J. C. Vanderleeden
Caltech, 1970

Donated to
Augustana University College
by

DR. H. VANDERLEEDEN

D1603145

THERMAL NEUTRON
SCATTERING

THERMAL NEUTRON SCATTERING

Edited by

P. A. EGELSTAFF

Atomic Energy Research Establishment
Harwell, Berkshire, England

1965  ACADEMIC PRESS
London and New York

ACADEMIC PRESS INC. (LONDON) LTD
Berkeley Square House
Berkeley Square
London, W.1.

U.S. Edition published by
ACADEMIC PRESS INC.
111 Fifth Avenue
New York, New York 10003

Copyright © 1965 By ACADEMIC PRESS INC. (LONDON) LTD

QC
721
.T53   /74893
1965

All Rights Reserved

No part of this book may be reproduced in any form by photostat, microfilm, or any other means, without written permission from the publishers.

Library of Congress Catalog Card Number: 65-14292

Printed in Great Britain at
The University Press
Aberdeen

Preface

This book presents the theoretical and experimental basis of neutron scattering by condensed matter in a form suitable for experimentalists whether they be postgraduate students, teachers or research workers. Consequently, the mathematical presentation has been aimed at physical understanding rather than rigour, and generous space has been given to experimental methods and results. The book is concerned with inelastic neutron scattering processes only, because these yield much of the new information available through neutron experiments which is not made available by other radiation scattering work. In contrast, there is a close parallel between X-ray measurements and elastic or total neutron diffraction measurements, as described by G. Bacon ("Neutron Diffraction", Oxford University Press, 1962).

The inelastic scattering of thermal neutrons can yield information about many properties; for example, it can cover lattice vibration properties, molecular energy levels, magnetic energy levels, translational motion in gases and liquids, such as diffusion, and other similar properties in which motion is an important aspect. Many branches of the subject will be treated in the succeeding chapters, but it is impossible to cover every one. One branch which has been left out concerns defects in solids: this subject has developed later than the other areas. Another branch omitted concerns liquid helium, which is being covered in a forthcoming book* and elsewhere. This illustrates the fact that each branch of neutron scattering properly belongs to a branch of physics and should be seen in that context also.

The historical development of this subject is interesting. Early experimental work using the total cross-section method only was carried on from 1936 to 1950, and the potential of the neutron scattering technique was realized during this period by a number of physicists in various countries. Unfortunately, experimental difficulties (particularly the low source fluxes) prevented adequate exploitation. For example, in England, both the three-axis spectrometer method and the filter–chopper method were examined by J. M. Cassels in 1950 but were abandoned due to inadequate sources. However, the decade 1951–60 was a period of intensive development of both neutron sources and experimental methods, so that by it's end there were many instruments at work in various countries. Most of the experimental results discussed in this book have been taken since 1960, particularly during the past three years, and the amount of research undertaken is still rising.

The material presented here is a condensation of and guide to the original

* P. Nozieres and D. Pines (1965). The Superfluid Bose Liquid, Chapter 6 of "Theory of Quantum Liquids". Benjamin.

AUGUSTANA UNIVERSITY COLLEGE
LIBRARY

literature. Chapter 1 covers the basic nuclear and magnetic scattering theory and outlines the applications of this theory to crystal lattices. An introduction to the liquid scattering theory is given also. Readers who wish to omit the details of the experimental work can proceed immediately to Chapters 5 and 6 where the nuclear and magnetic results on crystals are discussed. In Chapters 2–4 the experimental equipment is reviewed, including the various types of neutron spectrometer, source and detector which are used in this work. The theory for liquids and molecules, which is not as fully developed as the theory for solids, is presented in detail in Chapters 7 and 9, respectively. It will be noticed that in these cases the theoretical work refers to particular systems or particular properties: the reason for this is that no general theory is available. Experimental results on liquids are reviewed in Chapter 8 and on molecules in Chapter 10.

Because this is a new and expanding field which touches many established subjects, the units and notation employed in the literature are various and sometimes confusing. To clarify the units, a conversion chart has been printed at the end of the book which relates nine ways of expressing neutron energy found in recent publications. Also to help the notation problem, a general list of the symbols used is given in the Appendix and special lists are printed at the beginning of each chapter. As far as possible a common notation has been adopted throughout the book. It is hoped, in spite of the flaws of this system, that it will contribute to the growth of an accepted and consistent notation.

The background of nuclear physics knowledge required to discuss neutron scattering by nuclei is, in the present context, quite marginal. In terms of the partial wave treatment of nuclear scattering only the s-wave component is important for thermal neutrons. Corrections for p-wave and higher components are of the order of the minor interactions mentioned below. Also, for all the nuclei which are suitable for scattering experiments, the nuclear scattering length, which represents the strength of the interaction, is independent of neutron energy. However, the sign and the amplitude of the scattering length depends upon the particular energy level (of the nucleus) whose virtual excitation dominates the interaction. The parameters of this level will vary, of course, from isotope to isotope and also with the spin of the compound nucleus (i.e. with the orientation of nuclear and neutron spins). Because of this the sign and amplitude of the nuclear scattering length can vary in an irregular way from one nucleus to another. This is unlike the case of electromagnetic radiation, where scattering lengths have the same phase and amplitude for each scattering centre, and the scattering is fully coherent.

The interaction of a neutron with atomic nuclei is much stronger than interactions between atoms but the range is very short compared with interatomic distances, and for this reason the scattering by a single nucleus

AUGUSTANA UNIVERSITY COLLEGE
LIBRARY

is essentially isotropic. On the other hand, due to its magnetic moment, the neutron also interacts with atomic magnetic fields which arise from unpaired electrons in the outer shells. Because this scattering originates from a source of dimensions comparable to the neutron wavelength, it is subject to a scattering form factor which is similar to the X-ray atomic form factor. In addition to these two main interactions there are several smaller ones which are typically of the order of 10^{-3} of the former. These include the electron–neutron interaction, the nuclear magnetic interaction and various second-order interactions. The conventional methods (e.g. Fermi pseudo-potential, Born approximation, etc.) used in this book for treating the nuclear and magnetic effects are accurate to the same order of magnitude as these smaller neutron interactions. Since the experiments discussed here yield results which are accurate to the region of 1%, the corrections to the basic theoretical method and effects due to the small interactions listed above are of little importance.

Inelastic neutron scattering may be represented in the following way. The condensed atomic system is equivalent to a set of moving scattering centres while the neutron is represented as a plane wave. In looking at the scattering of this wave by the moving scatterers, a Doppler effect (i.e. changes in the wavelength and direction of motion of the neutron) is seen. These changes in wavelength and direction give details of the motion and structure of the condensed system. Neutron scattering theory is complicated just because both the motion and the structure have to be considered in one treatment. In addition, the experimental measurements on scattering systems such as crystals need either to be very precise or to add a new unambiguity of interpretation, because in order to be valuable they must add to an extensive background of existing knowledge. Thus, in such cases the neutron work is useful only when in a highly developed form, and it will be seen from the discussion of the experimental work that this stage has now been reached.

It will be noted that the theoretical treatments of condensed matter given in this book are concerned with either idealized or simplified systems. In almost every case the experimental results show up the non-ideal character of real systems, and so require a deeper theoretical analysis. This is typical of inelastic neutron scattering data because the neutron is such a sensitive probe reflecting accurately the microscopic structure and dynamical behaviour of the sample.

The most useful collections of papers in this field are found in the proceedings of IAEA conferences on "Inelastic Scattering of Neutrons in Solids and Liquids". These conferences were held in 1960, 1962 and 1964, and material presented at the first two has been used extensively in the preparation of this book, while some material from the third has been included.

The responsibility for the notation used and for the allocation of material to the various chapters is the Editor's, and I should like to thank all the authors for co-operating so fully in these matters. It has been a pleasure to work with them and to have their help at all stages in this project. I should also like to thank those colleagues at AERE (particularly Ray Lowde and Peter Schofield) who have given me advice from time to time and to thank Robin Sharp for his extensive help in the preparation of the notation lists and the index. The co-operation of the Academic Press at all stages of the production, especially over last-minute revisions, was particularly helpful.

PETER EGELSTAFF

Abingdon
March 1965

List of Contributors

ROBERT M. BRUGGER. *Phillips Petroleum Co., Atomic Energy Division, Idaho Falls, Idaho, U.S.A.* (p. 53)

S. J. COCKING. *Nuclear Physics Division, Atomic Energy Research Establishment, Harwell, England* (p. 141)

G. DOLLING. *Atomic Energy of Canada Ltd., Chalk River, Ontario, Canada* (p. 193)

P. K. IYENGAR. *Atomic Energy Establishment, Trombay, Bombay, India* (p. 97)

B. JACROT. *Centre d'Etudes Nucléaires de Saclay, France* (p. 251)

J. A. JANIK. *Physical Institute of the Jagiellonian University, Krakow, Poland* (pp. 413, 453)

A. KOWALSKA. *Physical Institute of the Jagiellonian University, Krakow, Poland* (pp. 413, 453)

K. E. LARSSON. *Royal Institute of Technology, Stockholm, Sweden* (p. 347)

W. M. LOMER. *Solid State Physics Division, Atomic Energy Research Establishment, Harwell, England* (p. 1)

G. G. LOW. *Solid State Physics Division, Atomic Energy Research Establishment, Harwell, England* (p. 1)

T. RISTE. *Institutt for Atomenergi, Kjeller, Norway* (p. 251)

ALF SJÖLANDER. *Institute of Theoretical Physics, Gothenburg, Sweden* (p. 291)

F. J. WEBB. *Nuclear Physics Division, Atomic Energy Research Establishment, Harwell, England* (p. 141)

A. D. B. WOODS. *Atomic Energy of Canada Ltd., Chalk River, Ontario, Canada* (p. 193)

Contents

PREFACE.., .,.. v

LIST OF CONTRIBUTORS... ix

CHAPTER 1

Introductory Theory

W. M. LOMER and G. G. LOW

1.1   Introduction.. 2
1.2   Thermal Neutron Scattering Cross-sections............................ 6
1.3   The Time Dependent Correlation Formalism............................ 10
1.4   The Scattering Law for Nuclei....................................... 12
1.5   Self-correlation in Liquids... 13
1.6   The Eigenfunction Formulation....................................... 15
1.7   Nuclear Elastic Scattering in a Crystal............................. 17
1.8   Nuclear Bragg Scattering.. 18
1.9   Scattering from Alloys and Incoherent Elastic Scattering............ 21
1.10 Inelastic Scattering: Ideal Lattice Vibrations...................... 23
1.11 Nuclear Inelastic Scattering in a Crystal........................... 26
1.12 One Phonon Coherent Scattering...................................... 28
1.13 Incoherent Scattering and the Density of Phonon States.............. 30
1.14 Multi-phonon Scattering and Total Cross-sections for Inelastic Scattering.... 31
1.15 Magnetic Scattering Cross-sections.................................. 33
1.16 Elastic Magnetic Scattering in Ferromagnets, etc.................... 36
1.17 Spin Wave Scattering.. 38
1.18 Critical Magnetic Scattering.. 45
References... 48

CHAPTER 2

Mechanical and Time-of-flight Techniques

ROBERT M. BRUGGER

2.1   Introduction.. 54
2.2   Transmission of Single Choppers..................................... 56
2.3   Chopper Construction.. 57
2.4   Helical Slot Velocity Selectors..................................... 65
2.5   Polycrystalline Filter Monochromators plus Chopper Time-of-flight Analyzers 67
2.6   Single-chopper Monochromators plus Time-of-flight Analyzers......... 69
2.7   Discussion of Phased Chopper Velocity Selectors..................... 70
2.8   Resolution of Phased Chopper Velocity Selectors..................... 72
2.9   The Harwell-Chalk River Velocity Selector........................... 76
2.10 The MTR Phased Chopper Velocity Selector............................ 80
2.11 The Saclay Cold Neutron Velocity Selector........................... 85
2.12 Rotating Crystal Time-of-flight Spectrometers....................... 85
2.13 Spinning Sample Method.. 88
2.14 Linear Accelerator and Pulsed Reactor Methods....................... 89

2.15 Multichannel Time Analyzers... 90
2.16 Timing Signals.. 92
2.17 Safety... 93
References... 94

CHAPTER 3

Crystal Diffraction Techniques

P. K. IYENGAR

3.1 Introduction... 98
3.2 Brief Theory of Crystal Diffraction.................................. 98
3.3 Collimator Design... 103
3.4 Types of Crystals Used.. 104
3.5 Parasitic Reflections... 106
3.6 Order Contamination.. 108
3.7 Luminosity of Diffraction Patterns and Collimators.................. 109
3.8 Basic Design of a Crystal Spectrometer.............................. 111
3.9 Triple Axis Spectrometer at Chalk River............................. 113
3.10 Other Triple Axis Spectrometers.................................... 117
3.11 Automation for a Triple Axis Spectrometer.......................... 118
3.12 Special Experimental Methods for the Triple Axis Spectrometer....... 119
3.13 Constant "Q" Method.. 123
3.14 Shape of Neutron Group and Focusing Effects........................ 124
3.15 Problems in "Scalar Q" Experiments................................. 125
3.16 Neutron Filters.. 127
3.17 Single Crystal Filters... 130
3.18 Polycrystalline Filter as an Analyser.............................. 132
3.19 Window Filter.. 134
3.20 Filter Detectors used with Pulsed Sources.......................... 136
3.21 Brief Comparison with Time-of-flight Methods....................... 137
References... 138

CHAPTER 4

Neutron Sources and Detectors

S. J. COCKING AND F. J. WEBB

4.1 Introduction... 142
4.2 Research Reactors and their Neutron Beam Holes..................... 142
4.3 Collimators for Neutron Beams..................................... 146
4.4 Moderator Temperature... 148
4.5 Pulsed Reactors... 150
4.6 Electron Linear Accelerator Neutron Sources....................... 152
4.7 Comparison of Pulsed and Continuous Neutron Sources............... 155
4.8 Cold Neutron Moderators in Reactors............................... 158
4.9 Cold Moderating Materials... 160
4.10 Brief Theory of Cold Moderators.................................. 162
4.11 Liquid Hydrogen Moderators in Low Flux Reactors.................. 164

4.12 Liquid Hydrogen Moderators in High Flux Reactors.................... 165
4.13 Increases in Cold Neutron Flux....................................... 167
4.14 Safety of Liquid Hydrogen Moderators................................ 169
4.15 General Properties of Thermal Neutron Detectors..................... 171
4.16 Boron Trifluoride (BF_3) Filled Proportional Counters............... 175
4.17 Helium–3 Filled Proportional Counters............................... 178
4.18 Boron or Lithium (with Zinc Sulphide) Scintillation Detectors........... 178
4.19 Scintillating Glasses Containing Boron or Lithium...................... 184
4.20 Other Detectors... 190
4.21 Summary of Detector Performance.................................. 190
References.. 191

CHAPTER 5

Thermal Vibrations of Crystal Lattices

G. DOLLING and A. D. B. WOODS

5.1 Introduction.. 193
5.2 Metals and Alloys: Introduction...................................... 198
5.3 Face-centred Cubic Metals... 201
5.4 Body-centred Cubic Metals... 207
5.5 Other Metals and Alloys... 212
5.6 Semiconductors: Introduction.. 216
5.7 Force Models for Semiconductors.................................... 219
5.8 Semiconductors: Comparison of Theory and Experiment................. 221
5.9 Determination of Polarization Vectors................................ 223
5.10 Ionic Crystals: Introduction... 225
5.11 Shell Models for Alkali Halides....................................... 226
5.12 Longitudinal Optic Modes of Alkali Halides........................... 229
5.13 Calcium Fluoride and Uranium Dioxide............................... 231
5.14 Strontium Titanate.. 233
5.15 Carbon... 235
5.16 Hydrogen Vibrations in Compounds.................................. 238
5.17 Anharmonic Effects... 239
5.18 Summary... 243
References.. 244

CHAPTER 6

Magnetic Inelastic Scattering of Neutrons

B. JACROT and T. RISTE

6.1 General Remarks on Magnetism and Neutron Scattering................. 251
6.2 Uncoupled Ions; Paramagnetic Scattering at High Temperatures.......... 253
6.3 Coupled Ions.. 256
6.4 Experimental Results on Coupled Systems............................. 259
6.5 Magnetic Inelastic Scattering at Low Temperatures.................... 261
6.6 Methods for Distinguishing Spin Wave Scattering from Other Inelastic
     Components... 264

6.7   Experimentally Observed Dispersion Curves.............................. 267
6.8   The Effect of Temperature on the Spin Wave Dispersion Curve and Line
      Width... 272
6.9   Conclusion on Spin Wave Experiments.................................. 275
6.10 The Theory of Critical Scattering...................................... 277
6.11 Experimental Results on Critical Scattering in Iron and Nickel.......... 281
6.12 Critical Scattering in Antiferromagnetic and Ferrimagnetic Substances..... 286
6.13 Conclusions.. 288
References.. 288

CHAPTER 7

Theory of Neutron Scattering by Liquids

ALF SJÖLANDER

7.1   Introduction.. 291
7.2   Van Hove Correlation Functions....................................... 294
7.3   Moment Relations... 298
7.4   Fluctuation-dissipation Theorem....................................... 301
7.5   Scattering by Harmonic Solids... 303
7.6   Scattering by Anharmonic Solids....................................... 306
7.7   General Discussion of Classical Liquids................................ 309
7.8   Interference Effects... 320
7.9   Gaussian Approximation... 326
7.10 Introduction of the Velocity Frequency Function....................... 328
7.11 Discussion of Various Explicit Dynamical Models....................... 331
7.12 Concluding Remarks... 341
7.13 References.. 342

CHAPTER 8

Experimental Results on Liquids

K. E. LARSSON

8.1   Introduction.. 347
8.2   Neutron Scattering Experiments on Water.............................. 350
8.3   Liquid Hydrogen.. 367
8.4   Various Hydrogenous Liquids.. 373
8.5   Glycerol.. 378
8.6   Coherent Scattering from Liquid Metals................................ 387
8.7   Liquid Sodium.. 398
8.8   Liquid Argon... 402
8.9   Liquid Bromine... 407
References.. 409

CHAPTER 9

The Theory of Neutron Scattering by Molecules

J. A. JANIK and A. KOWALSKA

9.1   Introduction.. 414
9.2   The Isotropic Harmonic Oscillator..................................... 416
9.3   Sachs and Teller Mass Tensor Concept................................. 418

9.4 The Zemach and Glauber Formalism.................................. 422
9.5 Examples of Zemach and Glauber Cross-sections........................ 428
9.6 An Approximate Theory for the Thermal Energy Region................. 432
9.7 Diatomic Molecules (particularly H_2)................................. 437
9.8 Scattering by Rotators... 442
9.9 Time-dependent Correlation Function for an Atom in a Molecule.......... 447
References... 450

CHAPTER 10

Neutron Scattering Experiments on Molecules

J. A. Janik and A. Kowalska

10.1 Introduction.. 453
10.2 Total Cross-section Data on Hydrogenous Gases........................ 454
10.3 Angular and Energy Distribution Data on Hydrogenous Gases........... 460
10.4 Hydrogenous Liquids.. 467
10.5 Metal Hydrides... 476
10.6 Ammonium Salts.. 481
10.7 Various Hydrogenous Solids... 487
10.8 Experiments with Non-hydrogenous Molecules........................ 489
10.9 Concluding Discussion... 492
References... 493

AUTHOR INDEX.. 497
SUBJECT INDEX... 507
APPENDIX.. 519

CHAPTER 1

Introductory Theory

W. M. LOMER and G. G. LOW

Solid State Physics Division, Atomic Energy Research Establishment, Harwell, England

1.1 Introduction		2
1.2 Thermal Neutron Scattering Cross-sections		6
1.3 The Time Dependent Correlation Formalism		10
1.4 The Scattering Law for Nuclei		12
1.5 Self-correlation in Liquids		13
1.6 The Eigenfunction Formulation		15
1.7 Nuclear Elastic Scattering in a Crystal		17
1.8 Nuclear Bragg Scattering		18
1.9 Scattering from Alloys and Incoherent Elastic Scattering		21
1.10 Inelastic Scattering: Ideal Lattice Vibrations		23
1.11 Nuclear Inelastic Scattering in a Crystal		26
1.12 One phonon Coherent Scattering		28
1.13 Incoherent Scattering and the Density of Phonon States		30
1.14 Multi-phonon Scattering and Total Cross-sections for Inelastic Scattering		31
1.15 Magnetic Scattering Cross-sections		33
1.16 Elastic Magnetic Scattering in Ferromagnets, etc.		36
1.17 Spin Wave Scattering		38
1.18 Critical Magnetic Scattering		45
References		48
Appendix		49

List of Symbols

c	Velocity of sound	$\mathbf{v}(\tau)$	Atomic velocity
c_i, c_j	Concentrations of components in alloy	v_0	Velocity of incident neutrons
$\mathbf{G}$	Spin spiral vector	v	Velocity of scattered neutrons
$G_v(\mathbf{r},\tau)$	Vineyard's correlation function for liquids	v_T	Width of Maxwellian flux-distribution at temperature T
H	Hamiltonian	α	Angle between $\mathbf{Q}$ and $\boldsymbol{\mu}$
$\mathbf{k},\mathbf{l}$	Subscripts for positions in unit cells	Γ	Spin wave parameter
		$\Gamma(\mathbf{r},\tau)$	Correlation function
$\mathbf{m},\mathbf{n}$	Subscripts for positions of atoms	$\gamma(\tau)$	Spin correlation function
n	Occupation number for phonons etc.	ϵ	Degree of polarization of neutrons
		η	Spin deviation
$\mathbf{N}$	Magnetic scattering vector	$\boldsymbol{\lambda}$	Spin-polarization vector of neutrons
P_1	Thermal probability of occupation of state i	λ_T	Width of Maxwellian flux-distribution at temperature T
p	Magnetic scattering length	ξ	Variable; also creation operator for magnons
t	Time		
$\mathbf{u},\mathbf{v}$	Subscripts for positions on basis lattice	$\phi_{\mathbf{q}s}$	Creation operator for phonon specified by $\mathbf{q},s$
V	Volume of unit cell	ψ	Wave function

1.1 Introduction

The purpose of the present chapter is to outline the various types of neutron scattering process that occur in solids and liquids and to give formulae for the relevant cross-sections in each case. Arguments closely associated with elementary physical ideas are given with each discussion in an attempt to convey briefly some of the physics of the cross-sections quoted. It is hoped that this treatment will be of assistance to readers requiring a simple introduction to the subject, for even though the mathematics is not entirely elementary, it should be fairly easily understood and may be of interest even to those familiar with the usual derivations. The basis of the treatment is the setting up of retarded waves representing the scattering from individual atoms. These partial amplitudes contain the correct factors of relative phase so that they may be added to give a resultant total scattering amplitude. This principle is described in the following section and then developed in subsequent discussions throughout the chapter as required. The connection between this treatment and the time independent treatment is indicated in Section 1.6.

In a scattering process in which the scatterer is extended in space it is convenient to represent the effective scattering density by a sum of Fourier terms. One term of such a sum could be taken to be proportional to $e^{i(\mathbf{q} \cdot \mathbf{r} - ft)}$, where the explicit dependence on time has been included so that we shall be able to take account of atomic movement within the scatterer. If the incident particles in the scattering process are represented by a wave $e^{i(\mathbf{k}_0 \cdot \mathbf{r} - \omega_0 t)}$, where the particle mass defines a relationship between the energy $\hbar\omega_0$ and the momentum $\hbar\mathbf{k}_0$, it is clear that any interaction in the system will result in some scattered particles which are described by the wave $e^{i\{(\mathbf{k}_0 \pm \mathbf{q}) \cdot \mathbf{r} - (\omega_0 \pm f)t\}}$, where the same relationship holds between $\hbar(\omega_0 \pm f)$ and $\hbar|\mathbf{k}_0 \pm \mathbf{q}|$. The scattered intensity depends on the wave vector and the frequency of the Fourier wave in the scatterer and thus, in principle, both the atomic spatial arrangement and the energy levels in the scatterer can be studied. Because of the relationship between $\hbar\omega_0$ and $\mathbf{k}_0$, it is not to be expected in general that experimentally significant shifts of both wave vector and frequency will occur in the same experimental arrangement. In the case of the neutron, however, we are fortunate in that the energy–wavenumber relationship, $\hbar\omega_0 = \hbar^2 k_0^2 / 2m$, is such that wavelengths of atomic dimensions correspond to thermal energies. It follows that thermal neutrons can show appreciable shifts of both wave vector and energy after scattering in a solid or a liquid and that the observation of such shifts provides a valuable means for studying aggregated matter.

The wavelength of a neutron is in fact related to velocity and energy by

$$\lambda = \frac{h}{mv} = \frac{3 \cdot 96}{v} = \frac{0 \cdot 286}{\sqrt{E}} \text{ Å} \tag{1.1}$$

where v is in km sec^{-1} and E is in eV. A nomogram (Egelstaff, 1958) relating the various units is given at the back of the book.

Although the neutron was discovered in 1932 it has been possible to use it extensively as a tool in solid and liquid state research only since beams from high flux reactors have become available. The neutrons provided in this way show a velocity distribution which corresponds to a Maxwell spectrum. Thus for neutrons in equilibrium with a moderator of temperature T, a velocity distribution is expected of

$$n_d(v)\mathrm{d}v = \frac{4n_D}{\sqrt{\pi}}\frac{v^2\mathrm{d}v}{v_T^3}\,\mathrm{e}^{-v^2/v_T^2} \tag{1.2}$$

where the total number of neutrons per unit volume is

$$n_D = \int_0^\infty n_d(v)\mathrm{d}v \tag{1.3}$$

and

$$v_T = \left(\frac{2kT}{m}\right)^{\frac{1}{2}}. \tag{1.4}$$

The neutron flux is v times the velocity distribution so that it is given by

$$n_f(v)\mathrm{d}v = 2n_F\frac{v^3\mathrm{d}v}{v_T^4}\exp\left(-\frac{v^2}{v_T^2}\right) \tag{1.5}$$

where the total flux is

$$n_F = \int_0^\infty n_f(v)\mathrm{d}v = \frac{2n_D}{\sqrt{\pi}}v_T. \tag{1.6}$$

This spectrum has a maximum at $v = \left(\frac{3kT}{m}\right)^{\frac{1}{2}}$. The neutron flux spectrum in terms of λ is given by

$$n_f(\lambda)\mathrm{d}\lambda = 2n_F\frac{\lambda_T^4\mathrm{d}\lambda}{\lambda^5}\,\mathrm{e}^{-\lambda_T^2/\lambda^2} \tag{1.7}$$

where

$$\lambda_T = \frac{h}{mv_T}. \tag{1.8}$$

This spectrum has a maximum at $\lambda = h/(5kTm)^{\frac{1}{2}}$.

Figure 1.1 shows the flux spectrum $n_f(\lambda)$ for a moderator temperature of 40°C. The number of neutrons per second in a wavelength interval $\mathrm{d}\lambda$ is given by the shaded area. This number is just like the source brightness of an optical source, and the flux of useful neutrons in any beam experiment depends on collimation conditions. By use of a multi-slit collimator an area A of the source may be viewed, utilizing any desired angular divergences

$\delta\theta_h$ and $\delta\theta_v$ in two perpendicular directions. The number of neutrons accepted is $(1/4\pi)\ n_f(\lambda)\mathrm{d}\lambda A\delta\theta_h\delta\theta_v$ and the total beam area at a distance d from the collimator is approximately $A+d^2\delta\theta_h\delta\theta_v$. When d is small enough this gives a uniform beam intensity of $(1/4\pi)n_f(\lambda)\mathrm{d}\lambda\delta\theta_h\delta\theta_v$. Provided the specimen is covered by the beam, increase in source area is useless. At great distances, where $A/d^2\ll\delta\theta_h\delta\theta_v$ the beam intensity drops into a d^{-2} region given

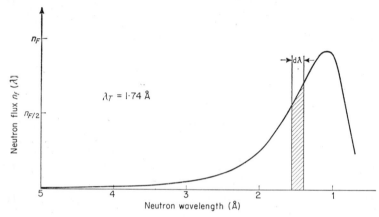

$$\lambda_T = 1{\cdot}74\ \text{Å}$$

Neutron flux $n_f(\lambda)$

Neutron wavelength (Å)

FIG. 1.1 The flux spectrum $n_f(\lambda)$ corresponding to a moderator temperature of 40°C.

by $n_f(\lambda)\mathrm{d}\lambda A/4\pi d^2$, and then relaxation of collimation is useless. For a spectrometer with vertical plane collimation of $\pm1°$ and a corresponding total collimator height of 2 inches this condition sets in at a specimen distance of some 5 ft. In the former regime, with a total flux of 10^{14} n cm^{-2} sec^{-1} at source, a $1°\times\frac{1}{4}°$ collimated beam has a total intensity of 6×10^8 n cm^{-2} sec^{-1}. If it is then monochromated to $\mathrm{d}\lambda/\lambda\sim1\ \%$ near the Maxwell spectrum peak, the beam has a final intensity of about 6×10^6 n cm^{-2} sec^{-1}.

As pointed out above, in general, scattered neutrons show a dependence on both the spatial atomic arrangement and the energy levels in the scatterer. Sometimes, however, conditions are such that one type of scattering largely predominates and the scattered neutron pattern develops distinctive features which can be interpreted immediately in terms of either a spatial or energetic arrangement within the sample. Thus, in Fig. 1.2(a) we see Bragg peaks in the plot of scattered intensity versus angle of scattering which can be straight away inverted to give information concerning the structure of the specimen. Fig. 1.2(b), on the other hand, refers to an experiment in which the scattered intensity shows much less angular dependence: on examining the energy spectrum of the scattered neutrons, however, a distinctive peak is found which provides a measure of certain of the energy levels within the material being studied. Cross-sections applicable to specific experiments, such as these, are developed in later sections after treatment of the general theory of neutron scattering in Sections 1.2, 1.3 and 1.4. A specific type of scattering which is not treated in this chapter at all, however, is that from molecules. The energy spectrum of a molecule has levels corresponding to internal vibrational modes of the atoms within the molecule, the energies of

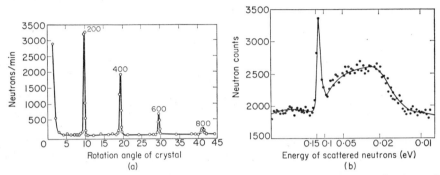

FIG. 1.2(a) Record from a neutron crystal spectrometer showing the Bragg peaks observed with a single crystal sample of KBr (Bykov *et al.*, 1957). (b) Energy spectrum of neutrons inelastically scattered by polycrystalline ZrH; the peak at 0·134 eV corresponds to an optical lattice vibration (Pelah *et al.*, 1957).

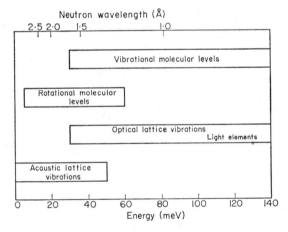

FIG. 1.3. Diagram indicating the possible energies of certain types of excitation in a solid or a liquid.

which depend on the atomic masses and interatomic forces. Such levels are in general comparatively energetic and persist with little modification in going from gas to liquid to crystalline phase. Less energetic are the librational or torsional modes originating in the rotational movement of a part or the whole of a molecule. These modes are modified from phase to phase, the rotations becoming hindered with increasing density. Finally, there are present in molecular crystals, lattice modes of vibration akin to ordinary lattice vibrations and dependent on molecular masses and intermolecular forces. Calculations of the scattering from molecular systems involve summations over the states of the particular system concerned and the detailed discussion of such scattering is left until Chapter 9. In Fig. 1.3 we give a schematic diagram indicating the energies of various excitations. The great utility of inelastic scattering measurements with thermal neutrons is immediately apparent.

1.2 Thermal Neutron Scattering Cross-sections

The Schrödinger equation for a neutron of energy $\hbar^2 k_0^2 / 2m$ in the presence of a single atom bound at the origin so that the centre of mass co-ordinates correspond to laboratory co-ordinates is

$$\left\{ \nabla^2 + k_0^2 - \frac{2m}{\hbar^2} V(\mathbf{r}) \right\} \psi = 0, \tag{1.9}$$

where $V(\mathbf{r})$ is the interaction potential between the neutron and the atom. $V(\mathbf{r})$ must take account of (a) the interaction of the neutron with nuclei via nuclear forces, and (b) the interaction of the neutron with electrons in atoms carrying a magnetic moment through the action of magnetic forces on the magnetic moment of the neutron. (b) is smaller than (a) but it extends over a much greater range so that the effects produced in the two cases are comparable.

On account of the short range nature of the forces in (a) the scattering from nuclei is isotropic and the asymptotic form of the wave function at large distances is

$$\psi_0 + \psi_1 = e^{ik_0 z} - \frac{b}{r} e^{ikr}, \tag{1.10}$$

where ψ_0 represents the incident neutron and ψ_1 the spherically symmetric scattered intensity. If the scattering is treated by first order Born approximation the form of $V(\mathbf{r})$ defined so as to give the correct isotropic scattering is the so-called Fermi pseudo-potential, i.e.

$$V(\mathbf{r}) = \frac{2\pi \hbar^2 b}{m} \delta(\mathbf{r}). \tag{1.11}$$

The scattering cross-section, defined as the ratio of the number of neutrons scattered per second to the incident neutron flux, is given by

$$\sigma = \frac{4\pi r^2 v \left| \frac{b}{r} e^{ikr} \right|^2}{v \left| e^{ik_0 z} \right|^2} = 4\pi b^2 \tag{1.12}$$

(v is the velocity of a neutron which is, of course, unchanged after scattering from a fixed nucleus which cannot accept energy from the neutron). The scattering length b of the nucleus can be complex only when absorption is large. Nonetheless, for completeness, the complex nature of b is allowed for in the master cross-section formula (1.18) (see below). Lists of scattering cross-sections are given in the "Barn Book" (Hughes and Schwartz, 1958). The cross-section of a free atom as opposed to the bound atom treated above is

$$\sigma_{\text{free atom}} = \frac{\sigma}{\left(1 + \dfrac{m}{M}\right)^2} \tag{1.13}$$

where M is the mass of the atom. This relationship may be understood by transferring to the centre of mass co-ordinates. In this system the scattering process may be regarded as the interaction through the potential $V(\mathbf{r})$ of a particle having the velocity of the incident neutron and a mass equal to the reduced mass $mM/(m+M)$, with a nucleus bound at the origin (see for example Schiff, 1949, p. 101). The problem, therefore, is exactly as above apart from the change of mass, and because of the manner in which mass enters equation (1.9) it is clear that the total cross-section, which is independent of co-ordinate system, will be reduced to the value given in equation (1.13).

In samples of macroscopic dimensions the centre of mass co-ordinates correspond to the laboratory system, and the total scattering may be evaluated by proper summation of independent but possibly coherent scattering from all nuclei present. (This is true only if the incident beam is not much attenuated by the sample—in X-ray terms, if extinction is negligible.) The phase of the scattering from each nucleus depends on its precise position, and in order to take account of atom movements it is necessary to introduce the idea of a retarded neutron wave. Because the neutron wave equation is unlike the classical wave equation, and the velocities of the scattering centres are comparable with the neutron velocities, the detailed derivation of the scattering power differs in detail from the normal optical Huygens' construction. This detailed derivation is given in the Appendix: the skeleton of that argument is reproduced here to give some physical basis for the following sections.

We consider the amplitude of the total wave field scattered from a system of moving nuclei, when a well collimated, mono-energetic neutron beam is incident. The incident neutron function is written

$$\psi_0 = e^{i(\mathbf{k}_0 \cdot \mathbf{r} - \omega_0 t)} \tag{1.14}$$

where $\hbar\omega_0 = \hbar^2 k_0^2/2m$ = neutron energy, and $\hbar\mathbf{k}_0$ = neutron momentum.

Every nucleus is at every instant the source of a spherical scattered wave coherent in phase with the incident wave; these waves combine and interfere until at large distance from the sample there is some total wave field which will represent outgoing neutrons of various energies and momenta. If the nuclei are static, the frequency of every scattered wave is equal to that of the incident wave, and only elastic scattering is possible. If the nuclei are not static, Doppler shifts change the scattered frequencies. Intuitively it seems plausible that if some scattered neutrons are found with their momenta changed by $\hbar\mathbf{Q}$ and their energy changed by $\hbar\omega$, then the scattering system is able to change its overall dynamical state by just these same quantities. In other words, it seems likely that the intensity of neutron scattering through $\mathbf{Q}$, ω is a measure of the density of the corresponding spatial and time Fourier components of scattering power in the sample.

To demonstrate this we proceed as follows. The scattering by any nucleus is found by regarding the nucleus as the centre of a scattering Fermi pseudo-potential, which is treated as a time dependent perturbation acting on the incident wave. Each nucleus $\mathbf{n}$ provides a potential

$$V_{\mathbf{n}} = \frac{2\pi\hbar^2}{m} b_{\mathbf{n}} \delta\{\mathbf{r} - \mathbf{R}_{\mathbf{n}}(t)\} \qquad (1.15)$$

The total scattered wave field from all nuclei is worked out by normal methods which, however, look unfamiliar because the neutron wave equation has the nature of a complex diffusion equation rather than a classical wave equation. This wave field is derived as an explicit function of $\mathbf{r}$ and t, in terms of the history of the scattering nuclei (equation (A1.5)). In principle the history from $t = -\infty$ occurs in the expressions, but it is clear that any neutron scattered at some velocity v, and detected at a point distant r' from the sample at time t', was scattered at a time near $t' - \dfrac{r'}{v}$. Thus the scattering history can be taken over a limited period. The wave field is much more easily used after Fourier transformation to give the scattering amplitude as a function of $\mathbf{k}$ and ω_1, the momentum and energy of the scattered neutron. The scattered amplitude is given in equation (A1.11) as

$$f(\mathbf{k},\omega_1) = \frac{1}{r'} \frac{1}{T} \int_0^T dt_0 \, e^{-i\omega t_0} \sum_{\mathbf{n}} b_{\mathbf{n}} \int d\mathbf{r} \delta\{\mathbf{r} - \mathbf{R}_{\mathbf{n}}(t_0)\} \, e^{i\mathbf{Q}\cdot\mathbf{r}}, \qquad (1.16)$$

where $\mathbf{Q} = \mathbf{k}_0 - \mathbf{k}$ and $\omega = \omega_0 - \omega_1$ and where T is a long time used as the period for the Fourier transformation. The flux in a given energy range ΔE, and given angular range $\Delta\Omega$, is usually required and this may be written

$$|f(\mathbf{k},\omega_1)|^2 \frac{T\Delta E}{2\pi\hbar} \times (\text{area}) \times (\text{velocity}) = |f(\mathbf{k},\omega_1)|^2 \frac{T\Delta E}{2\pi\hbar} r'^2 \Delta\Omega v_1. \qquad (1.17)$$

Hence the differential cross-section for N particles becomes (equations (A1.12) and (A1.14))

$$\frac{d^2\sigma}{d\Omega dE} = |f(k,\omega_1)|^2 \frac{Tr'^2}{2\pi\hbar} \frac{v_1}{v_0}$$

$$= \frac{v_1}{v_0} \frac{1}{2\pi\hbar} \iint d\tau\, e^{-i\omega\tau} \sum_{m,n} b_m^* b_n\, e^{i\mathbf{Q}\cdot(\mathbf{r}-\mathbf{r}'')}\delta\{\mathbf{r}'' - \mathbf{R}_m^{\times}(0)\}\delta\{\mathbf{r} - \mathbf{R}_n(\tau)\}d\mathbf{r}''d\mathbf{r}$$

$$= \frac{v_1}{v_0} \frac{1}{2\pi\hbar} \int_{-\infty}^{\infty} d\tau\, e^{-i\omega\tau} \sum_{m,n} b_m^* b_n\, \overline{e^{i\mathbf{Q}\cdot\{\mathbf{R}_n(\tau) - \mathbf{R}_m(0)\}}} \qquad (1.18)$$

where the bar denotes the time average, and where the second form neglects the operator nature of the nuclear co-ordinates.

This equation is taken as the starting point of many of the treatments in this chapter, since it throws emphasis on the correlations between spatial and time behaviour of the atoms. It may be transformed by standard methods into an eigenvalue form, equation (1.51), which is an equally general and valid starting point.

The inelastic scattering, corresponding to $\omega \neq 0$, thus arises because of systematic correlation between the atomic positions at different times. Consider, for example, a single atom undergoing small harmonic oscillation of frequency f. The exponential may be expanded to give

$$e^{i\mathbf{Q}\cdot\{\mathbf{R}_n(\tau) - \mathbf{R}_n(0)\}}$$

$$= e^{i\mathbf{Q}\cdot\mathbf{u}_n(\tau)}\, e^{-i\mathbf{Q}\cdot\mathbf{u}_n(0)}$$

$$= 1 + i\mathbf{Q}\cdot\{\mathbf{u}_n(\tau) - \mathbf{u}_n(0)\} + \{\mathbf{Q}\cdot\mathbf{u}_n(\tau)\}\{\mathbf{Q}\cdot\mathbf{u}_n(0)\} + \dots \quad (1.19)$$

where $\mathbf{u}(\tau) = \mathbf{u}\dfrac{e^{if\tau}+e^{-if\tau}}{2}$ gives the amplitude of the oscillation. Thus, the real terms in the above expression reduce to

$$1 + |\mathbf{Q}\cdot\mathbf{u}|^2 \frac{e^{if\tau}+e^{-if\tau}}{2} + \dots \qquad (1.20)$$

so that in view of the time integration in equation (1.18), in terms of the present approximation, only three distinct values of ω lead to non zero cross-sections, namely $\omega = \pm f$, and 0. These frequencies correspond to the neutron receiving energy from the oscillator, giving energy to it, or being scattered elastically. The elastic scattering ($\omega = 0$) arises from the time average distribution of the nuclei. It is perhaps worth pointing out here that the elastic scattering cross-section is quite different from that for X-ray diffuse scattering, which is often referred to as being effectively elastic. The X-ray cross-section is in fact an integral over all energy changes, $\hbar\omega$ (see also the following section). These are so small relative to $\hbar\omega_0$, that changes in $\mathbf{Q}$ may be neglected The diffracted intensity corresponds to a "snapshot" picture rather than a

2*

time-average picture since integration of the factor $e^{-i\omega\tau}$ over ω leads to a term $\delta(\tau)$. Thus for X-rays equation (1.18) becomes

$$\frac{d\sigma}{d\Omega} = \frac{1}{2\pi\hbar} \sum_{m,n} f_m^*(\mathbf{Q})f_n(\mathbf{Q})\ \overline{e^{i\mathbf{Q}\cdot[\mathbf{R_n}(0)-\mathbf{R_m}(0)]}} \tag{1.21}$$

where the form factors f_n replace the scattering lengths b_n.

1.3 The Time Dependent Correlation Formalism

If we return to equation (1.18) we may write the differential cross-section in the alternative form

$$\frac{d^2\sigma}{d\Omega dE} = \frac{b^2}{2\pi\hbar}\frac{k}{k_0}\int_{-\infty}^{\infty} d\tau\ e^{-i\omega\tau} \sum_{m,n} \int d\mathbf{r}'d\mathbf{r}'' e^{i\{\mathbf{Q}\cdot(\mathbf{r}'-\mathbf{r}'')\}} \overline{\delta\{\mathbf{r}''-\mathbf{R_m}(0)\}\delta\{\mathbf{r}'-\mathbf{R_n}(\tau)\}}$$

$$= \frac{b^2}{2\pi\hbar}\frac{k}{k_0}\int_{-\infty}^{\infty} d\tau\ e^{-i\omega\tau} \sum_{m,n} \int d\mathbf{r}'d\mathbf{r}\, e^{i\mathbf{Q}\cdot\mathbf{r}}\overline{\delta\{\mathbf{r}+\mathbf{R_m}(0)-\mathbf{r}'\}\delta\{\mathbf{r}'-\mathbf{R_n}(\tau)\}}$$

$$\tag{1.22}$$

where we assume for the moment that $\overline{b^2} = \overline{b}^2 = b^2$. The time average denoted by the bar can in fact be expressed in terms of a probability density $p\{\mathbf{R_m}(0),\mathbf{R_n}(t)\}$ which refers to the probability that given that nucleus $\mathbf{m}$ is at $\mathbf{R_m}(0)$ at $t=0$, nucleus $\mathbf{n}$ is at $\mathbf{R_n}(t)$ at time t. Thus, we may write

$$\frac{d^2\sigma}{d\Omega dE} = \frac{b^2}{2\pi\hbar}\frac{k}{k_0}\int_{-\infty}^{\infty} d\tau\ e^{-i\omega\tau} \sum_{m,n} \int d\mathbf{r}'d\mathbf{r}\ e^{i\mathbf{Q}\cdot\mathbf{r}} \times d\mathbf{R_m}d\mathbf{R_n}p\{\mathbf{R_m}(0),\ \mathbf{R_n}(\tau)\} \times$$

$$\delta\{\mathbf{r}+\mathbf{R_m}(0)-\mathbf{r}'\}\delta\{\mathbf{r}'-\mathbf{R_n}(\tau)\} \tag{1.23}$$

The form of this expression is important: the probability density $p\{\mathbf{R_m}(0),\mathbf{R_n}(\tau)\}$ is operated on by two delta functions. In order to carry out the integration over $\mathbf{r}$ it is not permissible simply to substitute $\mathbf{r}' = \mathbf{R_n}(\tau)$ into the first delta function because the variables $\mathbf{R_m}(0)$ and $\mathbf{R_n}(\tau)$ do not commute if $\mathbf{R_m}$ and $\mathbf{R_n}$ are dynamically coupled.

It is convenient now to introduce the space-time correlation function $G(\mathbf{r},\tau)$ of the system (Van Hove, 1954a) which is defined as

$$G(\mathbf{r},\tau) = \frac{1}{N} \sum_{m,n} \int d\mathbf{r}'\overline{\delta\{\mathbf{r}+\mathbf{R_m}(0)-\mathbf{r}'\}\delta\{\mathbf{r}'-\mathbf{R_n}(\tau)\}} \tag{1.24}$$

where N is the number of particles present. It has been pointed out by Van Hove (1958) that the imaginary part of $G(\mathbf{r},\tau)$ divided by $\hbar$ describes the local disturbance produced by a neutron in the density of the scattering system. In fact for a system in thermal equilibrium, because of the existence of a dispersion relation between the real and imaginary parts of $G(\mathbf{r},\tau)$ this local disturbance may be calculated from the equilibrium density fluctuations of the scattering system in the absence of a neutron (for example see Nelkin, 1961). This is simply a consequence of the fluctuation dissipation theorem (Callen and Welton, 1951) which relates the dissipative response of a system to a perturbation, to the equilibrium fluctuations of the system in the absence of the perturbation.

Using the correlation function $G(\mathbf{r},\tau)$ the cross-section (1.23) may be re-written as

$$\frac{d^2\sigma}{d\Omega dE} = \frac{Nb^2}{2\pi\hbar}\frac{k}{k_0}\int\limits_{-\infty}^{\infty} d\tau\, e^{-i\omega\tau}\int d\mathbf{r}\, e^{i\mathbf{Q}\cdot\mathbf{r}}\, G(\mathbf{r},\tau). \tag{1.25}$$

The correlation function can be split into two parts, a "self" correlation function $G_s(\mathbf{r},\tau)$ which is a measure of the positions of the same particle as a function of time, and the "distinct" correlation function $G_d(\mathbf{r},\tau)$ which is concerned with two different particles. Thus,

$$G_s(\mathbf{r},\tau) = \frac{1}{N}\sum_{\mathbf{n}}\int d\mathbf{r}'\,\overline{\delta\{\mathbf{r}+\mathbf{R_n}(0)-\mathbf{r}'\}\delta\{\mathbf{r}'-\mathbf{R_n}(\tau)\}}\,; \tag{1.26}$$

$$G_d(\mathbf{r},\tau) = \frac{1}{N}\sum_{\mathbf{m,n}}^{\mathbf{m}\neq\mathbf{n}}\int d\mathbf{r}'\,\overline{\delta\{\mathbf{r}+\mathbf{R_m}(0)-\mathbf{r}'\}\delta\{\mathbf{r}'-\mathbf{R_n}(\tau)\}}. \tag{1.27}$$

On the assumption that the various values of b present are distributed randomly among the nuclei, the complication of spin or isotope disorder which was ignored in equations (1.22) to (1.25) is now taken into account by replacing $b^2 G(\mathbf{r},\tau)$ by

$$\Gamma(\mathbf{r},\tau) = \overline{b^2}G_s(\mathbf{r},\tau) + \overline{b}^2 G_d(\mathbf{r},\tau). \tag{1.28}$$

(a moment's reflection makes it clear that $G_s(\mathbf{r},\tau)$ must be associated with $\frac{1}{N}\sum_{\langle m,n\rangle} b_m b_n \delta_{nm} = \overline{b^2}$ and $G_d(\mathbf{r},\tau)$ with $\frac{1}{N^2}\sum_{n,m}^{\mathbf{m}\neq\mathbf{n}} b_m b_n = \overline{b}^2$). Thus, if we eliminate $G_d(\mathbf{r},\tau)$ between $G(\mathbf{r},\tau) = G_s(\mathbf{r},\tau) + G_d(\mathbf{r},\tau)$ and equation (1.28), we find that we can replace equation (1.25) by

$$\frac{d^2\sigma^{coh}}{d\Omega dE} = \frac{\overline{b}^2 N}{2\pi\hbar}\frac{k}{k_0}\int d\mathbf{r}d\tau\, e^{i(\mathbf{Q}\cdot\mathbf{r}-\omega\tau)}G(\mathbf{r},\tau) \tag{1.29}$$

and

$$\frac{d^2\sigma^{inc}}{d\Omega dE} = \frac{(\overline{b^2}-\overline{b}^2)N}{2\pi\hbar}\frac{k}{k_0}\int d\mathbf{r}d\tau\, e^{i(\mathbf{Q}\cdot\mathbf{r}-\omega\tau)}G_s(\mathbf{r},\tau) \tag{1.30}$$

the so-called coherent and incoherent cross-sections.

It is sometimes possible to assume that the energy transfers are small compared with the incident neutron energy and in this case we may be interested in just the cross-section integrated over these energy transfers, i.e. the angular distribution irrespective of energy change. To get this we have merely to integrate equation (1.29) over ω. This is easily done provided that we may assume that $\mathbf{Q}$ is constant over the range of ω for which energy transfers are important. As $Q^2 = 2\left\{k_0^2 \pm \dfrac{m\omega}{\hbar} - k_0\left(k_0^2 \pm \dfrac{2m\omega}{\hbar}\right)^{\frac{1}{2}}\cos\phi\right\}$ (where ϕ is the scattering angle) we see that this assumption implies that $m\omega/\hbar k_0^2(1-\cos\phi) \ll 1$ or alternatively that $2m\omega/\hbar Q^2 \ll 1$. Thus, if $G(\mathbf{r},\tau)$ varies over a time scale τ_c, so that only values of $|\omega| \leq 1/\tau_c$ matter, the above condition is fulfilled when $2m/\hbar Q^2 \ll \tau_c$. In these circumstances the integration over ω produces a factor $\delta(\tau)$ and the subsequent τ integration gives rise to $G(\mathbf{r},0)$. In other words $G(\mathbf{r},\infty)$ is related to the strictly elastic scattering but, under these special conditions (which hold excellently for X-rays), $G(\mathbf{r},0)$ is related to the total scattering in what is known as the static approximation. Thus we have from equation (1.29) that

$$\frac{d\sigma}{d\Omega} = \frac{\bar{b}^2 N}{2\pi}\int d\omega \int d\tau\, e^{-i\omega\tau}\int d\mathbf{r}\, e^{i\mathbf{Q}\cdot\mathbf{r}}G(\mathbf{r},\tau) = \bar{b}^2 N\int d\mathbf{r}\, e^{i\mathbf{Q}\cdot\mathbf{r}}G(\mathbf{r},0)$$

$$= \bar{b}^2 N\left\{1 + \int d\mathbf{r}\, e^{i\mathbf{Q}\cdot\mathbf{r}}g(\mathbf{r})\right\} \qquad (1.31)$$

where

$$G_s(\mathbf{r},0) = \delta(\mathbf{r}) \quad\text{and}\quad G_d(\mathbf{r},0) = g(\mathbf{r}). \qquad (1.32)$$

The pair correlation function $g(\mathbf{r})$ is simply the instantaneous correlation factor defined by

$$g(\mathbf{r}) = \frac{1}{N}\sum_{m,n}^{m \neq n} \overline{\delta\{\mathbf{r} + \mathbf{R}_m(0) - \mathbf{R}_n(0)\}}. \qquad (1.33)$$

1.4 The Scattering Law for Nuclei

It will be seen from equation (1.25) that the quantity obtained directly from experimental measurements is the space and time transform of the correlation function $G(\mathbf{r},\tau)$, i.e.

$$S(\mathbf{Q},\omega) = \frac{1}{2\pi\hbar}\int d\mathbf{r}d\tau\, e^{i(\mathbf{Q}\cdot\mathbf{r}-\omega\tau)}G(\mathbf{r},\tau) \qquad (1.34)$$

This function is sometimes called the "scattering law". It depends solely on the dynamics of the scatterer. It has two general properties, however, which are independent of both the dynamics and structure of the scattering system. These are (see for example Nelkin, 1961):

(1) the sum rule due originally to Placzek which is given by

$$\int \omega\, d\omega S(\mathbf{Q},\omega) = \frac{Q^2}{2M} \qquad (1.35)$$

where M is the mass of a scattering particle, and

(2) the detailed balance condition which relates the energy loss and energy gain cross-sections, thus

$$S(-\mathbf{Q},-\omega) = e^{-\frac{\hbar\omega}{kT}} S(\mathbf{Q},\omega) \qquad (1.36)$$

(note $\hbar\omega$ is positive if the neutron loses energy).

A useful quantity often used in connection with scattering law discussions is the intermediate function corresponding to the spatial part of the transform (1.34), i.e.

$$I(\mathbf{Q},\tau) = \frac{1}{2\pi\hbar}\int d\mathbf{r}\ e^{i\mathbf{Q}\cdot\mathbf{r}} G(\mathbf{r},\tau). \qquad (1.37)$$

Schofield (1960 and 1961) has pointed out that $\tilde{I}(\mathbf{Q},\tau)$ defined by

$$\tilde{I}(\mathbf{Q},\tau) = I(\mathbf{Q},\tau+i\hbar/2kT) \qquad (1.38)$$

is a real function of τ, so that if $\tilde{S}(\mathbf{Q},\omega)$ is the Fourier transform of $\tilde{I}(\mathbf{Q},\tau)$ with respect to τ,

$$\tilde{S}(\mathbf{Q},\omega) = e^{-\hbar\omega/2kT} S(\mathbf{Q},\omega). \qquad (1.39)$$

From the properties of $\tilde{I}(\mathbf{Q},\tau)$ it follows that $\tilde{S}(\mathbf{Q},\tau)$ is even in both $\mathbf{Q}$ and ω so that equation (1.39) expresses the detailed balance condition.

1.5 Self-Correlation in Liquids

Attempts to derive a detailed scattering law function in the case of liquids are frustrated by the present status of theory and a useful method of approach appears to be to compare experimental results with simple models representing extreme physical situations. In this section we confine ourselves to some aspects of self-correlation in liquids; the detailed discussion of this topic and general correlations is given in Chapter 7. Pioneer work in this field has been carried out by Vineyard (1958) who evaluated $G_s(\mathbf{r},\tau)$ in a classical approximation. In view of Schofield's work it appears that the space-time transform of a real correlation function of this sort should be associated with $\tilde{S}(\mathbf{Q},\omega)$ rather than $S(\mathbf{Q},\omega)$ so that the condition of detailed balance is not violated. In other words in going to the classical limit $\hbar\to0$ one has to be careful as $\hbar\omega\to0$. The correlation function proposed by Vineyard is

$$G_v(\mathbf{r},\tau) = \{2\pi w^2(\tau)\}^{-\frac{3}{2}}\ e^{-r^2/2w^2(\tau)} \qquad (1.40)$$

where

$$w(\tau)\to\left(\frac{kT}{2M}\right)^{\frac{1}{2}}|\tau| \text{ for small times}$$

and

$$w(\tau)\to(2D|\tau|\ +C)^{\frac{1}{2}} \text{ for long times.}$$

The behaviour of the width function $w(\tau)$ for small times corresponds to that for a free particle (perfect gas) while for long times $w(\tau)$ is of the form appropriate to diffusive motion. Thus D is the coefficient of self-diffusion and C is a constant introduced to allow for the possibility of a departure, at long

14 W. M. LOMER AND G. G. LOW

times, from the ideal asymptotic value of mean square displacement of $6D|\tau|$ (as a result of complicated behaviour at intermediate times). The scattering law function corresponding to (1.40) is

$$\tilde{S}_v(\mathbf{Q},\omega) = \frac{1}{2\pi\hbar}\int d\tau \, e^{-i\omega\tau - \frac{1}{2}Q^2w^2(\tau)}. \tag{1.41}$$

Short interaction times correspond to large changes in momentum $\hbar Q$ while for large interaction times the only important atomic motions are diffusive in character.

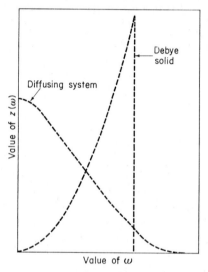

FIG. 1.4. Plots of the $z(\omega)$ function for (I) an ideal fluid and (II) a Debye solid (Egelstaff, 1961).

In dealing with the dynamics of liquids it is often simpler to consider the velocity correlation rather than treating the displacement directly (de Gennes, 1959 and Schofield, 1961). For a system in thermal equilibrium it can be shown that the second time derivative of the mean square displacement $u^2(\tau)$ is twice the correlation function for the velocity of the atoms, i.e.

$$\frac{d^2}{dt^2}\{u^2(\tau)\} = 2\,\overline{\mathbf{v}(0)\cdot\mathbf{v}(\tau)}. \tag{1.42}$$

For the Gaussian approximation of equation (1.40) the width function $w^2(\tau)$ is related to $u^2(\tau)$ by $w^2(\tau) = \frac{1}{3}u^2(\tau)$. Egelstaff (1961) has pointed out that the velocity correlation may be obtained from the experimental data via the even form of the scattering law (equation (1.39)). Thus, from $\tilde{S}(Q,\omega)$ the functions

$$p(\omega) = \frac{2M}{kT}\,\omega^2\left[\frac{\tilde{S}(Q,\omega)}{Q^2}\right]_{Q\to 0} \tag{1.43}$$

and

$$z(\omega) = \frac{2kT}{\hbar\omega} \sinh\left(\frac{\hbar\omega}{2kT}\right) p(\omega) \qquad (1.44)$$

may be obtained. $z(\omega)$ is the "spectral density" of the motion of a single atom in the system (see, for a mathematical discussion, Weiner, 1930). For a crystal $z(\omega)$ is equal to the usual frequency distribution. Examples for other systems are given in Fig. 1.4. The function $z(\omega)$ may be related immediately to the velocity correlation of a particle. Thus, according to the elegant discussion of Rahman $et\ al.$ (1962) the real and imaginary parts of $\overline{\mathbf{v}(0) . \mathbf{v}(\tau)}$, denoted respectively by Re (v) and Im (v), are connected with the frequency distribution by the relations

$$z(\omega) = \frac{4M}{3\pi\hbar} \frac{\tanh\left(\dfrac{\hbar\omega}{2kT}\right)}{\omega} \int\limits_0^\infty d\tau \cos(\omega\tau) \,\mathrm{Re}\,(v) \qquad (1.45)$$

$$= \frac{4M}{3\pi\hbar} \frac{1}{\omega} \int\limits_0^\infty d\tau \sin(\omega\tau) \,\mathrm{Im}\,(v). \qquad (1.46)$$

1.6 The Eigenfunction Formulation

The expression (1.18) is useful when studying any system, but in many simple cases it is advantageous to use some knowledge of the dynamics of the scatterer to evaluate the operator $\mathbf{R_n}(\tau)$. This is done by expressing the scattering cross-section in terms of the eigenstates of the scatterer. The time dependent operator $\mathbf{R_n}(\tau)$ may be transformed into the Schrödinger representation by the standard transformation

$$\mathbf{R_n}(0) = e^{\frac{iH\tau}{\hbar}} \mathbf{R_n}(\tau) \, e^{-\frac{iH\tau}{\hbar}} \qquad (1.47)$$

where H is the Hamiltonian governing the motion of the nucleus $\mathbf{n}$. Using this, the scattering potential in the Schrödinger representation becomes

$$V = \sum_\mathbf{n} \frac{2\pi\hbar^2}{m} b_\mathbf{n} \, e^{\frac{iH\tau}{\hbar}} \delta\{\mathbf{r} - \mathbf{R_n}(\tau)\} e^{-\frac{iH\tau}{\hbar}} \qquad (1.48)$$

The matrix element for a change of neutron state from $\mathbf{k}_0, E$ to $\mathbf{k}_0 + \mathbf{Q}$, $E + \hbar\omega$, is then ($\Delta E = E_\text{initial} - E_\text{final}$)

$$\frac{m}{2\pi\hbar^2} \langle \mathbf{k}_0 + \mathbf{Q} | V | \mathbf{k}_0 \rangle = \sum_\mathbf{n} b_\mathbf{n} \int d\tau \, e^{-i(\Delta E + \hbar\omega)\tau/\hbar} \langle f | \, e^{i\mathbf{Q}\cdot\mathbf{r}} \delta(\mathbf{r} - \mathbf{R_n}) | i \rangle$$

$$= 2\pi\hbar \sum_\mathbf{n} b_\mathbf{n} \langle f | e^{i\mathbf{Q}\cdot\mathbf{r}} \delta(\mathbf{r} - \mathbf{R_n}) | i \rangle \delta(\Delta E + \hbar\omega). \qquad (1.49)$$

This may now be substituted into the general formula (120.1) of Landau and Lifshitz (1958) giving, after rearrangement, the contribution to the cross-section of the process involving the excitation of the crystal from state i to state f, i.e.

$$\frac{d^2\sigma}{d\Omega dE} \propto \frac{k}{k_0} \sum_{m,n} b_m b_n \langle i|e^{-i\mathbf{Q}\cdot\mathbf{R_m}}|f\rangle \langle f|e^{i\mathbf{Q}\cdot\mathbf{R_n}}|i\rangle \delta(\Delta E + \hbar\omega). \tag{1.50}$$

The required cross-section is obtained by summing over all final states, and over all initial states weighted by their thermal occupation probability P_i. Thus,

$$\frac{d^2\sigma}{d\Omega dE} = \frac{k}{k_0} \sum_{\substack{m,n \\ i,f}} P_i b_m b_n \langle i|e^{-i\mathbf{Q}\cdot\mathbf{R_m}}|f\rangle \langle f|e^{i\mathbf{Q}\cdot\mathbf{R_n}}|i\rangle \delta(\Delta E + \hbar\omega). \tag{1.51}$$

This is a key expression. It corresponds to the eigenfunction formulation version of equation (1.18). Given a knowledge of the eigenstates of a system the neutron scattering cross-section is immediately calculable from equation (1.51). This method of approach has been widely used in connection with phonons and also for spin wave scattering (see Section 1.15 for a discussion of the modifications required to cover this case). When all the atoms concerned are identical and the scatterer is a perfect crystal the states i and f may be associated with wave vectors $\mathbf{q'}$ and $\mathbf{q}$. The matrix elements (1.49) then take the form

$$\sum_n e^{i\mathbf{q}\cdot\mathbf{R_n}} e^{i\mathbf{Q}\cdot\mathbf{R_n}} e^{-i\mathbf{q'}\cdot\mathbf{R_n}}.$$

$\mathbf{R_n}$ is restricted to be a lattice point and so this sum is

$$N\delta(\mathbf{q}-\mathbf{q'}+\mathbf{Q}-2\pi\boldsymbol{\tau})$$

where N is the number of atoms and $\boldsymbol{\tau}$ is a reciprocal lattice vector (it is assumed for the moment that the $\mathbf{n}$ correspond to a primitive lattice). This then leads to the conservation of crystal momentum relationship,

$$\mathbf{Q} = \mathbf{q'} - \mathbf{q} + 2\pi\,\boldsymbol{\tau}. \tag{1.52}$$

It is often useful to separate off the part of equation (1.51) which is dependent on the mean values of b associated with the various sets of equivalent atoms. This part of the expression is known as the coherent cross-section (cf. equation (1.29)). Thus, for a single element, assuming that the various values of b are randomly distributed among the nuclei, we have that

$$\frac{d^2\sigma^{coh}}{d\Omega dE} = \frac{k}{k_0} \bar{b}^2 \sum_{\substack{m,n \\ i,f}} P_i \langle i|e^{-i\mathbf{Q}\cdot\mathbf{R_m}}|f\rangle \langle f|e^{i\mathbf{Q}\cdot\mathbf{R_n}}|i\rangle \; \delta(\Delta E + \hbar\omega). \tag{1.53}$$

The remainder of the cross-section (1.51) which is left after subtracting off the coherent component (1.53) is known as the incoherent cross-section. For an element we see that the incoherent term is proportional to

$$\frac{1}{N} \sum_{\langle m,n \rangle} b_m b_n \delta_{mn} - \bar{b}^2 = \overline{b^2} - \bar{b}^2,$$

i.e. $\dfrac{\mathrm{d}^2\sigma^{inc}}{\mathrm{d}\Omega \mathrm{d}E} = \dfrac{k}{k_0} (\overline{b^2} - \bar{b}^2) \sum_{\substack{n \\ i,f}} P_i \langle i | e^{-i\mathbf{Q} \cdot \mathbf{R_n}} | f \rangle \langle f | e^{i\mathbf{Q} \cdot \mathbf{R_n}} | i \rangle \delta(\Delta E + \hbar\omega).$ (1.54)

(cf. equation (1.30)).

1.7 Nuclear Elastic Scattering in a Crystal

For the study of elastic scattering ω is set equal to zero by definition. The integration over τ in equation (1.18) is then dominated by times which are effectively infinitely great compared with the physical correlation times in the equation. Hence we may write :

$$\frac{\mathrm{d}\sigma}{\mathrm{d}\Omega} = \sum_{m,n} b_m b_n \overline{e^{i\mathbf{Q} \cdot \{\mathbf{R_n}(0) - \mathbf{R_m}(\infty)\}}}$$ (1.55)

If the nuclear positions are written as a sum of an equilibrium position $\mathbf{P_n}$ and a small displacement $\mathbf{u_n}$, then using

$$\mathbf{R_n} = \mathbf{P_n} + \mathbf{u_n},$$ (1.56)

equation (1.55) can be expanded as follows

$$\frac{\mathrm{d}\sigma}{\mathrm{d}\Omega} = \sum_{m,n} b_m b_n \, e^{i\mathbf{Q} \cdot (\mathbf{P_n} - \mathbf{P_m})} \overline{\left[1 + \frac{i}{1!} \mathbf{Q} \cdot \{\mathbf{u_n}(0) - \mathbf{u_m}(\infty)\} - \right.}$$
$$\overline{\left. \frac{1}{2!} \{\mathbf{Q} \cdot (\mathbf{u_n}(0) - \mathbf{u_m}(\infty))\}^2 - \frac{i}{3!} \{\mathbf{Q} \cdot (\mathbf{u_n}(0) - \mathbf{u_m}(\infty))\}^3 + \dots \right]}.$$ (1.57)

In the harmonic approximation (see Section 1.10) the nuclear displacements are distributed in a Gaussian fashion and in these circumstances equation (1.57) may be written in the form

$$\frac{\mathrm{d}\sigma}{\mathrm{d}\Omega} = \sum b_m b_n \, e^{i\mathbf{Q} \cdot (\mathbf{P_n} - \mathbf{P_m})} \, e^{-(W_n + W_m)}$$ (1.58)

where W_n, the Debye-Waller parameter, is equal to $\overline{(\mathbf{Q} \cdot \mathbf{u_n})^2}/2$. For spherical or cubic symmetry $W = Q^2\overline{u^2}/6$ where $\overline{u^2}$ is the mean square deviation of the positions of the nuclei concerned. For a crystal containing one atom per unit cell W may be evaluated in the Debye approximation and related to the Debye temperature Θ, thus (see Weinstock, 1944)

$$W = \frac{3\hbar^2 Q^2}{2Mk\Theta} \left\{ \frac{1}{4} + \frac{1}{\zeta^2} \int_0^\zeta \frac{\xi \mathrm{d}\xi}{e^\xi - 1} \right\}$$ (1.59)

where $\zeta = \dfrac{\Theta}{T}$. Equation (1.58) may be rewritten as

$$\frac{d\sigma}{d\Omega} = \sum_n b_n^2\, e^{-2W_n} + \sum_{m,n}^{m\neq n} b_m b_n\, e^{i\mathbf{Q}\cdot(\mathbf{P_n}-\mathbf{P_m})}\, e^{-(W_n+W_m)} \qquad (1.60)$$

and on the assumption that, among the atoms of a given chemical species there is no correlation between the value of the scattering length and position in the crystal, i.e. assuming isotopic disorder and a random distribution of spin orientations, this result can be expressed as follows:

$$\frac{d\sigma}{d\Omega} = N \sum_l (\overline{b_l^2}-\bar{b}_l^2)\, e^{-2W_l} + \sum_{u,v} e^{i\mathbf{Q}\cdot(\mathbf{P_v}-\mathbf{P_u})} \sum_{k,l} \bar{b}_k \bar{b}_l\, e^{i\mathbf{Q}\cdot(\rho_l-\rho_k)}\, e^{-(W_l+W_k)} \qquad (1.61)$$

where $\mathbf{P_u}$, $\mathbf{P_v}$ refer to positions on a basis lattice and ρ_k, ρ_l to positions in a unit cell. Thus, $\mathbf{u}$, $\mathbf{v}$ run over the N positions of the basis lattice and $\mathbf{k}$ and $\mathbf{l}$ over the L positions in a unit cell.

The cross-section has now been resolved into two parts very different in nature: namely the incoherent cross-section given by

$$\frac{d\sigma^{inc}}{d\Omega} = N \sum_l (\overline{b_l^2}-\bar{b}_l^2)\, e^{-2W} \qquad (1.62)$$

and the coherent cross-section

$$\frac{d\sigma^{coh}}{d\Omega} = |\sum_v e^{i\mathbf{Q}\cdot\mathbf{P_v}}|^2\, |\sum_l \bar{b}_l\, e^{i\mathbf{Q}\cdot\rho_l}\, e^{-W_l}|^2. \qquad (1.63)$$

The interference effects giving rise to the coherent cross-section depend only on the average scattering lengths of the nuclei: the mean square deviation from this average gives the incoherent scattering, i.e.

$$\overline{(b-\bar{b})^2} = \frac{1}{N} \sum_v (b_v^2 - 2b_v\bar{b} + \bar{b}^2) = \overline{b^2} - \bar{b}^2. \qquad (1.64)$$

(cf. equations (1.53) and (1.54) and also (1.29) and (1.30)).

1.8 Nuclear Bragg Scattering

It is convenient at this point to make use of the properties of the reciprocal lattice. Because the Fourier transform of the scattering power of the crystal involves only reciprocal lattice vectors $\boldsymbol{\tau}$ where $\boldsymbol{\tau}\cdot\mathbf{P} =$ integer, when $\mathbf{P}$ is a lattice vector, it follows that the coherent scattering cross-section can be expressed in terms of delta functions with arguments dependent on such vectors. Thus, in exact analogy with standard X-ray results (see Cassels, 1950)

$$\frac{d\sigma^{coh}}{d\Omega} = \frac{(2\pi)^3}{V}\, N \sum_\tau \delta(\mathbf{Q}-2\pi\boldsymbol{\tau})|F_\tau|^2 \qquad (1.65)$$

where V is the volume of a unit cell in the crystal and

$$F_\tau = \sum_l \bar{b}_l\, e^{i2\pi\tau \cdot \rho_l}\, e^{-W_l} \qquad (1.66)$$

is the structure factor for the reflection defined by $\mathbf{Q} = 2\pi\boldsymbol{\tau}$. The subscript l runs over the L sites in a unit cell.

A useful construction due to Ewald embodying the Bragg scattering condition $\mathbf{Q} = 2\pi\boldsymbol{\tau}$ is shown in Figure 1.5. This construction is made as

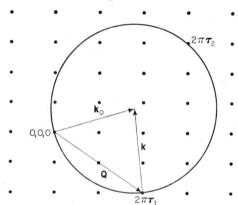

FIG. 1.5. Diagram showing a construction in reciprocal space for the determination of the conditions for Bragg reflection (the Ewald construction).

follows. In reciprocal space draw $\mathbf{k}_0$ from the 0,0,0 position and then with the position $\mathbf{k}_0$ as centre describe a sphere of radius k. Any point on this sphere corresponds to some $\mathbf{Q}$ given by $\mathbf{Q} = \mathbf{k}_0 - \mathbf{k}$, where $k_0 = k$. Should the sphere pass through a reciprocal lattice point $2\pi\boldsymbol{\tau}_1$, then Bragg reflection from the corresponding planes will occur in a direction given by the k of the construction for that point. On account of this property the sphere is known as the sphere of reflection.

It is clear that diffraction by a set of lattice planes can take place only if $|\boldsymbol{\tau}| \leqslant \dfrac{k}{\pi}$. The condition $\lambda = \dfrac{2}{|\boldsymbol{\tau}|_{\text{minimum}}}$ defines the so-called Bragg scattering cut-off. Neutrons with wavelengths exceeding the Bragg limit cannot suffer coherent diffraction in a perfect crystal.

For a polycrystal in which the planes have random orientations the total cross-section for coherent scattering is found to be (e.g. Cassels, 1950)

$$\frac{\lambda^2}{2V} N \sum_{|\tau| \leqslant \frac{2}{\lambda}} |F_\tau|^2\, |\tau|^{-1} \qquad (1.67)$$

This cross-section shows discontinuous decreases in magnitude with increasing wavelength as various planes cease to be effective as scatterers (see

Fig. 1.6). The Bragg cut-off corresponds to a sudden transition between low and high transmission properties. This feature is made use of in neutron apparatus and forms the basis of the neutron filter technique.

Mention may be made at this point of a topic which is of considerable practical importance in connection with diffraction experiments on account of the limitation it can impose on the ultimate accuracy of a measurement. This is the phenomenon known as extinction.

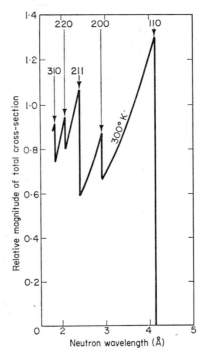

Fɪɢ. 1.6. The calculated total cross-section versus neutron wavelength corresponding to the elastic coherent scattering from the nuclei in a sample of polycrystalline iron. The ordinate scale is expressed in terms of the ratio of the cross-section per atom of the sample to the nuclear coherent cross-section of an iron atom (Cassels, 1950).

If single crystals were perfect almost all of the neutrons of Bragg wavelength would be reflected in a depth of crystal a few atomic layers thick and the majority of the specimen would not be irradiated by unscattered neutrons at all. In reality, however, all crystals are divided up by dislocations into small blocks which show a spread of misorientations relative to one another, known as the mosaic spread. This means that on the whole the various blocks will reflect neutrons of any given wavelength at slightly different angular settings of the crystal and the penetration into the crystal will be considerable. The integrated intensity is then greater, since reflection takes place over a greater angular range. However, diminution in neutron intensity still takes place as the incident beam traverses the specimen and unless this is negligible, extinction is said to prevail. If the diminution results from the beam passing through a considerable length of specimen and hence encountering a number of blocks of the same orientation each one of which is bathed in practically uniform radiation, the extinction is said to be secondary. Primary extinction would occur if the blocks were so large that the beam was attenuated appreciably by passing through one of them. A quantitative account of extinction is contained in the literature (Bacon and Lowde, 1948).

Finally, reference may be made of the phenomenon of multiple Bragg scattering. In Fig. 1.5 it will be seen that should the sphere of reflection pass through a second reciprocal lattice point τ_2, then it is possible to regard neutrons reflected by the lattice planes corresponding to τ_2 as being incident on to the planes denoted by τ_1. Doubly scattered neutrons reflected by first the τ_2 and then the $\tau_1 - \tau_2$ planes have just the direction and wavelength of neutrons reflected once by the τ_1 planes. Thus, the intensity of a particular single reflection may be either enhanced or diminished by multiple reflections. This can be a complication when careful measurements of the relative intensities of various Bragg reflections are being made. Other difficulties originating in double scattering can arise also. For example, as a result of such scattering, a crystal used as a monochromator may show scattering according to an undesired reflection which is nominally absent because it is forbidden by a structure factor when only single reflections are considered. Because double scattering can involve neutrons travelling between reflections in the crystal in a direction normal to the incident beam, appreciable broadening of the beam may result if the specimen is wider than the beam. The multiply scattered neutrons will, of course, also show a greater angular divergence than singly scattered neutrons. In experiments involving the examination of a polycrystal with a monochromatic beam, multiple Bragg scattering gives rise to a diffuse scattering having a complicated dependence on angle which can add considerably to the difficulty of a measurement (see Vineyard, 1954, Brockhouse *et al.*, 1955 and Lowde and Wheeler, 1962). Further discussion of the above points and their practical consequences may be found in Chapter 3.

1.9 Scattering From Alloys and Incoherent Elastic Scattering

As yet the deviations in the scattering length b which give rise to the incoherent scattering described in Section 1.7 have not been considered. In a crystal containing a single chemical species, variations in b from site to site will arise from the random distribution of nuclear spin orientations if the nuclei concerned have spin, or from the presence of isotopes. Both these effects are included in the cross-sections for elements quoted in the "Barn Book".

The incoherent cross-section per atom for a completely disordered alloy containing several chemical species may be found as follows (we omit the Debye-Waller factor throughout this section):

$$\mathscr{S}_{\text{alloy}} = 4\pi(\overline{b^2} - \overline{b}^2)$$

$$= 4\pi\left\{\sum_i c_i(\overline{b_i^2} - \overline{b}_i^2) + \sum_i c_i(1 - c_i)\overline{b}_i^2 - \overset{i \neq j}{\sum_{i,j}} c_i c_j \overline{b}_i \overline{b}_j\right\} \tag{1.68}$$

where c_i and b_i are the fractional concentration and scattering length for constituent number i.

For a binary alloy of intermediate order the differential cross-section per atom may be written

$$\frac{1}{NL} \sum_{m,n} b_m b_n\, e^{i\mathbf{Q}\cdot(\mathbf{P_n}-\mathbf{P_m})}$$

$$= c_1\overline{b}_1^2 + c_2\overline{b}_2^2 + \overset{\mathbf{r} \neq 0}{\sum_{\mathbf{r}}}\left\{g_{11}(\mathbf{r})\overline{b}_1^2 + g_{22}(\mathbf{r})\overline{b}_2^2 + g_{12}(\mathbf{r})\overline{b}_1\overline{b}_2\right\}e^{i\mathbf{Q}\cdot\mathbf{r}} \tag{1.69}$$

where

$$g_{ij}(\mathbf{r}) = \frac{1}{N(\mathbf{r})} \overset{m \neq n}{\sum_{m,n}} \delta\{\mathbf{r} + \mathbf{P_m}(i) - \mathbf{P_n}(j)\}. \tag{1.70}$$

$\mathbf{P_m}(i)$ denotes the set of positions of constituent i and $N(\mathbf{r})$ is the number of pairs of atoms in the crystal joined by vector $\mathbf{r}$: $g_{ij}(\mathbf{r})$ is the fraction of the total number of pairs of sites connected by the vector $\mathbf{r}$ in which an atom of constituent i is connected to an atom of constituent j. Such functions are known as pair distribution functions and they correspond to the static limiting case of the correlation functions described in Section 1.3. Because the values of pair distribution functions must be consistent with the gross composition of the crystal it follows that for the binary system at present under discussion

$$c_1 = g_{11}(\mathbf{r}) + \tfrac{1}{2}g_{12}(\mathbf{r}), \tag{1.71}$$

$$c_2 = g_{22}(\mathbf{r}) + \tfrac{1}{2}g_{12}(\mathbf{r}). \tag{1.72}$$

A short range order parameter is conveniently defined in terms of the deviation of $g_{12}(\mathbf{r})$ from the value $2c_1c_2$ corresponding to a random disordered system, divided by the deviation of a completely ordered system from $2c_1c_2$, i.e.

$$\frac{g_{12}(\mathbf{r}) - 2c_1c_2}{g'_{12}(\mathbf{r}) - 2c_1c_2} \tag{1.73}$$

where $g'_{12}(\mathbf{r})$ is the pair distribution function for complete order. Also it may be noted that

$$g_{12}(0) \equiv 0. \tag{1.74}$$

Thus, expression (1.69) for the differential scattering cross-section per atom may be rearranged as follows:

$$c_1\overline{b_1^2} + c_1\overline{b_2^2} + \sum_{\mathbf{r}}^{\mathbf{r} \neq 0} \{c_1\overline{b_1^2} + c_2\overline{b_2^2} - \tfrac{1}{2}g_{12}(\mathbf{r})(\overline{b_1^2} + \overline{b_2^2} - 2\overline{b_1}\overline{b_2})\} \; e^{i\mathbf{Q}\cdot\mathbf{r}}$$

$$= c_1\frac{\mathscr{S}_1}{4\pi} + c_2\frac{\mathscr{S}_2}{4\pi} + \overline{b}^2 \sum_{\mathbf{r}} e^{i\mathbf{Q}\cdot\mathbf{r}} + (\overline{b_1} - \overline{b_2})^2 \sum_{\mathbf{r}} \{c_1c_2 - \tfrac{1}{2}g_{12}(\mathbf{r})\} \; e^{i\mathbf{Q}\cdot\mathbf{r}}$$

It is seen that the cross-section is divided into the usual incoherent and coherent parts together with a term containing the pair distribution function $g_{12}(\mathbf{r})$. For a random distribution $g_{12}(\mathbf{r}) = 2c_1c_2$ and the latter disappears except for $\mathbf{r} = 0$.

1.10 Inelastic Scattering: Ideal Lattice Vibrations

An expression for the potential energy of a system of particles may be developed as a power series in particle displacements from equilibrium (see for example Ziman, 1960). For small amplitudes of vibration this series development can be broken off at the quadratic terms, resulting in a homogeneous quadratic form for the potential energy. If the potential energy is expressed in this way we may write it as

$$\tfrac{1}{2} \sum_{\substack{v,l,\alpha \\ u,k,\beta}} G_{\mathbf{u}\mathbf{k}\beta}^{\mathbf{v}\mathbf{l}\alpha} u_{\mathbf{v}\mathbf{l}}^{\alpha} u_{\mathbf{u}\mathbf{k}}^{\beta} \tag{1.76}$$

where $u_{\mathbf{v}\mathbf{l}}^{\alpha}$ is the α-component of the displacement of the atom labelled by $\mathbf{l}$ in the unit cell at position $\mathbf{v}$ on the basis lattice, and the $\mathbf{G}$ are the force constants which define the dynamics of the lattice. The kinetic energy is of course quadratic in the particle momenta, and the classical vibration problem can be solved in terms of $3NL$ normal modes, each of which behaves like an independent harmonic oscillator. The periodicity of the crystal lattice allows us to establish that these normal modes are wave-like states and a first step in setting them up is to define the Fourier transforms $\mathscr{U}$ of the atomic displacements u,

$$\mathscr{U}_{\mathbf{q}\mathbf{l}}^{\alpha} = \frac{1}{N} \sum_{\mathbf{v}} e^{-i\mathbf{q}\cdot\mathbf{P}\mathbf{v}} u_{\mathbf{v}\mathbf{l}}^{\alpha}$$

$$u_{\mathbf{v}\mathbf{l}}^{\alpha} = \sum_{\mathbf{q}} e^{i\mathbf{q}\cdot\mathbf{P}\mathbf{v}} \mathscr{U}_{\mathbf{q}\mathbf{l}}^{\alpha} \tag{1.77}$$

where the wave vector $\mathbf{q}$ may be regarded as occupying the first Brillouin zone with a density of $NV/(2\pi)^3$. The momentum of a single atom is simply

$M_1 \frac{\partial}{\partial t} u^\alpha_{vl}$; the momentum conjugate to the Fourier transformed displacement $\mathcal{U}^\alpha_{ql}$ is, however, easily seen (by evaluating the commutator in detail) to be $M_1 \frac{\partial}{\partial t} \mathcal{U}^\alpha_{-ql}$. Only the $3L$ states (distinguished by the label s) of the same q are interdependent (though we must remember that the vector $-q$ is associated with conjugate functions and must be carried for the time being as an independent state). Determination of the normal modes for any particular q then involves the solution of $3L$ simultaneous equations to determine the relative amplitudes of the various displacements $\mathcal{U}^\alpha_{ql}$ (i.e. to determine the polarization vector $V^{l\alpha}_s(\mathbf{q})$).

The Hamiltonian is

$$H = \tfrac{1}{2} \sum_{v,l,\alpha} M_l \left(\frac{du^\alpha_v}{dt}\right)^2 + \tfrac{1}{2} \sum_{\substack{v,l,\alpha \\ u,k,\beta}} G^{vl\alpha}_{uk\beta} u^\alpha_{vl} u^\beta_{uk} \tag{1.78}$$

and substitution for u in terms of $\mathcal{U}$ leads to

$$H = \frac{N}{2} \sum_{q,l,\alpha} M_l \frac{d\mathcal{U}^\alpha_{ql}}{dt} \frac{d\mathcal{U}^\alpha_{-ql}}{dt} + \frac{N}{2} \sum_{\substack{q,l,k \\ \alpha,\beta}} \mathcal{U}^\alpha_{ql} \Big\{ \sum_{u,v} G^{vl\alpha}_{uk\beta} \, e^{iq \cdot (\mathbf{P}_u - \mathbf{P}_v)} \Big\} \mathcal{U}^\beta_{-qk} \tag{1.79}$$

Introducing $U_l = \mathcal{U}_l M_l^{\frac{1}{2}}$ we have

$$H = \frac{N}{2} \sum_{q,l,\alpha} \frac{dU^\alpha_{ql}}{dt} \frac{dU^\alpha_{-ql}}{dt} + \frac{N}{2} \sum_{\substack{q,l,k \\ \alpha,\beta}} U^\alpha_{ql} E^{\alpha l}_{\beta k}(\mathbf{q}) U^\beta_{-qk} \tag{1.80}$$

where

$$E^{\alpha l}_{\beta k}(\mathbf{q}) = \sum_{u,v} G^{vl\alpha}_{uk\beta} \, e^{iq \cdot (\mathbf{P}_u - \mathbf{P}_v)} M_l^{-\frac{1}{2}} M_k^{-\frac{1}{2}} \tag{1.81}$$

is known as the dynamical matrix. Each term in $\mathbf{q}$ is now separated from all other $\mathbf{q}$ values.

The classical equations of motion for the Hamiltonian (1.80) may be written

$$\frac{\partial^2}{\partial t^2} U^\alpha_{ql} = -\sum_{\beta,k} E^{\alpha l}_{\beta k}(-\mathbf{q}) U^\beta_{qk} \tag{1.82}$$

and we may seek a solution where the displacements are of the form

$$\phi_{qs}(0) \, V^{l\alpha}_s(\mathbf{q}) \, e^{-if_{qs}t} \tag{1.83}$$

where $\phi_{qs}(0)$ is a scalar amplitude undetermined by the dynamical equations. The $3L$ eigenvalues of f_{qs} are the solutions of the secular equation

$$\det \{ E^{\alpha l}_{\beta k}(\mathbf{q}) - f^2_{qs} \delta_{kl} \delta_{\alpha\beta} \} = 0 \tag{1.84}$$

and the coefficients $V^{l\alpha}_s(\mathbf{q})$ are the components of the corresponding eigenvectors. They may be regarded as the components of a $3L$ dimensional vector of unit length called the polarization vector for mode $\mathbf{q}s$. These vectors may be shown to be orthogonal in the sense that

$$\sum_{\mathbf{l},\alpha} V_s^{l\alpha}(\mathbf{q}) V_{s'}^{*l\alpha}(\mathbf{q}) = \delta_{ss'}$$

The terms with the negative frequencies (the complex conjugate solutions) must be combined with the others to ensure real displacements, and finally we arrive at

$$u_{\mathbf{v}\mathbf{l}}^{\alpha} M_{\mathbf{l}}^{\frac{1}{2}} = \sum_{\mathbf{q},s} \{\phi_{\mathbf{q}s}(0)\, \mathrm{e}^{-if_{\mathbf{q}s}t + i\mathbf{q}\cdot\mathbf{P_v}} V_s^{l\alpha}(\mathbf{q}) + \phi_{\mathbf{q}s}^{*}(0)\, \mathrm{e}^{if_{\mathbf{q}s}t - i\mathbf{q}\cdot\mathbf{P_v}} V_s^{*l\alpha}(\mathbf{q})\} \qquad (1.85)$$

and conversely

$$\phi_{\mathbf{q}s}(t) = \frac{1}{2N} \sum_{\mathbf{v},\mathbf{l},\alpha} \mathrm{e}^{-i\mathbf{q}\cdot\mathbf{P_v}} V_s^{*l\alpha} M_{\mathbf{l}}^{\frac{1}{2}} \left(u_{\mathbf{v}\mathbf{l}}^{\alpha} + \frac{i}{f_{\mathbf{q}s}}\, \dot{u}_{\mathbf{v}\mathbf{l}}^{\alpha} \right). \qquad (1.86)$$

The total energy is then expressed in terms of the amplitude operators ϕ as

$$H = N \sum_{\mathbf{q},s} f_{\mathbf{q}s}^{2}\{\phi_{\mathbf{q}s}(t)\phi_{\mathbf{q}s}^{*}(t) + \phi_{\mathbf{q}s}^{*}(t)\, \phi_{\mathbf{q}s}(t)\}, \qquad (1.87)$$

where the form chosen is correct for quantization when ϕ and ϕ^* do not commute. The classical amplitude $\phi(0)$ is therefore determined by $|\phi(0)|^2 - E/2Nf^2$, where E is the energy in the mode. These "amplitude operators" are merely the creation and destruction operators (see for example Ziman, 1960) for the vibrational modes. If a state $\mathbf{q}s$ is occupied by n phonons, then the operator ϕ destroys a phonon; ϕ^* creates one (for convenience we drop the subscripts on ϕ and on f in the following equations and also in Sections 1.11 and 1.12):

$$\phi|n\rangle = \left(\frac{\hbar n}{2Nf}\right)^{\frac{1}{2}} |n-1\rangle$$

$$\phi^*|n\rangle = \left(\frac{\hbar(n+1)}{2Nf}\right)^{\frac{1}{2}} |n+1\rangle$$

and

$$\phi\phi^*|n\rangle = \frac{\hbar}{2Nf}(n+1)|n\rangle$$

$$\phi^*\phi|n\rangle = \frac{\hbar}{2Nf}n|n\rangle$$

$$\langle n|H|n\rangle = \sum \hbar f\,(n+\tfrac{1}{2}). \qquad (1.88)$$

The actual relations between the frequency and wave number in any crystal can be evaluated only if we have a detailed knowledge of the force constants $\mathbf{G}$. However, the few general properties are worth mentioning.

(i) In all crystals the modes associated with the three lowest branches of the dispersion relationship between f and q have $f \to 0$ as $q \to 0$, and are known as the acoustic modes. In these modes all atoms in a unit cell vibrate nearly in phase and the phonon is a normal sound wave. The frequency is linearly dependent on q for small q, and is related to the velocity c by $f = cq$. c depends on polarization; in isotropic media only two values, longitudinal and transverse, are distinct, but in general c is a function of polarization and of $\mathbf{q}$.

(ii) All other modes associated with the other $3(L-1)$ branches of the dispersion relationship are collectively known as optical modes because in simple ionic crystals the antiphase motion of the atoms in a unit cell produces a volume electric polarization which interacts with electromagnetic waves.

(iii) In molecular crystals the internal degrees of freedom may be little affected by the formation of the crystal, and the corresponding phonon branch may have an energy independent of wave number q and equal to that of the free molecule.

(iv) The mean occupation number of any phonon state in thermal equilibrium is related to its energy and the temperature by the Bose relationship

$$\bar{n} = (e^{hf/kT} - 1)^{-1}. \tag{1.89}$$

(v) The phonon states derived above are eigenstates of an ideal system in which the potential energy may be represented as a quadratic form in the displacements. A real crystal is "anharmonic" and higher terms in the potential give rise to finite phonon lifetimes and therefore a conjugate energy or frequency line width.

1.11 Nuclear Inelastic Scattering in a Crystal

The scattering amplitude in equation (1.16) may, with the aid of expressions (1.56) and (1.85), be expanded for the case of a Bravais lattice to give

$$
\begin{aligned}
|f(\omega)| &= \frac{1}{r'T} \int d\tau\, e^{-i\omega\tau} \sum_{\mathbf{n}} b_{\mathbf{n}}\, e^{i\mathbf{Q}\cdot\mathbf{R_n}(\tau)} \\
&= \frac{1}{r'T} \int d\tau \sum_{\mathbf{v}} b_{\mathbf{v}}\, e^{i(\mathbf{Q}\cdot\mathbf{P_v} - \omega\tau)} \times\ e^{i\mathbf{Q}\cdot\mathbf{u_v}(\tau)} \\
&= \frac{1}{r'T} \int d\tau \sum_{\mathbf{v}} b_{\mathbf{v}}\, e^{i(\mathbf{Q}\cdot\mathbf{P_v} - \omega\tau)} \times \\
&\quad \prod_{q,s}[1 + i\mathbf{Q}\cdot(\phi\, e^{-if\tau + i\mathbf{q}\cdot\mathbf{P_v}}\mathbf{V} + \phi^*\, e^{if\tau - i\mathbf{q}\cdot\mathbf{P_v}}\mathbf{V}^*)M^{-\frac{1}{2}} - \\
&\quad \tfrac{1}{2}\{\mathbf{Q}\cdot(\phi\, e^{-if\tau + i\mathbf{q}\cdot\mathbf{P_v}}\mathbf{V} + \phi^*\, e^{if\tau - i\mathbf{q}\cdot\mathbf{P_v}}\mathbf{V}^*)\}^2 M^{-1} + \ldots]
\end{aligned}
\tag{1.90}
$$

The form of the first and second terms in the expansion of the exponentials demonstrates immediately the existence of elastic and one-phonon processes in the scattering. Continuing with the consideration of a Bravais lattice and assuming that there is no correlation between the values of b_v and the lattice positions $\mathbf{P}_v$, we may write, from equation (1.18), that

$$\frac{d^2\sigma^{\mathrm{coh}}}{d\Omega dE} = \frac{\bar{b}^2}{2\pi\hbar}\frac{k}{k_0}\int_{-\infty}^{\infty} d\tau\, e^{-i\omega\tau} \times \sum_{\mathbf{u},\mathbf{v}} \overline{e^{i\mathbf{Q}\cdot\{\mathbf{R_v}(\tau)-\mathbf{R_u}(0)\}}} \tag{1.91}$$

and

$$\frac{d^2\sigma^{\mathrm{inc}}}{d\Omega dE} = \frac{\overline{b^2}-\bar{b}^2}{2\pi\hbar}\frac{k}{k_0}\int_{-\infty}^{\infty} d\tau\, e^{-i\omega\tau} \times \sum_{\mathbf{v}} \overline{e^{i\mathbf{Q}\cdot\{\mathbf{R_v}(\tau)-\mathbf{R_v}(0)\}}} \tag{1.92}$$

Thus, corresponding to the expansion in equation (1.90), we have for the coherent cross-section that

$$\frac{d^2\sigma^{\mathrm{coh}}}{d\Omega dE} = \frac{\bar{b}^2}{2\pi\hbar}\frac{k}{k_0}\int_{-\infty}^{\infty} d\tau\, e^{-i\omega\tau} \times \sum_{\mathbf{u},\mathbf{v}} e^{i\mathbf{Q}\cdot(\mathbf{P_v}-\mathbf{P_u})} \times$$

$$\prod_{\mathbf{q},s}[1+|\mathbf{Q}\cdot\mathbf{V}|^2\phi^*\phi\, e^{i\mathbf{q}\cdot(\mathbf{P_v}-\mathbf{P_u})-if\tau}M^{-1}+|\mathbf{Q}\cdot\mathbf{V}|^2\phi\phi^*\, e^{-i\mathbf{q}\cdot(\mathbf{P_v}-\mathbf{P_u})+if\tau}M^{-1}$$

$$-|\mathbf{Q}\cdot\mathbf{V}|^2(\phi^*\phi+\phi\phi^*)M^{-1}] \tag{1.93}$$

where only the lowest of those terms which do not sum to zero over the crystal are retained in the expansions of the exponentials. Using $\phi^*\phi+\phi\phi^* = \hbar(n+\tfrac{1}{2})/Nf$ and the relationship

$$\prod_{\mathbf{q},s}\left\{1-|\mathbf{Q}\cdot\mathbf{V}|^2\frac{\hbar(n+\tfrac{1}{2})}{NfM}\right\} \sim e^{-\sum_{\mathbf{q},s}|\mathbf{Q}\cdot\mathbf{V}|^2\frac{\hbar(n+\tfrac{1}{2})}{NfM}} = e^{-2W} \tag{1.94}$$

equation (1.58) may be re-derived for the case of a Bravais lattice if ω is put equal to zero. On the other hand if ω is non-zero and the factor corresponding to a particular phonon mode $\mathbf{q}s$ is withdrawn from the multiple product, we find that

$$\frac{d^2\sigma_1^{\mathrm{coh}}}{d\Omega dE} = \frac{\bar{b}^2}{2\pi\hbar}\sum_{\mathbf{q},s}\frac{k}{k_0}\int_{-\infty}^{\infty} d\tau\, e^{-i(\omega\mp f)\tau} \times \sum_{\mathbf{u},\mathbf{v}} e^{i(\mathbf{Q}\mp\mathbf{q})\cdot(\mathbf{P_v}-\mathbf{P_u})}|\mathbf{Q}\cdot\mathbf{V}|^2\frac{\hbar(n+\tfrac{1}{2}\pm\tfrac{1}{2})}{2NfM}e^{-2W}$$

$$= \bar{b}^2\sum_{\mathbf{q},s}\frac{k}{k_0}\delta(\hbar\omega\mp\hbar f) \times \frac{(2\pi)^3}{V}\sum_{\tau}\delta(\mathbf{Q}\mp\mathbf{q}-2\pi\tau)|\mathbf{Q}\cdot\mathbf{V}|^2\frac{\hbar(n+\tfrac{1}{2}\pm\tfrac{1}{2})}{2Mf}e^{-2W} \tag{1.95}$$

as the remainder of the multiple product is still equal very closely to e^{-2W} for N large. Thus, we have obtained the cross-section for one-phonon changes in the state of the crystal. The upper signs refer to phonon creation and the lower signs to phonon destruction processes. It will be recalled that $\hbar\omega = \frac{\hbar^2}{2m}(k_0^2-k^2)$ so that the first delta function is an expression of the law of conservation of energy. The second delta function defines the so-called crystal momentum conservation law. These two conditions stipulate the scattering surfaces in reciprocal space discussed in the next section. The phonon population is, of course, usually given by $\bar{n}$ of equation (1.89). If the crystal contains more than one atom per unit cell the cross-section becomes

$$\frac{d^2\sigma_1{}^{\text{coh}}}{d\Omega dE} = \frac{(2\pi)^3}{V} \sum_{q,s} \frac{k}{k_0} \delta(\hbar\omega \mp \hbar f) \times \sum_{\tau} \delta(\mathbf{Q} \mp \mathbf{q} - 2\pi\boldsymbol{\tau}) \frac{\hbar(n + \frac{1}{2} \pm \frac{1}{2})}{2f} \times$$
$$|\sum_{l} \bar{b}_l\, e^{i\mathbf{Q}\cdot\mathbf{p}_l}\mathbf{Q}\cdot\mathbf{V}^l M_l^{-\frac{1}{2}}\, e^{-W_l}|^2 \tag{1.96}$$

where the structure factor takes account of the amplitudes and phases of the various vibrating atoms through the polarization vectors $\mathbf{V}^l$ (Waller and Froman, 1952).

The incoherent scattering from a Bravais lattice due to one-phonon processes is

$$\frac{d^2\sigma_1{}^{\text{inc}}}{d\Omega dE} = (\overline{b^2} - \bar{b}^2) \sum_{q,s} \frac{k}{k_0} \delta(\hbar\omega \mp \hbar f)|\mathbf{Q}\cdot\mathbf{V}|^2 \frac{\hbar(n + \frac{1}{2} \pm \frac{1}{2})}{2Mf}\, e^{-2W} \tag{1.97}$$

where the same convention as regards signs is maintained. For a crystal containing more than one atom per unit cell the cross-section becomes

$$\frac{d^2\sigma_1{}^{\text{inc}}}{d\Omega dE} = \sum_{q,s} \frac{k}{k_0} \delta(\hbar\omega \mp \hbar f) \frac{\hbar(n + \frac{1}{2} \pm \frac{1}{2})}{2f} \sum_{l}(\overline{b^2} - \bar{b}^2)_l|\mathbf{Q}\cdot\mathbf{V}^l|^2\, M_l^{-1}\, e^{-2W_l}. \tag{1.98}$$

1.12 One-phonon Coherent Scattering

The physically observed cross-section is the result of summing over the phonon modes and integrating over the energy of the scattered neutrons. The summation is carried out by multiplying by the density of $\mathbf{q}$ vectors in reciprocal space, $NV/(2\pi)^3$, and integrating. Thus, from equation (1.95)

$$\frac{d^2\sigma_1{}^{\text{coh}}}{d\Omega dE} = Nb^2 \sum_{s} \frac{k}{k_0} \frac{\hbar(n + \frac{1}{2} \pm \frac{1}{2})}{2Mf}|\mathbf{Q}\cdot\mathbf{V}|^2\, e^{-2W}\delta(\hbar\omega \mp \hbar f) \tag{1.99}$$

where it is understood that $\pm \mathbf{q} = \mathbf{Q} - 2\pi\boldsymbol{\tau}$. As $\hbar\omega \mp \hbar f$ is a function of $E = \hbar^2 k^2/2m$, the integration over the δ-function involves the Jacobian

$$|\mathscr{J}| = \left|\frac{d(\hbar\omega \mp \hbar f)}{dE}\right|_{\omega \mp f = 0} = \left|1 \pm \frac{\hbar}{2E}\mathbf{k}\cdot\nabla_q f\right| \tag{1.100}$$

so that we find

$$\frac{d\sigma^{\text{coh}}}{d\Omega} = Nb^2 \sum_{s} \frac{k}{k_0} \frac{\hbar(n + \frac{1}{2} \pm \frac{1}{2})}{2Mf|\mathscr{J}|}|\mathbf{Q}\cdot\mathbf{V}|^2\, e^{-2W}. \tag{1.101}$$

The different behaviour at low temperatures of the two cross-sections is to be noted. The cross-section for the creation of phonons tends towards a

limiting finite value whereas the cross-section for phonon destruction tends
to zero as the temperature is reduced. At higher temperatures and for small
$\mathbf{q}$ vectors so that we may assume $\hbar f \ll kT$ and a linear relationship between f
and q such that $f/q = c$ (we are concerned only with acoustic phonons), we
have that

$$\frac{\mathrm{d}\sigma_1{}^{\mathrm{coh}}}{\mathrm{d}\Omega} \propto \frac{n + \frac{1}{2} \pm \frac{1}{2}}{f} \sim \frac{kT}{\hbar c^2 q^2} \qquad (1.102)$$

if we neglect the effect of the Jacobian.

The two conditions on the coherent scattering, namely

$$\pm\mathbf{q} = \mathbf{Q} - 2\pi\boldsymbol{\tau} \quad \text{and} \quad \pm\hbar f = \hbar\omega = \frac{\hbar^2}{2m}(k_0^2 - k^2)$$

define so-called scattering surfaces in reciprocal space. Under the approximations $f/q = c$ and $k_0/k \sim 1$, these may be discussed by elementary means

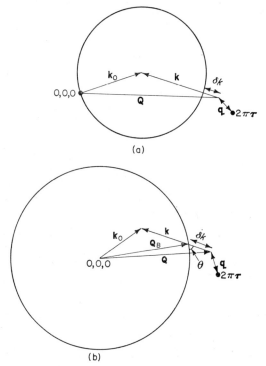

(a)

(b)

FIG. 1.7. Constructions in reciprocal space for determining the scattering surfaces in the
vicinity of a reciprocal lattice point corresponding to neutron–phonon interactions.

with the aid of the construction in Fig. 1.7(a). Thus, if the sphere of reflection is drawn in reciprocal space with radius k_0 about a centre at $\mathbf{k_0}$, the

distance from the surface of the sphere to the end of the $\mathbf{Q}$ vector (in a direction normal to the surface of the sphere) is

$$\delta k = \pm k_0 \mp k \sim \pm \frac{k_0^2 - k^2}{2k_0} = \frac{mf}{\hbar k_0} = \frac{c}{v}q \qquad (1.103)$$

where v is the velocity of the neutron. But this relationship between δk and q where both are small as assumed above simply defines a family of hyperboloids or ellipsoids with $2\pi\boldsymbol{\tau}$ as a pole and the sphere of reflection in the limit as a polar plane. Hyperboloids or ellipsoids, respectively, are obtained according to whether c/v is less than or greater than unity. These then, are the scattering surfaces traced out as the angle of scattering between $\mathbf{k_0}$ and $\mathbf{k}$ is varied. If this angle is maintained fixed and the orientation of the crystal varied then the surfaces defined may be found as follows (see Fig. 1.7(b)).

Draw the vector corresponding to $\mathbf{Q}_B = \mathbf{k_0} - \dfrac{k_0}{k}\mathbf{k}$ and with the origin of reciprocal space as centre describe a sphere of radius $|\mathbf{Q}_B|$. It is then found that the distance from the surface of the sphere to the end of the vector $\mathbf{Q}$ (in a direction normal to the surface of the sphere) is

$$\delta k' \sim \delta k \sin \theta \sim \frac{c}{v}\sin \theta q \qquad (1.104)$$

where θ is the semi-angle between $\mathbf{k_0}$ and $\mathbf{k}$, i.e. half the scattering angle. Again the surfaces are found to be hyperboloids and ellipsoids but with a different set of parameters.

1.13 Incoherent Scattering and the Density of Phonon States

If $|\mathbf{Q} . \mathbf{V}|^2$ in equation (1.97) is replaced by $\overline{|\mathbf{Q} . \mathbf{V}|^2}$ where the bar denotes that an average over a constant frequency surface has been taken, the incoherent cross-section may be written

$$\frac{d^2\sigma_1^{\text{inc}}}{d\Omega\,dE} = 3(\overline{b^2} - \bar{b}^2)\, N \int_0^\infty df\, z(f) \frac{k}{k_0} \overline{|\mathbf{Q} . \mathbf{V}|^2} \frac{\hbar(n + \frac{1}{2} \pm \frac{1}{2})}{2Mf} e^{-2W} \delta(\hbar\omega \mp \hbar f), \quad (1.105)$$

where the summation over $\mathbf{q}$ has been transformed to an integration over the density of phonon states. The factor 3 arises because of the three possible values of s. For cubic symmetry $\overline{|\mathbf{Q} . \mathbf{V}|^2} = Q^2/3$ so we then have

$$\frac{d^2\sigma_1^{\text{inc}}}{d\Omega dE} = (\overline{b^2} - \bar{b}^2)\, N\, \frac{z(f)}{f} \frac{k}{k_0} Q^2 \frac{n + \frac{1}{2} \pm \frac{1}{2}}{2M} e^{-2W} \qquad (1.106)$$

where it is understood that $\pm\hbar f = \hbar\omega$. The quantity $z(f)$ is just the number of phonon frequencies per unit frequency divided by the total number of frequencies of that polarization. Thus, $\int_0^\infty z(f)\,df = 1$.

1.14 Multi-phonon Scattering and Total Cross-sections for Inelastic Scattering

We give here a brief discussion of multi-phonon scattering and an evaluation of the total cross-sections for inelastic scattering, in particular from polycrystals. The treatment of such scattering is considerably simplified by two suggestions concerning the method of calculation to be used. These are, first, that to a reasonable approximation the coherent effects may be neglected and the cross-section evaluated as though all the scattering were incoherent, the coherent cross-section being added to the incoherent one. Thus, the scattering is taken to be proportional to $\overline{b}^2$. This is known as the incoherent approximation. The second suggestion concerns the method of summation to be used when evaluating the total cross-section for inelastic scattering. The sum over the terms representing 1-, 2-, 3-phonon processes, etc., is slowly convergent but Placzek pointed out that if the cross-section were expanded as a series in $1/M$ only a very few terms need be summed. This device is known as the Placzek mass expansion (see Placzek, 1954). The Debye frequency spectrum is often used in calculations of the present type. Marshall and Stuart (1961) have discussed the criterion determining the optimum Debye parameter.

Since phonons of different wave vector are independent in the present approximation, the generalization of equation (1.105) for the one-phonon incoherent scattering to the multi-phonon case is straightforward. We have now to consider a number of different phonon modes changing their populations by ± 1 and thus the p-phonon cross-section will contain a product of p factors of the type $|\mathbf{Q} \cdot \mathbf{V}|^2 |\phi|^2$. It can thus be shown that the scattering cross-section is (Marshall and Stuart, 1961)

$$\frac{\mathrm{d}^2\sigma_p^{\text{inc}}}{\mathrm{d}\Omega \mathrm{d}E} = \frac{(\overline{b^2} - \overline{b}^2)}{p!} N \frac{k}{k_0} \prod_{i=1}^{p} \left[\int_{-\infty}^{\infty} \mathrm{d}f_i \frac{z(f_i)}{f_i} \frac{\hbar Q^2/2M}{\mathrm{e}^{\hbar f_i/kT}-1} \right] \times \mathrm{e}^{-2W} \delta(\hbar\omega + \sum_i \hbar f_i), \quad (1.107)$$

where $z(f)$ for negative f is defined by $z(-f) = z(f)$ and cubic symmetry has been assumed. Using the Debye approximation it is possible to carry out the necessary integrations to obtain the cross-section σ_p^{inc}. The total inelastic incoherent cross-section is then given by

$$\sigma_{\text{inelastic}}^{\text{inc}} = \sum_{p=1}^{\infty} \sigma_p^{\text{inc}}. \quad (1.108)$$

However, as pointed out already, the series (1.108) is only slowly convergent and the total inelastic scattering cross-section is much more conveniently evaluated by means of the mass expansion where only a very few terms need be summed. Let us therefore write down the expression for incoherent scattering analogous to equation (1.93). We find that

$$\frac{d^2\sigma^{inc}}{d\Omega dE} = \frac{\overline{b^2}-\overline{b}^2}{2\pi\hbar}\frac{k}{k_0}\int_{-\infty}^{\infty} d\tau \; e^{-i\omega\tau} N\prod_{q,s}[1+|\mathbf{Q}.\mathbf{V}|^2 \; \phi^*\phi \; e^{-if\tau}M^{-1}+$$

$$|\mathbf{Q}.\mathbf{V}|^2 \; \phi\phi^* \; e^{if\tau}M^{-1}-|\mathbf{Q}.\mathbf{V}|^2 \; (\phi^*\phi+\phi\phi^*) \; M^{-1}]. \quad (1.109)$$

We now select those terms in the expression corresponding to inelastic scattering which depend on the first power of $1/M$, these are:

$$\frac{d^2\sigma^{inc}}{d\Omega dE}(1) = (\overline{b^2}-\overline{b}^2) \sum_{q,s} \frac{k}{k_0}\delta(\hbar\omega \mp \hbar f)|\mathbf{Q}.\mathbf{V}|^2\frac{\hbar(n+\frac{1}{2}\pm\frac{1}{2})}{2Mf} \quad (1.110)$$

There are two terms in $1/M^2$: the first is a correction to the one-phonon term arising from an expansion of the Debye-Waller term, and the second is the leading, uncorrected two-phonon term. Much of the two-phonon scattering is compensated by the loss of one-phonon cross-section. In the higher terms this kind of effect is even better matched and accounts for the success of the Placzek expansion for total cross-section. The term in $1/M^2$ is:

$$\frac{d^2\sigma^{inc}}{d\Omega dE}(2) = (\overline{b^2}-\overline{b}^2)2\frac{k}{k_0}\left[-W\delta(\hbar\omega\mp\hbar f)\sum_{q,s}|\mathbf{Q}.\mathbf{V}|^2\frac{\hbar(n+\frac{1}{2}\mp\frac{1}{2})}{2Mf}+\right.$$

$$\left.\frac{N}{4}\delta(\hbar\omega\mp\hbar f_1\mp\hbar f_2)\left\{\sum_{q,s}|\mathbf{Q}.\mathbf{V}_1|^2\frac{\hbar(n_1+\frac{1}{2}\pm\frac{1}{2})}{2MNf_1}\right\}\left\{\sum_{q,s}|\mathbf{Q}.\mathbf{V}_2|^2\frac{\hbar(n_2+\frac{1}{2}\pm\frac{1}{2})}{2MNf_2}\right\}\right] \quad (1.111)$$

The sums over $\mathbf{q}$ may be converted to integrals and, as $z(f) = z(-f)$, the expansions corresponding to phonon creation and destruction can be written in the same form, the integrations in the two cases being over the negative and positive half spaces, respectively. If this is done and if integrations over the scattered neutron energy and over scattering angle are carried out, then for cubic symmetry the total cross-sections for inelastic scattering corresponding to equations (1.110) and (1.111) are found to be (Marshall and Stuart, 1961)

$$\sigma^{inc}(1) = 4\pi \; (\overline{b^2}-\overline{b}^2)\frac{N\hbar}{2M}\frac{k}{k_0}(k_0^2+k^2)\times\int_{-\infty}^{\infty}\frac{df}{f}\frac{z(f)}{e^{\hbar f/kT}-1} \quad (1.112)$$

and

$$\sigma^{inc}(2) = 4\pi(\overline{b^2}-\overline{b}^2)\frac{N\hbar}{6M^2}\frac{k}{k_0}(3k_0^4+3k^4+10k_0^2k^2)\times$$

$$\left[-\frac{M\overline{u^2}}{3}\int_{-\infty}^{\infty}\frac{df}{f}\frac{z(f)}{e^{\hbar f/kT}-1}+\frac{\hbar}{2}\prod_i^2\int_{-\infty}^{\infty}\frac{df_i}{f_i}\frac{z(f_i)}{e^{\hbar f_i/kT}-1}\right] \quad (1.113)$$

where $k = \left(k_0^2 + \dfrac{2m}{\hbar} \sum_i f_i \right)^{\frac{1}{2}}$ and $\overline{u^2}$ is the mean square of the atomic displace-

ments. Except for rather high temperatures just these two terms in the mass expansion are sufficient in fact to give a good approximation for the total inelastic scattering.

If the differential scattering cross-section is required instead of the cross-section integrated over energy as above, the mass expansion may be inadequate and it is better to calculate the multi-phonon terms separately by some other method. Use may be made of a recursion formula expressing the p-phonon term as a convolution of the $p-1$ term and the one-phonon term. Terms above the two or three-phonon term may be evaluated in the approximation in which the one-phonon term in the convolution is approximated by a Gaussian (Schofield and Hassitt, 1958). Corrections for deviations from the Gaussian form may be applied by multiplying the Gaussian by a sum of Hermite orthogonal functions (Sjölander, 1958). If high energy incident neutrons or high sample temperatures are used so that many phonons are involved in the scattering process, the cross-section can be calculated using the method of steepest descent (Egelstaff and Schofield, 1962).

1.15 Magnetic Scattering Cross-sections

In these sections we shall be concerned with the scattering from magnetic materials in which co-operative magnetic phenomena are in operation and also briefly with the scattering from paramagnets. To deal with the former category first let us pick a particular material such as iron as an example in order to fix our attention. At very low temperatures the magnetic moments on the iron atoms are all aligned in accordance with the ground state condition arising from the presence of exchange interactions between the atoms. As the temperature is raised the spin arrangement begins to break down until, at the Curie temperature, all long range order disappears. Short range order persists above the Curie temperature, however, and in the region of the Curie point "critical" magnetic phenomena occur. These are discussed in Section 1.18.

The scattering of neutrons by atoms possessing magnetic moments requires the use of the Dirac equation for a proper treatment of the interaction between the neutron and the magnetic electrons (Halpern and Johnson, 1939). If no orbital moment† is present so that the atoms carry a spin moment

---

† Trammell (1953) has shown that the matrix element (see Section 1.6) for the magnetic scattering including orbital effects is approximately given by

$$\left\langle \left| \sum_j \{ e^{i\mathbf{Q} \cdot \mathbf{r}_j} \mathbf{S}_j + \tfrac{1}{4}(\mathbf{l}_j f_j + f_j \mathbf{l}_j) \} \right| \right\rangle$$

where $\mathbf{r}_j$ is the position of the jth electron relative to the nucleus of the atom concerned and only, the magnetic scattering may be found on the assumption that the atoms possess a magnetic scattering length, for neutrons of spin vector S', of ($\wedge$ denotes a unit vector):

$$p = \frac{2e^2\gamma}{mc^2} f(\mathbf{Q})\, \mathbf{S}' \cdot \{\mathbf{S} - \hat{\mathbf{Q}}(\mathbf{S} \cdot \hat{\mathbf{Q}})\} \qquad (1.114)$$

where γ is the magnetic moment of the neutron in nuclear magnetons ($= 1\cdot91$) and m is the electron mass. $\mathbf{S}$ is the atomic spin. The factor $e^2/2mc^2$ is simply the product of the nuclear and Bohr magnetons, which is the basic ingredient of the interaction potential, multiplied by $2m/\hbar^2$ (cf. equation (1.9)). $f(\mathbf{Q})$ is the form factor of the spin density. Thus, $f(\mathbf{Q}) = \int d\mathbf{r} \, e^{i\mathbf{Q} \cdot \mathbf{r}} |\psi(\mathbf{r})|^2$ where $\psi(\mathbf{r})$ is the wave function describing the magnetic electrons. It will be noted that

$$\mathbf{S} - \hat{\mathbf{Q}}(\mathbf{S} \cdot \hat{\mathbf{Q}}) = \hat{\mathbf{Q}} \times (\mathbf{S} \times \hat{\mathbf{Q}}) = \mathbf{S}^{\perp}$$

is the projection of $\mathbf{S}$ in the plane normal to the scattering vector $\mathbf{Q}$. Substituting equation (1.114) in the general formula (1.18) gives

$$\frac{d^2\sigma}{d\Omega dE} = \frac{1}{2\pi\hbar} \frac{k}{k_0} \int d\tau \, e^{-\omega\tau i} \sum_{m,n} \left(\frac{2e^2\gamma}{mc^2}\right)^2 f_m(\mathbf{Q}) f_n(\mathbf{Q}) \, \overline{e^{i\mathbf{Q} \cdot \{\mathbf{R_n}(\tau) - \mathbf{R_m}(0)\}}} \times$$

$$\{\mathbf{S}' \cdot \mathbf{S_m}(0) - (\mathbf{S}' \cdot \hat{\mathbf{Q}})(\mathbf{S_m}(0) \cdot \hat{\mathbf{Q}})\}\{\mathbf{S}' \cdot \mathbf{S_n}(\tau) - (\mathbf{S}' \cdot \hat{\mathbf{Q}})(\mathbf{S_n}(\tau) \cdot \hat{\mathbf{Q}})\}. \quad (1.115)$$

The factors involving spin may alternatively be written in the form

$$\{\mathbf{S}' \cdot \mathbf{S_m}^{\perp}(0)\}\{\mathbf{S}' \cdot \mathbf{S_n}^{\perp}(\tau)\}.$$

For unpolarized incident neutrons, this expression may be simplified by summing over neutron polarizations to reduce the product of the spin operators to

$$\tfrac{1}{4}(\delta_{\mu\nu} - \hat{Q}_\mu \hat{Q}_\nu) S_m^{\mu}(0) S_n^{\nu}(\tau) = \tfrac{1}{4}\mathbf{S_m}^{\perp}(0) \cdot \mathbf{S_n}^{\perp}(\tau)$$

giving finally

$$\frac{d^2\sigma}{d\Omega dE} = \frac{1}{2\pi\hbar} \frac{k}{k_0} \int d\tau \, e^{-i\omega\tau} \left(\frac{e^2\gamma}{mc^2}\right)^2 \sum_{m,n} f_m(\mathbf{Q}) f_n(\mathbf{Q}) \times$$

$$\overline{e^{i\mathbf{Q} \cdot \{\mathbf{R_n}(\tau) - \mathbf{R_m}(0)\}}} \sum_{\mu,\nu} (\delta_{\mu\nu} - \hat{Q}_\mu \hat{Q}_\nu) S_m^{\mu}(0) S_n^{\nu}(\tau). \quad (1.116)$$

The superscripts μ and ν refer to a set of Cartesian coordinate directions. In

---

$\mathbf{S}_j$ and $\mathbf{l}_j$ are the spin and orbital angular momentum operators. The function f_j is given by

$$f_j = 2\left[\frac{d}{d\xi}\left(\frac{e^{\xi} - 1}{\xi}\right)\right]_{\xi = i\mathbf{Q} \cdot \mathbf{r}_j}$$

In the forward direction the scattering intensities corresponding to equal values of orbital and spin moment are equal. See also Blume *et al.* (1962).

terms of the eigenstate formulation the part of this cross-section which refers specifically to the excitation of the magnetic system, is ($\Delta E = E_{\text{initial}} - E_{\text{final}}$)

$$\frac{d^2\sigma}{d\Omega dE} = \frac{k}{k_0}\left(\frac{\gamma e^2}{mc^2}\right)^2 \sum_{\mu,\nu} (\delta_{\mu,\nu} - \hat{Q}_\mu \hat{Q}_\nu) \sum_{\substack{m,n \\ i,f}} P_i \, e^{i\mathbf{Q}\cdot(\mathbf{P_n}-\mathbf{P_m})} \times$$

$$|f_{\mathbf{m}}(\mathbf{Q})||f_{\mathbf{n}}(\mathbf{Q})|\langle i|S_{\mathbf{m}}^\mu|f\rangle\langle f|S_{\mathbf{n}}^\nu|i\rangle \delta(\Delta E + \hbar\omega) \, e^{-2W}. \qquad (1.117)$$

(The other part of the cross-section corresponding to magnetovibrational scattering, i.e. phonon scattering acting through the magnetic cross-section, has been dropped simply by replacing the atomic positions $\mathbf{R}$ by the lattice positions $\mathbf{P}$ and adding a Debye-Waller factor).

In the case of elastic scattering from a system with all moments aligned parallel or antiparallel to one single direction it is possible to simplify the above expressions.† We introduce a vector $\mathbf{N}$ related to a unit vector $\hat{\boldsymbol{\mu}}$ parallel to the magnetization direction and unit vector $\hat{\mathbf{Q}}$ parallel to the scattering vector.

$$\mathbf{N} = \hat{\boldsymbol{\mu}} - (\hat{\mathbf{Q}} \cdot \hat{\boldsymbol{\mu}})\hat{\mathbf{Q}}. \qquad (1.118)$$

Denoting the magnitude of the spin vector by S, we may define a magnetic scattering length by

$$p = \frac{e^2\gamma}{mc^2} f(\mathbf{Q})S \, |\mathbf{N}|. \qquad (1.119)$$

The quantity $|\mathbf{N}|$ is simply $\sin \alpha$, where α is the angle between $\mathbf{Q}$ and $\boldsymbol{\mu}$. For neutrons polarized to degree ϵ in the direction $\boldsymbol{\lambda}$, the nuclear and magnetic elastic scattering may be summed to give

$$\frac{d\sigma^{\text{coh}}}{d\Omega} = \frac{(2\pi)^3 N}{V} \sum_\tau \delta(\mathbf{Q} - 2\pi\boldsymbol{\tau}) \, e^{-2W} \times (b^2 + p^2 + 2bp\epsilon\hat{\boldsymbol{\lambda}} \cdot \hat{\mathbf{N}}) \qquad (1.120)$$

Clearly the last term averages to zero for an unpolarized incident neutron beam.

At sufficiently low temperatures the deviations from complete spin alignment may be treated in the spin wave approximation. The magnetic fluctuations associated with the spin waves interact with the neutrons to produce inelastic scattering. Such scattering is in many ways similar to the phonon scattering described previously and is dependent on conditions of energy and crystal momentum conservation. A detailed discussion in this connection is given in Section 1.17.

Finally we must discuss the scattering from paramagnets. A "perfect" paramagnet with no coupling between atoms can scatter only elastically (unless

† Scattering from non-collinear arrays of spin density has been discussed by Blume (1963b). See also Blume (1963a).

some change of the internal state of the atoms takes place during the scattering process). Under conditions in which spin movement only is important, the scattering length will depend on the total spin eigenvalue $\sqrt{S(S+1)}$. The spins will be directed randomly in space and the mean value of the squares of the projections of the spins on to the plane normal to $\mathbf{Q}$ is $\frac{2}{3}S(S+1)$.

Thus, the cross-section for scattering is

$$\frac{\mathrm{d}\sigma^{\mathrm{para}}}{\mathrm{d}\Omega} = \frac{2}{3}N\left(\frac{e^2\gamma}{mc^2}\right)^2 f^2(\mathbf{Q})S(S+1). \tag{1.121}$$

If the coupling between the paramagnetic atoms is appreciable, inelastic scattering will be experienced. This is discussed in Section 1.18. Another type of inelastic scattering results if the paramagnetic atoms change their internal state during the scattering process. This can take place if the splitting between the atomic states is comparable with the neutron energy. Consider, for example, a crystal containing rare earth ions. The $2J+1$ fold degeneracy of the atomic states which ensues from Russell-Saunders coupling between the orbital and spin moments in an ion is lifted by the crystalline fields present. The magnitude of the resulting splitting is comparable with thermal energies and gives rise to inelastic scattering of thermal neutrons. The scattered neutrons show discrete energy changes corresponding to the energy splittings in the paramagnet. The evaluation of the relevant cross-sections involves summation over the states of the particular ions concerned. Such scattering is in some ways analogous to the scattering from molecules where again the energy levels of the scatterer are directly reflected in the scattered neutron energy spectrum.

1.16 Elastic Magnetic Scattering in Ferromagnets, etc.

If the spins in a magnetic crystal are all parallel or anti-parallel to a particular direction given by $\boldsymbol{\mu}$, the coherent elastic scattering cross-section for unpolarized neutrons due to magnetic effects may be written

$$\frac{\mathrm{d}\sigma^{\mathrm{coh}}}{\mathrm{d}\Omega} = \frac{(2\pi)^3 N}{V} \sum_{\tau} \delta(\mathbf{Q} - 2\pi\boldsymbol{\tau})|F_{\tau}|^2 \tag{1.122}$$

where the structure factor is

$$F_{\tau} = \sum_{l} p_l\, e^{i2\pi\boldsymbol{\tau}\cdot\boldsymbol{\rho}_l}\, e^{-W_l} \tag{1.123}$$

This expression applies to a ferromagnet, ferrimagnet or antiferromagnet providing that it is understood that p_l is positive or negative according to whether the spin concerned lies in a positive or negative direction along $\mathbf{\mu}$, the direction of magnetization. Thus, the unit cell to which F_τ refers may not be the same as the chemical unit cell. Any such difference must be taken into account in connection with N and V. If the scattering sample is divided up into domains whose directions of magnetization are oriented in a random manner, the factor $\sin \alpha$ in the cross-section must be replaced by its average value. For spherical or cubic symmetry this average is 2/3.

If polarized neutrons are used further terms in the expression for the cross-section appear. The additional scattering may be found by replacing $|F_\tau|^2$ in equation (1.122) by

$$2\epsilon\hat{\mathbf{\lambda}} \cdot \hat{\mathbf{N}} \sum_l p_l\, e^{i2\pi\tau \cdot \rho_l}\, e^{-W_l} \sum_k \bar{b}_k\, e^{-2\pi\tau \cdot \rho_k}\, e^{-W_k}. \tag{1.124}$$

These cross terms† are of considerable use for the study of weak magnetic reflections as in many cases their values exceed the magnitudes of the terms in p^2. A further important feature of the cross terms is that they provide a means of obtaining a beam of polarized neutrons. Consider the condition under which $\hat{\mathbf{Q}} \cdot \hat{\mathbf{\mu}} = 0$ and suppose that the neutrons in an unpolarized incident beam be divided into two equal groups defined by $\hat{\mathbf{\lambda}} \cdot \hat{\mathbf{\mu}} = \pm 1$. The cross-sections in a simple crystal for these two groups are $(\bar{b}+p)^2$ and $(\bar{b}-p)^2$ so that if a reflection in which $\bar{b} = p$ is found, only the neutrons for which $\hat{\mathbf{\lambda}} \cdot \hat{\mathbf{\mu}} = 1$ will be reflected.

Canted spin arrangements represent an increase in the complexities to be handled. Of particular interest in this connection is the scattering from crystals containing spin spirals (or antiphase domains) where a new periodicity equalling a number of chemical lattice spacings is present. Suppose we imagine such a periodicity exists in a crystal having only one atom per unit cell or alternatively we discuss only the scattering from one sublattice of a more complicated structure. Let the periodicity of the spin spiral or antiphase domains be represented by a wave vector $\mathbf{G}$. Then, in general, the value of $\sin \alpha$ at a given lattice site may be expanded in a Fourier series and to a first approximation we have a magnetic scattering length which varies from site to site in a manner described by $e^{i\mathbf{G} \cdot \mathbf{P}_v}$. It follows that the cross-section is proportional to $|\sum_v e^{i\mathbf{G} \cdot \mathbf{P}_v}\, e^{i\mathbf{Q} \cdot \mathbf{P}_v}|^2$ so that reinforcement and Bragg scattering occurs for $\mathbf{Q} + \mathbf{G} = 2\pi\mathbf{\tau}$. Thus, the Bragg peaks appear in reciprocal space slightly displaced from the reciprocal lattice positions. In principle, further satellite reflections will occur if the variation in $\sin \alpha$ is not fully represented by the single Fourier term above.

So far we have discussed only coherent effects. Incoherent magnetic

† If the spin structure is not collinear, polarization-dependent, purely magnetic scattering is possible (see, for example, Blume, 1963a).

scattering will occur in ferromagnetic alloys and in the case of a binary alloy the total incoherent elastic scattering is given by

$$\frac{d\sigma^{inc}}{d\Omega} = N\left[\overline{b^2} - \overline{b}^2 + c_1 c_2 \left\{\left(\frac{\gamma e^2}{mc^2}\right)^2 \sin^2\alpha \left\{f_1(\mathbf{Q})S_1 - f_2(\mathbf{Q})S_2\right\}^2 + 2\frac{\gamma e^2}{mc^2}\times\right.\right.$$

$$\left.\left.(\overline{b}_1 - \overline{b}_2)\{f_1(\mathbf{Q})S_1 - f_2(\mathbf{Q})S_2\} \, \epsilon\hat{\boldsymbol{\lambda}} . \mathbf{N}\right)\right\} e^{-2W} \qquad (1.125)$$

where S_1 and S_2 refer to the spins on the atoms of the two constituents. It is clear that measurements of such scattering taken together with the results of saturation magnetization experiments can be used to evaluate S_1 and S_2. The magnetic scattering is distinguished from the large nuclear background by changing the direction of magnetization of the sample. (Note that the use of a single Debye-Waller factor implies that the masses and force constants pertaining to the two constituents are similar. This in fact would be the case for an alloy of two metals of the same transition series.)

1.17 Spin Wave Scattering

First let us consider the nature of the spin fluctuations in a ferromagnet[†] under conditions of low temperature such that the spin wave description is

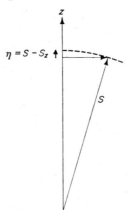

FIG. 1.8. Schematic diagram illustrating the deviation of the direction of an individual atomic spin in a ferromagnet from the direction of magnetization, which is assumed to lie along the z-axis. The fluctuation in the xy-plane, for small deviations, is seen to be approximately $(2\eta S)^{\frac{1}{2}}$.

valid (we shall also assume one atom per unit cell). If the direction of magnetization defines a z-axis, then classically the spin fluctuations in the x–y

[†] More exact descriptions of the spin wave approximation for both ferromagnets and antiferromagnets are given, for example, by Keffer et al. (1953) (introductory) and Oguchi (1960).

plane have a magnitude of approximately $(2\eta S)^{\frac{1}{2}}$, where $\eta = S - S^z$ is the spin deviation in the z-direction per atom (see Fig. 1.8). It is convenient to express these fluctuations in the x–y plane in terms of the quantities

$$S^\pm = S^x \pm iS^y \tag{1.126}$$

so that $S^+ S^- = 2\eta S$. Let us now carry out a Fourier transform over these spin parameters and thus establish a set of normal co-ordinates for the spin fluctuations, i.e. for a Bravais lattice we have

$$\xi_{\mathbf{q}} = (2NS)^{-\frac{1}{2}} \sum_{\mathbf{v}} e^{-i\mathbf{q} \cdot \mathbf{P_v}} S_{\mathbf{v}}^+$$

$$\xi_{\mathbf{q}}^* = (2NS)^{-\frac{1}{2}} \sum_{\mathbf{v}} e^{i\mathbf{q} \cdot \mathbf{P_v}} S_{\mathbf{v}}^- \tag{1.127}$$

and conversely

$$S_{\mathbf{v}}^+ = \left(\frac{2S}{N}\right)^{\frac{1}{2}} \sum_{\mathbf{q}} e^{i\mathbf{q} \cdot \mathbf{P_v}} \xi_{\mathbf{q}}$$

$$S_{\mathbf{v}}^- = \left(\frac{2S}{N}\right)^{\frac{1}{2}} \sum_{\mathbf{q}} e^{-i\mathbf{q} \cdot \mathbf{P_v}} \xi_{\mathbf{q}}^*. \tag{1.128}$$

If we now write out the time dependence of the normal co-ordinates explicitly, $\xi(t) = \xi(0) e^{-ift}$, we may express the spin fluctuation components in terms of these co-ordinates in the form

$$S_{\mathbf{v}}^x = \left(\frac{S}{2N}\right)^{\frac{1}{2}} \sum_{\mathbf{q}} (e^{i\mathbf{q} \cdot \mathbf{P_v}} \xi_{\mathbf{q}}\, e^{-ift} + e^{-i\mathbf{q} \cdot \mathbf{P_v}} \xi_{\mathbf{q}}^*\, e^{ift})$$

$$S_{\mathbf{v}}^y = i\left(\frac{S}{2N}\right)^{\frac{1}{2}} \sum_{\mathbf{q}} (e^{-i\mathbf{q} \cdot \mathbf{P_v}} \xi_{\mathbf{q}}^*\, e^{ift} - e^{i\mathbf{q} \cdot \mathbf{P_v}} \xi_{\mathbf{q}}\, e^{-ift}). \tag{1.129}$$

On the assumption that the exchange interactions between the spins may be dealt with in the approximation of the Dirac vector model the Hamiltonian for the spin system may now be written

$$\begin{aligned} H &= -2 \sum_{\mathbf{u,v}} J_{\mathbf{uv}} \mathbf{S_v} \cdot \mathbf{S_u} \\ &= -2 \sum_{\mathbf{u,v}} J_{\mathbf{uv}} S_{\mathbf{v}}^z S_{\mathbf{u}}^z - \sum_{\mathbf{u,v}} J_{\mathbf{uv}} (S_{\mathbf{v}}^+ S_{\mathbf{u}}^- + S_{\mathbf{v}}^- S_{\mathbf{u}}^+) \\ &= -zNS(S+1)J + zSJ \sum_{\mathbf{q}} (1 - \Gamma_{\mathbf{q}})(\xi_{\mathbf{q}} \xi_{\mathbf{q}}^* + \xi_{\mathbf{q}}^* \xi_{\mathbf{q}}) \end{aligned} \tag{1.130}$$

where the last line assumes that interactions with an exchange integral J between the z nearest neighbours are the only important ones and where

$$\Gamma_{\mathbf{q}} = \frac{1}{z} \sum_{\boldsymbol{\rho}} e^{i\mathbf{q} \cdot \boldsymbol{\rho}} \tag{1.131}$$

ρ running over the z neighbours concerned. The system can thus be treated as a set of independent harmonic oscillators. In fact the parameters $\xi_{\mathbf{q}}$, $\xi_{\mathbf{q}}^*$

are the spin destruction and creation operators and have the properties of altering the occupation n of a spin wave mode q by ± 1, i.e.

$$\xi|n\rangle = n^{\frac{1}{2}}|n-1\rangle$$
$$\xi^*|n\rangle = (n+1)^{\frac{1}{2}}|n+1\rangle \tag{1.132}$$

so that

$$\xi^*\xi|n\rangle = n|n\rangle$$
$$\xi\xi^*|n\rangle = (n+1)|n\rangle \tag{1.133}$$

and

$$\langle n|H|n\rangle = -zNS(S+1)J + \sum \hbar f(n+\tfrac{1}{2}) \tag{1.134}$$

where

$$\hbar f = 2z\,SJ(1-\Gamma). \tag{1.135}$$

Let us first find the cross-section for spin wave scattering in a ferro-magnetic crystal containing one atom per unit cell only. In order to do this we must evaluate terms of the type $\sum_{u,v} e^{i\mathbf{Q}\cdot(\mathbf{P_v}-\mathbf{P_u})}S_u^\mu(0)S_v^\nu(\tau)$ where μ, ν run over x and y. The terms corresponding to $\mu \neq \nu$ cancel and the two terms with $\mu = \nu$ are both equal to

$$\frac{(2\pi)^3 S}{2V} \sum_q e^{\mp if\tau} \sum_\tau \delta(\mathbf{Q}\mp\mathbf{q}-2\pi\boldsymbol{\tau})(n+\tfrac{1}{2}\pm\tfrac{1}{2}) \tag{1.136}$$

where use has been made of equations (1.133) and where the upper and lower signs refer to spin wave creation and destruction processes respectively. The dependence on $\mathbf{Q}$ of the scattering is contained in $(2-\hat{Q}_x^2-\hat{Q}_y^2)f^2(\mathbf{Q}) = (1+\cos^2\alpha)f^2(\mathbf{Q})$ (see equation (1.116)). Thus, the final expression for the inelastic scattering of unpolarized neutrons is of the form

$$\frac{d^2\sigma_1^{coh}}{d\Omega dE} = \left(\frac{\gamma e^2}{mc^2}\right)^2 \frac{S}{2} \sum_q (1+\cos^2\alpha)\frac{k}{k_0}\delta(\hbar\omega \mp \hbar f)\times$$
$$\frac{(2\pi)^3}{V}\sum_\tau \delta(\mathbf{Q}\mp\mathbf{q}-2\pi\boldsymbol{\tau})f^2(\mathbf{Q})(n+\tfrac{1}{2}\pm\tfrac{1}{2})\,e^{-2W}. \tag{1.137}$$

The physically observed cross-section found by summation over the spin wave modes and integration over the scattered neutron energy is

$$\frac{d\sigma_1^{coh}}{d\Omega} = \left(\frac{\gamma e^2}{mc^2}\right)^2 \frac{NS}{2}(1+\cos^2\alpha)\frac{k}{k_0}f^2(\mathbf{Q})\frac{(n+\tfrac{1}{2}\pm\tfrac{1}{2})}{|\mathscr{J}|}\,e^{-2W} \tag{1.138}$$

where the Jacobian $\mathscr{J}$ is given in equation (1.100).

For small spin wave energies $\hbar f \propto q^2$ (see for a simple discussion Keffer et al., 1953) and if this approximation and the condition $\hbar f \ll kT$ obtain, we have that

$$\frac{d\sigma_1^{coh}}{d\Omega} \propto n_q + \tfrac{1}{2}\pm\tfrac{1}{2} \sim \frac{kT}{\hbar f} \propto \frac{T}{q^2} \tag{1.139}$$

i.e. the cross-section shows similar dependences on temperature and wave vector as were found for the case of phonon scattering (cf. equation (1.102)).

It is instructive to discuss the scattering surfaces for ferromagnetic spin waves under the above simplifying conditions. We have that

$$\delta k = k - k_0 \sim (\mp 1)\frac{mf}{\hbar k} \sim (\mp 1)\frac{A}{2k}q^2 \qquad (1.140)$$

where the upper and lower signs refer respectively to magnon creation and destruction as before and A is a dimensionless constant for the particular crystal concerned. (A is related to the constant of proportionality in the spin wave dispersion relationship $\hbar f = Dq^2$, by $A = \dfrac{2m}{\hbar^2}D$.)

Thus, if we make a construction (see Fig. 1.9) in which a Cartesian co-ordinate system is set up in reciprocal space with the point $2\pi\boldsymbol{\tau}$ as origin, the distance q^2 may be written as $x_1^2 + y_1^2 + z_1^2$ where x_1, y_1, z_1 are the co-ordinates of the point $\mathbf{Q}$ in this co-ordinate system. Further if the x-axis lies

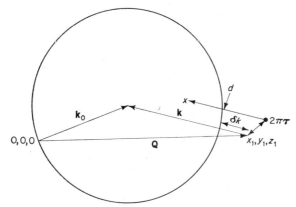

FIG. 1.9. Construction in reciprocal space for determining the scattering surfaces in the vicinity of a reciprocal lattice point corresponding to neutron scattering by spin waves in a ferromagnet.

parallel to and has the same sense as the vector $\mathbf{k}$, this axis will intersect the sphere of reflection normally with an intercept $x = d$ which will be positive or negative according as to whether the point $2\pi\boldsymbol{\tau}$ lies outside or inside the sphere respectively. Thus,

$$\delta k = k - k_0 \sim d - x_1$$

and

$$q^2 = x_1^2 + y_1^2 + z_1^2 \sim \frac{2k}{(\mp 1)A}\delta k \sim \frac{2k}{(\mp 1)A}(d - x_1) \qquad (1.141)$$

so that

$$\left\{ x_1 + \frac{k}{(\mp 1)A} \right\}^2 + y_1^2 + z_1^2 \sim \frac{k^2}{A^2} + \frac{2kd}{(\mp 1)A}. \qquad (1.142)$$

3*

Hence, the scattering surfaces are spheres. Under the present approximation
in which anisotropy forces are neglected and a simple isotropic, quadratic
dispersion law assumed, the spherical scattering surfaces are in fact an exact
result (e.g. see de Gennes, 1963). Provided that $\dfrac{k}{A} > 2|d|$ there occurs, for
each value of d, scattering corresponding to both magnon creation and
destruction. The surfaces described are those traced out by varying the
scattering angle at which the counter is held. If the scattering angle is fixed
and the crystal orientation is changed the scattering surfaces are also spheres
as can be shown by a construction similar to that used in the case of phonon
scattering in connection with the same type of experimental procedure (see
Section 1.12 and Fig. 1.7(b)).

The introduction into the problem of more than one magnetic atom per
unit cell results in a corresponding increase in the number of branches in the
spin wave dispersion law. Thus, the dispersion law for a ferromagnet with
two atoms per unit cell will contain both an acoustic and an optical branch.
The scattering from these more complicated structures is dependent on the
energy and crystal momentum conservation laws in just the manner described above for the Bravais lattice. However, the factor $Sf^2(\mathbf{Q})$ in the cross-
section formulae above must be replaced by a structure factor which takes
account of both the magnitudes and the relative phases of the spin fluctuations on the various atoms in a unit cell. Thus, cancellation can take place
and the cross-section is usually reduced in the vicinity of certain reciprocal
lattice points. Examples of this type of scattering that have been treated in
detail are ferromagnetic hexagonal cobalt and certain antiferromagnetic
structures (the latter must be included in the present discussion as they
clearly have more than one atom per magnetic unit cell). Thus, the spin
wave cross-section for hexagonal cobalt is correctly given by equation
(1.138) if S is replaced by $2S \cos^2\left\{\dfrac{\phi - 2\pi\boldsymbol{\tau} \cdot \boldsymbol{\rho}_{12}}{2}\right\}$ for acoustic magnons and by
$2S \sin^2\left\{\dfrac{\phi - 2\pi\boldsymbol{\tau} \cdot \boldsymbol{\rho}_{12}}{2}\right\}$ for optical magnons (Low, 1962). The vector $\boldsymbol{\rho}_{12}$
relates the two atoms in a unit cell. The parameter ϕ is a function of the wave
vector $\mathbf{q}$ which gives the relative phase of the fluctuations corresponding to the
mode concerned on the two atoms in the unit cell. The phase difference of the
scattering from the two atoms is in fact given by $\varDelta e^{i\phi} e^{i(\mathbf{q}\mp\mathbf{Q}) \cdot \boldsymbol{\rho}_{12}}$ where $\varDelta$ is $+1$
for acoustic magnons and -1 for optical magnons. The forms of the structure
factors above follow immediately remembering that $\mathbf{Q}\mp\mathbf{q} = 2\pi\boldsymbol{\tau}$ for coherent
scattering.

We turn now to the question of spin wave scattering in an antiferromagnet. The two branches of the dispersion law expected for two atoms per

unit cell are in this case degenerate. We shall consider a simple system in which the structure can be divided into two equivalent sublattices in each of which all the spins are similarly directed. It will be assumed that the only important magnetic interactions are exchange interactions between atoms on different sublattices and that only one set of neighbours is involved. Moreover, it will be necessary to assume that the chemical structure of the magnetic atoms (as contrasted with the magnetic structure) has only one atom per unit cell. Nevertheless the discussion still includes several structures of great importance, e.g. the body centred cubic and tetragonal structures with interactions between a central atom and the eight equally spaced neighbours at the unit cell corners; also the simple cubic structure with interactions between nearest neighbours.

As usual let us denote the direction of spin alignment as the z-direction. Then the magnitudes and phases of the magnetic fluctuations in the x–y plane arising from a spin wave may be written as

$$S^{\frac{1}{2}}\left\{\frac{1}{\sqrt{1-\Gamma^2}}+1\right\}^{\frac{1}{2}}e^{i\mathbf{q}\cdot\mathbf{R}_1} \quad \text{and} \quad S^{\frac{1}{2}}\left\{\frac{1}{\sqrt{1-\Gamma^2}}-1\right\}^{\frac{1}{2}}e^{i\mathbf{q}\cdot\mathbf{R}_2}$$

for the two sublattices concerned. $\Gamma = \frac{1}{z}\sum_{\rho}e^{i\mathbf{q}\cdot\mathbf{\rho}}$ where $\mathbf{\rho}$ runs over the z neighbours with which an atom is considered to have magnetic interactions. Now as pointed out at the beginning of this section, the spin deviation in the z-direction η is related to the fluctuations in the x–y plane through the expression $\sqrt{2\eta S}$. Thus, it follows that the deviations per spin wave on the two sublattices are

$$\frac{1}{2}\left\{\frac{1}{\sqrt{1-\Gamma^2}}+1\right\} \quad \text{and} \quad \frac{1}{2}\left\{\frac{1}{\sqrt{1-\Gamma^2}}-1\right\}.$$

It must be remembered that these deviations have opposite senses on the z-axis and therefore the overall change in magnetization for the whole crystal is their difference, i.e. 1 unit per spin wave. However, as there will usually be an equal number of spin deviations of each type excited on both sublattices, no net change in macroscopic magnetization is expected. On the average, each sublattice separately suffers a loss of magnetization given by the mean of the above expressions, i.e. $\frac{1}{2}(\sqrt{1-\Gamma^2})^{-1}$ units per spin wave.

From the above expressions for the magnetic fluctuations in the x–y plane it follows that the correct structure factor in the present case with which to replace S in equation (1.138) is

$$S\left|\left(\frac{1}{\sqrt{1-\Gamma^2}}+1\right)^{\frac{1}{2}}-\left(\frac{1}{\sqrt{1-\Gamma^2}}-1\right)^{\frac{1}{2}}e^{i(\mathbf{q}\mp\mathbf{Q})\cdot\mathbf{\rho}_{12}}\right|^2 = \frac{2S\{1-\Gamma\cos(\mathbf{Q}\mp\mathbf{q})\cdot\mathbf{\rho}_{12}\}}{\sqrt{1-\Gamma^2}}.$$

$$(1.143)$$

(It is assumed that N represents the number of magnetic unit cells.) The first point to consider is the value of $(\mathbf{Q} \mp \mathbf{q}) \cdot \boldsymbol{\rho}_{12}$. Let us denote the set of vectors in reciprocal space associated with the chemical structure of the magnetic atoms as $\boldsymbol{\tau}$ vectors. The introduction of the spin directions into the problem results, as we have discussed, in a reduction in symmetry so that we must now consider a structure having two atoms per unit cell. This gives rise to further reciprocal lattice vectors, each new vector being half of some $\boldsymbol{\tau}$ vector. Suppose these additional vectors are denoted by $\boldsymbol{\Omega}$. Now it is clear that $\boldsymbol{\tau} \cdot \boldsymbol{\rho}_{12}/2\pi$ is equal to an integer whereas $\boldsymbol{\Omega} \cdot \boldsymbol{\rho}_{12}/2\pi$ has half integer values. It follows that the structure factor above becomes

$$2\frac{S(1-\Delta\Gamma)}{(1-\Gamma^2)^{\frac{1}{2}}} = 2S\left(\frac{1-\Delta\Gamma}{1+\Delta\Gamma}\right)^{\frac{1}{2}} \tag{1.144}$$

where Δ is equal to $+1$ for a $\boldsymbol{\tau}$ type reflection and to -1 for an $\boldsymbol{\Omega}$ type reflection.

In order to discuss the scattering in the vicinity of a reciprocal lattice point we may use the dispersion law for an antiferromagnet (see Keffer *et al.*, 1953 or Elliott and Lowde, 1955)

$$\hbar f = 2z\, SJ(1-\Gamma^2)^{\frac{1}{2}}. \tag{1.145}$$

The first point to notice is that $\hbar f \propto q$ for $\mathbf{q} \cdot \boldsymbol{\rho} \ll 1$ so that the scattering surfaces for antiferromagnetic spin waves are just those discussed in connection with phonons (Section 1.12). Next we must consider the intensity of the reflections in the vicinity of $\boldsymbol{\tau}$ and $\boldsymbol{\Omega}$ reciprocal lattice points. Using the usual approximation for the Bose population function (cf. equation (1.139)) and equations (1.144) and (1.145) we find that the cross-section is proportional to $\dfrac{kT}{zJ(1+\Delta\Gamma)}$. Thus, in the vicinity of $\boldsymbol{\tau}$ lattice points ($\Delta = +1$) the cross section is simply proportional to $\dfrac{kT}{2zJ}$ and no intensification occurs as the lattice point is approached. For $\boldsymbol{\Omega}$ type reflections, on the other hand, $\Delta = -1$ and the scattering varies approximately as $\dfrac{kT}{Jq^2a^2}$, where a is some lattice parameter. Hence, the cross-section is inversely proportional to q^2 as in the cases of ferromagnetic spin waves and phonons.

Magnon scattering has received extensive discussion in the literature, and has been treated for example by Elliott and Lowde (1955), Maleev (1957) and Sáenz (1960 and 1962). Recent work has included the spin wave scattering of polarized neutrons. For this, the factor $1+\cos^2\alpha$ in equation (1.138) must be replaced by $1+\cos^2\alpha \mp 2\cos(\alpha)\boldsymbol{\epsilon}\hat{\boldsymbol{\lambda}} \cdot \hat{\mathbf{Q}}$ (Sáenz, 1962b). In any real cooperatively magnetic system, the dispersion law is likely to be complicated by anisotropy forces and by the presence of exchange between more than one set of neighbours. Also, the spin wave energies depend on temperature as a result of spin wave interactions (see e.g. Okazaki *et al.*, 1964; Low, 1965).

Finally, mention should be made of magnetovibrational scattering. This is the inelastic scattering associated with lattice vibrations but dependent on the magnetic cross-section of the atoms. During such scattering the energy of the spin wave system does not change. This scattering is of little intrinsic interest as it does not yield any information that cannot be derived more directly by ordinary phonon scattering experiments. However, it must be studied because of its nuisance value in connection with certain spin wave scattering measurements. In order to distinguish ferromagnetic spin wave scattering from phonon scattering one may apply a magnetic field and so alter the value of $1+\cos^2\alpha$ in the spin wave cross-section between the limits of 1 and 2. Any magnetovibrational scattering present will, however, also be changed, its dependence on magnetic field direction being proportional to $\sin^2\alpha$. In fact the magnetovibrational scattering cross-section may be obtained by substituting p^2 (equation (1.119)) for $\bar{b}^2$ in equation (1.101). Spin wave scattering may be clearly separated from magnetovibrational effects with the aid of polarized neutrons.

1.18 Critical Magnetic Scattering

Our discussion of the magnetic inelastic scattering of neutrons has so far been limited to a small range of temperature of the scatterer, namely to temperatures well below the Curie or Neél temperature where the spin wave approximation is valid. Discussion of magnetic scattering at general temperatures is difficult but there are two other regions where a certain amount of simplification in the processes involved takes place. At very high temperatures of several times the critical point, the scattering from the paramagnetic spins show an energy spread which is related to the exchange parameters of the system in a fairly simple manner. This has been discussed by de Gennes (1958) and by Sáenz (1960). A second temperature region where a certain amount of simplification takes place is in the vicinity of the Curie or Neél temperature where critical phenomena prevail. Because of the resulting large correlation distances and long relaxation times, the scattering may over a limited range be treated as quasi-elastic and discussed in the static approximation.

A general formalism for treating magnetic scattering may be set up in terms of a correlation function which takes account of both particle position and spin direction. Thus

$$\Gamma^{\mu\nu}(\mathbf{r},\tau) = \frac{1}{N} \sum_{\mathbf{m},\mathbf{n}} \overline{\int d\mathbf{r}' S_{\mathbf{m}}^{\mu}(0) \, \delta\{\mathbf{r}+\mathbf{R}_{\mathbf{m}}(0)-\mathbf{r}'\} \, S_{\mathbf{n}}^{\nu}(\tau)\delta\{\mathbf{r}-\mathbf{R}_{\mathbf{n}}(\tau)\}} \qquad (1.146)$$

where μ,ν refer to directions along a set of Cartesian axes. It is a good approximation to assume that there is no coupling between the atomic positions $\mathbf{R_n}$ and the spins $\mathbf{S_n}$ so that equation (1.146) becomes

$$\Gamma^{\mu\nu}(\mathbf{r},\tau) = \sum_n \gamma_n^{\mu\nu} G_n(\mathbf{r},\tau) \tag{1.147}$$

where

$$\gamma_n^{\mu\nu}(\tau) = \overline{S_0^\mu(0)S_n^\nu(\tau)} \tag{1.148}$$

and

$$G_n(\mathbf{r},\tau) = \overline{\int d\mathbf{r}' \, \delta\{\mathbf{r}+\mathbf{R}_0(0)-\mathbf{r}'\}\delta\{\mathbf{r}'-\mathbf{R}_n(\tau)\}}. \tag{1.149}$$

(Note that, on the assumption that all the atoms are identical, the sum in equation (1.146) has been restricted to $\mathbf{n}=0$ and the factor N^{-1} dropped.) If it is assumed that only exchange interactions between the magnetic atoms are important then the above expressions simplify to

$$\Gamma(\mathbf{r},\tau) = \sum_n \gamma_n(\tau) G_n(\mathbf{r},\tau) \tag{1.150}$$

and

$$\gamma_n(\tau) = \overline{\mathbf{S}_0(0) \cdot \mathbf{S}_n(\tau)} \tag{1.151}$$

The cross-section may now be written

$$\frac{d^2\sigma}{d\Omega dE} = \left(\frac{e^2\gamma}{mc^2}\right)^2 \frac{2N}{3\hbar} \frac{k}{k_0} f^2(\mathbf{Q}) \frac{1}{2\pi} \int d\mathbf{r}d\tau \, e^{i(\mathbf{Q}\cdot\mathbf{r}-\omega\tau)}\Gamma(\mathbf{r},\tau) \tag{1.152}$$

where it has been assumed that, over the crystal as a whole, the spin directions are distributed randomly, i.e. below the Curie temperature a ferromagnet is assumed to consist of domains of random orientation.

The separation into elastic and inelastic scattering may be effected by separating $\Gamma(\mathbf{r},\tau)$ into its asymptotic value for $\tau = \pm\infty$ and a term converging to zero when $\tau\to\infty$. Thus,

$$\gamma_n(\tau) = \overline{S}^2 + \gamma_n'(\tau) \tag{1.153}$$

where $\overline{S}$ is the mean spin value in the direction of magnetization (or some other specified direction if the crystal is paramagnetic). The term dependent on the mean spin component represents long range order and gives rise to Bragg scattering. Also, we may write

$$G_n^i(\mathbf{r},\tau) = G_n(\mathbf{r},\infty)+G_n'(\mathbf{r},\tau). \tag{1.154}$$

Thus, taking the terms on the right hand sides of equations (1.153) and (1.154) in pairs, we have four types of scattering: elastic, inelastic in the spin system but elastic in the phonon system, inelastic in the phonon system and finally inelastic in both the spin and the phonon systems. We shall consider only the scattering which is inelastic in the spin system and for this purpose we shall replace $G_n(\mathbf{r},\tau)$ by $\delta(\mathbf{r}-\mathbf{P_n})$, thus ignoring the effects of lattice vibrations. Hence, we have for a polycrystal

$$\frac{\mathrm{d}^2\sigma}{\mathrm{d}\Omega\mathrm{d}E} = \left(\frac{e^2\gamma}{mc^2}\right)^2 \frac{2N}{3\hbar}\frac{k}{k_0}\,f^2(\mathbf{Q})\frac{1}{2\pi}\sum_n\int\mathrm{d}\tau\,e^{i(\mathbf{Q}\cdot\mathbf{P_n}-\omega\tau)}\gamma_n'(\tau). \qquad (1.155)$$

If the scattering is examined in the static approximation the cross-section (1.155) reduces by integration over all neutron energies to

$$\frac{\mathrm{d}\sigma}{\mathrm{d}\Omega} = \left(\frac{e^2\gamma}{mc^2}\right)^2 \frac{2N}{3}f^2(\mathbf{Q})\sum_n e^{i\mathbf{Q}\cdot\mathbf{P_n}}\gamma_n'(0). \qquad (1.156)$$

It will be noted that for negligible interaction between spins, $\gamma_n'(0)$ is zero except for $\mathbf{P_n} = 0$ in which case $\gamma_n'(0) = S(S+1)$ and equation (1.156) reduces to the expression for paramagnetic scattering of equation (1.121).

We turn now to a discussion concerned specifically with critical magnetic scattering. Such scattering is an example of a general physical phenomenon, another instance of which is the critical opalescence which occurs when light is passed through a liquid or dense gas at constant pressure, in the vicinity of the critical point. The critical magnetic effect may be described by considering the properties of a ferromagnet in the temperature range above the Curie temperature. Suppose a region of the ferromagnet, small compared with the total volume, but containing a large number of spins is selected. This region will have a magnetic moment $\boldsymbol{\mu}$ which will fluctuate about zero. The probability of observing a magnetic moment $\mu = |\boldsymbol{\mu}|$ will have a Gaussian form and if we neglect anisotropic interactions $\mu^2 = 3\chi kTN_\delta$ where N_δ is the number of spins in the region and χ is the magnetic susceptibility per spin. But χ approaches infinity as T approaches T_c so that the fluctuations in μ become great. It can be shown that a similar behaviour results if T_c is approached from below. Detailed arguments show in fact that (Van Hove, 1954b)

$$\gamma_n'(0) \sim \frac{S(S+1)V}{4\pi r_1^2 P_n}e^{-K_1 P_n} \qquad (1.157)$$

where V is the volume per spin, and the lengths r_1 and K_1^{-1} are related by the formula

$$(K_1 r_1)^2 = \chi_0/\chi \qquad (1.158)$$

where χ is the susceptibility and χ_0 is the paramagnetic susceptibility for perfectly non-interacting spins. Thus, for $T\to\infty$, $K_1\to r_1^{-1}$ while for $T\sim T_c$, $\chi\to\infty$ and $K_1\to 0$.

If the scattering is examined near a reciprocal lattice point $\boldsymbol{\tau}$, so that $\mathbf{Q}-2\pi\boldsymbol{\tau} = \mathbf{q}$ where q is small then equations (1.156) and (1.157) give (Van Hove, 1954b)

$$\frac{\mathrm{d}\sigma}{\mathrm{d}\Omega} = \left(\frac{e^2\gamma}{mc^2}\right)^2 \frac{2N}{3}S(S+1)f^2(\mathbf{Q})\frac{1}{r_1^2(K_1^2+q^2)}. \qquad (1.159)$$

Actually the expression (1.157) is invalid for P_n small. Nevertheless equation (1.159) gives the cross-section correctly provided q is small. This point and details concerning the extension of the formulae to more complicated lattices are discussed in the literature (see for example Elliott and Marshall, 1958 and de Gennes and Villain, 1960) and also in Chapter 6.

References

Bacon, G. E. and Lowde, R. D. (1948). *Acta Cryst.* **1**, 303.

Blume, M. (1963a). *Phys. Rev.* **130**, 1670.

Blume, M. (1963b). *Phys. Rev.* Letters **10**, 489.

Blume, M., Freeman, A. J. and Watson, R. E. (1962). *J. chem. Phys.* **37**, 1245.

Brockhouse, B. N., Corliss, L. M and Hastings, J. M. (1955). *Phys. Rev.* **98**, 1721.

Bykov, V. N., Vinogradov, F., Levdik, V. A. and Golovkin, V. S. (1959). *Soviet Phys. Crystallography* **2**, 626.

Callen, H. B. and Welton, T. A. (1951). *Phys. Rev.* **83**, 34.

Cassels, J. M. (1950). *Progr. nucl. Phys.* **1**, 185.

de Gennes, P. G. (1958). *J. Phys. Chem. Solids* **4**, 223.

de Gennes, P. G. (1959). *Physica*, **25**, 825.

de Gennes, P. G. (1963). *In* "Magnetism", ed. by H. Suhl and G. T. Rado, Vol. III. Academic Press, New York.

de Gennes, P. G. and Villain, J. (1960). *J. Phys. Chem. Solids*, **13**, 10.

Egelstaff, P. A. (1958). Neutrons, pp. 10–15 of "The Nuclear Handbook", ed. by O. R. Frisch. Newnes, London.

Egelstaff, P. A. (1961). *In* "Inelastic Scattering of Neutrons in Solids and Liquids", p. 25. IAEA, Vienna.

Egelstaff, P. A. and Schofield, P. (1962). *Nucl. Sci. Engng* **12**, 260.

Elliott, R. J. and Lowde, R. D. (1955). *Proc. roy. Soc.* **A230**, 46.

Elliott, R. J. and Marshall, W. (1958). *Rev. mod. Phys.* **30**, 75.

Halpern, O. and Johnson, M. H. (1939). *Phys. Rev.* **55**, 898.

Hughes, D. J. and Schwartz, R. B. (1958). "Neutron Cross Sections", 2nd Ed. B.N.L. 325, U.S. Gov. Printing Office, Washington.

Keffer, F., Kaplan, H. and Yafet, Y. (1953). *Amer. J. Phys.* **21**, 250.

Landau, L. D. and Lifshitz, E. M. (1958). "Quantum Mechanics". Pergamon Press, London.

Low, G. G. (1962). *Proc. phys. Soc.* **79**, 473.

Low, G. G. (1965). *In* "Inelastic Scattering of Neutrons", Vol. I, p. 413. IAEA, Vienna.

Lowde, R. D. and Wheeler, D. A. (1962). *J. Phys. Soc. Japan* **17**, Suppl. B-II, 342.

Maleev, S. V. (1957). *Zh. eksp. teor. Fiz.* **33**, 1010.

Marshall, W. and Stuart, R. (1961). *In* "Inelastic Scattering of Neutrons in Solids and Liquids", p. 75. IAEA, Vienna.

Nelkin, M. (1961). *In* "Inelastic Scattering of Neutrons in Solids and Liquids", p. 3. IAEA, Vienna.

Oguchi, T. (1960). *Phys. Rev.* **117**, 117.

Okazaki, A., Turberfield, K. C. and Stevenson, R. W. H. (1964). *Phys. Letters* **8**, 9.

Pelah, I., Eisenhauer, C. M., Hughes, D. J. and Palevsky, H. (1957), *Phys. Rev.* **108**, 1091.

Placzek, G. (1954). *Phys. Rev.* **93**, 895.

Rahman, A., Singwi, K. S. and Sjölander, A. (1962). *Phys. Rev.* **126**, 986.

Sáenz, A. W. (1960). *Phys. Rev.* **119**, 1542.

Sáenz, A. W. (1962a). *Phys. Rev.* **125**, 1940.

Sáenz, A. W. (1962b). *In* "Pile Neutron Research in Physics", p. 423. IAEA, Vienna.

Schiff, L. I. (1949). "Quantum Mechanics", McGraw-Hill, New York.

Schofield, P. (1960). *Phys. Rev. Letters* **4**, 239.

Schofield, P. (1961). *In* "Inelastic Scattering of Neutrons in Solids and Liquids", p. 39. IAEA, Vienna.

Schofield, P. and Hassitt, A. (1958). "Second United Nations International Conference on the Peaceful Uses of Atomic Energy", **16**, 217.

Sjölander, A. (1958). *Ark. Fys.* **14**, 315.

Trammell, G. T. (1953). *Phys. Rev.* **92**, 1387.

Van Hove, L. (1954a). *Phys. Rev.* **95**, 249.

Van Hove, L. (1954b). *Phys. Rev.* **95**, 1374.

Van Hove, L. (1958). *Physica* **24**, 404.

Vineyard, G. H. (1954). *Phys. Rev.* **96**, 93.

Vineyard, G. H. (1958). *Phys. Rev.* **110**, 999.

Waller, I. and Froman, P. O. (1952). *Ark. Fys.* **4**, 183.

Weiner, N. (1930). *Acta Math.* **55**, 117.

Weinstock, R. (1944). *Phys. Rev.* **65**, 1.

Ziman, J. M. (1960). "Electrons and Phonons". Oxford University Press, London.

Appendix

The incident neutron beam is represented by

$$\psi_0(\mathbf{r},t) = e^{i(\mathbf{k}_0 \cdot \mathbf{r} - \omega_0 t)} \tag{A1.1}$$

In the presence of an assembly of nuclei this is acted on by the time-dependent Hamiltonian operator

$$H = H_0 + \sum_n \frac{2\pi \hbar^2}{m} b_n \delta\{\mathbf{r} - \mathbf{R}_n(t_0)\} \tag{A1.2}$$

where $H_0 = -\frac{\hbar^2}{2m}\nabla^2$, $\mathbf{R}_n(t)$ is the position of nucleus $\mathbf{n}$ at time t and b_n is the scattering length of nucleus at $\mathbf{n}$. ($\mathbf{R}_n$ is an operator and care must be exercised in manipulation not to violate commutation properties with other nuclear co-ordinates to which $\mathbf{n}$ is dynamically coupled). The scattered wave field now develops according to the usual time dependent Schrödinger equation (Wick, G. C. (1937). *Phys. Z.* **38**, 403–406),

$$i\hbar \frac{\partial}{\partial t} \psi(\mathbf{r},t)|_{t_0} = \left[H_0 + \sum_n \frac{2\pi \hbar^2}{m} b_n \delta\{\mathbf{r} - \mathbf{R}_n(t_0)\} \right] \psi(\mathbf{r},t)|_{t_0}. \tag{A1.3}$$

Writing $\psi = \psi_0(\mathbf{r},t) + \psi_s(\mathbf{r},t)$ and restricting ourselves to first order perturbations, we have

$$\left(i\hbar \frac{\partial}{\partial t} + \frac{\hbar^2}{2m}\nabla^2 \right) \psi_s(\mathbf{r},t)|_{t_0} = \frac{2\pi \hbar^2}{m} \sum_n b_n \delta\{\mathbf{r} - \mathbf{R}_n(t_0)\} \psi_0(\mathbf{r},t_0) \tag{A1.4}$$

The total scattered wave field is the result of the superposition of the solutions representing waves originating at all earlier times from the source terms on the right. The solution is obtained readily by the normal Green's function method. The solution of the related equation

$$\left(\nabla^2 + \frac{i2m}{\hbar}\frac{\partial}{\partial t}\right)G(\mathbf{r}-\mathbf{r}',t-t') = 4\pi\delta(\mathbf{r}-\mathbf{r}')\,\delta(t-t')$$

is

$$G(\mathbf{r}-\mathbf{r}',\,t-t') = \frac{i}{(t-t')^{\frac{3}{2}}}\left(\frac{m}{2\pi\hbar}\right)^{\frac{1}{2}}e^{\frac{im|\mathbf{r}-\mathbf{r}'|^2}{2\hbar(t-t')}}.$$

The solution of equation (A1.4) is then given by

$$\psi_s(\mathbf{r}',t) = \int d\mathbf{r}dt_0 G(\mathbf{r}-\mathbf{r}',t-t_0)\sum_n b_n\,\delta\{\mathbf{r}-\mathbf{R}_n(t_0)\}\,\psi_0(\mathbf{r},t_0)$$

$$= i\left(\frac{m}{2\pi\hbar}\right)^{\frac{1}{2}}\int_{-\infty}^{t}dt_0(t-t_0)^{-\frac{3}{2}}\sum_n b_n\int d\mathbf{r}\delta(\mathbf{r}-\mathbf{R}_n(t_0))\,e^{\frac{im|\mathbf{r}-\mathbf{r}'|^2}{2\hbar(t-t_0)}}\psi_0(\mathbf{r},t_0) \qquad (A1.5)$$

This is an explicit form for the scattered wave field, and it only remains to reduce it to convenient form. We shall evaluate it at large $\mathbf{r}'$, and carry out a Fourier transformation with respect to time so that we obtain an energy resolution of the scattered neutrons rather than a time-dependent neutron field. We first carry out the Fourier transform over some long arbitrary period T. We write

$$\psi_s(t) = \sum_\omega f(\omega)\,e^{-i\omega t}$$

$$f(\omega) = \frac{1}{T}\int_0^T dt\,e^{i\omega t}\psi_s(t) \qquad (A1.6)$$

Substituting the explicit expressions for $\psi_s(\mathbf{r}',t)$ and for $\psi_0(\mathbf{r},t_0)$ we have, where $\hbar\omega_1$ is the energy of the scattered neutron,

$$f(\mathbf{r}',\omega_1) = \frac{i}{T}\left(\frac{m}{2\pi\hbar}\right)^{\frac{1}{2}}\int_0^T dt\,e^{i\omega_1 t}\int_{-\infty}^{t}dt_0(t-t_0)^{-\frac{3}{2}}\sum_n b_n\int d\mathbf{r}\delta\{\mathbf{r}-\mathbf{R}_n(t_0)\}\times$$

$$e^{\frac{im|\mathbf{r}-\mathbf{r}'|^2}{2\hbar(t-t_0)}}\,e^{i(\mathbf{k}_0\cdot\mathbf{r}-\omega_0 t_0)}$$

$$= \frac{i}{T}\left(\frac{m}{2\pi\hbar}\right)^{\frac{1}{2}}\int_0^T dt\int_{-\infty}^{t}\frac{dt_0}{(t-t_0)^{\frac{3}{2}}}\,e^{i(\omega_1-\omega_0)t_0}\,e^{i\omega_1(t-t_0)}\sum_n b_n\int d\mathbf{r}\delta\{\mathbf{r}-\mathbf{R}_n(t_0)\}\times$$

$$e^{i\mathbf{k}_0\cdot\mathbf{r}+\frac{im|\mathbf{r}'-\mathbf{r}|^2}{2\hbar(t-t_0)}}.$$

$$(A1.7)$$

Changing the variables of integration to t_0 and $s = t-t_0$, and writing $\omega = \omega_0 - \omega_1$ we have that

$$f(\mathbf{r}',\omega_1) = \frac{i}{T}\left(\frac{m}{2\pi\hbar}\right)^{\frac{1}{2}} \int\limits_0^\infty \frac{ds}{s^{\frac{3}{2}}} \int dt_0 \, e^{-i\omega t_0} \, e^{i\omega_1 s} \sum_n b_n \int d\mathbf{r}\delta\{\mathbf{r}-\mathbf{R}_n(t_0)\} \, e^{i\mathbf{k}_0 \cdot \mathbf{r}+\frac{im|\mathbf{r}'-\mathbf{r}|^2}{2\hbar s}}.$$

$$(A1.8)$$

The integration over s involves the exponential expression

$$e^{i\left\{\omega_1 s + \frac{m|\mathbf{r}'-\mathbf{r}|^2}{2\hbar s}\right\}}\delta\{\mathbf{r}-\mathbf{R}_n(t_0)\}.$$

The oscillations in phase of this expression are very rapid, with changes in s, except near the stationary position

$$\omega_1 = \frac{m|\mathbf{r}'-\mathbf{R}_n(t_0)|^2}{2\hbar s_0^2} \qquad (A1.9)$$

The main contribution to the integral therefore comes from this region of s. This is natural enough, for the kinetic energy of the scattered neutron $\hbar\omega_1 = \frac{1}{2}m\frac{|\mathbf{r}'-\mathbf{R}_n(t_0)|^2}{(t-t_0)^2} = \frac{1}{2}mv^2$. Thus provided our time of flight from specimen to detector is short compared with the time over which we analyse the energy spectrum we may treat the limit of the s integration as infinite, as written in equation (A1.8).

It is simplest now to take the approximation that r', the sample to detector distance, is large compared with the sample dimensions (which contain all $\mathbf{R}_n(t)$) and write

$$|\mathbf{r}'-\mathbf{r}|^2 \sim r'^2 - 2\mathbf{r}' \cdot \mathbf{r}.$$

By expanding round the value s_0 given by equation (A1.9), the integral over s in equation (A1.8) becomes ($s_1 = s - s_0$)

$$\int \frac{ds}{s^{\frac{3}{2}}} e^{i\omega_1 s} \, e^{i\left(\frac{mr'^2}{2\hbar s} - \frac{mr' \cdot r}{\hbar s}\right)} \sim s_0^{-\frac{3}{2}} \, e^{i\left(\omega_1 s_0 + \frac{mr'^2}{2\hbar s_0} - \frac{mr' \cdot r}{\hbar s_0}\right)} \int ds_1 \, e^{-\frac{imr'^2}{2\hbar s_0^3}s_1^2}. \quad (A1.10)$$

Carrying out the integration and dropping the phase factors which are independent of specimen coordinates r, we get the result:

$$\frac{1}{r'}\left(\frac{2\pi\hbar}{m}\right)^{\frac{1}{2}} e^{-i\mathbf{k} \cdot \mathbf{r}}$$

where $\mathbf{k}$ has been written for $\dfrac{m\mathbf{r}'}{\hbar s_0} = \dfrac{m\mathbf{v}}{\hbar}$. Substituting this reduction into (A1.8), we have

$$f(\mathbf{r}',\omega_1) = \frac{i}{r'T} \int\limits_0^T dt_0 \, e^{-i\omega t_0} \sum_n b_n \int d\mathbf{r}\delta\{\mathbf{r}-\mathbf{R}_n(t_0)\} \, e^{i\mathbf{Q} \cdot \mathbf{r}} \qquad (A1.11)$$

where $\mathbf{Q} = \mathbf{k}_0 - \mathbf{k}$.

To form the scattered intensity we require the value of $\sum|f(\omega_1)|^2$ in a small energy range ΔE, where the sum is over the discrete energy values allowed by the finite time T of our energy analysis. The number of terms in ΔE is $T\Delta E/2\pi\hbar$, so that we have

$$\sum|f(\omega_1)|^2 = \frac{T\Delta E}{2\pi\hbar}\,\frac{1}{T^2 r'^2}\int\limits_0^T dt_0 \int\limits_0^T dt\; e^{-i\omega(t_0-t)}[\sum_{m,n} b_m^* b_n \times$$

$$\int dr'' \int dr\; e^{i\mathbf{Q}\cdot(\mathbf{r}-\mathbf{r}'')}\delta\{\mathbf{r}''-\mathbf{R}_m(t)\}\delta\{\mathbf{r}-\mathbf{R}_n(t_0)\}]. \qquad (A1.12)$$

In many circumstances we are concerned to evaluate the cross-sections after solution of the dynamic problem of the nuclei, and may treat the $\mathbf{R}_n$ as ordinary vectors rather than operators. We may then carry out the δ function integrations to obtain

$$\sum|f(\omega)_1|^2 = \frac{T\Delta E}{2\pi\hbar}\cdot\frac{1}{T^2 r'^2}\int\limits_0^T dt_0 \int\limits_0^T dt\; e^{-i\omega(t_0-t)}\sum_{m,n} b_m^* b_n\, e^{i\mathbf{Q}\cdot\{\mathbf{R}_n(t_0)-\mathbf{R}_m(t)\}}. \qquad (A1.13)$$

Changing the integration variables to t_0, and $\tau = t_0-t$, we may assume the time T to greatly exceed the maximum time over which physical correlations of the motion of atoms persists, so that the limits of integration for τ are effectively infinite. Then

$$\sum|f(\omega_1)|^2 = \frac{1}{r'^2}\frac{\Delta E}{2\pi\hbar}\frac{1}{T}\int\limits_0^T dt_0 \int\limits_{-\infty}^{\infty} d\tau\; e^{-i\omega\tau}\sum_{m,n} b_m^* b_n\, e^{i\mathbf{Q}\cdot\{\mathbf{R}_n(t_0)-\mathbf{R}_m(t_0-\tau)\}}$$

$$= \frac{1}{r'^2}\frac{\Delta E}{2\pi\hbar}\int\limits_{-\infty}^{\infty} d\tau\; e^{-i\omega\tau}\sum_{m,n} b_m^* b_n\, \overline{e^{i\mathbf{Q}\cdot\{\mathbf{R}_n(\tau)-\mathbf{R}_m(0)\}}} \qquad (A1.14)$$

where the bar denotes "time average of". The corresponding cross-section is readily found from the flux represented by this intensity. The number of neutrons passing through the area $r_1^2\, d\Omega$ is in the ratio $(v_1/v_0)r_1^2\, d\Omega\sum|f(\omega_1)|^2$ to the incident flux. The differential cross-section is thus

$$\frac{d^2\sigma}{d\Omega dE} = \frac{v_1}{v_0}\frac{1}{2\pi\hbar}\int d\tau\; e^{-i\omega\tau}\sum_{m,n} b_m^* b_n\, \overline{e^{i\mathbf{Q}\cdot\{\mathbf{R}_n(\tau)-\mathbf{R}_m(0)\}}}. \qquad (A1.15)$$

Note added in proof. Since the preparation of this chapter, another treatment of neutron scattering based on the use of time-dependent operators has appeared. This is Prof. I. Waller's article in "Advanced Methods of Crystallography", edited by Prof. G. N. Ramachandran (Academic Press, London, 1964).

CHAPTER 2

Mechanical and Time-of-flight Techniques

ROBERT M. BRUGGER

Phillips Petroleum Company, Atomic Energy Division,
Idaho Falls, Idaho, U.S.A.

2.1 Introduction... 54
2.2 Transmission of Single Choppers....................................... 56
2.3 Chopper Construction.. 61
2.4 Helical Slot Velocity Selectors....................................... 65
2.5 Polycrystalline Filter Monochromators plus Chopper Time-of-flight
    Analyzers.. 67
2.6 Single-chopper Monochromators plus Time-of-flight Analyzers 69
2.7 Discussion of Phased Chopper Velocity Selectors 70
2.8 Resolution of Phased Chopper Velocity Selectors...................... 72
2.9 The Harwell-Chalk River Velocity Selector........................... 76
2.10 The MTR Phased Chopper Velocity Selector........................... 80
2.11 The Saclay Cold Neutron Velocity Selector.......................... 85
2.12 Rotating-crystal Time-of-flight Spectrometers 85
2.13 Spinning Sample Method.. 88
2.14 Linear Accelerator and Pulsed Reactor Methods...................... 89
2.15 Multichannel Time Analyzers.. 90
2.16 Timing Signals... 92
2.17 Safety... 93
References.. 94

List of Symbols

A	Area of chopper slots	v_{co}	Minimum neutron velocity for transmission by plane slot chopper
a	Separation of two choppers		
B	Transmission function of chopper for fast neutrons	X	Distance from chopper near sample to detectors
d	Width of slot in chopper		
$D(\theta)$	Chopper thickness (in direction of neutron beam) as a function of its angular position	y	Shadow factor for choppers
		Y	Distance from sample to detectors
		a	Extreme angle allowed by collimator between neutron trajectory and plane through centre of collimator
L	Length of helical slot velocity selector		
$n(\tau)$	Number of neutrons with reciprocal velocity τ	β	Velocity of neutrons in units of v_{co}
		Δt	Burst time (full-width at half-height)
R	Length of chopper slot (axis-to-edge)		
S	Standard deviation of time-burst	ρ	Radius of curvature of chopper slot
T	Transmission of phased chopper system	τ	Time of flight (or reciprocal velocity)
		ϕ	Angular rotation (about axis of helix) of one end of helical slot with respect to the other
v	Neutron velocity		
v_0	Neutron velocity for maximum transmission through chopper	ω	Angular velocity of chopper

2.1 Introduction

Three functions must be performed in conventional inelastic scattering experiments: (1) neutrons in a small velocity interval must be selected for the incident neutron beam, (2) the energy of the scattered neutrons must be analyzed to determine the energy change, and (3) the angle of scattering with respect to the incident beam and with respect to the sample orientation must be measured to determine the momentum change. These three functions can be achieved by coherent diffraction techniques, by mechanical and time-of-flight techniques, or by a combination of the two. The integrated mechanical and time-of-flight systems and the time-of-flight components that are combined with coherent diffraction components are discussed in this chapter. Coherent diffraction components and systems are discussed in Chapter 3.

Time-of-flight techniques † are those in which a burst of polychromatic neutrons is produced and the times for these neutrons to travel from the source of the burst to a detector are measured. A single "chopper" interrupting a beam from a reactor is quite often the source of pulsed neutrons. An example of such a chopper time-of-flight system used with an incident neutron beam composed of neutrons having a Maxwellian velocity distribution (see Fig. 1.1 and equation (1.2)) is given at Fig. 2.1. The chopper opens at time t_0 and successive subscripts indicate later times; the figure illustrates the principle of this technique in which the slower neutrons take longer to travel to the detector so that they are counted at a later time. A multichannel time analyzer records the pulses from the counter and presents them as a time spectrum (or reciprocal velocity or wavelength spectrum) of the neutron beam. In recent years, pulsed linear accelerators, pulsed reactors, and other methods of interrupting reactor beams have been developed to replace choppers in some experimental arrangements.

Time-of-flight techniques have high data accumulation rates because of their concurrent energy (i.e. velocity) analysis of all neutrons in the burst. These techniques have been widely adapted to inelastic scattering measurements in order to analyze the energies of the scattered neutrons and a variety of combinations will be described later.

Mechanical techniques are those in which neutrons of one narrow velocity band are passed by a chopper or system of choppers while neutrons of all other velocities are excluded. The original example of this type device using a single rotor is the helical slot velocity selector. In this system the polychromatic neutrons in a parallel beam try to pass through a helical shaped slot cut on the periphery of a rotating drum. Only those neutrons whose velocities allow them to stay in the slot and not hit the sides as the drum rotates pass out through the far end of the velocity selector. With many

† Many details of these techniques are described in the volume by Spaepen (1961).

closely spaced slots, a continuous beam of monochromatic neutrons is produced.

In recent years mechanical monochromatization has been achieved by combining two choppers (Egelstaff, 1956a) which are spaced several metres apart and which open at interrelated times. In these phased chopper velocity selectors the first chopper passes bursts of polychromatic neutrons, while the second passes bursts of neutrons having only a narrow band of velocities.

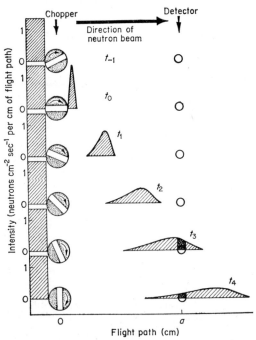

Fig. 2.1. Space distribution of neutrons at successive times in a chopper time-of-flight experiment. The time when the chopper is "open" is t_0. The heavily shaded part of the distribution at t_3 and t_4 represents neutrons being detected at times t_3 and t_4.

The mean velocity of the band is determined by the distance between the choppers and the time lag or phase between the opening of the first chopper and the opening of the second chopper.

The mechanical techniques, since they are inefficient analysers, are used principally as monochromatizing methods. Although velocity selectors similar to the helical slot velocity selectors (Section 2.4) were the first instruments used to make energy dependent neutron measurements (Dunning et al., 1935), helical slot velocity selectors have seen only limited application to total cross section measurements. The phased chopper velocity selectors, because they monochromatize the incident beam of neutrons and because they produce bursts for time-of-flight analysis of the scattered neutrons, are the most promising of the mechanical time-of-flight methods being used for inelastic scattering experiments (see Sections 2.7 to 2.12).

The mechanical techniques and the time-of-flight techniques are similar. As an example, the phased chopper velocity selector can be considered as a single chopper with the second chopper acting as a single channel time analyzer. Both methods depend upon the relationship of velocity and energy of the neutrons to their time of flight. Inelastic scattering measurements are presently important for neutron energies betweeen 0·001 and 1 eV. Above 1 eV the neutrons are insensitive to the binding of the atoms in molecules, liquids or solids; the total cross-section reaches the free atom cross-section. Below 0·001 eV the counting rates are too small. Thus neutrons with velocities between 500 and 14,000 metres per second are important for inelastic scattering. For reference, a nomogram is given in the back of the book comparing the magnitude of the energy, velocity, and wavelength in this range.

Single choppers are essential parts of many time-of-flight systems and different types of choppers have been developed that stress simplicity or minimum burst time or maximum background suppression. A knowledge of the transmission and construction of these choppers is important to the understanding and successful interpretation of the experimental results. Several instruments that do not use choppers have been developed for inelastic scattering experiments. In the rotating crystal arrangement (Brockhouse, 1958), a crystal spinning at a high rotational speed both monochromatizes and pulses the neutrons for time-of-flight analysis before they are scattered by the sample. In the spinning sample method (Brugger et al., 1959), a sample rapidly passing through the beam of beryllium filtered neutrons produces pulses of scattered neutrons. These scattered neutrons are energy analyzed by time of flight. The wide variety of instruments described in this chapter illustrates the versatility of time-of-flight techniques.

All time-of-flight techniques depend upon the magnitude, speed, and versatility of a time analyzer to sort and store signals initiated by the neutrons. Development of multi-channel multi-input analyzers has advanced hand in hand with choppers and velocity selectors. Analyzers with tens of thousands of channels and several score inputs are being developed and the proper selection of the optimum analyzer is an important step in the planning of any experimental equipment.

2.2 Transmission of Single Choppers

The design of choppers has advanced rapidly from the first "Fermi" chopper (Fermi et al., 1947) to high speed choppers with divergent, curved or multiple slots. The purpose of all these designs is to interrupt a poly-chromatic beam of neutrons, thus producing bursts of short time duration.

Figure 2.2 shows the two conventional designs of a single chopper. In the chopper of Fig. 2.2(a) the beam passes through a hole or slot cut in the chopper perpendicular to the axis of rotation. Since the path of the neutrons having the desired velocity v_0 in the rotating coordinates of this chopper is an Archimedian spiral $r = v_0\theta/\omega$, the slot is usually cut in a circular arc

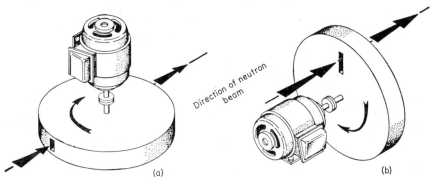

Direction of neutron beam

(a)   (b)

FIG. 2.2. Two designs of choppers: (a) Perpendicular-beam-to-rotational-axis chopper (which may be a single slot as shown or many slots side by side). (b) Parallel-beam-to-rotational-axis chopper.

$\rho = v_0/2\omega$ to approximate this path. This slot then excludes fast and very slow neutrons and the chopper acts as a coarse velocity selector. The advantages of this design are: (1) a large amount of material with respect to the total mass of the chopper is put into the beam when the chopper is closed, (2) it can easily accommodate different shaped slots, (3) multiple slots can be used without increasing the burst time, and (4) the chopper acts as a coarse monochromator.

In the chopper of Fig. 2.2(b) the beam of neutrons passes through a hole or slot cut parallel to the axis of rotation near the periphery. One advantage of this design is that a hole is not cut through the axis of rotation. Disadvantages are the large mass that must be spun if an appreciable amount of material is to be in the beam when the chopper is closed and that multiple slots for each burst may not be used if short bursts are to be produced. For this chopper design to act as a velocity selector, it must be lengthened and the slot cut in the shape of a helix.

The transmission probability of an idealized Fermi type chopper (Fig. 2.2(a)) has been determined in detail (Egelstaff, 1953; Mostovoi, 1956; Stone and Slovacek, 1956). These calculations are for a parallel beam of neutrons passing through a single slot having plane parallel sides. The neutrons pass through the slot perpendicular to the axis of rotation which is midway between the two sides of the slot. The burst obtained is triangular in time for infinite velocity neutrons, changing to a triangle with rounded top, to a parabola as the neutron velocity decreases till no neutrons are transmitted through the slot at velocities lower than $v_{co} = \omega R^2/d$. The angular velocity of the slot is ω, the length of the slot from the axis of rotation to the edge of the rotor is R and the distance between the two plane sides is d. The integral of the burst shape over time gives the transmission as a function of velocity v for the single rotating slot. This function normalized to unity for infinite velocity neutrons is

$$T(\beta) = 1 - \frac{8}{3}\beta^2 \qquad\qquad\qquad 0 < \beta < \frac{1}{4}$$

$$T(\beta) = \frac{16}{3}\beta^{1/2} - 8\beta + \frac{8}{3}\beta^2 \qquad\qquad \frac{1}{4} < \beta < 1 \qquad\qquad (2.1)$$

$$T(\beta) = 0 \qquad\qquad\qquad\qquad \beta > 1$$

and it is shown in Fig. 2.3, which shows transmission function plotted against the parameter $\beta = \dfrac{\omega R^2}{dv}$. The points are the ratios of counting rates obtained at different values of ω and experimentally verify the formulae (Stone and Slovacek, 1956).

For neutrons with velocities such that the transmission is near the maximum, the burst time of a chopper can be estimated by the time for the slot to pass through the centre of the beam. For this case the full width at half maximum height Δt of the neutron burst generated by rotating the chopper of Fig. 2.2(a) in a parallel beam is $\Delta t = d/2\omega R$. The full width at half height of the chopper of Fig. 2.2(b) or the chopper of Fig. 2.2(a) with a divergent slot so that it only chops on one edge is $\Delta t = d/\omega R$. If the beam is not parallel, but spread evenly over an angle 2α, the former burst time becomes $\Delta t = \dfrac{1}{2\omega}\left(\dfrac{d}{R} + 2\alpha\right)$. However, if a fixed collimator providing a divergent beam of width d is placed before the chopper of Fig. 2.2(b) the beam divergence does not affect the pulse length. In practice the neutron beam divergence has only a minor effect on the transmission. The major effect of this divergence is that the beam is swept from one side of the sample to the other as the chopper opens and closes. The sweep increases the burst time and worsens the time resolution. In some cases this sweeping of the beam across the sample can be used in time focusing by having the sweep start on the side of the sample that is the farthest from the detectors or in inelastic scattering by arranging that the neutrons arriving first are least accelerated and conversely.

From Fig. 2.3 one notes that the transmission for fast neutrons approaches one, but to pass neutrons with very small velocities, either the slot width d must be large or the rotational speed ω must be small. Either change produces a very large time width of the burst. Since accurate time analysis depends on a small time width of the burst, this is an undesirable effect.

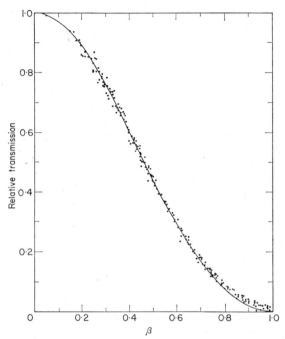

FIG. 2.3. Transmission of a single rotating slot with plane parallel sides. $\beta = \omega R^2/dv$ for a straight slot chopper.

The path of a neutron in the rotating system of coordinates of a chopper is an Archimedean spiral $r = v_0\theta/\omega$, but as stated above for the usual curvatures encountered in chopper design this can be approximated by a parabola or a circle. By using a slot with curved sides instead of a slot with plane sides, neutrons with small velocities are transmitted with large probability while d and ω can be adjusted to give a small burst width. For maximum transmission of neutrons of velocity v_0, the radius of curvature ρ of the circular shaped slot and the angular velocity ω of the chopper must be such that $v_0 = 2\omega\rho$.

Marsaguerra and Pauli (1959) have calculated the burst shapes of a rotating parabolic shaped slot which is a close match to the circular or Archimedean shaped slot. They present detailed equations and figures of these bursts in time and velocity. In this case

$$\beta = \frac{\omega R^2}{d}\left(\frac{1}{v} - \frac{1}{v_0}\right). \tag{2.2}$$

AUGUSTANA · UNIVERSITY COLLEGE
LIBRARY

For velocities v greater than v_0, the transmission curve of Fig. 2.3 is reflected about the ordinate axis into the negative plane. Thus the plane slot chopper is a high pass filter while the curved slot chopper can be made a band pass filter. Most choppers have too wide a band to be effective monochromators but the crude monochromatizing is used to eliminate frame overlap or order and to shape a polycrystalline filtered beam (see Section 2.5 and 2.6).

For a curved slot chopper that acts like a velocity selector excluding very fast neutrons and for which $v_0 \ll \omega R^2/d$, the full width of the velocity band passed by the chopper is $2dv_0^2/\omega R^2$ and the full width in velocity at half height Δv of the band is $0.95 dv_0^2/\omega R^2$. The resolution of this chopper for the neutrons of the desired velocity is then $\Delta v/v_0 = 0.95 dv_0/\omega R^2$.

If the total slot area is A, the number of neutrons per cm^2 per sec falling on the slot is $n(\tau)$ in a reciprocal velocity interval $\delta\tau$, and the open fraction of the chopper is $d/4\pi R$, then the total number of neutrons transmitted per sec is

$$N = \frac{dA}{4\pi R} \int_{-\infty}^{\infty} n(\tau) T \, d\tau. \tag{2.3}$$

If we assume that the spectrum $n(\tau)$ is flat over the range of τ transmitted by the chopper, then using (2.1) we find

$$N = 0.47 A n(\tau) \frac{d^2}{2\pi \omega R^3} \tag{2.4}$$

The transmission discussed in the previous paragraphs is that for neutrons of the desired velocity through the slot of the chopper when the chopper is "open". Another transmission that must be considered when designing choppers is that for passage of the neutrons through the material of the chopper when it is "closed". This transmission B_{eff} can be calculated from the known cross-sections $\sigma(v)$ of the materials from which the chopper is made, the thickness of the chopper $D(\theta)$ at each angle θ when it is "closed", and the flux distribution $n(v)$ in the incident beam. This transmission is

$$B_{\text{eff}}(\theta) = \int n(v) B(v,\theta) dv \Big/ \int n(v) dv \quad \text{where} \quad B(v,\theta) = \exp(-nD(\theta)\sigma(v)). \tag{2.5}$$

The number of atoms per cubic centimetre is n and the cross-section $\sigma(v)$ has to be interpreted as a "removal" cross-section. This is an operationally defined cross-section describing the actual attenuation of the beam, including the effects of multiple scattering capture and other processes.

Since the incident beam is usually from a reactor, the range of integration is from thermal to greater than 15 MeV. The regions of this range that allow more neutrons to pass are those where the cross-sections are low, such as the "windows" in nickel at 60 keV and in iron at 25 keV or above 1 MeV for the hydrogen in plastics. Cross-sections for aluminium and magnesium are

AUGUSTANA UNIVERSITY COLLEGE
LIBRARY

relatively small in the electron-volt energy range, so choppers made from these materials are not effective against fast neutrons. Nickel, iron, and plastic are much more effective in this region. The very fast neutrons are the most difficult to stop since all materials have relatively low-cross-sections for fast neutrons. This transmission depends upon the amount of material $(nD(\theta))$ in the beam. Just as the chopper is closing nD is small and the background at this angle can be high. The choppers should therefore be designed to insert rapidly a large amount of material into the beam.

The transmission B_{eff} of the choppers at Fig. 2.4 is about 10^{-3} when the chopper slots are perpendicular to the beam. This is not sufficient and a B_{eff} of 10^{-6} is desired so that no effects of background from this source can be seen above the room background in an inelastic scattering experiment. The choppers shown in Fig. 2.5 because they are broader, are more effective in suppressing background.

2.3 Chopper Construction

The most common chopper, the Fermi type, follows the design of Fig. 2.2(a). It consists of alternating sheets of a neutron transmitting material, the windows, and a neutron absorbing or scattering material, the chopping foils, in a supporting shell. The chopper is rotated about an axis parallel to the plane of the windows while the neutron beam strikes the chopper perpendicular to this axis. During the short time when the path of the beam and the windows are parallel, neutrons are transmitted while at all other times the neutrons are absorbed by the chopping foils. Thus bursts of neutrons are produced. To be an effective chopper, the windows must allow a large percentage of the neutrons of the desired energy to pass when the planes of these sheets are parallel to the beam, and the chopping foils must scatter or absorb most of the neutrons of all energies when the planes of these sheets are not parallel to the beam. Since no materials are perfect windows or chopping foils, materials are selected that optimize the combination of high "open" transmission, low "closed" transmission and easy construction.

Aluminium frequently is selected for the windows of Fermi type choppers because of its high macroscopic transmission for neutrons of all energies, its strength, and its machineability. Then cadmium is selected for the chopping foil because of its large macroscopic absorption cross-section for neutrons below 0·3 eV. With cadmium the chopper is effective below 0·3 eV only and the aluminium windows supply the necessary rigidity. The thickness of the window and chopper foils are adjusted to maximize the "intensity" when the chopper is open, minimize the leakage when the chopper is closed, and deliver short bursts.

Many modifications (Hughes, 1953; Larsson *et al.*, 1958; Mostovoi *et al.*,

1956; Vladimivskii *et al.*, 1956; Whittemore, 1964) of Fermi's original design
have appeared that incorporate curved windows, or more transparent
windows to increase the transmission, or larger sizes to suppress backgrounds.

The Fermi type choppers of the Materials Testing Reactor (MTR) velocity
selector (Brugger *et al.*, 1961) shown in Fig. 2.4 have aluminium as the

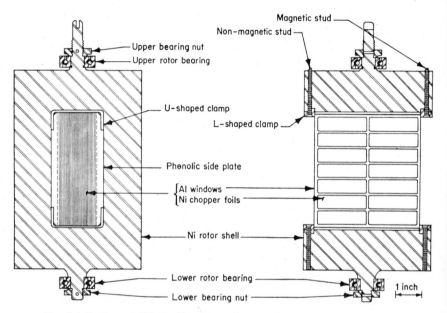

FIG. 2.4. Sections at 90° of a Fermi type chopper of the MTR velocity selector.

window material. However, to decrease to 10% the loss of neutrons due
to scattering from the window material, 87% of the aluminium window
material has been removed to form a grid or spacer. Then, since the aluminium no longer has rigidity or strength, cadmium coated nickel sheets are
used as the chopping foils. The nickel supplies the rigidity and more effectively scatters neutrons above 0·3 eV than does cadmium alone. Each window is
0·032 in. thick while each nickel plus cadmium foil is 0·011 in. thick. This
allows a possible 75% window area of the chopper when it is "open" and
produces 17 μsec burst when the chopper is spinning at 4700 rev/min. The
multiple foils allow a 4 in. by 1·3 in. beam area to be used. This chopper is
not as effective as desired in removing fast neutrons from the beam when it
is "closed" because of the limited radial dimensions and because of the
limited amount of chopping foil material.

To transmit neutrons efficiently in the thermal range (see Section 2.2), sets
of chopping foils with radii of curvature of ∞, 83, 42, 21 and 12 in. have been

made for the MTR choppers. The 12-in. radius of curvature foils efficiently pass 0·005 eV neutrons when a chopper is spinning at 15,000 rev/min. The curvature is obtained by cutting the phenolic side pieces to the desired shape and then pressing the flat foils between them.

These choppers which are usually operated at about 12,000 rev/min are designed to spin at speeds up to 15,000 rev/min. At 15,000 rev/min a burst is produced every 4 msec and with 2–2·5 m flight paths, no "frame overlap" is encountered. Frame overlap occurs when slower neutrons from a first burst arrive at the detector late enough to be intermixed with faster neutrons from a second burst. To realize the maximum intensity, the chopper should open and illuminate the sample with full intensity for most of the burst time. Since the windows of these choppers have an angular acceptance of 0·5°, the

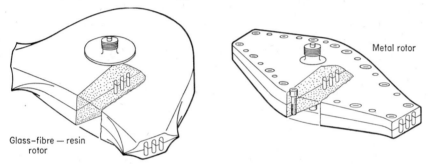

Fig. 2.5. Two models of the Harwell high speed slow neutron choppers.

external collimation must be less than 0·5° to realize this maximum intensity condition. In some experiments, where high intensity is desirable and angular resolution is not critical, this is an undesirably small acceptance angle.

Operating choppers at the highest possible peripheral speeds has the advantages of producing shorter pulses or allowing wider slot and beam sizes to be used. The strength of materials limits this tip speed to about 500 m/sec and choppers designed by Pickles and Hazlewood (1960) and used in the Harwell-Chalk River velocity selector (Section 2.9) approach this limit. Figure 2.5 shows two designs, the left one for relatively slow neutrons and the right one for relatively fast neutrons. These choppers have a 5-in. radius from the centre of rotation to the tip of the chopping slots. Curved slots are necessary to allow the desired velocity neutrons to pass while still preserving small burst widths. Therefore an asymmetrical shape is required to preserve balance and strength, the shape being different for each curvature of the slots. Only a few slots of a larger width (0·25 in.) than in a Fermi chopper are used; thus machining the slots is simple and no window material is necessary. For improved reslution the most recently made choppers of this design have twelve slots 0·1 in. wide.

These choppers are designed for speeds up to 45,000 rev/min. While the slots should have the shape of an Archimedean spiral, a circular slot with parallel sides (for these 10-in. diameters rotor spinning at 36,000 rev/min) is nowhere more than 0·004 in. different from the Archimedean. A perfectly designed slot would be of constant width as measured perpendicular to the beam of neutrons in the laboratory system, each measurement being made as the centre of the slot passes through the centre line of the beam. These choppers have a parallel sided slot in the rotating frame of reference, which is a good approximation in this case.

While Fermi type choppers are rigidly supported at both ends by bearings and can spin in any orientation, the high speed Harwell choppers spin about vertical axes and are suspended from thin flexible shafts. Each shaft allows its chopper to seek its own axis of rotation. Spinning asymmetrical choppers in this fashion has revealed the presence of resonances, in some of which the motions are unstable. Hay et al. (1961) discuss the problem of spinning asymmetric choppers at very high speeds and mention methods for accelerating through these resonances.

The choppers shown in Fig. 2.5 are constructed of three types of material: (1) Nimonic 90 (a high nickel content metal), (2) an alloy of 10% cadmium–90% magnesium and (3) laminated glass fibre plastic. Because of the cadmium in the alloy, these are very effective choppers for neutrons with energies below the cadmium cut-off but "rotating collimators" (see Section 2.9) must be used to stop the faster neutrons. The glass and hydrogeneous plastic make the laminated glass fibre type choppers effective for neutrons with energies above the cadmium cut-off. The Nimonic rotors, because of the high nickel content, are effective stoppers of neutrons of any energy. These choppers are made in two pieces; the two halves of the chopper are bolted together, gluing or brazing having proved inferior. The metal choppers can be operated safely at 36,000 rev/min and are tested at 45,000 rev/min. Their calculated breaking speed is in the neighbourhood of 60,000 rev/min. The plastic choppers fail at 36,000 rev/min and therefore must operate somewhat slower. Failure usually occurs across the midplane. The stress, strength and balance properties and the determination of the shapes and sizes of this type chopper have been determined in detail (Pickles and Hazlewood, 1960).

The Harwell designed choppers put a large amount of material into the beam when they are closed, thus effectively reducing the background of fast neutrons. When the slots are narrow, the high speed operation produces very short bursts. With 0·25-in. wide slots, the angular acceptance of the choppers is about 1·3° and the external collimation can be equivalent. This produces increased intensities over the previously mentioned MTR designed Fermi choppers. At 36,000 rev/min, bursts are produced every 1·6 msec.

Thus to limit frame overlap arising from inelastically scattered neutrons in an experiment with 2-m scattered flight paths, only every second burst is accepted. This discards some of the potential intensity.

Choppers similar to the Fig. 2.2(a) type but with curved divergent slots have been developed for slow neutron experiments (Dyer and Low, 1961). In these choppers the narrow end chops in the manner of the chopper of Fig. 2.2(b) while the wide end allows neutrons from a divergent beam with a wide velocity range to pass. This design is advantageous when using a narrow beam for small sample work. An analysis of the stress distribution in this type has been given by Umakantha (1959).

A chopper for specific application to cold neutrons that has achieved a peripheral speed of 700 msec has been developed at Argonne National Laboratory (A.N.L.) by Connor et al. (1964). Following the design of fig. 2.2(b) a thin aluminium disk of 23·5-in. diameter is spun at speeds up to 23,000 rev/min. The disk is cadmium coated except for a number of 1 in. × 3 in. areas near the edge. These areas are the slots for chopping the neutrons when the neutron beam is travelling parallel to the axis of rotation. Since no holes are cut into the chopper structural material, the high peripheral speeds are possible. The advantage of this design is the very short slot length along the beam direction (0·25 in.) which allows of a large angular acceptance. Therefore large source sizes can be used and high intensities realized. One difficulty is obtaining short enough bursts while still using a large beam area. Only one slot per burst can be used, while in a Fermi chopper many narrow slots are used. In the ANL design, two closely spaced choppers spinning in opposite directions chop the beam from both sides. This will halve the burst time and make the burst symmetric in time about the beam axis. However, the added difficulty of chopper phasing will be introduced.

Other methods of chopping might be possible. Lowde (1959) has suggested the use of slotless choppers, called "blotors", that chop on the side. Since these choppers do not have slots, they might operate at very high speeds.

2.4 Helical Slot Velocity Selectors

A helical slot monochromator is designed to produce either bursts or a continuous beam of monochromatic neutrons. Figure 2.6 shows the Argonne National Laboratory helical slot velocity selector (Nasuhoglu and Ringo, 1960) that has been used to measure total cross sections of hydrogenous liquids for neutrons with wave lengths between 5–20 Å (see Chapter 10). This velocity selector is made by aligning many 0·031-in. thick cadmium coated steel disks on a single shaft. The disks have narrow radial slots punched in the edges; the slots are aligned to form helical channels along the periphery of the rotor parallel to the axis. A simpler design uses straight slots but turns

4

the axis of the selector with respect to the beam (Dash and Sommer, 1953). If these channels make a partial rotation ϕ in the length of the rotor L, when the angular velocity of the selector is ω, the selector will pass neutrons travelling parallel to the shaft at a velocity $v = \dfrac{L\omega}{\phi}$. The resolution of such a selector is approximately

$$\Delta v/v = 2\alpha + dv/LR\omega. \tag{2.6}$$

In this equation Δv is the full width at half height of the velocities passed, d is the width of the channels at the radial distance R, and α is the extreme angle that the external collimation permits between the neutron trajectory

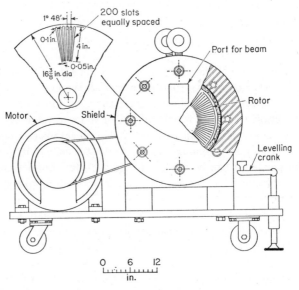

FIG. 2.6. Sketch of the Argonne helical slot velocity selector as viewed from the neutron source. The length of the rotor is 12 in.

and the plane passing through the centre of the collimating system. Since material strengths limit $R\omega$ to values of not much greater than 200 m/sec, these selectors are limited to very slow neutrons or very small values of d/L. Small values of d/L limit the angular acceptances (not α) of the selector to such a small value that the intensity is much reduced.

Helical slot velocity selectors have the advantages of being relatively easy to operate and (unless the slot width is small) they are easy to build. Since these selectors can be made long, their discrimination against fast neutrons is good. These velocity selectors are free from order or frame overlap effects and can be made to deliver a continuous monochromatic beam. In addition, no complicated electronic time analyzer is needed. Besides their use in total neutron cross-section measurements, helical slot velocity selectors with transmissions of 0·8–0·9 are finding wide use for removing orders from the beams of crystal diffracted systems (Holt, 1957; Smith and Miller, 1963).

2.5 Polycrystalline Filter Monochromators plus Chopper Time-of-flight Analyzers

A polycrystalline filter for producing a beam of cold monoenergetic neutron and a chopper time-of-flight system to analyze the energy of the scattered neutrons is a useful combination (Palevsky, 1961). The filter-chopper experimental equipment at the Stockholm reactor (Larsson *et al.*, 1961) as shown in Fig. 2.7 is an example of one system of this type. A filter of polycrystalline

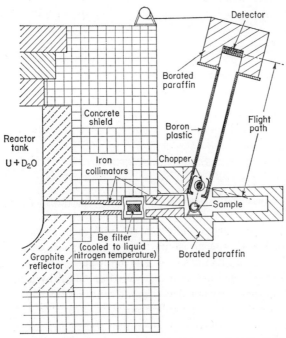

FIG. 2.7. The filter chopper experimental arrangement at the Stockholm reactor.

beryllium at liquid nitrogen temperatures, which passes only neutrons below 0·005 eV, is mounted in the beam inside the reactor shielding (see Chapter 3). Since the energy interval between 0 and 0·005 eV is small compared to the energy gain usually observed in an inelastic scattering event, the beam is essentially monoenergetic. A sample whose orientation is known and can be adjusted is placed in the beam after the filter. A set of BF_3 counters is mounted in a large shielded box at the end of the 4 metre shielded flight path. A simple Fermi type chopper interrupts the neutrons scattered in the direction of the counters and allows time-of-flight analysis of the scattered neutrons to be made.

While many filter-chopper systems are fixed to analyze scattering at only 90° since the backgrounds are usually lowest at this angle, the scattering angle of this instrument can be varied from 20° to 90° to the incident beam.

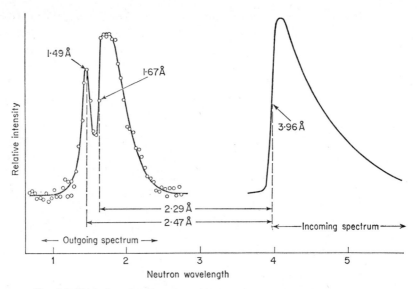

FIG. 2.8. Typical scattered neutron spectrum from the Stockholm apparatus.

For coherent inelastic scattering measurements, such as the dispersion relation measurements this is necessary to reach the pertinent regions of frequency ω and wave number Q space. The flight path is pivoted at the sample position and the shielded detector is lowered or raised by a hoist.

The filter-chopper method has the advantages of (1) simplicity and reliability, (2) low fast neutron backgrounds, and (3) relatively high intensities. The disadvantages are that (i) the initial energy is fixed, thus all regions of ω and Q space cannot be reached and that (ii) the incident neutrons' energy spread for some measurements is relatively large.

The experimental equipment at Stockholm has been used to measure the dispersion relations of aluminium in three principal crystalline directions. An example of the experimental data is given in Fig. 2.8; peaks due to the one-phonon process (Chapter 1, Section 1.12) are clearly seen. The evaluation of the phonon energy depends upon the shape of the peak, and is discussed in detail by Larsson *et al.* (1961). These results are discussed also in Chapter 5 and are plotted in Fig. 5.2. The error in the measurements arises mainly from the uncertainty in the magnitude of the initial wave vector and in the angular resolution of both the initial and final beams. The resolution introduced through the chopper burst time uncertainty can be easily made small. Many other measurements with this type of equipment are reported in Chapters 8 and 10.

2.6 Single-chopper Monochromators plus Time-of-flight Analyzers

One method of reducing the initial neutron energy uncertainty of the filter-chopper method is to mount a specially designed chopper (Turberfield and Egelstaff, 1961; Dahlborg *et al.*, 1961; Haas *et al.*, 1961; Harris *et al.*, 1963) after the filter and before the sample in Fig. 2.7. Thus improved energy resolution of the initial neutrons is achieved through the monochromatizing action of the single chopper. Dahlborg *et al.* (1961) describe a chopper of 30 cm diameter with curved slots 0·175 cm wide that demonstrates this action. The slots, which have a radius of curvature of 50 cm, are shaped to pass with optimum efficiency neutrons at the beryllium cut-off. For this optimum operation, the rotor turns at 9,600 rev/min. The width at half maximum of the burst between the beryllium cut-off and the low energy edge is reduced from 1·1 Å to 0·31 Å, and gives an initial wave length resolution $\Delta \lambda/\lambda$ of about 8%. Besides the advantage of shaping the burst by putting the chopper before the sample, data at several angles may be recorded simultaneously, thus increasing the overall data accumulating capacity (Dolling, 1961).

This arrangement of a filter plus a single chopper velocity selector is not restricted to neutrons with wavelength near the Bragg cutoff, but the incident wavelength can be varied over a wide range. For example the apparatus described by Harris *et al.* (1963) is used with incident wavelengths chosen between 4 Å and 10 Å. An important reason for using longer wavelengths is that the energy width of the incident neutron-spectrum decreases with increasing wavelength (at least as λ^{-2}) and small energy transitions are more accurately determined. Results with equipment of this kind are discussed in Chapters 5, 6, 8 and 10.

Single-chopper time-of-flight equipment as in Fig. 2.7 could be combined with other monochromators such as a single crystal spectrometer (Saunderson and Duffill, 1961) or a helical slot velocity selector. Both of these will have low intensities because of the small angular acceptance but this may not be a disadvantage when conducting experiments such as the measurement of dispersion relations where good angular resolution is important. Neither of these arrangements is limited to long wavelengths, $\lambda > 4$ Å, as is the filter-chopper arrangement.

2.7 Discussion of Phased Chopper Velocity Selectors

The first mechanical monochromator was two cadmium disks with a few holes near the periphery (Dunning *et al.*, 1935). The disks, mounted several feet apart on a single shaft, acted like two choppers. The first disk allowed bursts of polychromatic neutrons travelling parallel to the axis to pass. The second disk passed only neutrons of one velocity, those that arrived when a hole was in line. The phasing of the "open" times of the two disks was accomplished by the proper orientation of the disks on the shaft. A modernized version of this system in which the phase between the two choppers is maintained mechanically, is in use at Saclay measuring the inelastic scattering of cold neutrons (Gobert and Jacrot, 1958). Another instrument of this type with electrical phasing is being built at Brookhaven National Laboratory (Otnes and Palevsky, 1963). A velocity selector composed of two divergent slot choppers of the Fig. 2.2(a) has been built by Dyer and Low (1961). All these instruments employ choppers in which the effective chopping point is at the surface of the rotor.

In addition to this combination of two single slot choppers which forms a velocity selector, there is the combination of two multi-slot choppers like Fig. 2.2(a) which form a phased chopper velocity selector. Several velocity selectors of this type are now in operation. The phased chopper velocity selector designed at Harwell and first put into operation at Chalk River in 1958 (Egelstaff *et al.*, 1961a) is based upon the high speed Harwell choppers (see Section 2.2) while a modification of this machine is being used at the University of Michigan (Vincent, 1961). The phased chopper velocity selector at the Materials Testing Reactor (Brugger *et al.*, 1961) is built around the Fermi type choppers (see Section 2.2). The relative alignment or phase of the slots in the two choppers of these velocity selectors is produced electrically. A second phased chopper velocity selector which derives its power from a motor generator source is in operation at the MTR (Brugger *et al.*, 1962).

In these instruments two choppers are spaced several metres apart in the beam from the reactor. Both choppers spin at the same speed and the time of opening of one and then the other is precisely controlled. Tolk *et al.* (1960) have calculated examples of the burst shapes at different points along the beam in such a velocity selector and these calculations demonstrate the operation of a phased chopper velocity selector. The first chopper chops the reactor beam into bursts of polychromatic neutrons as shown in Fig. 2.9(a). These neutrons spread out in time as they travel to the second chopper as shown in Fig. 2.9(b). The second chopper, which opens at a set time after the first chopper opens (in this example 700 μsec), selects one small velocity range from this distribution. After the second chopper, the burst has both a small time range and small velocity range as shown in Fig. 2.9(c). The neutrons which do not interact with a sample are still in a well defined burst when they arrive at the beam monitor detector several metres after the sample. The burst is wider at the beam monitor detector than just after the second chopper because of the finite range of velocities passed by the second chopper as shown in Fig. 2.9(d).

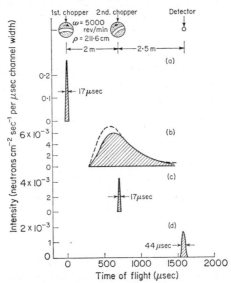

Fig. 2.9. Time distributions of neutron at different positions in a phased chopper velocity selector. (a) Time distribution immediately after first chopper. (b) Time distribution immediately before second chopper (solid line) and time distribution if transmission of the first chopper were one for neutrons of all velocities (dashed line). (c) Time distribution immediately after second chopper. (d) Time distribution at detector.

The neutrons that pass through the second chopper of the phased chopper velocity selector are well defined in energy and time. In slow neutron inelastic scattering experiments a sample is placed a short distance beyond the second chopper and the scattered neutrons are detected by sets of counters placed around the sample and several metres from it.

Lowde (1959) has considered the possible arrangements of phased chopper velocity selectors with optimum operating characteristics. With the designs considered, resolutions comparable to those of coherent diffraction devices, but with more versatility and overall counting rates are realized. Lowde discusses also the method of choosing the parameters of these instruments.

Phased chopper velocity selectors have several advantages when compared to other techniques. Since inelastic scattering experiments are low intensity measurements, an outstanding advantage is the large amount of data that is accumulated for any given operating period. By producing a burst of monochromatic neutrons and then measuring the energy of all scattered neutrons at many angles simultaneously, the several operations that are done successively by other instruments are measured concurrently with this system. The amount of information obtained concurrently more than compensates for the loss in intensity due to chopping the beam into bursts. The amount of data depends upon the extent of the equipment, that is the number of detectors and number of time channels, and the limit of these has not been reached by the existing velocity selectors.

Another advantage of the phased chopper velocity selectors is that the effect of drifts or changes in the neutron velocity or intensity are observed in all channels by the detectors and the beam monitor simultaneously. Thus the data taken at many angles and final energies concurrently, can be normalized and corrected for resolution and backgrounds more easily than with other methods. On the other hand "point-by-point" data collection methods (e.g. the constant Q method discussed in Chapter 3) are difficult to handle in the same way without a considerable loss of efficiency.

Once the phased chopper is built and operating and the calibrations are made, the operation is relatively simple. The initial energy or resolution may be changed in a few minutes: they are continuously variable and such changes do not necessitate moving any shielding or the detectors. Usually there are no overlap or second order effects. A final advantage of the velocity selector is that its resolution may be improved without a great loss in data accumulation suffered by other instruments. By increasing the rotational speed, the resolution is improved by the ratios of new to old speed while the number of neutrons/min in the burst is decreased by only the same factor.

2.8 Resolution of Phased Chopper Velocity Selectors

The resolution, intensity and pulse shapes have been calculated by a number of authors (Egelstaff, 1956b; Lowde, 1959; Tolk and Brugger, 1960; Dyer and Low, 1961; Brugger and Evans, 1961b; Zweifel and Carpenter, 1961; Cocking, 1961b, 1965; Vertebnii et al., 1963; Royston, 1964) who derive expressions (2.8) and (2.12) below, among other results. They show that it is advantageous to build a machine of large dimensions. Practical considerations (e.g. sample size, chopper construction etc.) lead to a compromise which may vary from case to case as illustrated by the various instruments discussed in this chapter.

Figure 2.10 indicates how the time resolution of a phased chopper velocity selector changes with initial neutron energy and with final neutron energy. These curves were obtained from calculations by Brugger and Evans (1961b) for the MTR velocity selector (see Section 2.10) with the choppers spinning at 4720 rev/min. The resolution is defined as the full width at half maximum of the burst Δt as measured at the detectors divided by the time of flight from the sample to the detectors. The initial energy is changed by changing the chopper phase (the relative time of opening of the first chopper and then the second) while keeping the rotational speed constant. The dashed line shows the variation in resolution when the neutrons do not change energy (elastic scattering) upon interaction with the sample. Since the burst time is essentially a constant, this follows the relation $\Delta t/t = \text{constant}/t$. The solid lines show the resolution variation when the neutrons do change energy (inelastic

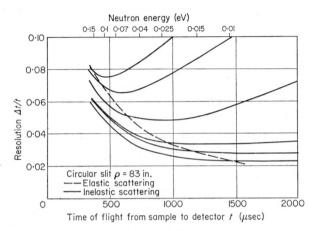

FIG. 2.10. Resolution of a phased chopper velocity selector.

scattering) upon interaction with the sample, the change being the difference between the abscissa of the intercept of dashed and solid lines and the abscissa of another point on the curve. The intersection of each solid line and the dashed line indicates the initial energy for each solid line.

Royston (1964) and Cocking (1961b, 1965) have determined the resolution of a phased chopper velocity selector (see also Vertebnii et al., 1963) by starting from the expressions of Marsaguerra and Pauli (1959) for the transmission of a single chopper as a function of time and velocity. If the distance between the centres of the choppers is greater than twice the diameter of the choppers, they show that the transmission function can be approximated by a triangle. With this simplification the transmission function of a phased chopper velocity selector normalized to unity for the neutrons of velocity v_0 is

$$T = 1 - 6\beta_1^2 + 6\beta_1^3 \qquad\qquad 0 < \beta_1 < \frac{1}{2}$$

$$T = 2(1 - \beta_1)^3 \qquad\qquad \frac{1}{2} < \beta_1 < 1 \qquad\qquad (2.7)$$

$$T = 0 \qquad\qquad \beta_1 > 1$$

Here $\beta_1 = \dfrac{\omega R a}{d}\left(\dfrac{1}{v} - \dfrac{1}{v_0}\right)$ and a is the distance between the choppers.

4*

When the transmission function is half its maximum value $\beta_1 = \pm 0\cdot37$. Hence the full width at half maximum of the velocity distribution Δv is

$$\Delta v = 0\cdot74 \left(\frac{d}{\omega R a}\right) v_0^2. \tag{2.8}$$

Comparing this expression with that for the single chopper (Section 2.2), the distance between chopper centres a has replaced the chopper radius R. This formula is independent of the direction of rotation for parallel sided multi-slot choppers, but for single divergent slot choppers or choppers like Fig. 2.2(b) it is necessary for the choppers to chop in the same direction to obtain the minimum Δv.

To determine the time resolution for a phased chopper velocity selector, let $\Delta\tau_1$ be the open time of the chopper near the reactor, $\Delta\tau_2$ the open time of the chopper near the sample, a the distance between the two choppers and X the distance from the chopper near the sample to the detectors. Royston finds the resolution in time of flight for elastic scattering of the velocity selector to be given by

$$S^2 = \{(X+a)^2\,\Delta\tau_2^2 + X^2\Delta\tau_1^2\}/24a^2 \tag{2.9}$$

where S is the standard deviation of a Gaussian representing the burst as observed at the detector. Optimum intensity for a given resolution is obtained when

$$\Delta\tau_1/\Delta\tau_2 = (X+a)/X \tag{2.10}$$

For inelastic scattering, when all neutrons in the burst change energy by the same amount, the standard deviation of the time burst of inelastically scattered neutrons observed at the detector is

$$S^2 = \left\{ \left(X + \left[\left(\frac{\tau}{\tau_0}\right)^3 - 1\right]Y + a\right)^2 \Delta\tau_2^2 + \left(X + \left[\left(\frac{\tau}{\tau_0}\right)^3 - 1\right]\right)^2 \Delta\tau_1^2 \right\} \Big/ 24a^2 \tag{2.11}$$

and Y is the distance from the sample to the detector, τ is the reciprocal velocity for the inelastically scattered neutrons and τ_0 is the reciprocal velocity for the neutrons incident on the sample. In these equations the length of time the chopper is open is $2\Delta\tau$. Equations (2.9) and (2.11) are for a parallel beam and for a velocity selector assembled from single-slot choppers. The width obtained by Royston (1964) agrees reasonably well with those obtained by Brugger and Evans (1961b).

Equation (2.9) may be tested experimentally by measuring tne standard deviation of the neutron burst shapes observed on a sequence of counters placed in the beam of a phased chopper spectrometer. At Fig. 2.11 data obtained with the Harwell-Chalk River spectrometer (Section 2.9) are given for each of the chopper svstems employed, which verifies this equation.

For a phased chopper velocity selector the total number of neutrons passed per second, N, is found in the same way as for the single chopper but using (2.7) for T. In this case

$$N = 0{\cdot}25An(\tau_0)\frac{d^2}{2\pi\omega aR^2} \tag{2.12}$$

Here it is assumed that the beam is parallel so that the first rotor does not cast a "shadow" on the second and it is assumed that both choppers are identical. Royston (1964) discusses the case of two dissimilar choppers and arrives at the condition (2.10) for optimum intensity and resolution.

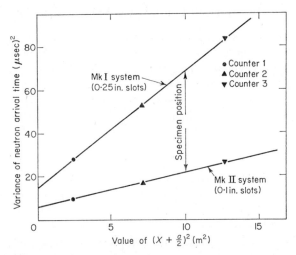

FIG. 2.11. Behaviour of the square of the variance of the neutron burst shape with distance from choppers for a phased rotor spectrometer (Haywood and Thorson, 1963).

When the beam is divergent, the first rotor can cast a shadow on the second and the number of neutrons transmitted will be less than N. This reduction is most pronounced when the first rotor has such a small angular acceptance that it does not open and illuminate the second chopper with full intensity, but it sweeps the beam across the second chopper. With multislot choppers, some loss is incurred because the area A of the first chopper does not exactly overlap the area of the second chopper for all paths of the divergent beam. Egelstaff (1961) suggests that the number of neutrons passed is yN where $y\sim0{\cdot}5$ for a well designed system and $y\ll0{\cdot}5$ if consideration is not taken of the conditions mentioned above. For velocity selectors using choppers like Fig. 2.2(b) or 2.2(a) with a divergent slot, $y\sim1$.

It is useful to consider the restrictions imposed upon the resolution and intensity of a velocity selector by external factors. For example, the strength of rotor materials limits the maximum value of ωR as discussed in Section 2.3. If ωR is fixed (usually near its maximum value) the width of the velocity distribution is determined by the ratio d/a, while the intensity is governed by the ratio d^2/Ra. This shows that the performance is governed by the proportions of the machine in addition to the expected dependence upon the available beam area and source intensity. The actual magnitudes of d, a and R are thus determined by a balance between the factors discussed in this section and those considered in Section 2.3. For the case of the single slot chopper, Lowde (1959) gives a detailed discussion of these questions.

2.9 The Harwell-Chalk River Velocity Selector

A phased chopper velocity selector designed around the high speed Harwell choppers was developed at Harwell (Egelstaff *et al.*, 1961a), but was assembled at Chalk River to take advantage of the high flux of the N.R.U. reactor. The choppers of this velocity selector are 2·7 m apart and spin at speeds between 24,000 and 36,000 rev/min. The half width of the bursts immediately after the second chopper when the 0·1-in. slot choppers are used are as small as 7 μsec and at the detectors are as small as 10 μsec. A sample is placed 0·5 m after the second chopper while up to 20 B_2O_3 or LiF scintillation counters are placed around the sample between 12° and 155° at 1·27 m distance to detect the scattered neutrons. Two banks of 12 counters at distances of 3 m but covering restricted angular ranges are in use also. The velocity selector and the scattering flight plaths are shielded with large concrete blocks and borated paraffin.

Two rotating collimators help the choppers suppress the fast neutron background and can be used to control burst repetition rate. These intercept the beam, one before and one after the first chopper. They are circular disks made of plastic cemented glass fibre, 10 in. in diameter with two $1\frac{1}{4}$-in. square holes at right angles passing through the axis of rotation. Since the rotating collimators rotate at one-quarter the speed of the choppers, the holes at right angles are needed to pass every burst produced by the choppers. Rotating collimators with only a single hole can be used to stop every other burst thus eliminating frame overlap arising from inelastically scattered neutrons. Placing the rotating collimators several metres apart, one before and one after the first chopper, guarantees that one is always closed to fast neutrons.

Each chopper is driven by a separate motor, while the coupling between choppers which achieves the desired phasing relation is obtained through the common electrical system used to drive the motors. Figure 2.12 is a cross-section diagram of one of these motors with its bearing and support system (Egelstaff *et al.*, 1961b). Each motor is a hysteresis, synchronous, 3 phase,

2 pole, 60-W motor that can develop an accelerating torque of 0·02 lb ft and a synchronous pull-out torque of 0·01 lb ft.

Figure 2.13 shows the electrical circuit used for driving the motors. The 100 kc/s output of the primary crystal oscillator is frequency divided to give square waves with periods of 40, 200, 1000 and 4000 μsec. By the proper

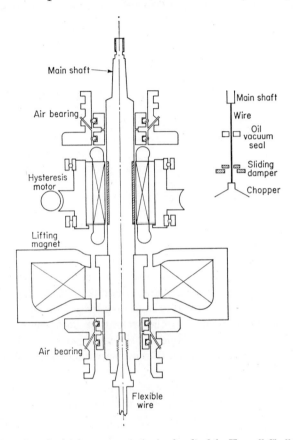

Main shaft

Air bearing

Hysteresis motor

Lifting magnet

Air bearing

Flexible wire

Main shaft

Wire

Oil vacuum seal

Sliding damper

Chopper

Fig. 2.12. A section of a driving system (spinning head) of the Harwell-Chalk River velocity selector.

combination of these square waves and then filtering, a sine wave output with a period between 240 and 20,000 μsec (variable in 40-μsec steps) is obtained. There are several ways of coupling two motors, such as (1) a 3-phase oscillator to three amplifiers and then to the motors, (2) a single phase oscillator, one amplifier to each motor and phase splitting, (3) a single phase oscillator, one amplifier to a pair of motors, each motor with phase splitting as in Fig. 2.14 or (4) a single phase oscillator, one amplifier and phase splitting circuit to a pair of motors whose windings are joined together. System 4 gives the least uncertainty in phase. Phase stabilities of one motor with respect to another of $\pm 0.3°$ have been achieved with this system and synchronous speed is held to better than 1 part in 10^5. The acceleration time of a Mg–Cd chopper to 36,000 rev/min is about 60 min, while 180 min are required for the nimonic choppers. These acceleration times are not a disadvantage, since once at speed, the chopper operates for many hundreds of hours.

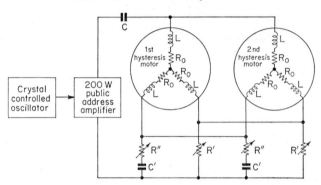

FIG. 2.13. Electrical circuit for driving a pair of motors of the Harwell-Chalk River velocity selector.

The motor and chopper support and bearing system were designed to have minimum power losses due to bearing friction or windage; the loss at 600 c/s is approximately 10 W. Thus fluctuations in the losses are small. Air bearings which exclude any metal to metal contact confine the motor, and a magnetic support system carries the weight of both the motor and the chopper. Since it is desirable to operate the motor at atmospheric pressures but with the chopper in a vacuum to remove windage losses, the chopper is coupled to the motor by a 0·095-in. diameter steel wire passing through an oil lubricated journal bearing acting as a vacuum seal. This wire serves to decouple the chopper from the motor so that unbalance due to inaccuracies in manufacture or uneven expansion of the chopper at speed does not throw large loads onto the bearings.

Because of shaft whirls and regions of unstable motion encountered during acceleration (Hay *et al.*, 1961) a sliding disk damper is placed on the wire near the chopper. This removes energy from any motion that causes the wire to move more than 0·001 in. from its normal position. At operating speeds the rotor axis remains fixed to 0·0005 in. and the thin shaft flexes synchronously to take up the rotor unbalance.

After accelerating, the hysteresis motors lock in synchronism at arbitrary position. In the Harwell-Chalk River velocity selector, coarse phasing is achieved by decreasing the power to a motor until it slips to the correct position. Fine phasing adjustments are made by rotating the stator of the motor and for this purpose the stator is fixed to a worm gear which is driven by a remotely controlled motor. The signal used for comparing phases is developed by a photomultiplier tube detecting light reflected from a mirror

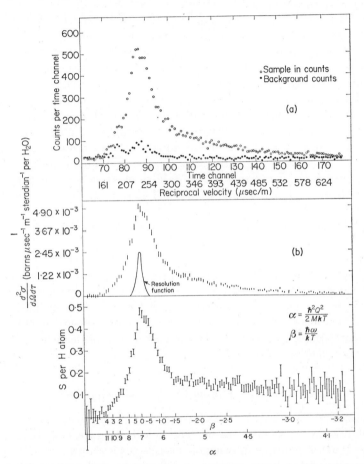

FIG. 2.14. Scattering of 0·12 eV neutrons by water at room temperature at an angle of 86·9°, showing raw data and background (a), and steps in conversion to scattering law (c).

surface on the top of each motor. The time of this signal has been previously compared to the time of the neutron or gamma burst passing through the chopper. Another method of changing the initial energy of the neutron selected is to change the rotational speed of the choppers at a fixed angular phase. For choppers with relatively narrow slits this method is used since it preserves efficiency by maintaining the relation $v_0 = 2\omega\rho$ (see Section 2.2).

This velocity selector is used at the N.R.U. reactor on a beam hole where the source flux has been measured by gold foil irradiation to be 6×10^{13} neutrons $sec^{-1} cm^{-2}$. For the mark I system (0·25-in. slot choppers) the measured flux on the sample is $1·3 \times 10^4$ neutrons/sec at 0·07 eV (Cocking, 1961a) compared to $1·6 \times 10^4$ neutrons/sec that is calculated. In the case of mark II system (0·1-in. slot choppers) the results at 0·07 eV are 6×10^3 neutrons/sec (Thorson, 1963) and 5×10^3 neutrons/sec respectively. (For both calculations a value of $y = \frac{1}{2}$ was used.) The mark II system gives a flux of about 10 neutrons/burst. Time resolutions for elastic scattering $\Delta t/t$ may be obtained from Fig. 2.11, and are as precise as 2% where Δt is the full width at half maximum as measured at the detectors and t is the time of flight from the sample to the detectors. Since 1958 this velocity selector has been measuring the scattering of slow neutrons from samples of reactor moderator materials. Figure 2.14 shows one example of data on water obtained by Haywood and Thorson (1962). Figure 2.14(a) is the raw data and background, Fig. 2.14(b) is the conversion of this data to cross section as a function of time-of-flight, while Fig. 2.14(c) is the final conversion to the scattering law (Chapter 1, Section 1.4).

The advantage of this particular design of velocity selector is that high speed choppers are used. This realizes the fast chopping speed, the large acceptance angle, and effective fast neutron suppression of these choppers. The choppers may be changed easily so that it is possible to insert another set of choppers with a different curvature to their slots, or to insert choppers with single divergent slots, into the same instrument. The spinning system has low power loss. The disadvantages are that the suspension and driving system are complex and delicate. In two instances rotors have been damaged when they spun out of control.

2.10 The MTR Phased Chopper Velocity Selector

A phased chopper velocity selector designed around Fermi type choppers was built and is in operation at the Materials Testing Reactor (Brugger and Evans, 1961). A cutaway drawing of this selector is shown in Fig. 2.15. The choppers are 3·4 m apart, spin at 12,000 rev/min and produce bursts immediately beyond the second chopper that are 6·5 μsec half-width at half maximum. The sample is placed 0·5 m beyond the second chopper while the sets of detectors are 2 m from the sample. The velocity selector and scattering area are enclosed by thick paraffin shielding. Since the choppers are not effective fast neutron scatterers, two rotating collimators which are coarse resolution choppers 12 in. in diameter and made of nylon are placed between the choppers. The phasing of the choppers of this velocity selector is achieved by electrical coupling.

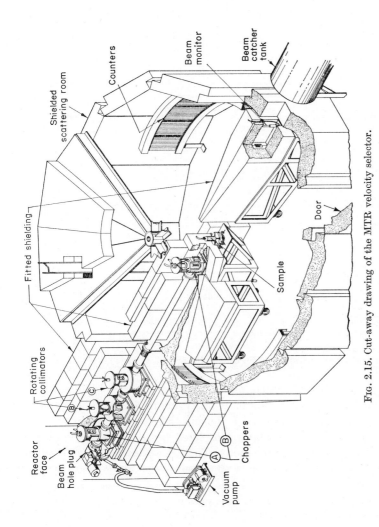

FIG. 2.15. Cut-away drawing of the MTR velocity selector.

The motors which drive each chopper are 2-phase, 4-pole hysteresis synchronous motors rated at 1/6 horse power at 6000 rev/min. Each motor which has standard ball bearings is located in the common vacuum housing and drives the choppers through a no-backlash flexible coupling. Each chopper is supported at top and bottom by bearings.

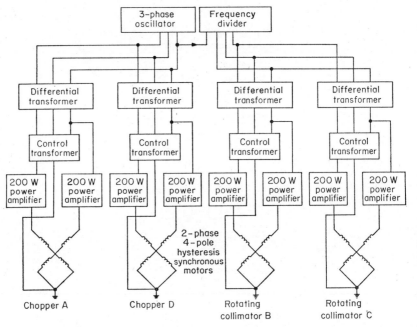

FIG. 2.16. Electrical circuit for driving the motors of the MTR velocity selector.

Figure 2.16 is a block diagram of the electronic supply for the motors. A precision three phase oscillator is the primary standard. Four differential transmitters which are used for phasing the choppers follow the oscillator. One phase from the oscillator, amplified by a 200 W audio amplifier, is supplied to one phase of the motor. The three phases from the oscillator are mixed by a control transformer which supplies a single phase output which can be adjusted in angle with respect to the input phase. This output is supplied to the motor after amplification. By adjusting the control transformer, the 90° between the two phases of the motor can be adjusted.

The time between opening of one chopper and the opening of a second is changed by using the differential transmitters. These transmitters shift the three output phases relative to the three input phases from the oscillator thus allowing each motor and chopper to be turned easily and quickly relative to the other choppers.

In the development of the MTR velocity selector, it was found that the drag introduced through bearings and flexible couplings was not the principal cause of phase instability between choppers. The major source is instability in the signal generated by the oscillator and amplified by the amplifiers. The signal must be free from amplitude and period fluctuations. With the present electronic supply, the time of opening between the two choppers is held to $\pm 1\ \mu$sec. Since the burst as measured at the detectors is 13 μsec, the small amount of jitter between the phases of the rotors causes little broadening of the burst. No further control or feedback systems are needed.

The advantages of this particular velocity selector lie in its conservative design. Limited speed operation with rigid axis of rotation has limited the chances for failure. The large beam area allowed adequate counting rates with a source flux in the reactor of only 10^{13} thermal neutrons/cm^2 sec. About $1\cdot5 \times 10^5$ neutrons/min with an energy of 0·07 eV impinged upon the sample. In 1965 (Brugger, 1965) this velocity selector was moved to another beam hole of the MTR which has a source flux of 2×10^{14} neutrons/cm^2 sec. An additional improvement was realized by doubling the width of the slits in the first chopper to get maximum intensity (see Equation 2.10). By this second change the intensity at the sample increased by a factor of 2·7 while the burst width at the counters only increased from 13 μsec to 15 μsec. The disadvantages, which arise mainly from the choppers, are partial suppression of fast neutron background and somewhat limited angular acceptance. Some problems were encountered, but solved, in running motors and bearings in a vacuum.

An example of data obtainable with the MTR velocity selector is given at Figs. 10.6 and 10.7. The choppers were spinning at 12,000 rev/min and the channel widths of the time analyser were 5 μsec. A sample of methane gas in a thin-walled aluminium container was placed at the sample position. A similar sample container was used as the blank to obtain the background effects. Data were recorded at eight angles for 27 h of sample and 27 h of blank. By subtracting the blank from the sample data, the effects of "room background", of scattering from the aluminium container, and of scattering by air near the sample are eliminated and the effects of scattering from the methane are obtained. The effects of backgrounds could also be obtained by reversing the rotational direction of the choppers, thus excluding slow neutrons but reproducing the conditions encountered by the fast neutrons. Further discussion of the methane data is given in Chapter 10.

While phased chopper velocity selectors are ideally suited for measuring such data which lead to scattering law (see Chapter 1, Section 1.4), they have been successful also in measuring special properties of solids, such as the dispersion relation. Figure 2.17 shows how the scattering surface method is used to measure the dispersion relations of beryllium with the MTR velocity

selector (Schmunk *et al.*, 1961). In these measurements, seven 1-in. diameter by 4-in. active length counters were placed side by side at 2 m from
the sample. Their centre wires were perpendicular to the scattered beam.
Each counter was connected to a separate section of the time analyzer.
Neutrons that scattered inelastically from the single crystal of beryllium

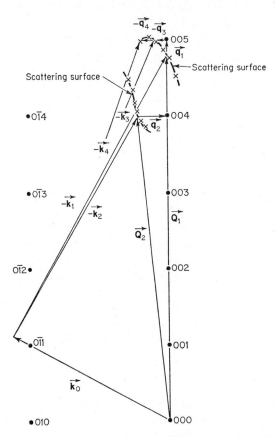

Fig. 2.17. Reciprocal space for beryllium crystal with neutrons wave vector before scatter-
ing $\mathbf{k}_0$ and wave vectors after scattering $\mathbf{k}$ which show how the end points of the $\mathbf{k}$'s trace out
a scattering surface.

and obeyed the equation for coherent inelastic scattering (see Chapter 1,
equation (1.99)) produced peaks in the time distributions from which the
wave vectors $\mathbf{k}$ of the neutrons after scatter were determined. By plotting
$\mathbf{k}$'s for each counter in reciprocal space, the results from all the counters
traced out a portion of a scattering surface. These scattering surfaces usually
crossed a symmetry direction as shown in Fig. 2.17. Schmunk *et al.* (1962)

report that this method competes favourably with the alternative constant Q method discussed in Chapter 3, and the dispersion law results they obtained are discussed in Chapter 5.

2.11 The Saclay Cold Neutron Velocity Selector

The Saclay mechanical velocity selector (Gobert and Jacrot, 1958) is a direct application, incorporating many advances, of the original velocity selector (Dunning et al., 1935). Figure 2.18 is a diagram of this selector.

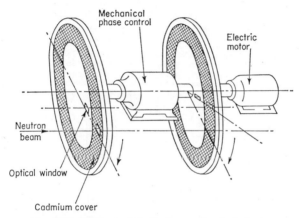

Fig. 2.18. Diagram of the Saclay mechanical selector.

Two choppers like Fig. 2.2(b) one metre in diameter and one metre apart spin about a common axis at 6000 rev/min. Eight 1·5 cm wide by 5 cm high slots on the periphery of the rotors chop the beam. Phasing between the slots of the two choppers is achieved by a 1 : 1 ratio gear mechanism between the choppers which allows adjustments in phase while the choppers are at speed. Burst times of 50 μsec are obtained. A beryllium filter is used to limit fast background and thus the initial energy of the neutrons is below the beryllium cutoff. A sample is placed after the second chopper and the scattered neutrons are observed by a counter 4 m from the sample. While this system is relatively simple and trouble free, it suffers from the principal limitations of choppers in which the rotational axis and beam are parallel. One limitation is that either the beam sizes are too small or that the burst widths are too wide.

2.12 Rotating-crystal Time-of-flight Spectrometers

Several methods for time-of-flight experiments have been developed that do not rely on conventional choppers to pulse the beam. The most productive of these is the rotating-crystal spectrometer (Brockhouse,

1961; O'Connor, 1960; Gläser, 1961, 1963; Harling, 1965). Figure 2.19 shows the pertinent parts of the model in use at the N.R.U. reactor at Chalk River. A beam of neutrons from the reactor strikes a crystal rotating at a high angular velocity. Each time a set of crystal planes satisfies the Bragg condition to reflect neutrons through the slits C_2, a burst of monoenergetic neutrons is passed to the sample. Thus with a single rotor, burst of monoenergetic neutrons are produced for performing inelastic scattering experiments.

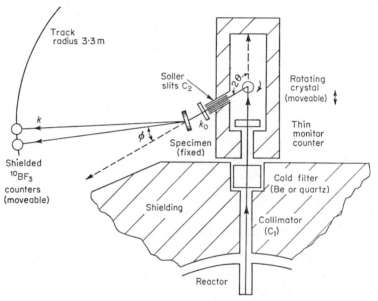

FIG. 2.19 Schematic diagram of the rotating crystal spectrometer at the N.R.U. reactor at Chalk River.

In the Chalk River arrangement the rotating crystal is mounted on a lathe bench and linked to the collimator C_2 so that the diffraction angle and thus the energy of the initial neutrons of the bursts may be easily changed. A sample is mounted beyond collimator C_2 and several detectors are placed in a shielded cart 3·3 m from the sample. As with other time-of-flight systems, data at several angles may be taken simultaneously when the output of each detector is fed into a time analyzer.

The crystal is a single aluminium crystal machined to a sphere and mounted on a shaft through the centre of the sphere. The crystal is spun at 8000 rev/min. With the [111] axis vertical, the (220) planes produce six bursts per revolution. The crystal selected should have little incoherent scattering to limit non-Bragg scattering that will cause background and it should have a high melting temperature compared to room temperature so that thermal diffuse scattering will be small. A flat crystal or a Fankuchen cut crystal would add intensity and focusing advantages. A thicker crystal than in a stationary spectrometer is tolerable because the Doppler shifts make extinction less effective.

The rotating crystal spectrometer will have order contamination not only from the second and higher orders of the (220) planes but also six bursts per revolution from the (422) and (440) planes at 3 times and at 4 times the first order energy. For some initial planes, neutrons from these secondary

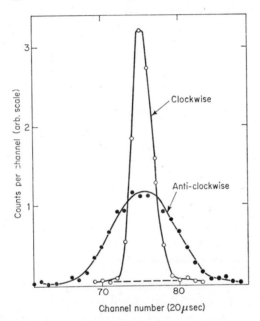

FIG. 2.20. Example of time focusing of the burst from a rotating crystal spectrometer.

planes can be eliminated by proper orientation of the crystal (Gläser, 1961). In the Chalk River experiment these orders are removed by filtering the initial beam through cold polycrystalline beryllium or cold single crystal quartz filters. Other possible methods of removing the higher order neutrons and frame overlap would be to phase a rotating collimator or a second rotating crystal with the principal rotating crystal.

With the proper geometrical orientation of the experiment and the proper rotational direction of the crystal, time focusing of the burst may be realized by reflecting the slower neutrons first. The width of the burst in time as measured at the detectors depends upon the thickness of the detectors, the shape, size and orientation of the sample, the shape and size of the rotating crystal, the mosaic spread of the rotating crystal, and the velocity of rotation and the direction of rotation of the crystal. Figure 2.20 shows an example of how the burst may be time focused or de-focused in a rotating-crystal spectrometer according to the direction of rotation. Similar focusing of time or velocity are possible with some systems of phased rotors (Lowde, 1959).

Figure 2.21 is an example of data obtained with the Chalk River rotating-crystal time-of-flight spectrometer. It shows the frame overlap and the initial resolution as determined by scattering from vanadium. This type spectrometer has the advantages of being relatively simple, inexpensive, and

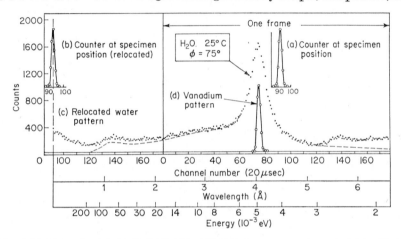

FIG. 2.21. Example of data obtained with the Chalk River rotating-crystal spectrometer.

durable. The backgrounds are low since the monoenergetic beam is deflected away from the line of the initial beam and the backgrounds are time independent. The pulsed beam can have a large area, high resolution, and be time focused. The disadvantages are possible order contamination of the initial beam, frame overlap and small angular acceptance of the initial beam because of limited mosaic spread in the crystal. The intensity of initial neutrons depends on the reflectivity of the crystal which decreases with increasing energy. By setting up two collimators (C_2) at two different values of 2θ (Fig. 2.19), two pulsed monokinetic beams may be obtained. Gläser (1963) discusses the advantages of this technique to cover a large region of (Q,ω) space in a short time.

2.13 Spinning Sample Method

A time-of-flight technique developed at the Materials Testing Reactor produces bursts of scattered neutrons by rapidly passing a sample through the initial beam of monochromatic neutrons (Brugger et al., 1959). A beam of neutrons from the reactor is monochromatized by filtering through 6·5 in. of polycrystalline beryllium and is then collimated by a cadmium slit to a 3-in. high by 0·064-in. wide area. Samples contained in 3-in. long by 0·064-in. diameter aluminium tubes are placed on the ends of a 3-ft rod. This rod is spun about its centre so that the samples pass perpendicular to the beam through the beam. Thus bursts of scattered neutrons are produced that can be analyzed by time of flight.

With the samples spinning at 1250 rev/min, bursts 29 μsec wide are produced. The advantages of the spinning sample method are its simplicity and that all backgrounds are time independent. Some of the method's disadvantages are the difficulty of varying the samples' properties, such as temperature, and the small beam area. Since the sample is moving, the experimental co-ordinate system is not the laboratory system and Lowde (1957) (see also Shull and Gingrich, 1964) has indicated that this has interesting experimental applications. As with many of the other techniques discussed in this chapter the spinning sample can be used with monochromatic beams produced by some other method.

2.14 Linear Accelerator and Pulsed Reactor Methods

Electron linear accelerators, which are intense sources of bursts of neutrons, are being used for high resolution time-of-flight measurements of nuclear properties at neutron energies from 10 eV to 500 keV (e.g. Spaepen, 1961). Recently, results have been obtained using these accelerators for inelastic scattering experiments at lower energies (Whittemore and Danner, 1963; Kirouac et al., 1964). Pulsed reactors are also intense sources of neutrons and are being used for inelastic scattering measurements (Bondarenko et al., 1963; Bayorek et al., 1964; Golikov et al., 1964). The methods used with both sources are similar, the major difference being the longer flight paths required with the pulsed reactors because of their longer bursts. Linear accelerators and pulsed reactors as sources are discussed in Chapter 4.

To use the bursts of neutrons from a linear accelerator for inelastic scattering experiments, a device must be added to monochromatize the neutrons before they are scattered from the sample. In Whittemore's arrangement, the principle of the phased chopper velocity selector is applied. The linear accelerator target acts as the first chopper because bursts of polychromatic neutrons are produced there. A chopper placed several metres from the neutron source is phased with the accelerator and passes only neutrons of one small velocity range. Thus bursts of monoenergetic neutrons are obtained that are scattered from a sample placed after the chopper. The neutrons scattered at several angles are time analyzed over a 1·6 m flight path. The initial energy is fixed by the distance between the chopper and the target and by the time between the electron burst and the chopper opening. In this arrangement the linear accelerator is triggered with a signal from the chopper (see also Rainwater *et al.*, 1962) and the speed control of the chopper does not have to be as precise as in phased choppers.

The advantage of the pulsed sources, if intensity is adequate, is that the background source of neutrons is not on when data is being recorded. This allows less shielding and simpler rotors to be used. The need to work near the source and the gamma flash is a disadvantage. Many scattering angles and a large multi-channel-time analyzer are needed to exploit fully this system. The use of coherent scattering methods and filters as monochromators with pulsed sources are discussed in Chapter 3. With coherent diffraction mono-chromators, time-of-flight is still needed for analyses of the energy of the neutrons after scattering. If the filter detector method (see Chapter 3) is used with the linear accelerator, the time of flight technique is used to determine the energy of the neutrons before scattering.

The methods discussed in the preceding paragraphs for use with a linear accelerator can also be adapted to the pulsed reactor sources. In this case since the burst of thermal neutrons is greater than 100 μsec wide while with linear accelerators the burst is about 20 μsec wide, longer flight paths must be used to have comparable resolution. For the experiments at the IBR(1) reactor at Dubna (Chapter 4), the distance between the reactor and the phased chopper is 8·5–14 m while the distance from the sample to the detectors is 3–10 m.

2.15 Multichannel Time Analyzers

All inelastic scattering experiments are low intensity measurements. With time-of-flight methods a duty cycle of the order of 0·001 is introduced to pulse the beam, and this loss of intensity can only be recovered by using large multichannel analyzers. While analyzers of limited capacity have been used in some early measurements or are being used for special experiments, the desirable analysers to match the most advanced choppers and rotating crystal spectrometers have the following properties.

Channel widths of 2–10 μsec are desirable since they are smaller than the burst time of 5–30 μsec now being introduced with slow neutron choppers. These channel widths are usually small enough to introduce only a small resolution broadening of the burst but wide enough to allow an appreciable number of counts per channel in a reasonable running time.

While many experiments have been performed with one input (counters at one scattering angle), multiple inputs are desirable to fully utilize the potential of the equipment even in the beryllium filtered beam and rotating crystal devices. Multi-angle operation has the advantages of more data, and data acquired simultaneously that can be correlated. The "scattering surface method" for dispersion relations (Schmunk *et al.*, 1962) is an example of the desirability of multiple inputs. Ten to thirty is a reasonable number of inputs to match the other existing equipment. Provision should also be made for the accumulation and storing of data from several samples and a standard, these being cycled into the beam at periods which are short compared to the overall running time of the experiment.

With the number of channels per input and the number of parallel inputs selected, the total number of channels is at least 2000. The desirable capacity for total counts per channel is about 100,000. These are needed to record the large number of elastically scattered neutrons in a run sufficiently long to observe a few hundred counts per channel from inelastically scattered neutrons. To be compatible with these counting rates at multiple parallel inputs, the dead time of the analyzer needs to be only a few microseconds in order to limit counting losses.

Immediate access to or observation of at least part of the data is desirable. Without this, data that require 24–48 h of running time can be lost because of trouble that could have been observed in less than 1 h. A display of counting rate per channel versus time that can immediately be interpreted qualitatively, but not necessarily quantitatively, meets this need.

With thousands of channels of data, the recording of the data can take an appreciable part of the data accumulating time. Since most data runs are 24–48 h, up to 1 h can be allowed for data recording. The speed of recording on punched paper tape, punched cards, or magnetic tape can usually be made sufficiently fast. If an on-line analyzer is used with a tape recorder storage system this time is zero. The recording system that is selected should be compatible with the electronic computer used to process the data.

The analyzer's storing and recording of data must be reliable. Exhaustive error analysis on as much data as are accumulating in an inelastic scattering experiment with a multi-channel analyzer cannot be performed because of the time required (Westcott, 1961). Once the data from initial runs have been checked, only spot checks on future runs can be justified. In processing the data to obtain differential cross-sections, electronic computers are essential, either as auxiliary systems in the time analyzers or as separate research support facilities. An automatic plotter of the data is also needed. Conversion of the data to partial differential cross-sections takes at least a day of organizing and several hours of electronic computer time. One overriding consideration in all time analyzers is cost and some of the above desirable features will have to be compromised or sacrificed to limit cost. For measuring dispersion relations, where only small parts of the time spectra are of interest or where absolute intensity is usually not important, more restricted analyzers are adequate.

The time analyzer (Petree, 1959) used with the MTR velocity selector is a transistorized magnetic core storage device with the following properties:

(1) 2·5–160 μsec channel widths, (2) 16 simultaneous inputs, (3) a double
storage system, 4096 channels total of sample and 4096 channels of empty
sample container, (4) 16 inputs with 256 channels per input of sample and
256 channels per input of empty, (5) 65,000 total counts per channel,
(6) 2·5 μsec dead time, (7) immediate visual inspection of data as oscilloscope
display, (8) punch card read out in 30 min, and (9) no internal logic; all
processing of data performed on a separate IBM 7040 computer.

This analyzer has the advantage of immediate access to the data but has
reached practical limits on the number of channels and inputs until more
economical magnetic core storage systems are developed (Alexander *et al.*,
1961a; Rockwood, 1961; Pagès *et al.*, 1961). The time required to process and
analyze this data suggests that more channels are not desirable at the present
time.

The time analyzer used with the Harwell-Chalk River velocity selector
(Alexander *et al.*, 1961b) uses magnetic tape as a storage system. Each pulse
from the detectors is coded as to flight time and angle and the code is stored
on magnetic tape. In this way the total count and number of channels and
inputs can be made very large. After a complete roll of tape is used (usually
24 h) the codes are sorted on a limited core storage analyzer by passing the
tape many times through the sorter to extract all of the information.

The advantages of this type of analyzer are that for large storage systems it
is less expensive, more channels and more total counts can be stored, and one
sorter can service several analyzer storage systems. The disadvantage is that
the data are not immediately available for qualitative analysis. This can be
overcome to some extent by having a combination of core storage and
magnetic tape storage. A limited core storage system allows immediate
access to sensitive parts of the data while all the data is stored on magnetic
tape for later analysis.

To overcome some of the disadvantages of the previously mentioned time
analysers, recent systems are using the storage capacity of computers
(Moore, 1965; Safford, 1965). With modest size computers, 8,000 total channels, multi-inputs, immediate display, and small dead times are available.
Computers allow simultaneous storage and processing so that the data can be
presented after background corrections and conversion to cross-sections have
been made. The data can also be stored in channels equal in energy for more
efficient use of the storage capacity. Because of the many advantages, this
type storage system is superseding the earlier time analyzers.

2.16 Timing Signals

Timing signals can be derived from a spinning chopper by several methods.
A photo multiplier cell which detects light reflected from a mirror on the
chopper can give a very sharp positive signal. This system introduces no

interaction between the chopper and its surroundings, can operate over a long distance and can be made insensitive to small distance changes. In a second system, a magnetic pickup detects the change in magnetic field as a piece of magnetic material on the chopper passes under the pickup. The pickup must be placed close to the chopper and the distance between the pickup and the chopper must not change. This system is durable, positive, and is well suited to the case where the chopper is rigidly supported. Knowledge of the operation of these signal systems, such as the zero time, the jitter and the delay, is important to the time calibration of the equipment (Deruytter et al., 1961; Brugger et al., 1961).

2.17 Safety of High Speed Choppers

The energy stored in the higher speed choppers can be of the order of 10^5 ft lb and at these large values, failure of the choppers not only can destroy the choppers (Thomas et al., 1961), but if precautions are not taken can damage the surrounding experiments, the reactor, and be a danger to personnel. Because of their high rotational speed, safety has been a major consideration in the design of the Harwell choppers and their housings (Pickles and Hazlewood, 1960). The steel housings and their special mountings around the choppers are designed to contain all of the energy in the event of a chopper explosion. If the chopper shaft fails, the chopper falls into a bearing and can continue to spin. A loose fitting sleeve inside the housing, which closes over the beam entrance and exit ports if hit by the chopper, prevents pieces escaping from the housing. The neutron and gamma shielding placed around each chopper housing provides additional protection for personnel and experiments. In the Harwell velocity selector, electrical safety circuits are incorporated to detect abnormal operation such as magnetic support failure, air bearing failure, instabilities, and power failures. These safety circuits activate a chopper shutdown procedure. So far, none of the incidents with choppers has done more than damage the choppers and the rotating sleeves.

By using two phased choppers instead of one large chopper, similar background suppression, burst times, and monochromatization can be obtained with a smaller amount of stored energy. The parallel-axis-to-beam choppers have the safety advantage over the perpendicular-beam-to-axis choppers in that flying pieces are not aimed at the core of the reactor. High speed choppers are carefully designed and are constructed of pre-inspected materials. Before being put into routine operation they are brought to speed in steps, inspections for inelastic expansion being made after each step. These pre-operation tests include over speed runs at 20 % higher than operation speed. Models of some choppers are tested to destruction to determine the limit of safe operating speed.

References

Alexander, T. K., Goulding, F. S., and Howell, W. D. (1961a). *In* "Neutron Time-of-Flight Methods", ed. by J. Spaepen, p. 449. Euratom, Brussels.

Alexander, T. K., Long, J. and Howell, W. D. (1961b). *In* "Neutron Time-of-Flight Methods", ed. by J. Spaepen, p. 491. Euratom, Brussels.

Bayorek, A., Machekhina, T. A., Palinski, K. and Shapiro, F. L. (1965). *In* "Inelastic Scattering of Neutrons in Solids and Liquids". IAEA, Vienna.

Bondarenko, I. I., Liforov, V. G., Nikolayev, M. N., Orlov, V. V., Parfenov, V. A., Syemyenov, V. A., Smirnov, V. I. and Turchin, V. F. (1963). *In* "Inelastic Scattering of Neutrons in Solids and Liquids", Vol. I, p. 127. IAEA, Vienna.

Brockhouse, B. N. (1958). *Bull. Amer. phys. Soc.* Ser. II, **3**, 233.

Brockhouse, B. N. (1961). *In* "Inelastic Scattering of Neutrons in Solids and Liquids", p. 113. IAEA, Vienna.

Brugger, R. M., McClellan, L. W., Streetman, G. B. and Evans, J. E. (1959). *Nucl. Sci. Engng* **5**, 99.

Brugger, R. M. and Evans, J. E. (1961a). *In* "Inelastic Scattering of Neutrons in Solids and Liquids", p. 277. IAEA, Vienna.

Brugger, R. M. and Evans, J. E. (1961b). *Nucl. Instrum. Methods* **12**, 75.

Brugger, R. M., and Strong, K. A. (1962). *Nucl. Instrum. Methods* **17**, 129.

Brugger, R. M. (1965). *Nucl. Instrum. Methods* **32**, 303.

Cocking, S. J. (1961a). *In* "Neutron Time-of-Flight Methods", ed. by J. Spaepen, p. 251. Euratom, Brussels.

Cocking, S. J. (1961b). *In* "Neutron Time-of-Flight Methods", ed. by J. Spaepen, p. 283. Euratom, Brussels.

Cocking, S. J. (1965). AERE Report R/4920. H.M.S.O., London.

Connor, D. W., Kleb, R. and Ostrowski, D. (1964). A phased-chopper monochromator for thermal neutron inelastic scattering spectrometry. ANL 6946.

Dahlborg, U., Holmryd, S., Larsson, K. E. and Otnes, K. (1961). *In* "Neutron Time-of-Flight Methods", ed. by J. Spaepen, p. 293. Euratom, Brussels.

Dash, J. G. and Sommer, H. S. (1953). *Rev. sci. Instrum.* **24**, 91.

Deruytter, A., Ceulemans, H.,and Neve d Mevergnies, M. (1961). *In* "Neutron Time-of-Flight Methods", ed. by J. Spaepen, p. 275. Euratom, Brussels.

Dolling, G. (1961). *In* "Inelastic Scattering of Neutrons in Solids and Liquids", p. 563. IAEA, Vienna.

Dunning, J. R., Pegram, G. B., Fink, G. A., Mitchell, D. P. and Segre, E. (1935). *Phys. Rev.* **48**, 704.

Dyer, R. F. and Low, G. E. (1961). *In* "Inelastic Scattering of Neutrons in Solids and Liquids", p. 179. IAEA, Vienna.

Egelstaff, P. A. (1953). "A Thermal Neutron Time-of-Flight Spectrometer", Report AERE–N/R–1131 (1954). *J. nucl. Engng* **1**, 57.

Egelstaff, P. A. (1956a). "Proceedings of the First International Conference on the Peaceful Uses of Atomic Energy, Geneva", Vol. IV, p. 119, United Nations, New York.

Egelstaff, P. A. (1956b). "The Measurement of the Scattering Law for a Moderator" (reprinted 1960). AERE R/3593. H.M.S.O., London.

Egelstaff, P. A. (1961). *In* "Neutron Time-of-Flight Methods", ed. by J. Spaepen, p. 261. Euratom, Brussels.

Egelstaff, P. A., Cocking, S. J. and Alexander, T. K. (1961a). *In* "Inelastic Scattering of Neutrons in Solids and Liquids", p. 165. IAEA, Vienna.

Egelstaff, P. A., Hay, H. J., Holt, N., Raffle, J. and Pickles, J. R. (1961b). *J. Instn elect. Engrs* **108B**, 26.

Fermi, E., Marshall, J. and Marshall, L. (1947). *Phys. Rev.* **72**, 193.

Gläser, W. (1961). *In* "Neutron Time-of-Flight Methods", ed. by J. Spaepen, p. 301. Euratom, Brussels.

Gläser, W. (1963). *In* "Inelastic Scattering of Neutrons in Solids and Liquids", Vol. I, p. 307. IAEA, Vienna.

Gobert, G. and Jacrot, B. (1958). *J. Phys. Radium* **19**, 51A.

Golikov, V. V., Zhukobskaya, I., Shapiro, F. L., Shkatula, A. and Janik, J. A. (1965). *In* "Inelastic Scattering of Neutrons", Vol. II, p. 201. IAEA, Vienna.

Haas, R., Kley, W., Krebs, K. and Rubin, R. (1961). *In* "Neutron Time-of-Flight Methods", Saclay, p. 289, Euratom, Brussels.

Harling, O. K. (1965). *Bull. Amer. phys. Soc.* Ser. II, **10**, 435.

Harris, D. M. C., Cocking, S. J., Egelstaff, P. A. and Webb, F. J. (1963). *In* "Inelastic Scattering of Neutrons in Solids and Liquids", Vol. I, p. 107. IAEA, Vienna.

Hay, H., Egelstaff, P. A. and Raffle, J. (1961). *In* "Pile Neutron Research in Physics", p. 559. IAEA, Vienna.

Haywood, B. C. and Thorson, I. M. (1962). *In* Proceedings of Brookhaven Conference on "Neutron Thermalisation", Vol. I, p. 26. B.N.L. 719 (C–32.)

Haywood, B. C. and Thorson, I. M. (1963). Private communication.

Holt, N. (1957). *Rev. sci. Instrum.* **28**, 1.

Kirouac, G. J., Moore, W. E., Seemann, K. W. and Yeater, M. L. (1964). Rensselaer Polytechnic Institute Linear Accelerator Project Report July-Sept.

Larsson, K. W., Stedman, R. and Palevsky, H. (1958). *J. nucl. Energy* **6**, 222.

Larsson, K. E., Holmyard, S. and Dahlborg, U. (1961). *In* "Inelastic Scattering of Neutrons in Solids and Liquids", p. 589. IAEA, Vienna.

Lowde, R. D. (1957). "Possibilities and Limitation of the Use of Swiftly Moving Specimens in Neutron Diffraction", Proc. Meeting "Use of Slow Neutrons to Investigate the Solid State", Swedish Atomic Energy Report, Stockholm.

Lowde, R. D. (1959). *J. nucl. Energy* **11**, 69.

Moore, W. E. (1965). Private communication.

Marsaguerra, M. and Pauli, G. (1959). *Nucl. Instrum. Methods*, **4**, 140.

Mostovoi, V. I., Pevzner, M. I. and Tsitovich, A. P. (1956). *In* "Proceedings of the First International Conference on the Peaceful Uses of Atomic Energy", Geneva, Vol. IV, p. 12. United Nations, New York.

Nasuhoglu, R. and Ringo, G. R. (1960). *J. chem. Phys.* **32**, 476.

O'Connor, D. A. (1960). *Nucl. Instrum. Methods* **8**, 244.

Otnes, K. and Palavsky, H. (1963). *In* "Inelastic Scattering of Neutrons in Solids and Liquids" Vol. I, p. 95. IAEA, Vienna.

Pagès, A., Avril, M. and Moreau, R. (1961). *In* "Neutron Time-of-Flight Methods", ed. by J. Spaepen, p. 473. Euratom, Brussels.

Palevsky, H. (1961). *In* "Inelastic Scattering of Neutrons in Solids and Liquids", p. 265. IAEA, Vienna.

Petree, F. (1959). *In* "Proceedings of the 1959 Biennial National Nuclear Instrumentation Symposium, Idaho Falls, Idaho", p. 81.

Pickles, J. R. and Hazlewood, R. (1960). "Design Development and Supply of Twin Rotor Neutron Spectrometers—Thermal Neutron Analyzer and Rotors for these Equipment", AERE X/PR/2357.

Rainwater, J., Peterson, J. S., Garg, J. D. and Havens, W. W. (1962). *Bull. Amer. phys. Soc.* **7**, 288.

96   R. M. BRUGGER

Rockwood, C. S. (1961). *In* "Neutron Time-of-Flight Methods", ed. by J. Spaepen, p. 473. Euratom, Brussels.
Royston, R. J. (1964). *Nucl. Instrum. Methods* **30**, 184.
Safford, G. J. (1965). Private communication.
Saunderson, D. H. and Duffill, D. (1961). "A Neutron Chopper for the DIDO Crystal Spectrometer", AERE R/3779. H.M.S.O., London.
Schmunk, R. E. and Brugger, R. M. (1961). *Nucl. Instrum. Methods* **12**, 365.
Schmunk, R. E., Brugger, R. M. and Randolph, P. D. (1962). *Phys. Rev.*, **128**, 562.
Selove, W. (1952). *Rev. Sci. Instrum.* **23**, 350.
Shull, C. G. and Gingrich, N. S. (1964). *J. appl. Phys.* **35**, 678.
Smith, J. R. and Miller, H. G. (1963). "A Mechanical Neutron Filter for a Crystal Spectrometer." USAEC Report IDO 16878.
Spaepen, J. (ed.) (1961). "Neutron Time-of-Flight Methods". Euratom, Brussels.
Stone, R. S. and Slovacek, R. E. (1956). "Reactor Spectrum Measurements Using a Neutron Time-of-Flight Spectrometer". United States Atomic Energy Commission Report KAPL 1499.
Thomas, G. E., Cote, R. E. and Bollinger, L. M. (1961). *In* "Neutron Time-of-Flight Methods", ed. by J. Spaepen, p. 297. Euratom, Brussels.
Thorson, I. M. (1963). Unpublished.
Tolk, N. H. and Brugger, R. M. (1960). *Nucl. Instrum. Methods*, **8**, 203.
Turberfield, K. C. and Egelstaff, P. A. (1961). *In* "Inelastic Scattering of Neutrons in Solids and Liquids", p. 581. IAEA, Vienna.
Umakantha, N. (1959). "On the Design of Rotors for Neutron Velocity Selection", AERE R/2992. H.M.S.O., London.
Vincent, D. H. (1961). Private communication.
Vladimirskii, V. V., Radkevich, I. A. and Sokolvikii, W. W. (1956). *In* "Proceedings of the First International Conference on the Peaceful Uses of Atomic Energy, Geneva", Vol. IV, p. 22. United Nations, New York.
Vertebnii, V. P., Koltyy, V. V. and Maystryenko, A. N. (1963). *In* "Inelastic Scattering of Neutrons in Solids and Liquids", Vol. I, p. 147. IAEA, Vienna.
Westcott, C. H. (1961). *In* "Neutron Time-of-Flight Methods", ed. by J. Spaepen, p. 523. Euratom, Brussels.
Whittemore, W. L. (1964). "Differential Neutron Thermalization". USAEC Report GA 5554.
Whittemore, W. L. and McReynolds, A. W. (1961). *In* "Inelastic Scattering of Neutrons in Solids and Liquids", p. 421. IAEA, Vienna.
Whittemore, W. L. and Danner, H. R. (1963). *In* "Inelastic Scattering of Neutrons in Solids and Liquids", Vol. I, p. 273. IAEA, Vienna.
Zweifel, P. F. and Carpenter, J. M. (1961). *In* "Inelastic Scattering of Neutrons in Solids and Liquids", p. 199. IAEA, Vienna.

CHAPTER 3

Crystal Diffraction Techniques

P. K. IYENGAR

Atomic Energy Establishment, Trombay, Bombay, India

3.1 Introduction... 98
3.2 Brief Theory of Crystal Diffraction 98
3.3 Collimator Design... 103
3.4 Types of Crystals Used... 104
3.5 Parasitic Reflections... 106
3.6 Order Contamination... 108
3.7 Luminosity of Diffraction Patterns and Collimators..................... 109
3.8 Basic Design of a Crystal Spectrometer............................... 111
3.9 Triple Axis Spectrometer at Chalk River.............................. 113
3.10 Other Triple Axis Spectrometers 117
3.11 Automation for a Triple Axis Spectrometer........................... 118
3.12 Special Experimental Methods for the Triple Axis Spectrometer.......... 119
3.13 "Constant $\mathbf{Q}$" Method....................................... 123
3.14 Shape of Neutron Group and Focusing Effects 124
3.15 Problems in "Scalar $\mathbf{Q}$" Experiments 125
3.16 Neutron Filters.. 127
3.17 Single Crystal Filters... 130
3.18 Polycrystalline Filter as an Analyser................................ 132
3.19 Window Filter.. 134
3.20 Filter Detectors Used with Pulsed Sources........................... 136
3.21 Brief Comparison with Time-of-Flight Methods........................ 137
References 138

List of Symbols

a	Dispersion parameter, $\tan\theta_B/\tan\theta_M$	$W(\eta)$	Number of mosaic blocks with normals at angle η to mean normal
B_0	Integrated intensity from mosaic block/unit volume	w	Width of slots in collimator
d_{hkl}	Spacing of planes (hkl)	x_0	Crystal thickness
$G(\phi_1)$	Relative intensity of neutrons at angle ϕ_1 to axis of Soller slit	x	Depth in crystal
h	Height of collimator	β	Half-width of Gaussian distribution of mosaic block normals ("mosaic spread")
L	Length of collimator		
N_c	Number of unit cells/unit volume		
P_0	Intensity of incident beam	γ_0	Direction cosine of incident beam with respect to inward normal of crystal face
P_H	Intensity of scattered beam		
R^θ	Integrated reflecting power from rotated crystal	η	Angle between normal of mosaic block and mean
R	Integrated intensity of Bragg peak	θ_B	Bragg angle for sample
R^λ	Integrated reflection for stationary crystal in white beam	θ_A	Bragg angle for analyser
		θ_M	Bragg angle for monochromator
r	Reflectivity per unit volume of crystal	ψ	Angle between k_0 and a crystallographic direction in the specimen

3.1 Introduction

The fortunate circumstance that the wavelength of thermal neutrons is of the same order as the inter-atomic distances in crystal lattices has led to the use of neutron diffraction in structure analysis and to a means for the selection of neutrons of a given wavelength. It was pointed out in Chapter 1 that a beam of neutrons from a nuclear reactor has a Maxwellian velocity distribution, and in Chapter 2 the necessity of selecting monokinetic neutrons from this distribution was discussed. By placing a suitably oriented single crystal in the beam, neutrons of a particular wavelength may be Bragg reflected (see Fig. 1.4) and used as the primary beam for various experiments. This method is employed in the study of the static structure of crystals by familiar diffraction techniques (Bacon, 1962). However it is also possible by an extension of this technique, to study the effects of the thermal motion of the atoms which were discussed in Chapter I.

This chapter deals with the method of crystal diffraction as a tool to measure energy changes in an inelastic scattering experiment. The fact that a single crystal can diffract neutrons of a unique wavelength into a definite direction makes it possible to analyse scattered neutrons with respect to energy. Brockhouse and Stewart (1955) describe the first application of this technique to the study of the dispersion law of crystal lattice modes. Since then it has found a wide field of application, and many of the developments in this technique will be described in the following sections. Polycrystalline substances because of their inability to scatter coherently neutrons whose wavelengths are greater than twice the largest interplanar distance of the lattice, are able to transmit all wavelengths greater than this value without much attenuation and thus act like a filter. Egelstaff (1951) reported the first use of the filter technique for the determination of energy changes which occur on scattering of cold neutrons. These two phenomena are made use of in a number of instruments to be described here, and so form the basis for many experiments on inelastic scattering.

3.2 Brief Theory of Crystal Diffraction

The theory of coherent neutron scattering by a crystalline solid shows in analogy with X-ray diffraction, that the structure factor F_τ per unit cell is given by the relation (see equation (1.66)):

$$F_\tau = \sum_l b_l\, e^{2\pi i \tau \cdot \rho_l}\, e^{-W_l} \tag{3.1}$$

where τ is the reciprocal lattice vector of the planes (hkl) considered, b_l the nuclear coherent scattering amplitude of atom l, ρ_l its position vector in the unit cell and W_l the Debye Waller factor. The summation is over all the atoms in the unit cell. The scattering from an extended single crystal has been considered in detail by Bacon and Lowde (1948) and Bacon (1962). The resultant scattering amplitude due to atoms in a plane is shown in diffraction theory to be half of that due to the atoms in the first Fresnel zone. It is shown in standard text books (e.g. James, 1958) that this quantity is

$$N_c d_{hkl} \frac{\lambda}{\sin \theta} F_{hkl} = 2 N_c d_{hkl}^2 F_{hkl} \tag{3.2}$$

where N_c is the number of unit cells per unit volume and d the interplanar distance of (hkl) planes. For neutrons this quantity has a magnitude of the order of few times 10^{-5}. Thus, an incident beam of neutrons will get highly attenuated if it traverses 10^4 layers of the crystal in which case the inner layers of a crystal of this thickness will not contribute to the reflected intensity as much as the top layers. This is called primary extinction. But the crystals are not usually perfect over such a large depth as 10^4 planes. A single crystal actually consists of mosaic blocks which are themselves perfect. Its dimension is of the order of a thousand angstroms. Thus, the neutron beam does not get attenuated within a single mosaic block. But, as the beam passes through the crystal it will meet further blocks which are identical in orientation and hence will suffer attenuation. This is called secondary extinction.

The scattered waves from separate blocks of a mosaic crystal are not coherent. If a single crystal is rotated in a monochromatic beam, reflection will occur over an angular range, dependent on the distribution of the mosaic blocks which is much larger than the intrinsic width of reflection from a perfect lattice which is of the order of few seconds only. The integrated intensity reflected from a mosaic block by rotation is given by the quantity $B_0 \Delta v$ where B_0 is given (James, 1958) by the relation

$$B_0 = \frac{\lambda^3 N_c^2}{\sin 2\theta} F_\tau^2 \tag{3.3}$$

and Δv is the volume of the mosaic block. Such a linear relation between the intensity reflected and the volume does not apply to large crystals; consequently we will now calculate the reflection from an extended crystal. Processes which cause neutron beam attenuation like nuclear absorption need not be considered since, in general, absorption is small in materials of interest as monochromators.

Following Bacon (1962), let the angular distribution of the mosaic blocks have a Gaussian form given by

$$W(\eta) = \frac{1}{\beta \sqrt{2\pi}} e^{-\eta^2/2\beta^2} \tag{3.4}$$

where β is the half width of the Gaussian distribution and $W(\eta)$ the number with their normals making an angle η with the mean normal of the mosaic blocks. Let r be the reflectivity per unit volume at any particular angular setting θ of the crystal. Then r will be related to B_0 and $W(\eta)$ by the relation

$$r = \frac{B_0}{\gamma_0} W(\theta - \theta_B) \qquad (3.5)$$

where θ is the glancing angle between the incident beam and the planes whose reflectivity is being considered, θ_B the Bragg angle for these planes and γ_0 the direction cosine of the incident beam relative to the inward normal to the crystal face. $W(\theta - \theta_R)$ will obviously give the number of mosaic blocks which will contribute to the reflected intensity. Considering

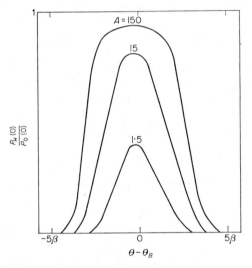

Fig. 3.1. The ratio of reflected intensity to incident intensity of neutrons reflected from an ideally imperfect crystal as the crystal is rotated, for different thickness of the crystal (Bacon and Lowde, 1948).

reflection from an infinitely wide crystal of thickness x_0, let P_0 and P_H represent the power of the incident and diffracted beams respectively at a depth x below the surface of the crystal, then

$$dP_0 = P_H r\, dx - P_0\, r\, dx$$
$$dP_H = P_H r\, dx - P_0\, r\, dx \qquad (3.6)$$

With the boundary conditions that P_0 assumes the value $P_0(0)$ at $x = 0$ and P_H is zero at $x = x_0$, it is found

$$P_0(x) = P_0(0)\, \frac{1 + r(x_0 - x)}{1 + r x_0} \qquad (3.7)$$

This gives the strength of the forward going beam at a depth x. The quantity

$$\frac{P_H(0)}{P_0(0)} = \frac{rx_0}{1+rx_0} = \frac{B_0 x_0}{\gamma_0} W(\theta-\theta_B) \Big/ \left\{ 1+B_0 \frac{x_0}{\gamma_0} W(\theta-\theta_B) \right\} \quad (3.8)$$

is the reflecting power of the slab. The variation of this function with θ, gives the intensity distribution, as the crystal is rotated. Figure 3.1 shows this distribution for various values of $A = \dfrac{B_0 x_0}{\beta \gamma_0}$. Only for the smallest value is the curve a true Gaussian reflecting the shape of the mosaic block distribution. When A is large the value of this expression is close to unity for an appreciable range of θ, showing that secondary extinction prevails. This curve

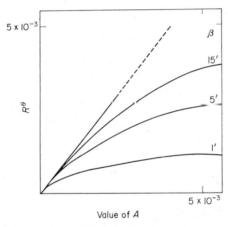

FIG. 3.2. Dependence of the integrated reflection R^θ on the thickness and mosaic spread, for reflection from finitely thick non-absorbing ideally imperfect crystal plates for different mosaic spread (Bacon and Lowde, 1948).

is of particular significance to the requirements for single crystal neutron crystallography. If x_0 is decreased or β is increased, the value of A is decreased and extinction effects will be less.

Another important quantity relating to total reflected intensity is the quantity R^θ, which is the integrated reflecting power obtained by rotating a crystal. This is obtained by integrating the expression (3.8).

$$R^\theta = \int_{-\infty}^{+\infty} \left[\frac{B_0 x_0}{\gamma_0} W(\eta) \Big/ 1 + \frac{B_0 x_0}{\gamma_0} W(\eta) \right] d\eta \quad (3.9)$$

When the peak reflection is small, the denominator is nearly unity and the integral is equal to $B_0 V$. On the other hand for an intense reflection where extinction prevails the integrated reflection falls from this value, the departure being greater, the smaller the value of β. Figure 3.2 shows the variation of R^θ with A for various values of β. This shows that for a large value of R^θ, β should be large.

In order to produce a monochromatic beam, a beam of neutrons of limited angular divergence is incident on the reflecting face of a crystal. Figure 3.3 illustrates the principle. A collimator of length L and width W defines a beam of angular divergence α. Neutrons of all wavelengths will radiate from a

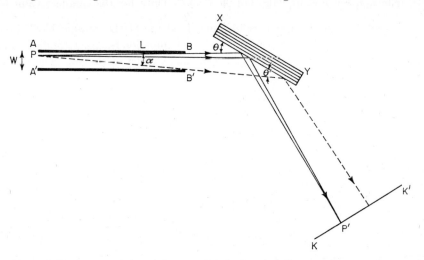

FIG. 3.3. Illustration of the production of monochromatic beam using a single crystal (Bacon, 1962).

point such as P at the entrance of the collimator, defined by the limits PB and PB'. For any given orientation of crystal XY there will be some wavelength which is at the right glancing angle to be Bragg reflected, when it is incident along PB. For a mosaic crystal, neutrons of wavelength λ could be reflected over an angular range of the order of the mosaic spread of the crystal about PB. Over this angular range all neutrons will pass through P'. Similarly, point B' will define an extreme ray PB' which will be incident at an angle $\theta' = \theta - \alpha$ and a wavelength $\lambda - d\lambda$ will be reflected to K'. Differentiating the expression $\lambda = 2d_{hkl} \sin\theta$, we obtain $\Delta\lambda = 2\alpha d_{hkl} \cos\theta$. If now P is imagined to move across AA' the total range in the angle of incidence among the neutrons incident on the crystal will be 2α, and the range of wavelength in the reflected beam will be $2\Delta\lambda$. One could calculate the intensity reflected by knowing the value of R^θ. R^λ defined as the integrated reflection for a crystal in a beam of white radiation can be calculated from R^θ using the relation

$$R^\lambda = R^\theta \, 2d_{hkl} \cos\theta \qquad (3.10)$$

R^λ is thus the range of wavelength over which the reflection may be considered to be complete. The beam intensity can be calculated knowing the spectrum of neutrons radiating from the source. If $n(\lambda)d\lambda$ gives the distribution in wavelength of the incident neutron spectrum then the total number of neutrons reflected by the monochromator will be $R^\lambda n(\lambda)$.

When a crystal is used as a monochromator in the reflection geometry the thickness chosen should be such that the ratio of reflected beam to incident beam intensity saturates as shown in Fig. 3.1 so that maximum intensity of neutrons is obtained. Too large a thickness for the crystal will cause any incoherent scattering to produce a contamination of thermal neutrons which should be avoided. The reflectivity R^θ may be calculated for various reflections by knowing the value of β. This has been done for a number of planes of the h.c.p. crystal of beryllium by Holm (1955).

3.3 Collimator Design

If the neutron wavelength is to be defined by the Bragg relation $\lambda = 2d_{hkl} \sin \theta$, we require a well defined direction for the incident beam of neutrons. In a nuclear reactor there is a gas of neutrons and they escape from the walls of the reactor vessel in all directions. Beam ports through the concrete biological shield are provided for taking out a beam of neutrons. Collimators (see Section 4·3) are inserted into these beam ports in order to obtain a beam of neutrons of well defined direction. Because the only effect is neutron attenuation by the materials of the collimator, one can design the collimators from purely geometrical considerations. A long vertical slit of horizontal width W and length L will transmit a beam of neutrons with the maximum horizontal angular divergence α equal to $\pm W/L$, about the straight direction. In general, this would be affected only by the non-uniformity of the surface of the collimating channels and by total reflection of neutrons from the walls of the collimator, which is important in cases where the collimation is of the order of minutes of arc. The considerations which limit the design of the primary collimators for an experiment are the following.

(1) The horizontal and vertical divergences required for optimum resolution and intensity of reflected neutrons.

(2) The size of the beam when it falls on the crystal.

(3) The area of radiating surface available in the reactor.

(4) The distance of the monochromating crystal from the source of radiation.

In general, the vertical divergence is limited only by the vertical dimensions of the beam at the crystal and the distance from the source. The optimum horizontal divergence of the beam is roughly of the order of the mosaic spread of the crystal used. For metallic crystals like aluminium and lead this is of the order one-quarter to one-half of a degree. If the beam width is large, say 5 cm or more, it is necessary to use Soller slits to obtain the required collimation. These are made out of a number of thin cadmium sheets kept apart by spacers, the separation being dictated by the allowable angular divergence. Soller collimators with cadmium sheets are easily made for use in the thermal neutron region, since the spacings are fairly large. In the case of neutron monochromators for cross-section measurements, the angular divergences permissible are very small. Sailor *et al.* (1956) have described a method of making good Soller slits of angular divergence of a few minutes of arc used in high resolution cross-section measurements in the electron volt region. It is also possible to make Soller slits by piling rectangular tubes made commercially for wave guides. By using these tubes the vertical divergence is also reduced. The intensity of neutrons transmitted as a function of angular divergence by a combination of beam tube with Soller slits is a complicated function involving a few integrals. The intensity depends, for a fixed collimation dictated by the Soller slits, on the position and distance of the Soller collimator from the source. The mathematics of the neutron transmission functions for such a system of collimators has been worked out by Szabo (1959). He has also discussed how to optimize the dimensions of the Soller slit to gain maximum intensity. In effect, while the channels of the Soller slit restrict the angular divergence they allow a larger area of the radiating surface to contribute to the intensity.

The above discussion pertains to primary collimation. Secondary collimators are used to restrict the angular divergence and define the direction after the monochromator and also before and after the analysing crystal, in an inelastic scattering experiment. They are also of the Soller slit type. Since the diffracted neutrons will have a larger angular spread than the incoming beam falling on the crystal, the secondary collimator should allow a larger angular spread. Suitable sequences of angular divergence to be chosen in the case of a diffraction experiment are discussed by Caglioti *et al.* (1958, 1960, 1962) and will be considered in Section 3.7. A general discussion of collimators is given in Chapter 4.

3.4 Types of Crystal Used

The monochromating crystal should reflect a portion of the neutron spectrum of width at least of the order of a few per cent of the selected wavelength in order to get sufficient intensity. This spread in the wavelength of reflected neutrons is provided by two factors, one the divergence of the incident neutron beam and the other the mosaic spread of the crystal. The resultant angular width of the beam $\Delta\theta$ is given by $[\beta^2+\frac{1}{2}\alpha^2]^{\frac{1}{2}}$ where β is the half width of the crystal mosaic spread and α the angular divergence of the collimator (defined as in equations (3.11) and (3.12)). The best compromise is made by making $\alpha\approx\beta$.

The material of the single crystals chosen should contain nuclei which have very small nuclear absorption for neutrons, negligible incoherent scattering and fairly large coherent scattering cross section. In the earliest experiments alkali halide crystals were used as monochromators, particularly NaCl, LiF_2 and CaF_2. These were chosen because sufficiently big crystals were readily available. However, metallic crystals were found to have higher reflectivity and mosaic spreads of the right order, and their mosaic spreads could be controlled during the process of growing. Nowadays, crystals of aluminium, copper and lead are used commonly as monochromators. In the higher energy region for cross section measurements, beryllium is used. The hexagonal structure of beryllium provides many planes of small lattice spacings for selecting higher energies and it has a small mosaic spread.

Metallic single crystals of large sizes often 5–10 cm in diameter are grown by the Bridgman technique. In this method the material of the crystal in pure form is melted in a graphite crucible and the melt cooled uniformly at the rate of few millimetres per hour. For this purpose either the furnace or the melt is moved. The factors determining the choice between the various arrangements are control of the speed of growth, temperature gradient, the shape of the isothermal surfaces (this requiring some control over the cooling as well as of the heat output) and minimization of stresses on the crystal, though stresses are unavoidable. Preparation of large single crystals of zinc, aluminium, copper and magnesium are described in reports by Modrzejewski and Bednarski (1955, 1958). These have been grown specially for neutron monochromators.

The measurement of mosaic spread is carried out by the X-ray back reflection technique or by taking a rocking curve with neutrons. If a well collimated beam of neutrons falls on the crystal, the counter being fixed for Bragg reflection from a vertical plane, and the crystal alone rotated the neutron intensity distribution gives the rocking curve. The half width of the distribution gives the mosaic spread. A finer measurement could be made by using a double axis spectrometer, where the highly monochromatic beam obtained by using a crystal of small mosaic spread (like quartz) as monochromator is used to obtain the rocking curve. Since the size of the crystal used as monochromator is large, it is necessary to measure the rocking curve for different regions of the same crystal to get an average value of the mosaic width. Shull (1960) has measured the mosaic width at different regions of a lead crystal using a silicon crystal as the monochromator. By compressing

5*

the crystal he has been able to increase its total mosaic spread. A quantitative measurement of the gain in reflectivity due to different types of plastic deformations in a germanium crystal has been reported recently by Barrett *et al.* (1963). The order of mosaic spreads of crystals ordinarily used are around one-quarter to one-half of a degree which may be obtained in single crystals of aluminium, lead and copper. Germanium has a much smaller mosaic spread. Natural crystals of magnetite have larger mosaic spreads often greater than 1°.

Metallic crystals are generally used in the reflection position for monochromatization. They could be cut in the Fankuchen (1937) way with the surface making an angle of a few degrees with the reflecting planes, which results in narrowing of the reflected beam and an increase in the intensity per unit area. However, this focusing effect will act strongly only in those crystals where the largest fraction of reflection occurs within a short depth from the surface. If the mean free path for neutrons for reflection in the crystal is large then this effect is not very prominent. Thus, it has been found experimentally that in lead the Fankuchen effect operates well, whereas in aluminium it is not very effective.

Different crystals have been used over different energy ranges. The choice is decided by the availability of reflecting planes of high reflectivity, lattice spacing to suit the energy needed and the permissible scattering angle. Using crystals of aluminium, lead and copper which have the face-centred cubic structure, the planes (111), (200), 311), etc., can be used to cover a wavelength range from 2 Å to about 0·5 Å. For neutron wavelengths greater than 2 Å, germanium and magnetite (McReynolds, 1952) are useful. They have the required larger lattice spacing. Thermica crystals have large lattice spacings and large mosaic spread, and are used for longer wavelength neutrons even up to 8 Å. The (111) planes of germanium and magnetite have the additional advantage that the second order reflection is absent. This is because second order reflection can be considered to be a reflection of neutrons of half the wavelength by the higher order planes (222) for which the structure factor is zero in germanium and very small in magnetite due to the structure of the unit cell.

3.5 Parasitic Reflections

When a single crystal is used to obtain monochromatic neutrons one of the sets of planes (hkl) is oriented with its normal in the plane in which the incident and reflected neutrons lie. In Fig. 1.5, the reciprocal lattice in this plane is shown and also the conditions under which reflection takes place due to the lattice planes indicated by the reciprocal lattice vector τ_1, the condition being that the wave vectors of the incident and outgoing neutrons should end at the origin and the reciprocal lattice point respectively. The angle included by these two vectors in the diagram gives the angle 2θ for the reflection. It is easy to see this construction satisfies the Bragg relation $\lambda = 2d_{hkl} \sin \theta$ since $|\mathbf{k}_0 - \mathbf{k}| = 2\pi\tau_1 = 2\pi/d_{hkl}$. One can now consider a sphere of reflection in reciprocal space with the radius equal to $|\mathbf{k}|$. It is easy to see that if any other reciprocal lattice point falls on the surface of this sphere then it represents another possible plane of reflection. In Figure 1.4 the point τ_2 also falls on this sphere and reflection could take place from that plane as well. Thus, two sets of planes τ_1 and τ_2 are competing and share the neutrons, but only the reflection from one set of planes is being observed. Therefore, the intensity is somewhat reduced. Sometimes there is an increase in intensity due to this phenomenon. This can happen because neutrons reflected from τ_2 can be reflected again by a plane $(\tau_2 - \tau_1)$ and this will have the same wavelength and direction as that of the reflection from τ_1 (see Section 1.8).

This phenomenon is actually observed when one measures the spectrum of neutrons from the reactor using a crystal spectrometer. As the neutron wavelength selected gets larger the sphere of reflection contracts, and as this is a continuous process it is found that at certain values of the radius of the sphere more than one reciprocal lattice point falls on the surface of the sphere. Instead of a smooth Maxwellian distribution, one sees large dips occasionally (e.g. Pattenden and Baston, 1957; Duggal, 1959). These dips are due to other competing planes as shown above. This phenomenon of multiple Bragg scattering has also been observed in the case of X-rays (Renninger, 1937). Various experimenters have made calculations of the angles at which double Bragg scattering can occur (see Hay, 1958; Duggal *et al.*, 1961; Spencer *et al.*, 1960; O'Connor and Sosnowski, 1961).

From these certain generalizations are possible. For all crystals of cubic symmetry and for the same conditions of incidence of the neutron beam, the multiple Bragg reflections will always occur at the same angle of incidence independently of the value of the lattice constant. For other symmetry systems multiple Bragg reflection will occur at the same angles of incidence in crystals which have the same ratios between lattice constants and the same angles between crystal axes. When multiple Bragg reflection occurs for the first order reflection then it also occurs for higher order reflections at the same angles of incidence. Another effect which occurs as a consequence of this double Bragg scattering is the simulation of a forbidden reflection. In the case considered in Figure 1.4 even if τ_1 represents a set of planes whose structure factor is zero, reflection can occur via τ_2 and an equivalent set of planes $\tau_3 = \tau_1 - \tau_2$ and emerge as though it was reflected from τ_1. Such a simulation of the (222) planes of germanium crystal was observed by Wajima *et al.* (1960). Double Bragg reflection can also affect the intensities of reflection observed in experiments with single crystal specimens. This effect is important in the accurate determination of the form factor for magnetic scattering by measurements on polarized neutron reflections from single domains. Shull (1962) has made a study of this effect in a single crystal of iron.

3.6 Order Contamination

The distribution in wavelength of the intensity of neutrons from a reactor was shown in Fig. 1.1. If a set of planes (hkl) of a crystal is used to select a range of wavelength $d\lambda$ at λ of the spectrum satisfying the Bragg relation $\lambda = 2d_{hkl} \sin \theta$, then neutrons of wavelength $\lambda/2$, $\lambda/3$, etc., are also reflected by the crystal. Fortunately the relative amount of higher order neutrons can be controlled. If the first order wavelength is near the peak of the Maxwellian around 1 Å, then the second order is around 0·5 Å where the intensity in the incident flux distribution is small and the higher orders are much smaller. The reflectivity of a crystal and also the detector efficiency fall off as the wavelength decreases. These factors enable the higher order contamination to be kept low in diffraction experiments using 1 Å neutrons. The percentage of higher order contamination can be calculated if the spectrum of incident neutrons and the reflectivity of the crystal are known. However, the calculations are not very accurate and whenever the effect of higher orders is important it is actually measured and allowed for. One method would be to measure the transmission through absorbers of known transmission (Wajima et al., 1960). If the transmission is measured for different thicknesses then the higher order intensity can be obtained.

In inelastic scattering experiments it is not always necessary to measure and correct for higher order contamination because the experiments involve measurement of energy changes. It is preferable to find ways of eliminating or reducing the percentage of higher order neutrons in the monochromatic beam or to remove their effects with a background measurement. In the region of wavelength 1–2 Å used for diffraction experiments the percentage of higher order, apart from second order, is small because of the Maxwellian wavelength distribution. This could be removed altogether if a background run is taken with resonance filter like gadolinium or plutonium which has an appreciable cross-section for neutrons less than 0·3 eV in energy. Thus, it can be made to be opaque to first order and transparent to higher orders. The effect of higher order neutrons is then included in the background. Alternatively, if the second order energy is chosen to be coincident with the resonant energy, a filter placed in the main beam will eliminate the second order neutrons before they reach the sample. Resonance filters are commonly used in nuclear cross-section measurements (Sturm, 1947). Suitable elements are samarium, indium, cadmium, etc. Also coherent Bragg reflection from a mosaic crystal can simulate a resonance by scattering neutrons of discrete wavelengths off the beam. By choosing a suitable set of planes of a mosaic crystal, second order neutrons alone have been reflected off the beam (Iyengar et al., 1965).

In the lower energy region (i.e. for wavelengths above 2 Å) mechanical monochromators can be used (Section 2.4). These mechanical monochromators select a broad region of neutron spectrum around the required wavelength, from which the crystal monochromator could select a monochromatic beam. Holt (1957) has built a monochromator with helical slots which has good transmission in the region 5 Å–12 Å. The theory of these monochromators is discussed in Chapter 2.

Polycrystalline filters offer an easy means of reducing second order contamination if the first order energy is below the Bragg cut-off of the filter element. Thus, for neutron wavelengths between 4 Å and 8 Å a beryllium filter is ideal.

3.7 Luminosity of Diffraction Patterns and Collimators

The intensity of a diffraction pattern and its resolution or angular width are dependent on many factors such as (1) the angular divergence of the primary collimator, (2) the angular divergence of the secondary collimator and (3) the acceptance angle of the collimator in front of the counter. There is also the mosaic width of the monochromator and the sample. Though the luminosity problem is not completely relevant to inelastic scattering, it is applicable in so far as the collimators before and after the monochromator are concerned. It has been dealt with in detail by Caglioti and Ricci (1962) and Caglioti et al. (1958, 1960). We shall summarize the essential points only.

We define by α_1, α_2 and α_3 the horizontal angular divergences of each slit of the Soller collimators at the respective positions from the primary collimator in the sequence 1-3 above. The angle α is the full width at half maximum of the triangular transmission function of a Soller slit. Let β be the similar width of the angular spread of the mosaic blocks. The transmission function of each Soller slit can be approximated to a Gaussian instead of a triangle for easier calculation. Thus, the transmission functions are given by the expression

$$G(\phi_1) = \exp-\left(\frac{\phi_1}{\alpha_1'}\right)^2 \quad \text{where } \alpha_1' = \frac{\alpha_1}{2(\log 2)^{\frac{1}{2}}} \qquad (3.11)$$

$G(\phi_1)$ gives the relative intensity of neutrons transmitted at an angle (ϕ_1). The distribution of mosaic blocks is assumed to be

$$W(\eta_1) = \exp-\left(\frac{\eta_1}{\beta_1'}\right)^2 \quad \text{where } \beta_1' = \frac{\beta_1}{2(\log 2)^{\frac{1}{2}}} \qquad (3.12)$$

β_1 is the half width of the mosaic spread and $W(\eta_1)$ the number having their normals at an angle η_1 to the mean normal.

Now the procedure adopted by Caglioti is to write down the probability for a neutron with a certain initial angular divergence ϕ_1, and wavelength λ to be transmitted by the first collimator, to be reflected by the mono-chromator, to pass through the second collimator, to be reflected again by the sample (powder or a single crystal) and then accepted by the counter; the angular setting of the monochromator being such that the neutron of wavelength λ_0 passing centrally through the first collimator will be Bragg scattered by the central mosaic blocks and will be Bragg reflected from the sample into the counter corresponding to the centre of the Bragg peak. The final probability will therefore be a product of the probabilities of these independent processes.

In the case of a powder sample where the mosaic structure should not matter, for the crystal planes are oriented at random, the full width at half maximum $A_{\frac{1}{2}}$ is given by:

$$A_{\frac{1}{2}} = \left[\frac{\alpha_1^2\alpha_2^2 + \alpha_1^2\alpha_3^2 + \alpha_2^2\alpha_3^2 + 4\beta_1^2(\alpha_2^2+\alpha_3^2) - 4a\alpha_2^2(\alpha_1^2+2\beta_1^2) + 4a^2(\alpha_1^2\alpha_2^2 + \alpha_1^2\beta_1^2 + \alpha_2^2\beta_1^2)}{\alpha_1^2 + \alpha_2^2 + 4\beta_1^2} \right]^{\frac{1}{2}}$$

(3.13)

The parameter a is connected to the mean Bragg angles θ_M and θ_B at the monochromator and sample respectively by the relation

$$a = \frac{\tan \theta_B}{\tan \theta_M} \tag{3.14}$$

This may be termed the dispersion parameter.

The integrated intensity (L) is given by

$$L = \frac{\alpha_1\alpha_2\alpha_3\beta_1}{(\alpha_1^2 + \alpha_2^2 + 4\beta_1^2)^{\frac{1}{2}}} \tag{3.15}$$

Similar expressions for a single crystal sample have also been obtained. Here there are two cases, one in which the crystal is moved at half the rate of the counter and the second in which the crystal alone is rotated with the counter fixed at $2\theta_B$. We quote a result for the first case only (see Caglioti et al., 1960, for the second case). The half width is given by a complex ex-pression similar to equation (3.13); it is dependent on a, going to a minimum at a value of $a \sim \frac{1}{2}$ and then increasing in a way proportional to a as its value tends to infinity. The integrated intensity is given by

$$L = \frac{\alpha_1\alpha_2\alpha_3\beta_1}{(4\beta_2^2 + \alpha_3^2)(\beta_1^2 + \frac{1}{4}\alpha_1^2 + \frac{1}{4}\alpha_2^2) + \frac{1}{4}\alpha_2^2(4\beta_1^2 + \alpha_1^2)} \tag{3.16}$$

Since the coefficient of a^2 in (3.13) is independent of α_2, one may choose comparatively large values of α_3 without loss of resolution. This gives good luminosity. Since luminosity is a symmetric function of α_1 and α_2 it is reasonable to have $\alpha_1 \approx \alpha_2$. In order to take greater advantage of the focusing action expressed by the coefficient of a in (3.13) it seems convenient to have $\alpha_1 \leqslant \alpha_2$. Thus, for a powder sample, the choice should be $\alpha_1 \leqslant \alpha_2 < \alpha_3$. For analysis of single crystals using 1 : 2 coupling, $\beta_2 < \alpha_3/2$ and $\alpha_1 \leqslant \alpha_2 < \alpha_3$.

In the case of the choice of a monochromator crystal mosaic spread is the important quantity which should match the collimator divergence. Measurement of mosaic spread has already been discussed. From the equations discussed above the luminosity of a spectrometer is practically a linear function of β_1 for small values of β_1 then tends to saturation as β_1^2 reaches a value of the order of $\frac{1}{4}(\alpha_1^2 + \alpha_2^2)$. The resolution of a spectrometer is not strongly affected by the value of β_1^2 as long as the latter is kept smaller or of the same order of magnitude as $\frac{1}{4}(\alpha_1^2 + \alpha_2^2)$. Hence a proper choice of the value of β_1 would be $\frac{1}{2}(\alpha_1^2 + \alpha_2^2)^{\frac{1}{2}}$. These conclusions have been experimentally verified by Caglioti and Ricci (1962).

3.8 Basic Design of a Crystal Spectrometer

A neutron crystal spectrometer, defined either as a device for measuring the neutron wavelength or for choosing a beam of monochromatic neutrons is essentially the same. The first instrument of this type was built by Zinn (1947) to select neutrons of different wavelengths and to measure the total cross-section of different nuclei as a function of neutron energy. These are now known as either neutron monochromators or single crystal spectrometers. The basic design of all subsequent spectrometers for solid state research in the field of neutron diffraction and inelastic scattering remains the same.

Nuclear cross-sections have been measured with crystal monochromators even at energies greater than 50 eV: however they are most useful below 20 eV. The resolutions obtainable in such experiments are usually defined in terms of the resolving power $\Delta E/E$ with ΔE the width at half maximum of the resolution function. The value of ΔE can be expressed approximately by the relation $\Delta E = KE^{3/2}$ where K is an instrumental constant. In the application of neutron monochromators to the study of solids and liquids it is not necessary to obtain as high a resolution as is used for cross-section measurements, nor is it necessary to select high neutron energies. Because of the high neutron intensity and longer wavelength required for diffraction and inelastic scattering experiments, the neutron energy used is in the thermal and sub-thermal region, and never larger than about 0·5 eV. However, the techniques of producing monochromatic beams are quite similar to those used for cross-section measurements and hence in this section we will discuss some of the details of a crystal monochromator, referring where necessary to the cross-section work.

The requirements of a spectrometer are simple, a table on which the single crystal sits and an arm which carries the neutron detector in a sufficiently big shield and which may be swung around the crystal axis. It is also necessary that as the arm is swung around the crystal, the crystal table follows this angular movement at half the rate so that crystal planes will always be oriented for reflection. The angular positions of both the arm and the crystal table should be able to be determined accurately to a minute or less. Since the neutron detector is housed inside a shield of paraffin and boron carbide, weighing about 200 lb and carried at a fairly large distance of 3–5 ft from the axis of the crystal table in order to have sufficient angular resolution, the main axis is built robustly with heavy bearings which carry the long arm with the heavy cantilever load on it. This part is important to a smooth performance of the crystal spectrometer. Alternatively the arm may be supported from the floor, to reduce the cantilever loading. It should also be possible to drive the arm by a motor at fairly low speed and to be able to move in steps of a quarter degree or less in certain cases.

An important consideration is the half-angling device. There are many methods of achieving this, mechanical, electrical and optical. The mechanical systems are by far the simplest. Some of the methods employed in different spectrometers are the following.

Two sets of gears in the ratio 1 : 2 have been used so that the crystal table moves at half the rate at which the counter arm moves. In this method a backlash error is possible if the direction of motion is reversed in the course of a run. Another method is the pulley system used by Hurst et al. (1950). Two sets of pulleys are used to transfer the angular rotation of the arm to the crystal table at half its rate, this being achieved by using two disks one of which has half the diameter of the other. This system has worked quite satisfactorily except that it occupied too much space. A very compact pulley system, using two such sets each giving a ratio of $\sqrt{2}$, has been used in a commercial spectrometer (Bacon and Dyer, 1959).

Crawford (see Brockhouse, 1961) has designed a new half angling system on the principle that the axis of a cylinder moves at half the rate of the periphery if it is held between two plates and rolled without slipping. Three cones are held between a fixed plate and a plate rotating with the counter arm. The axis of these cones is coupled to the crystal table such that only the translatory movement is applied to it and as a result, the crystal table follows the counter arm at half the speed. This design has the advantage of being very compact.

If one of the sides of a triangle is turned to change the included angle by θ, then the bisector of the included angle will change by $\theta/2$. Breton et al. (1957) have designed a half angling system on this principle. Mechanically, this is achieved by making a complete parallelogram with pivoted joints.

One corner coincides with the axis of the spectrometer, and a diagonal rod from this to the opposite corner is fixed to the crystal table. One arm of the parallelogram from this corner is fixed to the counter arm and the other is fixed in space. The free corner is made to slide along the diagonal rod. Thus, when the arm is rotated to decrease the included angle, the moving corner slides outwards and the crystal table will rotate through half the angle. Due to the finite lengths of the arms it is not possible to use this method if the angular movement of the arm is more than 60°.

Mueller *et al.* (1961) use two "Slo-Syn" motors to drive the arm and the crystal table independently. These motors operate in steps when pulses are fed to them, each step being a small fraction of a degree. By keeping the ratio of the number of pulses applied to the two motors to 2 : 1, half angling is achieved.

Another method uses optical coupling (Knowles, 1959). As the counter arm is rotated, a beam of light from the counter arm reflected from a mirror fixed on the axis of the crystal table is picked up by a photocell. The crystal table is driven by a servomotor controlled by the photocell current. This ensures that the crystal table rotates at half the rate.

The neutron detector is almost always a BF_3 proportional counter (see Chapter 4) having an efficiency of 80% or more when neutrons enter axially through an end window. This is enclosed in a big shield with an inch or more of boron carbide nearest to the counter and about 15 cm of paraffin or some other hydrogenous material all round, leaving a hole along the axis for the neutron beam to enter.

Many single axis spectrometers have been described in the literature (Zinn, 1947; Wollan and Shull, 1948; Bacon *et al.*, 1950; Hurst *et al.*, 1950; Ohno *et al.*, 1962).

3.9 The Triple Axis Spectrometer at Chalk River

The two basic requirements for an inelastic scattering experiment are a source of monochromatic neutrons and a device for energy analysing the scattered beam. In the instrument to be discussed in this section, these two requirements are satisfied by the use of two single crystal spectrometers. The first spectrometer provides monochromatic neutrons and the second energy analyses the scattered neutrons. Combining these two basic requirements with the sample mounting table results in a triple axis spectrometer. The versatility of an instrument for inelastic scattering experiments can be considered in terms of the two physical parameters, namely, the momentum transfer $\mathbf{Q} = \mathbf{k}_0 - \mathbf{k}$ and the energy transfer $E_0 - E = \hbar\omega$ as explained in Section 1.2. It is in terms of these two quantities that the whole dynamics of the scattering system is described. The magnitude of the momentum transfer depends on the values of the incoming and outgoing neutron propagation vectors $\mathbf{k}_0$ and $\mathbf{k}$ and the angle between them. In order to be able to cover experimentally a large range in momentum transfer, one should be able to cover continuously a large range in the magnitudes of $\mathbf{k}_0$ and $\mathbf{k}$ and in the scattering angle ϕ. This would automatically ensure a large range in energy transfer also.

One distinction must be made in the definition of $\mathbf{Q}$. In liquids and polycrystalline samples only the magnitude $|\,\mathbf{Q}\,|$ matters. In single crystals $\mathbf{Q}$ is a vector in relation to the crystallographic direction in the specimen. Thus,

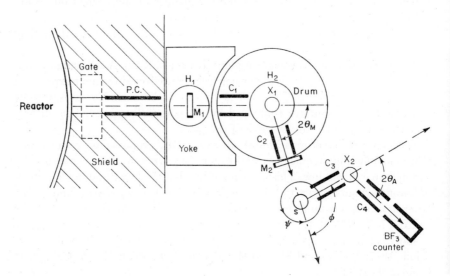

FIG. 3.4. Schematic drawing of the Chalk River triple axis spectrometer (Brockhouse, 1961). X_1 is the monochromator; the sample S and analyser X_2 are mounted on one spectrometer (the "positional spectrometer").

as will be shown later the orientation of $\mathbf{k}_0$ and $\mathbf{k}$ with respect to the crystallographic directions should be known and the instrument must be capable of changing the orientation at will.

Figure 3.4 gives a sketch of a triple axis spectrometer, and Fig. 3.5 is a photograph of this spectrometer partly assembled. X_1 and X_2 are two single crystals which function as the monochromatizing and analysing crystals respectively. The variations in the magnitudes of $\mathbf{k}_0$ and $\mathbf{k}$ are determined by the ranges of $2\theta_M$ and $2\theta_A$ of the monochromator and analysing spectrometer respectively, and the "d" spacing of the crystal planes (hkl) used for X_1 and X_2. In general, the angles $2\theta_M$ and $2\theta_A$ are limited by the physical size of the instrument, the space available around the reactor and the available neutron

FIG. 3.5. Photograph of the Chalk River triple axis spectrometer in a partially completed state. The sample, analysing crystal, the counter and some shielding have been removed.

spectrum of the source. Different sets of planes (hkl) having different spacings can be chosen, consistent with the resolution in wavelength required. The angle of scattering is also limited by the geometry of the apparatus.

When deciding the overall dimensions such as the distance between the sample and the analyser it is necessary to consider the space available for Soller collimators and for cryostats and magnets to be mounted on the sample table. In fact these considerations favour keeping these distances fairly large, which would enhance the versatility of the instrument for different types of problems.

The angle between the incident neutron wave vector $\mathbf{k}_0$ and one of the crystallographic directions in the specimen will be referred to as ψ. An ideal triple axis instrument will allow all the parameters $\mathbf{k}_0$, $\mathbf{k}$, ψ and ϕ to be varied continuously. This calls for a complicated design. To follow any given locus in (ω, $\mathbf{Q}$) space, it is necessary to vary at least three of these quantities; consequently the experimental arrangements can be simplified by fixing one of them. One simplification would be to make $\mathbf{k}_0$ or $\mathbf{k}$ fixed, i.e. either the incident or scattered neutron energy fixed. If the incident energy is fixed, the monochromator can be decoupled from the rest of the apparatus. The scattered neutron energy can be fixed by keeping $2\theta_A$ fixed, which means that the rotation about the analysing crystal axis is not required. In this case detected energy of the scattered beam can be chosen to a certain extent by changing the crystal planes used for reflection. Another method is to use a filter to define $\mathbf{k}$ employing the method discussed in Section 3.19.

The neutron beam from the reactor (Fig. 3.4) is collimated by an inpile collimator P.C. and passes through a large yoke. The hole H_1 in the yoke is to provide easy access to the neutron beam, without having to remove heavy equipment. In this case the hole is used to introduce a monitor counter to measure the neutron flux and also to be able to introduce single crystal filters in the beam which remove a substantial part of the epicadmium neutrons. The use of these filters will be discussed in a later section.

A large part of the shielding around the monochromator crystal X_1 consists of a large drum which can rotate about the axis of X_1. At the inlet end of the neutron beam the drum has a wedge shaped hole to allow for continuous variation in $2\theta_M$. However, large variations in $2\theta_M$ will require a large wedge which will result in ineffective shielding. Hence, the drum is made in the form of two concentric drums, the inner one having two port holes 60° apart and the outer four port holes 30° apart for the reflected beam to pass through. By combining two of these holes at one time the required angular range is selected. The unused port holes are plugged. The outer ends of the plugged holes can be seen in the photograph (Fig. 3.5). The angle $2\theta_M$ can be varied from 32° on one side to 92° on the other in four ranges. The central hole in the drum houses the monochromating crystal. The crystal table is coupled to either a half angling device fixed to the bottom of the drum of the roller type described earlier, or to a motor through two independent magnetic clutches. By energizing the proper magnetic clutch the crystal table can either be made to follow the rotation of the drum at half the rate, or rotated independently by remote operation as is required while adjusting for a Bragg reflection.

Additional Soller slit collimators may be introduced at positions C_1 and C_2. The drum is mechanically coupled to a large platform which moves on rails around the first axis and the angle $2\theta_M$ is read on a scale attached to this rotating platform. The positional spectrometer sits bodily on this platform. Since the monochromatizing crystal is mounted on a half angling system, the crystal always remains in the Bragg reflecting position as the angle $2\theta_M$ is changed continuously. This monochromator facility which allows a continous variation of the energy of incident neutrons has many advantages in inelastic scattering experiments. Since good resolution is obtained by working with as small an energy for the incident and scattered neutrons as possible, this may be achieved only by keeping the incident energy variable. Another advantage is that the analysing spectrometer angle $2\theta_A$ can be kept constant and the incident energy varied to cover a range of energy transfers. This allows the analysing spectrometer sensitivity to be kept the same, its variation with energy being difficult to determine accurately. Corrections for the change in incident flux may be made accurately from the counting rate of a thin fission counter used as the monitor. The incident wavelength range is chosen so that it is possible to observe a phonon as a neutron energy loss, which usually has a higher cross-section than the energy gain processes.

The positional spectrometer (Fig. 3.4) is the same as that described by Hurst *et al.* (1950), which was previously designed for use as a single crystal spectrometer. The advantage of using this spectrometer is that it has a large "Bofors" gun bearing and can take a large cantilever load. This enabled the analysing spectrometer to be mounted on its arm which can be moved in $\frac{1}{8}°$ steps by a motor and cam arrangement and the angle read on a scale. The sample table of this spectrometer is also capable of independent rotation by a motor in steps of $\frac{1}{8}°$ or can be coupled to the arm when it will rotate at half the speed of the arm of the positional spectrometer using a half angling device based on the pulley system.

The analysing spectrometer is seen in the photograph (Fig. 3.5). The arm rotates around the shaft which is rigidly fixed to the positional spectrometer arm. Rotation takes place through a worm and wheel drive, the driving motor being mounted on the arm itself. There is a magnetic clutch which couples the motor to the drive shaft and by using microswitches on the drive shaft, the clutch is de-energized exactly after $\frac{1}{8}°$ rotation. Thus, the analysing spectrometer can be moved in steps of $\frac{1}{8}°$. The half angling system of the analysing spectrometer is based on the principle of "rollers" as described previously.

The neutron detector in the analysing spectromer is a BF_3 counter, enriched in ^{10}B to 96%, housed inside a shield of boron carbide and paraffin. Neutrons enter the counter axially. Counters of different lengths are used depending on the energy of the scattered neutrons in order to obtain optimum values of signal to background ratios (see Section 4.15). The monitor counters are single foil low sensitivity fission counters with aluminium windows.

Monochromatizing and analysing crystals are aluminium single crystals in cylindrical form with their 110 axis vertical. They are fixed to a special mount on an indexing plate, so that the reflecting planes can be readily changed. Soller slit collimators are used at C_1, C_2, C_3 and C_4 in Fig. 3.4. The angular divergence of the collimators used depends on the counting rate obtainable for a particular experiment. For optimum resolution α_1 should be less than α_2, and α_3 less than α_4. A full description of this spectrometer has been given by McAlpin (1963).

3.10 Other Triple Axis Spectrometers

A number of triple axis spectrometers are in operation at other laboratories. Many of them use a fixed incident energy: thus, the monochromator is decoupled from the rest of the instrument, and the positional and analysing spectrometers form a single unit. At the Los Alamos Scientific Laboratory, Yarnell et al. (1959) has built an instrument of this kind. By using a high pressure BF_3 counter vertically, he has reduced the length of the counter shield, and thus the overall dimensions of the unit. The angular settings of the three parameters ψ, ϕ and $2\theta_A$ can be set to within $0.01°$, $0.01°$ and $0.001°$, respectively. This spectrometer also uses a sophisticated automatic system, with a tape punch input for feeding programme information.

A triple axis spectrometer has been built by Caglioti and Ascarelli (1963) at Ispra (Italy) which also uses a constant incident energy. The whole unit consisting of the positional and analysing spectrometers is mounted such that lateral displacement of the positional spectrometer is possible. A corresponding rotation of the monochromator drum to let the neutron beam fall on the specimen will change the neutron energy. Thus, although it is possible to vary the incident neutron energy easily, it is fixed during an experiment.

At Trombay, Iyengar et al. (1963) have built a triple axis spectrometer which again consists of single unit comprising the positional and analysing spectrometers. The angular increments in ψ, ϕ, and $2\theta_A$ are in steps of $\frac{1}{20}°$, $\frac{1}{8}°$ and $\frac{1}{8}°$, respectively. Simpler automation is used and is described in a later section. Another instrument has been built by Hagihara et al. (1962) for the

Japan Atomic Energy Institute which is very nearly the same as those described above. A second spectrometer has been built at Trombay in which the incident energy is varied continuously, but the analysing spectrometer angle $2\theta_A$ is fixed at any convenient angle but not variable automatically. Triple axis spectrometers have been brought into operation at other laboratories and are now in wide use.

3.11 Automation for a Triple Axis Spectrometer

Though the basic quantity to be measured in an inelastic scattering experiment is the differential scattering cross-section as a function of energy change and angle of scattering $d^2\sigma/d\Omega dE$, it is not always necessary or possible to measure this for all angles and energies. What is required is the quantity $S(\mathbf{Q}, \omega)$ where $\mathbf{Q}$ and ω are the two variable parameters which are related to the differential cross-section by the relation (see (1.25) and (1.34)).

$$\frac{d^2\sigma}{d\Omega dE} = AS(\mathbf{Q}, \omega) \qquad (3.17)$$

It may be necessary to measure (for certain samples) this quantity with one parameter variable and the other kept constant. The advantage of the triple axis spectrometer is that such selective experiments can be performed, while in other methods like the chopper time-of-flight experiments (Chapter 2), both the parameters are varied. Though the mechanical design of the triple axis instrument makes it possible to vary parameters like E_0, E, ψ and ϕ continuously, automation plays a major part in enabling specialized experiments, like the "constant $\mathbf{Q}$" method for measuring phonon dispersion relations, to be performed.

The increments in the various angles like $2\theta_M$, and $2\theta_A$ are usually set by cam contacts, while the actual steps are decided by the requirements of the experiment (with a basic minimum). At each setting of the different parameters, the spectrometer collects signal counts for a predetermined number of monitor counts, then if necessary, takes a background reading either by flipping the analysing crystal off the Bragg reflection position or by introducing a cadmium shutter in the beam. These normal operations are controlled by a basic circuit consisting of relays and timers. What is special about the triple axis instrument is the ability to command the spectrometer to take up positions where the values of ψ, ϕ and $2\theta_A$ or $2\theta_M$ are different and the steps are non-linear, without an attendant loss of efficiency.

This is best illustrated with respect to an experiment for determining phonon energies at "constant $\mathbf{Q}$". As will be described in section 3.13, for equal increments of one of the parameters say $2\theta_A$, the values of ψ and ϕ are computed by solving the equations (3.18). The values are rounded off to the nearest fraction of a degree chosen so that the increments are obtained as integral numbers, positive or negative. Then it is necessary to make the different drive motors of the spectrometer set the different increments required. This is done by a programming unit.

Various arrangements are used for feeding in the information and controlling the motion of the motors. The simplest is the one used by Iyengar and Vijayaraghavan (1964) consisting of two programme boards of 300 positions each for ψ and ϕ. These 300 positions are obtained by a matrix of 26 position uniselector switch and a 12 position, 25 wafer rotary switch.

The feeding of the information is carried out more elegantly by punched paper tapes. In this case, the tape reader will translate the command to electro-mechanical devices which will command the motors to take up their new positions. In the automatic operation of the spectrometer, a programme tape is prepared and inserted in to the tape reader. Signals from the reader go through a translator set to recognize the tape codes for commands such as read the angle, set the spectrometer, reset the scalar and start the counting and finally to print out the data. Other operations can be added to suit the requirements. Such automation is similar to that found in other branches of spectrometry, for example the collection of data from single crystal neutron diffraction instruments (Prince and Abrahams, 1962) and in X-ray diffractometers (Abrahams, 1962).

For other specialized experiments like that of constant energy transfer, the programming is suitably changed.

3.12 Special Experimental Methods for the Triple Axis Spectrometer

One of the important fields in which the triple axis spectrometer has been used extensively is the measurement of phonon dispersion relations in specific directions in a crystal lattice (see Chapter 5). The three equations which determine the conditions for observing a neutron group of energy E and wave vector $\mathbf{k}$, by exchange of energy with a phonon of wave vector $\mathbf{q}$, for incident neutrons of energy E_0 and wave vector $\mathbf{k}_0$ have already been discussed in Chapter 1. The theory of one phonon processes indicates that in general if neutrons are incident in a particular direction in a crystal lattice, and those scattered in another direction at an angle ϕ are energy analysed, then there should exist one or more neutron groups. This is because the outgoing neutron wavevector will always cut one or more scattering surfaces, and each point of intersection corresponds to a discrete neutron group in the scattered neutron spectrum provided the intensity factor is favourable. The scattering surface in any crystal depends on the detailed dispersion relation, and thus it is not possible to draw the scattering surfaces beforehand, except for small values of $\mathbf{q}$ for which the frequency ν can be calculated in crystals of high symmetry if the elastic constants are known.

In the earliest experiments on aluminium by Brockhouse and Stewart (1955, 1958), the experimental set up was such that $E_0(\mathbf{k}_0)$ and ϕ were fixed. Corresponding to any direction of incidence the outgoing neutrons were energy analysed. Any neutron groups which were observed gave the corresponding values of $\mathbf{k}$. These were marked in the reciprocal lattice diagram and the corresponding values of ν and $\mathbf{q}$ were obtained by joining these points to the nearest reciprocal lattice point. Then ψ was changed by rotating the sample crystal alone and the experiment was repeated. Figure 3.6 shows the

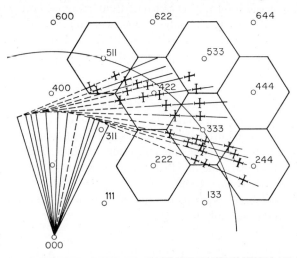

Fig. 3.6. The reciprocal lattice diagram for the 110 plane of aluminium, with the results of experiment in which incident neutrons of 0·022 eV were employed at a scattering angle of 95·1°. The solid lines along $\mathbf{k}$ indicate the range covered by the analysing spectrometer. Observed phonon positions are marked with estimated errors (Brockhouse and Stewart, 1958).

reciprocal lattice in which the different phonons observed are marked. From these results, those phonons whose $\mathbf{q}$ vectors lie in the required direction can be selected and the dispersion relation obtained.

This method is the same in principle, as the one described for time-of-flight spectrometers in Chapter 2. It suffers from the limitation that though a number of phonons are observed, very few are useful for direct interpretation, because only for certain symmetry directions is the dispersion relation easily interpretable. Secondly, the intensity of a neutron group depends on the component of the polarization vector of the phonon along $\mathbf{Q}$. This factor cannot be optimized at will in this method.

For these reasons a new method was developed, based on the use of a positional spectrometer which allows ϕ to be varied continuously and easily. This gives freedom of choice of one more parameter in the equations which give the conditions for one phonon scattering. For small values of $\mathbf{q}$, the dispersion relation for the symmetry directions can be calculated from the elastic constants. This straight line relation for $(\nu, \mathbf{q})$ can be the starting point to observe a phonon in a specific direction. The angles ψ and ϕ are calculated and set to observe a phonon. The actual energy distribution may not give the phonon of required $\mathbf{q}$, for the actual phonon energy may be different. From the observed phonon position and its $\mathbf{q}$ value, it could be inferred whether the actual energy is smaller or larger than the assumed value. The angles ψ and ϕ are then recalculated and set up to observe the phonon. By an iterative process, the frequency for the required $\mathbf{q}$ from the reciprocal lattice point is obtained. This method is called the method of successive approximations and has been used in the work on germanium (Brockhouse and Iyengar, 1958). A previous theoretical knowledge of the dispersion relation, even if obtained approximately on the basis of a force constant model, helps in arriving quickly at the right value of ν for a chosen value of $\mathbf{q}$ in a few steps.

Figure 3.7 is a reciprocal lattice diagram of a f.c.c. lattice and various methods for observing a zone-boundary phonon in the 111 direction will be discussed. In this figure OAB represents the vectors $\mathbf{k_0}$ and $\mathbf{k}$. From previous approximate knowledge of the dispersion relation ψ, ϕ and $\mathbf{k}$ are calculated such that a longitudinal phonon in the 111 direction will be observed at B. Actually, it may happen that instead of at B the neutron group appears at B′. This corresponds to a different value of $\mathbf{q}$, but a more accurate value of the frequency for B could be guessed and ψ and ϕ recalculated so that neutron group appears at B.

It is useful to point out a few features of this type of experiment. In an energy gain experiment, if the setting of ψ and ϕ are such that as $\mathbf{k}$ increases, $\mathbf{q}$ also increases then the phonon observed will be broad (provided ν increases with $\mathbf{q}$ as it does normally) for the equations will be satisfied for a range of values of $\mathbf{q}$. In other words the $\mathbf{k}$ direction cuts the scattering surface obliquely. If on the other hand as $\mathbf{k}$ increases the value of $\mathbf{q}$ decreases then the equations will be satisfied only in a limited region, and the observed neutron group will be narrower. One could make use of the first method to get the approximate value for the phonon and then improve by resorting to a different point in reciprocal space where the latter condition holds good. In Fig. 3.7, OCD represents this condition. As $\mathbf{k}$ is always less than $\mathbf{k_0}$, the energy change decreases as $\mathbf{q}$ increases. This produces a sharp phonon when the conservation conditions are satisfied. Also, in this direction, $\mathbf{q}$ almost lies along the 111 direction, which is the desired direction. By changing ψ and ϕ suitably, $\mathbf{k}$ can be made to lie along the 111 direction, and phonons of different $\mathbf{q}$ values observed.

By varying any two of the three variables, ψ, ϕ and $\mathbf{k}$ or $\mathbf{k_0}$ simultaneously, it is possible to keep **q** in the desired direction. By changing ϕ and **k** in step, the terminus of **k** lies along the 111 direction as shown in Fig. 3.7 by OEF and OEF'. In going from F to F', **k** changes by a certain value, and if there should occur any value of **q** for which the energy lies within the range of energy changes covered, a phonon will be observed. Then this phonon has the right direction and polarization. Again OGH and OG'H' represent conditions in which ψ and **k** are changed in steps. One advantage of this

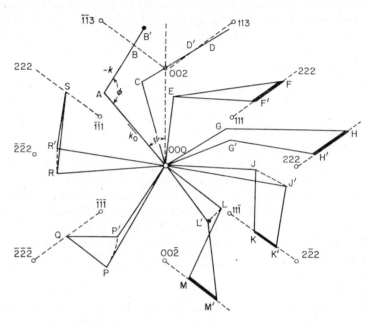

Fig. 3.7. Vector diagrams which illustrate the methods of measuring ν and **q** for phonons. Diagram OAB is the conventional method, OAB and OCD refer to the method of successive approximations. The next three diagrams illustrate how to measure phonons in the required direction by varying only two parameters non-linearly. Diagram OLM, OL'M' illustrates the method in which the energy transfer is kept fixed. The last two diagrams illustrate the method of "constant **Q**".

method is that it can be used with instruments in which ϕ is not controlled automatically. Thus, this method is applicable to the instruments used by Brockhouse and Stewart (1958) prior to 1957, and to those described by Iyengar et al. (1961) and Blinowski (1962). Similar conditions can also be achieved by changing $\mathbf{k}_0$ and ψ as illustrated by OJK and OJ'K' of Fig. 3.7.

This method of varying two parameters alone can give only one phonon in the desired direction. The experiment must be repeated with another value of the third parameter in order to observe a phonon of different **q**.

Another method is illustrated by OLM and OL'M' of Fig. 3.7, in which the energy change is kept constant and $\mathbf{q}$ is varied. This method was used by Sinclair and Brockhouse (1960) in measuring steep dispersion relations.

3.13 "Constant Q" Method

In this method (introduced by Brockhouse, 1960) $\mathbf{Q}$ is kept constant and the energy allowed to vary so that the conservation conditions may be satisfied for some value of the energy change. In Fig. 3.7, OPQ, OP'Q and ORS, OR'S illustrate the method. In the first, ψ and ϕ are varied together with $\mathbf{k}_0$ (or $2\theta_M$), $\mathbf{k}$ (or $2\theta_A$) being fixed such that $\mathbf{Q}$ ends at a given point in reciprocal space. Similarly, in the second example ψ and ϕ are both varied for successive values of $\mathbf{k}$ in such a way that $\mathbf{Q}$ remains constant. Now in these experiments if $\mathbf{k}_0$ or $\mathbf{k}$ is allowed to vary over a range of energy within which the energy transfer equals the energy of the phonon represented by $\mathbf{Q}$, then one is sure to observe a neutron group which will have the required $\mathbf{q}$.

The vector $\mathbf{Q}$ may be resolved in the plane of the spectrometer into the two components $\mathbf{Q}_1$ and $\mathbf{Q}_2$. Then the conservation conditions can be written as

$$\mathbf{Q}_1 = -\mathbf{k}_0 \sin \psi + \mathbf{k} \sin (\phi + \psi)$$
$$\mathbf{Q}_2 = \quad \mathbf{k}_0 \cos \psi - \mathbf{k} \cos (\phi + \psi) \qquad (3.18)$$

Given the values of $\mathbf{Q}_1$ and $\mathbf{Q}_2$ which are to be held constant and the fixed value of $\mathbf{k}_0$ to be used, corresponding values of ψ, ϕ and $\mathbf{k}$ (or $2\theta_A$) can be computed. $2\theta_A$ is allowed to vary in equal increments (say $\frac{1}{8}°$) to cover the range within which the phonon energy should occur. The corresponding angles ψ and ϕ are rounded off to the nearest angular interval the spectrometer is able to take. The spectrometer automation is programmed to take up these positions one by one and counts accumulated for a fixed time or number of monitor counts. Then the plot of counting rate as a function of one of the variables $2\theta_A$ alone gives the neutron distribution, and the centre of this distribution is taken as the correct phonon energy.

Figure 3.8 shows the $\mathbf{b}_2\mathbf{b}_3$ plane of the reciprocal lattice of magnesium, with a typical "constant $\mathbf{Q}$" experiment designed to measure the frequency of a transverse acoustic phonon in the [0001] direction. The vectors shown are the end positions of a 22 point experiment. Typical variations in ψ, ϕ and $2\theta_A$ are shown in the Fig. 3.8. The counting rate is also plotted for the observed phonon.

The "constant $\mathbf{Q}$" method has many advantages. It has become possible to observe phonons of predetermined $\mathbf{q}$, which saves time by giving only the required information. Besides, in the earlier methods the width of the observed neutron distribution is caused to a certain extent by the changing value of **q**. In other words, the distribution samples a region in reciprocal space which is dependent on factors like the angular collimation of the incident and outgoing neutrons as well as the gradient of the (ν, q) relation at the value of **q**. In the "constant **Q**" method, every time the momentum conservation condition is satisfied the **Q** value is predetermined and hence the phonons are usually sharper. In specialized experiments, for example those concerning the temperature variation of phonon frequency, this method

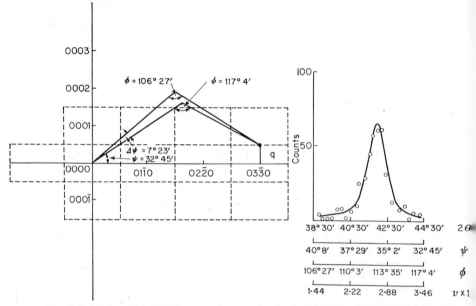

FIG. 3.8. Reciprocal lattice diagram of magnesium in the $\mathbf{b_2 b_3}$ plane. The limits of $\mathbf{k_0}$ and $\mathbf{k}$ for a typical "constant **Q**" run for the zone boundary transverse acoustic phonon in the [0001] direction are shown. The measured neutron counting rate in a 22 point run is also shown.

makes sure that one is always observing the phonon for the same **q** and hence the widths are readily comparable, whereas in the earlier methods this is not so. In general, one can choose any value of **Q** and obtain all the values of ν pertaining to different polarizations easily, provided the intensity factor is favourable. These advantages have made the triple axis instrument highly suited for phonon studies even though in rate of data collection, pulsed time-of-flight instruments are better.

3.14 Shape of Neutron Group and Focusing Effects

The shape of the neutron group depends on instrumental factors like the angular collimation defining $\mathbf{k_0}$ and $\mathbf{k}$ and the spread in their magnitudes, the mosaic spread of the crystal and the nature of the dispersion curve in the region of reciprocal space in which measurements are made. It is difficult to obtain a detailed mathematical expression for the shape of the neutron group. The angular divergence of k_0 and k makes the region of q space investigated a small volume which is not necessarily spherical. The vertical divergences are usually fairly large and this makes the problem of a detailed mathematical treatment even more difficult. In using the method of successive approximations it was pointed out how the nature of the dispersion curve in the direction of k influences the width of the peak. In the "constant Q" method this is not as serious, because the end point of Q does not vary, but nevertheless the gradient of the dispersion curve has some influence in the shape of the distribution though not in the integrated intensity. As before it is preferable if the k direction is normal to the scattering surface.

From an intuitive point of view one might expect the arguments detailed in Section 3.7 for diffraction patterns, to hold reasonably well for the inelastic scattering pattern. The choice of the collimator angles according to this reasoning should follow $\alpha_1 < \alpha_2$ and $\alpha_3 < \alpha_4$. An antiparallel arrangement of analysing spectrometer with respect to monochromatizing spectrometer would be preferred as shown in Fig. 3.4. Collins (1963) has derived mathematical expressions for the peak counting rate for the triple axis spectrometer similar in principle to the treatment of Caglioti et al. (1960) for the diffraction patterns. It still looks unrewarding to go into detailed calculations, while the intuitive reasonings in the choice of the collimator angles α_1, α_2, α_3 and α_4 and the point in reciprocal space where observations are made seem to be adequate. However, Peckham (1964) gives a graphical method of finding the optimum focusing geometry, and Caglioti (1964) has discussed focusing action for the special case of elastic diffraction using a triple axis spectrometer.

The shape of the neutron distribution at normal temperatures when anharmonic effects are not large is assumed to be equal to the overall resolution function which is approximately Gaussian. When the anharmonic forces are large the shape of the distribution broadens and assumes the Lorentz function rather than the Gaussian. The centre of the distribution can usually be found by a geometrical construction if corrections like the variation in detector sensitivity are properly taken into account. Alternatively the observed data can be fitted to a Gaussian by the least squares method, deriving values for the standard deviation and the centre of the distribution.

3.15 Problems in "Scalar Q" Experiments

With scattering samples in the form of liquids or polycrystalline solids, only the magnitude of Q is important, and the dynamics of the scattering specimen depends on the quantity $S(Q,\omega)$. The time dependent correlation functions $G(r,\tau)$ can be obtained by fourier inversion of the complete function $S(Q,\omega)$. Hence, it is necessary to obtain experimentally as much data as possible for the function $S(Q,\omega)$, and a series of experiments in each of which one of the variables is given a finite value and the distribution measured as the other variable is changed is perhaps the proper procedure to adopt. This can be done with the triple axis spectrometer provided the ranges required are small (as with phonons). For example the analysing spectrometer could be set at one energy, and the incident energy changed to maintain Q constant, the variation of the flux of incident neutrons being taken into account

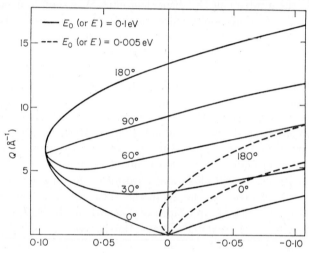

Fig. 3.9. The wave vector transfer $|\mathbf{Q}|$ as a function of the energy transfer $\hbar\omega$ for the incident energies (E_0) and several angles of scattering. The curves are the same using outgoing energies E except that the sign of $\hbar\omega$ is reversed (Brockhouse, 1961) (abscissa units are eV).

by the monitor counter whose energy sensitivity follows the $1/v$ law. Unfortunately the energy distributions in liquid and polycrystalline work are usually much wider than for phonon work, and in many cases it is possible to hold Q constant only by swinging the incident neutron energy and angle of scatter over very wide ranges. For example, if Q is to be kept constant at a value of $1 \cdot 0$ Å^{-1} for energy transfers of zero–50 meV, the incident neutron energy must be changed from 1 meV and a 90° angle to 800 meV and a 3° angle of scatter. This range is too great for any of the methods described above, and for this reason many of the advantages described in Section 3.13 do not apply here. However, for larger values of Q and cases where the energy transfers are not high (e.g. $Q = 2$ Å^{-1} over a range 0–10 meV) it is possible to use the "constant Q" method to advantage.

The neutron momentum and energy conservation laws impose restrictions on the range of (Q, ω) covered in an experiment. Some regions of (ω, Q) space covered for different incident energies and scattering angles are shown in Fig. 3.9. It is seen that, with incident cold neutrons, it is possible to cover only a small region of (ω, Q) space. It is impossible to obtain large energy transfers for small momentum transfer using cold neutrons. This problem arises in the study of the optical branch of spin waves because of the rapid fall of the magnetic scattering amplitude as a function of scattering angle (see Section 1.17).

3.16 Neutron Filters

For a polycrystalline material composed of coherently scattering nuclei, the total cross section varies markedly with incident neutron energy. In the thermal neutron energy range the wavelength of the neutrons is of the order of the interplanar distances, which leads to coherent Bragg scattering. The measured as well as calculated total cross-section shows discrete jumps each corresponding to the operation of one set of (hkl) planes (cf. Fig. 1.5). The wavelength at which such a step will be observed is given by the relation $\lambda = 2d_{hkl}$. In a polycrystalline substance there is a maximum spacing (d_{max}) corresponding to the lowest index reflection possible, and for neutrons of wavelength greater than $2d_{max}$ the material should be nearly transparent. It happens that for most materials, the largest value of d is of the order of 2–3 Å, so that transmission of a beam through a block of polycrystalline solid provides an easy means of selecting long wavelength neutrons. The first of such filters was made by Anderson et al. (1946) using graphite.

The use of polycrystalline filters has two aspects, one in which it is used to obtain a pure beam of cold neutrons which is employed as a "monochromatic" beam for inelastic scattering experiments, and the other in which it is used to discriminate against higher energy neutrons. Egelstaff (1951, 1953) in the early experiments on scattering from polycrystalline materials used them to provide a "monochromatic" beam. Beryllium is used as the filter material in the usual filter-chopper apparatus (Carter et al., 1957; Larsson et al., 1958). It is also used in the filter-pulsed reactor experiments (Golikov et al., 1963). The steep slope of the "cut-off" is very important in most of these experiments especially those involving small energy changes such as the measurement of diffusion broadening from liquids (Chapter 8).

There are other experiments where the filter precedes a monochromator in which case the monochromatic beam energy is less than 0·005 eV. Brockhouse (1961) has used a Be filter with the rotating crystal spectrometer, so that the higher order reflections will be absent when the first order is below the beryllium cut-off. In this case the total transmission of the filter below the cut-off is not very important. This instrument has been described in Section 2.12. The use of filters as energy analysers is discussed in Section 3.18.

In order to obtain a beam of pure cold neutrons it is necessary to consider several important aspects. The first is that the length of the filter should be sufficient to remove all neutrons of short wavelengths. This obviously depends on the cross-section for the "cut-off" planes. However, for neutrons of longer wavelength, the process of inelastic scattering can take place, and hence, too long a filter (even if maintained at a low temperature) will permit considerable inelastic scattering and consequent loss in intensity. Thus, though in principle the filter is a very elegant and easy way of selecting a beam of cold neutrons, its practical design should take into account many factors.

1. The material of the filter should have very low incoherent scattering and absorption cross-sections.

2. The cut-off wavelength of the filter will depend on the largest interplanar spacing of the filter material, and the cross-section for these planes should be high if a well defined "edge" to the transmitted spectrum is required.

3. Length of the filter should be such that there is complete scattering away of the thermal neutrons.

4. Lateral dimensions should be such as to minimize multiple scattering which will throw the faster neutrons back into the beam. This requires that the filter is covered by a neutron absorbing material like cadmium on the longer sides. Also it may be worth interleaving the filter material with cadmium sheets. The limitation to this would be the fact that by interleaving with cadmium, some of the cold neutrons passing at an angle will be lost and the effective solid angle for transmission will be reduced.

5. The filter should be cooled to a temperature much less than the Debye temperature so that inelastic scattering will be minimum. Since the cross-section for inelastic scattering depends on the Debye temperature, a high Debye temperature for the substance will be preferred.

6. The physical nature of the materials may cause small angle scattering especially by defects, pores and occlusions. Thus, the metallurgical process of making the filter material is also important.

The flux of cold neutrons which can be obtained ideally, may be calculated from the known wavelength distribution of incident neutrons and the cut-off wavelength of the filter. This will be given by:

$$
\begin{aligned}
n_c &= \int_{\lambda_c}^{\infty} 2n_F \left(\frac{\lambda_T}{\lambda}\right)^4 \exp -\left(\frac{\lambda_T}{\lambda}\right)^2 \frac{d\lambda}{\lambda} \\
&= n_F \left[1 - \left(1 + \left(\frac{\lambda_T}{\lambda_c}\right)^2\right) \exp -\left(\frac{\lambda_T}{\lambda}\right)^2 \right]
\end{aligned} \tag{3.19}
$$

where n_F is the total flux of the Maxwellian spectrum λ_T a constant for a given moderator temperature (equation 1·8), and λ_c the cut-off wavelength. For the normal moderator temperature around 300° K and λ_c in the region of 4–7 Å, the fraction $n_c/n_F \sim 10^{-2}$–10^{-3}. This is the fraction of the neutron flux which can be obtained ideally. In order to keep the contamination of higher energy neutrons small, to say within 1 % of the cold neutron flux, the attenuation factor of the filter for the thermal neutron region should be of the order of 10^5 times than that for cold neutrons. The mean wavelength of the cold

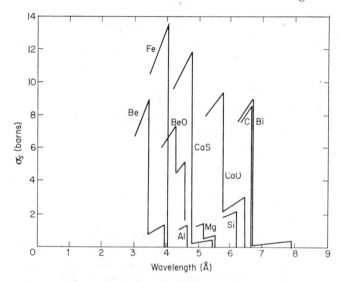

FIG. 3.10. The cross section for the cut-off planes for various polycrystalline substances indicating their cut-off wavelengths (Hughes, 1953).

neutrons filtered from a Maxwellian spectrum of neutrons has an approximate value of $4/3\lambda_c$. It may be seen from equation (3.19), that by lowering the temperature of the moderator which provides the neutrons, the relative intensity of cold neutrons can be enhanced (cf. Chapter 4).

The properties of various materials for filters have been discussed by Egelstaff and Pease (1954). The choice is often limited by one or other of the above requirements, and by the sort of use made of the filter. In some cases the contamination of thermal neutrons is not a big problem, but if the entire cold neutron beam is used for inelastic scattering experiments, then the purity is important. The sharpness of the cut-off is also important in such cases. Sharpness of the cut-off will depend on the cross-section of the cut-off plane or planes near it which in turn depends on the structure factor. This factor for various substances is shown in Fig. 3.10. If the filter material consists of heavy atoms, it also provides a fair amount of shielding against γ-rays as well. It is possible to provide attenuation of fast neutrons and γ-rays by using single crystals of bismuth and lead preceding the filter.

Due to a variety of factors, beryllium and beryllium oxide have proved to be the best filter materials and have been used in almost all inelastic scattering experiments. They have the convenient cut-off wavelengths of 3·96 and 4·7 Å respectively, small absorption, low incoherent scattering cross-sections and high Debye temperatures. By cooling the beryllium filter to liquid nitrogen temperature a sevenfold increase in the intensity of cold neutrons has been reported, although four- or fivefold increases are more usual for filters of the standard length. The length of the filter depends on the incident neutron spectrum: the normal length used for the filter-chopper apparatus (Chapter 2) is about 40 cm.

3.17 Single Crystal Filters

The total scattering cross-section for atoms in a crystal lattice depends on the neutron energy, and for fast neutrons Bragg scattering is negligible; inelastic scattering being the dominant effect. In the thermal neutron range interference effects predominate giving rise to sharp discontinuities in the cross-section curve. If a single crystal is used the number of planes that contribute to Bragg scattering is less than for a polycrystal and therefore the structure in total cross-section curve is not so prominent. In addition extinction is often important in reducing the observable cross section. For these reasons single crystals can be used to pass low energy neutrons while stopping fast neutrons. The neutron spectrum transmitted by such a filter can be quite different from that incident on it, the peak shifting to lower energy and the fast neutrons well attenuated. Egelstaff (1954) describes how a "modified bismuth filter" consisting of a mosaic of large crystallites can be used in this manner. Iyengar et al. (1965) describe the use of a single crystal with a large mosaic spread in selectively removing second order neutrons from a beam by Bragg reflection. Single crystal filters help in reducing the higher order contamination in crystal monochromators in the range 0·02–0·1 eV. With pool type reactors, the flux of resonance and fast neutrons in the beam are high, and single crystal filters are useful to obtain a pure thermal neutron beam.

The choice of the single crystal depends on many factors. The atoms in the solid should have negligible capture, incoherent and paramagnetic scattering cross-sections for thermal neutrons. The crystal mosaic should be small and perfect crystals would be preferred. Disorder and dislocations cause diffuse scattering, and some loss in intensity. The Debye temperature should be high thus reducing thermal diffuse scattering. Crystals of quartz, beryllium and bismuth have been considered.

Quartz offers a cheap and perfect crystal. This has been used by Brockhouse (1959) and Rustad *et al.* (1959). The total cross-section of quartz single crystals has been measured by Brockhouse (1959) for two temperatures and is shown in Fig. 3.11. For neutrons higher than 1 eV the attenuation coefficient is greater than 0·28 while in the region of interest below 0·2 eV

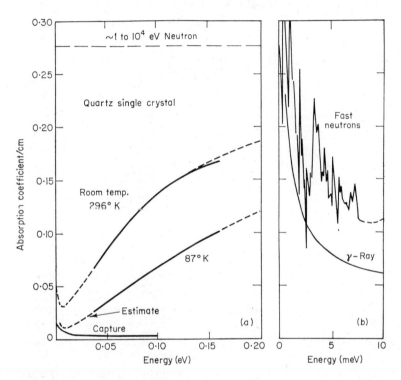

FIG. 3.11. (a) The measured total cross-section of a quartz single crystal (in units of absorption coefficient per cm length) as a function of neutron energy, for temperatures of 296°K and 87°K. The measurements of Rustad *et al.* (1959) for room temperatures are shown as dashed lines. An estimate for quartz at 87°K over a more extended energy range, as well as the capture cross-section for the silicon in the crystal are also shown. (b) Similar cross-sections for fast neutrons and γ-rays (Brockhouse, 1961).

the value varies from 0·05 to 0·10 per cm length of filter. At very low neutron energies the absorption of silicon is not negligible. The calculated capture is also indicated in the figure. Similar measurements have also been made by Møller *et al.* (1961).

From the point of view of high Debye temperatures beryllium is the best and it is also effective in attenuating resonance neutrons. Single crystals of beryllium with small mosaic spread are expensive. Cross-section measurements for a single crystal of beryllium are reported by Duggal and Thapar (1962). Dyer and Low (1961) have used a bismuth single crystal with a chopper apparatus. Menardi et al. (1963) have reported measurements on a single crystal of bismuth. The mosaic spread of their bismuth was fairly large and hence produced many peaks in the cross-section curve due to Laue-Bragg scattering. Because of its mass, bismuth reduces the γ-rays as well.

3.18 Polycrystalline Filter as an Analyser

The property of the polycrystalline filter to transmit all neutrons of energy less than the cut-off energy, with little attenuation, affords an easy means of selectively detecting neutrons. The use of a graphite filter placed in front of a BF_3 counter to define a given energy is described by Hughes (1953, p. 298, figs. 11–18). This kind of arrangement selects an energy interval between zero and the cut-off energy which in the case of beryllium is 5 meV. A beryllium "filter detector" was used by Brockhouse et al. (1960) and Stiller and Danner (1961) for inelastic scattering studies. In their case the energy of neutrons falling on the sample was varied and the counting rate at the detector recorded, which gave the counting rate as a function of energy transfer $E_0 - E_f$ (where E_0 is the incident neutron energy and E_f the mean energy of the detector sensitivity function.) In the set-up used by Woods et al. (1961) monochromatic neutrons, continuously variable in energy, were obtained from a crystal spectrometer. The detector consisted of a beryllium filter made of 4 in. $\times \frac{3}{8}$ in. $\times 2$ in. blocks interleaved with cadmium to give a cross-sectional area of 2 in. $\times 1$ in., and placed in front of a low pressure BF_3 chamber serving as the detector.

Figure 3.12 illustrates schematically a typical "beryllium detector" set up. It would be an advantage to have the detector mounted on an arm rotatable about the sample. If the filter is not cooled, the length has to be kept small. The mean energy of the detector is not half the cut-off energy because the detector sensitivity function is more like a right angled triangle tending to zero as the energy tends to zero. This type of spectrometer is useful for studying inelastic scattering from incoherently scattering samples since only the energy transfers are measured accurately.

Mikke and Kroh (1963), Venkataraman et al. (1963) and Saunderson and Rainey (1963) have built experimental set-ups similar to that of Woods et al. The energy transfer spectrum is usually obtained, by measuring the detector counting rate as a function of monochromator angle, the counting time being decided by preset counts from a monitor. This way of recording the data has some advantages, namely the factor k/k_0 (equation 1.22) in the inelastic scattering cross-section is automatically removed, the detector sensitivity is a constant and the energy distribution is readily obtained by varying the incident energy. These factors enable relative values of the van Hove scattering function $S(Q,\omega)$ to be obtained straight away from the data; the scattering angle adjustment enables Q to be changed to a limited extent.

The effect of second order neutrons and contaminant thermal neutrons have to be properly eliminated if the observed energy distributions are continuous. When using polycrystalline samples the scattered neutron spectrum contains a high proportion of Bragg reflected neutrons. These may leak through the filter if the length is inadequate causing spurious peaks in

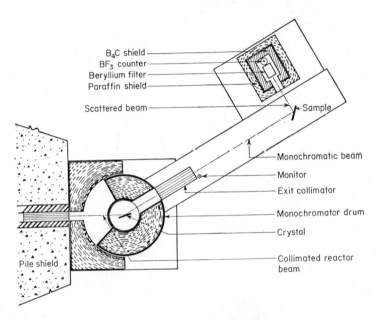

FIG. 3.12. Schematic drawing of a beryllium detector spectrometer using a crystal monochromator for obtaining neutrons continuously variable in energy.

the pattern. Since the position of occurrence of a Bragg reflection varies with scattering angle, it is possible to check for this effect either by changing the angle of scattering, in which case the peak will shift, or by removing the filter and repeating the run which will be equivalent to recording the diffraction pattern. The method has however been very effective in the study of hydrogen vibrations in many hydrides and in measuring the levels associated with molecular rotation in the solid state which occur for example with ammonium halides and methane (these results are described in Chapter 10). The full potentiality has still not yet been exploited. For example, cooling the filter and using detectors at different angles would provide higher intensities.

3.19 Window Filter

A further development of the beryllium detector spectrometer involves the use of two filters in cascade making a "window filter". In this case the

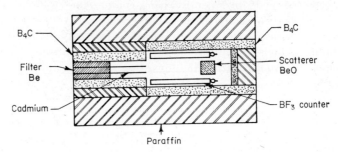

FIG. 3.13. Drawing of the window filter. Ten BF_3 counters form a cylindrical detector (Iyengar, 1964).

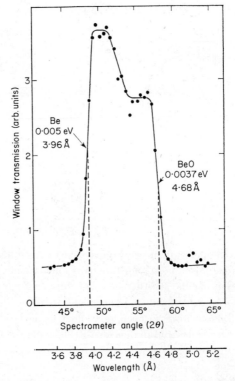

FIG. 3.14. Measured sensitivity function of the window filter using a crystal monochromator (Iyengar, 1964a).

neutrons transmitted by the first filter are scattered by a second filter with a lower energy cut-off. Neutrons in the energy interval between the two cut-offs are mostly scattered in the backward direction and hence may be counted in a cylindrical array of BF_3 counters or a ring counter.

The energy sensitivity characteristic of such a device has been measured by Iyengar (1964). He has used 4 in. long $\frac{1}{4}$ in. thick beryllium bricks interleaved with cadmium for the first filter forming a cross-section 2 in. × 2 in.

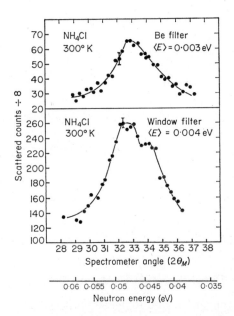

FIG. 3.15. Neutron energy transfer distribution due to the torsional oscillations in NH_4Cl at room temperature using the conventional beryllium filter in transmission and the window filter. The higher energy resolution achieved is indicated.

and a block of BeO as the scatterer. The BF_3 counters are 12 in. long and 1 in. diameter forming a cylindrical ring. Figure 3.13 shows a sketch of the assembly. The energy sensitivity was measured using monochromatic neutrons from a magnetite crystal monochromator which was fed by neutrons from a mechanical velocity selector. Figure 3.14 shows the measured sensitivity function, which has the expected sharp rise and fall at the respective cut-offs.

Different materials could be used to widen or narrow the energy width of the window. Using molybdenum for the scatterer a narrower window is obtained and the upper cut-off would then be at 4·5 Å. The background counting rate for incident neutron energies above and below the window region is dependent on the length of the scatterer and could be optimized.

With this improved resolution, the neutron group due to torsional oscillations in NH_4Cl was re-measured (Venkataraman et al., 1964) and found to be a composite peak while earlier measurements with the beryllium detector spectrometer showed only one peak. The results are shown in Fig. 3.15 and demonstrate the improved resolution obtained. Another incidental advantage seems to arise from the fact that the Bragg contamination from polycrystalline samples is less likely to be counted in this set-up compared to the normal beryllium detector set-up.

The nature of the energy sensitivity curve of the window filter allows the wave vector of the detected neutron to be defined accurately. This property makes the detector adaptable for phonon studies since both the energy and the momentum transfer are well defined. Iyengar et al. (1964) have used this device with the "constant $\mathbf{Q}$" method to measure the phonon dispersion relations in magnesium. The window filter assembly was mounted on the detector arm of a two axis spectrometer. Automatic programming for positioning ψ and ϕ as in the "constant $\mathbf{Q}$" method was provided. Some of the characteristics of this method are the following, (i) the spectrometer need be only a two axis instrument, (ii) the energy loss process is used, (iii) the incident neutron energy is fixed for a given phonon energy and (iv) for phonon frequencies in the range 4–13×10^{12} c/s, the incident neutron energy is in the peak region of the Maxwellian spectrum. Thus the conditions are optimized for a high counting rate and it is estimated that there is an improvement of a factor of five compared to conventional triple axis methods.

3.20 Filter Detectors Used with Pulsed Sources

The filter detector can be used to define the scattered neutron energy in a pulsed neutron beam experiment. The filter difference method in which a "window" is selected is the most practical method according to Webb (1964). Webb's method is shown diagrammatically in Fig. 3.16. Neutrons from the source travel along the flight path (l_1) to the sample, and after scattering travel along the short flight path (l_2) though the filters to the detectors. Only those neutrons which have lost sufficient energy to pass the filters are detected. The differences in the counts in the two detectors after some corrections for transmission through the sample and differential attenuation through the filters give the neutron intensity in the energy interval between the two cut-offs. To eliminate differences in the counter efficiencies, the position of the counters are alternated in a sequence of runs. If $l_2 \ll l_1$, the time of flight from source to detector is a measure of the incident neutrons' energy, so that all the scattering parameters are determined. Results for metal hydrides (Pan and Webb, 1965) covered energy transfers from $0\cdot1$ to 1 eV and gave data on the first, second and third vibrational modes of the proton. A single

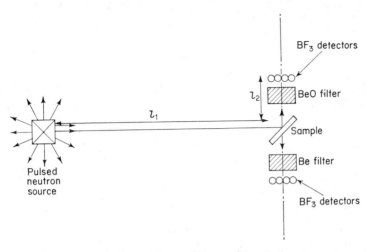

FIG. 3.16. Illustration of use of filter techniques with pulsed neutron source.

filter before the detectors (i.e. as in Fig. 3.16 but with the BeO filter detector) has been used in similar experiments with a pulsed reactor (Bajorek *et al.*, 1965).

3.21 Brief Comparison with Time-of-flight Methods

The crystal diffraction techniques as discussed in the previous pages have been applied to a variety of problems with great success. A comparison of this technique with that of the time-of-flight technique should take into consideration the particular problem in which one is interested. If the object is to measure $d^2\sigma/d\Omega dE$ as is required for scattering law work, the multi-rotor multi-detector time-of-flight devices yield data at a faster rate than the triple axis spectrometer. For specialized experiments, as in the "constant $\mathbf{Q}$" method, the triple axis spectrometer is better. An advantageous factor in the multirotor system is that one can easily use many detectors (with little additional investment in electronics) and so make measurements on neutrons scattered at many angles, while so far in a crystal spectrometer only one scattering angle is used. But recently crystal spectrometers have been designed by Brockhouse (1964) and Iyengar (1965) such that instead of one, there are five or six analysing spectrometers measuring the energy distribution at different angles. In the study of phonon dispersion relations, by a judicious choice of $\mathbf{Q}$'s in reciprocal space and branches of the dispersion curves the "constant $\mathbf{Q}$" method can be applied with each analysing spectrometer. Consequently this instrument should yield data on phonon dispersion relations at a favourable rate.

6*

References

Abrahams, S. C. (1962). *Rev. sci. Instrum.* **33**, 9, 973.

Anderson, H. L., Fermi, E. and Marshall, L. (1946). *Phys. Rev.* **70**, 815.

Bacon, G. E. (1962). "Neutron Diffraction". Oxford University Press, London.

Bacon, G. E. and Dyer, R. F. (1959). *J. sci. Instrum.* **36**, 419.

Bacon, G. E. and Lowde, R. D. (1948). *Acta cryst.* **1**, 303.

Bacon, G. E., Smith J. C. and Whitehead, C. D. (1950). *J. sci. Instrum.* **27**, 330.

Bajorek, A. Machehina, T. A., Parlinski, K. and Shapiro, F. L. (1965). *In* "Inelastic Scattering of Neutrons", Vol. II, p. 519. IAEA, Vienna.

Barrett, C. S., Mueller, M. H. and Heaton, L. (1963). *Rev. sci. Instrum.* **34**, 8, 847.

Blinowski, K. (1962). *In* "Pile Neutron Research in Physics", p. 369. IAEA, Vienna.

Breton, C., Hubert, P. and Meriel, P. (1957). *J. Phys. Radium* **18**, 25–35.

Brockhouse, B. N. (1959). *Rev. sci. Instrum.* **30**, 136.

Brockhouse, B. N. (1960). *Bull. Amer. phys. Soc.* II, 5, 462.

Brockhouse, B. N. (1961). *In* "Inelastic Scattering of Neutrons in Solids and Liquids", p. 113. IAEA, Vienna.

Brockhouse, B. N. and Iyengar, P. K. (1958). *Phys. Rev.* **111**, 747.

Brockhouse, B. N. and Stewart, A. T. (1955). *Phys. Rev.* **100**, 756.

Brockhouse, B. N. and Stewart, A. T. (1958). *Rev. mod. Phys.* **30**, 236.

Brockhouse, B. N. Sakamoto, M., Sinclair, R. N. and Woods, A. D. B. (1960). *Bull. Amer. phys. Soc.* II, 5.

Brockhouse, B. N. (1964). Private communication.

Caglioti, G. and Ricci, F. P. (1962). *Nucl. Instrum. Methods,* **15**, 155.

Caglioti, G. and Ascarelli, P. (1963). *In* "Inelastic Scattering of Neutrons in Solids and Liquids", Vol. I, p. 259. IAEA, Vienna.

Caglioti, G., Paoletti, A. and Ricci, F. P. (1958). *Nucl. Instrum. Methods* **3**, 223.

Caglioti, G., Paoletti, A. and Ricci, F. P. (1960). *Nucl. Instrum. Methods* **9**, 195.

Caglioti, G. (1964). *Acta cryst.* **17**, 1202.

Carter, R. S., Palevsky, H. and Hughes, D. J. (1957). *Phys. Rev.* **106**, 1168.

Collins, M. F. (1963). *Brit. J. Appl. Phys.* **14**, 805.

Duggal, V. P. (1959). *Nucl. Sci. Engng* **6**, 76.

Duggal, V. P., Rao, K. R., Thapar, C. L. and Singh, V. (1961). *Proc. Indian Acad. Sci.* **A 53**, 2.

Duggal, V. P. and Thapar, C. L. (1962). *Rev. sci. Instrum.* **33**, 49.

Dyer, R. and Low, G. G. E. (1961). *In* "Inelastic Scattering of Neutrons in Solids and Liquids", p. 179. IAEA, Vienna.

Egelstaff, P. A. (1951). *Nature, Lond.* **168**, 290.

Egelstaff, P. A. (1953). AERE Report No. R/1164. H.M.S.O., London.

Egelstaff, P. A. (1954). *J. nucl. Energy* **1**, 57.

Egelstaff, P. A. and Pease, R. S. (1954). *J. sci. Instrum.* **31**, 207.

Fankuchen, I. (1937). *Nature, Lond.* **139**, 193.

Golikov, V., Shapiro, F. L., Shkatula, A. and Janik, J. A. (1963). *In* "Inelastic Scattering in Solids and Liquids", Vol. I, p. 119. IAEA, Vienna.

Hagihara, S., Myashita, K. and Yoshie, T. (1962). Mitsubushi Denki Lab. Rep. 3, 1.

Hay, H. J. (1958). AERE Report No. R/2982. H.M.S.O., London.

Holm, M. W. (1955). IDO Report No. 16115.

Holt, N. (1957). *Rev. sci. Instrum.* **28**, 1.

Hughes, D. J. (1953). "Pile Neutron Research". Addison-Wesley.

Hurst, D. G., Pressesky, A. J. and Tunnicliffe, P. R. (1950). *Rev. sci. Instrum.* **21**, 705.

Iyengar, P. K. (1964). *Nucl. Instrum. Methods* **25**, 367.

Iyengar, P. K. (1965). *In* "Inelastic Scattering of Neutrons", Vol. II, p. 483. IAEA, Vienna.

Iyengar, P. K. and Vijayaraghavan, P. R. (1964). AEE/NP/12.

Iyengar, P. K., Satya Murthy, N. S. and Dasannacharya, B. A. (1961). *In* "Inelastic Scattering of Neutrons in Solids and Liquids", p. 555. IAEA, Vienna.

Iyengar, P. K., Venkataraman, G., Vijayaraghavan, P. R. and Roy, A. P. (1965). *In* Inelastic Scattering of Neutrons", Vol. I, p. 153. IAEA, Vienna.

Iyengar, P. K., Venkataraman, G., Rao, K. R., Vijayaraghavan, P. R. and Roy, A. P. (1963). *In* "Inelastic Scattering of Neutrons in Solids and Liquids", Vol. II, p. 99. IAEA, Vienna.

Iyengar, P. C., Soni, J. N., Navarro, O. D., Pineda, V. M., Natera, M. G., Lee, T. C., Marsongkohadi, Song, J. and Nimnanandon, T. (1965). Report No. PAEC(D) PH651.

James, R. W. (1958). "The Optical Principles of the Diffraction of X-rays". Bell, London.

Knowles, J. W. (1959). *Canad. J. Phys.* **37**, 203.

Larsson, K. E., Stedman, R. and Palevsky, H. (1958). *J. nucl. Energy*, **6**, 222.

McAlpin, W. (1963). AECL Report No. 1695; also see *Nucl. Instrum. Methods* **25**, 205 (1964).

McReynolds, A. W. (1952). *Phys. Rev.* **88**, 958.

Menardi, S., Hass, R. and Kley, W. (1963). *In* "Inelastic Scattering of Neutrons in Solids and Liquids", Vol. II, p. 139. IAEA, Vienna.

Mikke, K., and Kroh, A. (1963). *In* "Inelastic Scattering of Neutrons in Solids and Liquids", Vol. II, p. 237. IAEA, Vienna.

Modrzejewski, A. and Bednarski, S. (1955). Polish Academy of Sciences Report 112/I-B.

Modrzejewski, A. and Bednarski, S. (1958). Polish Academy of Sciences Report 32/I-B.

Moller, H. B., Shore, F. J. and Sailor, V. L. (1961). *Rev. sci. Instrum.* **32**, 654.

Mueller, M. H., Heaton, L. and Johanson, E. W. (1961). *Rev. sci. Instrum.* **32**, 456.

O'Connor, D. A. and Sosnowski, A. (1961). *Acta cryst.* **14**, 192.

Ohno, Y., Asami, T. and Okamoto, K. (1962). *In* "Pile Neutron Research in Physics", p. 585. IAEA, Vienna.

Pan, S. S. and Webb, F. J. (1965). *Nucl. Sci. Engng.* In press.

Pattendon, N. J. and Baston, A. H. (1957). AERE Report No. NP/R 2251. H.M.S.O., London.

Peckham, G. (1964). AERE Report No. R. 4380.

Prince, E. and Abrahams, S. C. (1959). *Rev. sci. Instrum.* **30**, 581.

Renninger, M. (1937). *Z. Phys.* **106**, 141.

Rustad, R. M., Wajima, L. T. and Melkonian, E. J. (1959). *Bull. Amer. phys. Soc.* **4**, 245.

Sailor, V. L., Foote, H. L., Landon, H. H. and Wood, R. E. (1956). *Rev. sci. Instrum.* **27**, 26.

Saunderson, D. H. and Rainey, V. S. (1963). *In* "Inelastic Scattering of Neutrons in Solids and Liquids", Vol. I, p. 413. IAEA, Vienna.

Sinclair, R. N. and Brockhouse, B. N. (1960). *Phys. Rev.* **120**, 1638.

Shull, C. G. (1960). Technical Report No. 5. Structure of Solids Group, MIT.

Shull, C. G. (1962). Advanced Course on Neutron Crystal Spectrometry. Institute for Atomic Energy, Kjeller, Norway.

Spencer, R. R. and Smith, J. R. (1960). *Nucl. Sci. Engng* **8**, 393.

Stiller, H. H. and Danner, H. R. (1961). *In* "Inelastic Scattering of Neutrons in Solids and Liquids", p. 363. IAEA, Vienna.

Sturm, W. J. (1947). *Phys. Rev.* **71**, 757.

Szabo, P. (1959). *Nucl. Instrum. Methods* **5**, 184.

Venkataraman, G., Usha, K., Iyengar, P. K. and Vijayaraghavan, P. R. (1963). *In* "Inelastic Scattering of Neutrons in Solids and Liquids", Vol. II, p. 253. IAEA, Vienna.

Venkataraman, G., Usha, K., Iyengar, P. K., Vijayaraghavan, P. R. and Roy, A. P. (1964). *Solid State Communications* **1**, 17.

Wajima, L. T., Rustad, R. M. and Melkinian, E. J. (1960). *J. phys. Soc. Japan*, **15**, 4, 630.

Webb, J. (1964). AERE Report No. 4263. H.M.S.O., London.

Woods, A. D. B., Brockhouse, B. N., Sakamoto, M. and Sinclair, R. N. (1961). *In* "Inelastic Scattering of Neutrons in Solids and Liquids", p. 487. IAEA, Vienna.

Wollan, E. O. and Shull, C. G. (1948). *Phys. Rev.* **73**, 830.

Yarnell, J. L., Arnold, J. L., Bendt, P. J. and Kerr, E. C. (1959). *Phys. Rev.* **113**, 1379.

Zinn, W. H. (1947). *Phys. Rev.* **71**, 752.

CHAPTER 4

Neutron Sources and Detectors

S. J. Cocking and F. J. Webb

Nuclear Physics Division, Atomic Energy Research Establishment, Harwell, England

4.1 Introduction.. 142
4.2 Research Reactors and their Neutron Beam Holes....................... 142
4.3 Collimators for Neutron Beams....................................... 146
4.4 Moderator Temperature.. 148
4.5 Pulsed Reactors.. 150
4.6 Electron Linear Accelerator Neutron Sources......................... 152
4.7 Comparison of Pulsed and Continuous Neutron Sources................. 155
4.8 Cold Neutron Moderators in Reactors................................ 158
4.9 Cold Moderating Materials.. 160
4.10 Brief Theory of Cold Moderators 162
4.11 Liquid Hydrogen Moderators in Low Flux Reactors.................... 164
4.12 Liquid Hydrogen Moderators in High Flux Reactors................... 165
4.13 Increases in Cold Neutron Flux..................................... 167
4.14 Safety of Liquid Hydrogen Moderators............................... 169
4.15 General Properties of Thermal Neutron Detectors.................... 171
4.16 Boron Trifluoride (BF_3) Filled Proportional Counters 175
4.17 Helium-3 Filled Proportional Counters.............................. 178
4.18 Boron or Lithium (with Zinc Sulphide) Scintillation Detectors...... 178
4.19 Scintillating Glasses Containing Boron or Lithium 184
4.20 Other Detectors... 190
4.21 Summary of Detector Performance................................... 190
References.. 191

List of Symbols

A	Area of source viewed by beam hole	P	Filling pressure of BF_3 counter
a	Radius of wire in BF_3 counter	R	Radius of moderator sphere
B	Background counts/minute	r	Radial position
c	Radius of tube in BF_3 counter	S	Scattered neutron counts/minute
d	Length of beam hole in reactor	T	Temperature of moderator
E_γ	Energy of γ-ray	T_n	Temperature of neutrons after n collisions in moderator
E_e	Energy of Compton electron due to γ-rays of energy E_γ	T_0	Temperature of neutrons incident on moderator
G	Gain in neutron intensity due to total reflection from walls of collimator	t	Thickness of moderator
h	Height of collimator	V	Voltage applied to counter
L	Length of collimator	w	Width of collimator slot
N_i	Density of nuclei of type i	α	Mobility of electron
n_i	Average number of collisions with nuclei of type i in moderator	ϵ	Fraction of absorbed neutrons producing detector pulses

4.1 Introduction

The wide range of investigations discussed in this book has been made possible by the development of the moderated nuclear fission reactor. Progress in reactor engineering since 1945 has led to successive increases totalling a factor of several hundred in the thermal neutron fluxes available to the experimenter. This has resulted in increasingly detailed and sophisticated investigations, illustrated by the steps from early measurements of total scattering cross-section to the angular variation of scattered intensity and finally to the detailed energy analysis of scattered neutrons. The range of these experiments has been outlined in previous chapters and will be discussed in detail later.

Progress has also been made in defining and satisfying the experimenter's needs for special beam reactors. One result is the very high flux reactor ($\sim 10^{15}$ neutrons cm^{-2} sec^{-1}) designed specifically for the extraction of neutron beams (Kouts, 1963). Other developments have been aimed at modifying the mean energy of the neutron spectrum at the experimenter's source position in the reactor; the low temperature moderator discussed in this chapter has been used for several years.

In addition the pulsed reactor and the accelerator pulsed neutron source have begun to yield results in scattering measurements. While most work so far has been carried out using the continuous nuclear reactor, these other sources are being rapidly developed and may compete in the future. A description of pulsed sources operating at present is given in this chapter and a brief comparison of the pulsed sources and continuous reactor is made.

Due to the high interaction cross-section of low energy neutrons with boron and lithium the detection of thermal neutrons is fortunately rather easy, detection efficiencies from 20 % to nearly 100 % being possible. While the well known boron trifluoride proportional counter satisfies the needs of most experimenters, the time-of-flight method calls for a well defined position of neutron detection as well as a high detection efficiency. This need has resulted in the development of the scintillation detector using a very thin neutron absorbing layer. The scintillation and proportional counters which have found application in experimental studies are discussed in this chapter and their use in modern apparatus is illustrated.

4.2 Research Reactors and their Neutron Beam Holes

Neutron inelastic scattering studies have been made using reactors with maximum fluxes ranging from $\sim 10^{12}$ neutrons cm^{-2} sec^{-1} to $\sim 5 \times 10^{14}$ neutrons cm^{-2} sec^{-1}. So many different reactor types are now employed in this research that it is impossible to give here a comprehensive survey.

Instead the example of the N.R.U. reactor at Chalk River, Canada, is used to illustrate the general features of greatest importance to the experimenter. Since scattering experiments are performed with neutron beams taken from the reactor our main interest will be in the beam holes. In Fig. 4.1 the arrangement of experimental holes in the N.R.U. reactor is shown. This large (200 MW) heavy water cooled and moderated reactor has a central flux of 3×10^{14} neutrons cm^{-2} sec^{-1}. There are 27 horizontal beam holes mostly of 30 cm or 15 cm diameter. These holes extend into the thermal

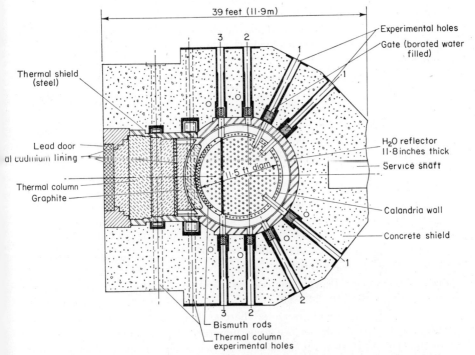

FIG. 4.1. The arrangement of horizontal beam holes in the N.R.U. reactor. Beam tubes reach (1) to the reactor core, (2) to the light water reflector, (3) through the reactor core.

column, to the light water reflector, into the core of the reactor via a re-entrant thimble or in the case of two holes pass right across the reactor through the core. Such arrangements are found in most thermal reactors which provide for beam research. In research reactors operating at present, the core and reflector design is such that the maximum thermal flux is near the core where unfortunately the fast neutron flux is also high. At greater distances from the fuel elements, while the fast flux falls off the thermal flux is also attenuated. Most experimenters have preferred to use beams from the central core of the reactor and use subsidiary means such as crystal filters (Section 3·17) or rotating shutters (Section 2.9) to reduce the unwanted fast neutron and γ-radiation. This fall-off in thermal flux away from the fuel elements is particularly evident in light water moderated reactors due to the short moderation length of fast neutrons in light water and also to the appreciable absorption cross section of hydrogen.

Very high flux reactors (maximum thermal flux approximately 10^{15} neutrons $cm^{-2}\,sec^{-1}$) are now being designed. The core geometry with these reactors is designed so that the thermal flux peaks in a moderator which is separated from the undermoderated core. The core may surround a central zone of moderator in which the thermal flux peaks (this is called the "flux trap" design) or alternatively the thermal flux is arranged to peak in a reflector surrounding the core. The later design is used at the Brookhaven High Flux Reactor (HFBR) which has been described by Kouts (1963). Improvements in the thermal-to-fast flux ratios are expected over present reactor designs.

Of more interest for beam research than the flux at the inner end of the beam hole is the flux at the point outside the reactor at which measurements are made. This reduced flux is estimated by multiplying the flux at the source by the solid angle subtended by the source area viewed, i.e. by $A/4\pi d^2$ where A is the area of the source viewed and d is the distance from the experimental position to the source block. The beam hole sizes and distances from the source block vary greatly for different reactors and beam holes. Typical figures are $A = 100$ cm^2, $d = 500$ cm, giving a solid angle factor 3×10^{-5}. The solid angle subtended by the source block may also be limited by necessary restriction of the angular divergence of the emerging beam as in the use of crystal spectrometers, for example, discussed in Section 1.1 and in detail in Section 3.3. Table 4.1 summarizes the parameters of some reactors covering a wide range of thermal fluxes and gives examples of the beam tubes available to the experimenters. The calculated performance of the High Flux Beam Reactor is given; other reactors have all been used as neutron sources in scattering studies and experimental equipment associated with these, and similar reactors, is discussed in Chapters 2, 3 and 4.

The use of beam holes passing right through the reactor often has advantages. Since the experiment does not "view" directly the fuel elements, the γ-radiation and fast neutron fluxes are reduced. The experimenter then arranges his own scattering "source block" in the hole. This arrangement has been used on the N.R.U. reactor by Zimmerman et al. (1961) who describe a source block of heavy water in an aluminium container. Dyer et al. (1959) describe tests made on a thin light water slab used as a source block in a through hole of the PLUTO reactor at Harwell. They find a maximum emergent flux when the water slab is set at a grazing angle of 18°

TABLE 4.1

Reactor and site	Power (MW)	Maximum thermal flux (neutrons cm^{-2} sec^{-1})	Moderator fuel and reflector	Horizontal beam holes				
				Number	Position	Thermal flux	Size (cm)	Length* (cm)
BEPO Harwell England	6·5	$1·5 \times 10^{12}$	graphite enriched U graphite	>30	to core	$0·1$-1×10^{12}	typically 10×10	typically 400–600
R1 Stockholm Sweden	0·6	$2·2 \times 10^{12}$	D$_2$O natural U graphite	1+2+2† 3+1+3 1+2+2+1	to core to reflector through core	$0·2$-$0·7 \times 10^{12}$ $0·5$-$2·2 \times 10^{12}$ $0·5$-$2·0 \times 10^{12}$	$15 \times 15 : 7$ diam. $17 \times 8·5 : 17 \times 16$ $5·6$ and $7·4$ diam.	285 380 380–450
BGRR Brookhaven U.S.A.	20	2×10^{13}	graphite enriched U graphite	>30	to core	$0·3$-2×10^{13}	typically $9·5 \times 9·5$	typically 360
EL3 Saclay France	15	1×10^{14}	D$_2$O enriched U D$_2$O and graphite	4+2 10+2 1	to core to reflector	$1·3$-$7·8 \times 10^{12}$ $2·8$-$4·3 \times 10^{13}$ $2·7 \times 10^{13}$	$18·4 \times 18·4$ 15 and 25 diam. 19×19	385 330
DIDO Harwell England	15	2×10^{14}	D$_2$O enriched U graphite	1+1+6 10 1	to core to reflector through core	3-5×10^{13} $0·5 \times 10^{13}$ $1·4 \times 10^{14}$	10–25 diam. 15 diam. 10×5	290 230 330
N.R.U. Chalk River Canada	200	3×10^{14}	D$_2$O natural U D$_2$O and H$_2$O	9 15 2	to core to reflector through core	5×10^{13} 5×10^{13} 3×10^{14}	30 diam. 15 diam. $8·3 \times 11·4$	440 340 460
MTR Idaho Falls U.S.A.	40	$4·8 \times 10^{14}$	H$_2$O enriched U Be and graphite	6 7 1	to core to reflector through core	3-4×10^{14} $0·1$-$1·0 \times 10^{13}$ 2×10^{14}	15 diam. 10–20 diam. $12·3 \times 12·3$	490 400–450 500
HFBR Brookhaven U.S.A.	40	$7·5 \times 10^{14}$	D$_2$O enriched U D$_2$O	8 1	in reflector outer reflector	$\sim 7·5 \times 10^{14}$ 5×10^{14}	9 diam. 30 diam.	346–376 326

* Length from end of hole to reactor face
† This notation indicates a number of different sizes of holes in the " to core " category, etc.

to the emergent beam. In these high flux reactors the water from the source block must be circulated through a cooler to remove the heat produced by reactor radiation, principally by γ-radiation.

4.3 Collimators for Neutron Beams

Detailed design of beam hole collimators depends on the configuration of beam holes and several examples of collimator design are given in the references quoted at the end of this chapter. The general features of collimator design are first, fix the required collimation angles for the beam, secondly,

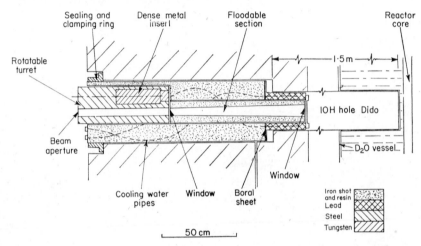

Fig. 4.2. An example of a neutron beam collimator used in a reactor beam hole.

define this collimation path using appropriate shielding materials and finally, provide some means of shutting off the beam. Figure 4.2 illustrates these points with the example of a beam collimator used with crystal spectrometer equipment at the high flux reactor DIDO. The hole in the reactor shield is stepped, as is usual, to prevent streaming of unwanted radiation through gaps between the collimator and the reactor shield. The inner end of the collimator is made of lead to absorb most of the γ-rays from the reactor core which would lead to troublesome heating in the rest of the shielding. This lead plug is cooled by circulating water. The main shielding plug consists of a steel tube filled with iron shot and resin. This mixture forms an efficient shield against fast neutrons and γ-rays. At the inner end of this main plug a sheet of "boral" (boron carbide and aluminium powder sandwiched between aluminium sheets) absorbs the thermal neutrons outside the collimated beam. This prevents heating of the resin by thermal neutron absorption; the boral is fixed in good thermal contact with the cooled lead section. The collimated beam may be shut off by flooding the tapering section of the collimator with water. The water scatters and absorbs the fast and thermal neutron beam but is insufficient to stop the γ-rays. The outer section of the collimator can therefore be rotated to present a shield of heavy metal (tungsten) and steel in the beam in place of the open beam tube. In application with its crystal spectrometer this beam tube contains further collimators of the Söller type.

At the N.R.U. reactor a borated-water filled vessel (or gate) is installed in the reactor shield at each beamhole (Fig. 4.1). This vessel can be lowered remotely to shut off the neutron beam. This provision simplifies the design of beam collimators which need only provide a massive insert to attenuate γ-rays to shut off the beam. Materials used for shielding in collimators include lead, steel, concrete, steel-loaded concrete, boron-loaded resins and wood. A collimator made of wood (oak) with a lead inner end was used in the high flux reactor at N.R.U. The inner part of this inexpensive collimator had, however, become structurally unsound after two years in the reactor.

The beam collimator illustrated in Fig. 4.2 is one in which the neutron beam spectrum is not altered in the collimator. Other collimators are designed to include beam filters, either single crystals or polycrystal filters (Chapter 3), together with provision for cooling by liquid nitrogen. The more complicated arrangements for low temperature moderators in beam holes are discussed in Sections 4.11 and 4.12.

The total reflection of low energy neutrons by walls is a well-known effect in collimators which attempt to define very closely ($<1°$) the angular divergence of the beam. Total reflection of neutrons by walls of refractive index μ takes place for scattering at angles less than the critical angle θ_c given by

$$\theta_c = \sqrt{2(1-\mu)} \tag{4.1}$$

where

$$(1-\mu) = \frac{\lambda^2 N b}{2\pi}$$

N is the number of atoms per cm³ and b the coherent scattering length of the wall. The critical angles for nickel and copper are 0·017 and 0·014 radians respectively, for neutrons of wavelength 10Å.

Maier-Leibnitz and Springer (1963) have discussed the use of totally reflecting collimator tubes for low energy neutrons. More neutrons are transmitted by total reflection than pass straight down the tubes. They show that for a smooth, straight tube the gain in intensity G, is given by

$$G = \frac{4\theta_c^2 L^2}{hw} \quad \text{if} \quad \theta_c > \frac{h}{L} \quad \text{and} \quad \frac{w}{L} \tag{4.2}$$

L, h and w are the length, height and width of the tube, respectively.

Taking $L = 7$ m and $hw = 10$ cm², a copper tube gives a gain of 40 for 10 Å neutrons. The beam divergence is then $\sim 2\theta_c = 2 \cdot 8 \times 10^{-2}$ radians instead of $\sim 0 \cdot 5 \times 10^{-2}$ radians. Total reflection of long wavelength neutrons may be used to conduct these neutrons along a curved reflecting tube to remove them from the direct beam of high energy neutrons, which are not reflected. Such a neutron conducting tube has been installed at the FRM reactor at Munich (Christ and Springer, 1962). The copper tube, 7 m long, 3·4 cm diameter, is bent into an arc of radius 310 m. A gain in intensity of about 40 over that expected from geometrical paths if the tube were straight was found for neutrons of 10^{-3} eV. The exit of the "conducted" beam was moved 8 cm from the direct beam to provide a clean beam of low energy neutrons. The extension of totally reflecting collimators to the provision of polarized neutron beams using walls of magnetized iron has been pursued by Møller et al. (1963).

4.4 Moderator Temperature

The thermal neutron flux distribution in equilibrium with a moderator at temperature T, expressed as flux per energy interval dE at energy E may be written down immediately from equations (1.5) and (1.6) (Section 1.1), as

$$n_f(E)\mathrm{d}E = 2n_F \frac{E}{(kT)^2} \mathrm{e}^{-\frac{E}{kT}} \mathrm{d}E \qquad (4.3)$$

Reactors used for neutron beam experiments have moderator temperatures in the range 30° to 150°C. Heavy or light water moderated research reactors usually operate at temperatures near 60°C. Graphite moderated reactors are usually operated near 150°C to avoid the complication of Wigner energy storage. Thus the maximum flux of thermal neutrons for moderators at these temperatures is in the neighbourhood of 0·03 eV, as shown by Fig. 4.3, the flux falling off rapidly at higher and lower energies. It has proved difficult to perform scattering experiments when the flux is less than about one-tenth of the peak flux, that is with neutron energies below 5×10^{-3} eV and above 0·2 eV.

It is clear that an increase of flux might be achieved if the reactor moderator temperature could be varied to suit any particular experiment. For example, Fig. 4.3 shows how the flux of "cold" neutrons ($< 5 \times 10^{-3}$ eV) is increased if the Maxwell distribution is shifted from 295°K to 77°, 20° or 4·2°K, corresponding to the boiling points of nitrogen, hydrogen and helium respectively. At 5×10^{-3} eV an order of magnitude increase is possible, and much higher increases are possible at lower neutron energies. It was suggested by Egelstaff et al. (1955) that since liquid hydrogen has a small slowing down length, due to its low atomic mass and high scattering cross-section, as little as 200 ml of liquid hydrogen situated near the centre of a reactor would form a useful cold neutron source. Such a moderator was first installed in the low power reactor BEPO at Harwell (Butterworth *et al.*, 1957).

In view of the considerable importance of enhancing available fluxes for cold neutron measurements, liquid hydrogen moderators and other cold neutron sources will be dealt with in some detail in Sections 4.8–4.14, where the factors affecting their efficiency will be discussed.

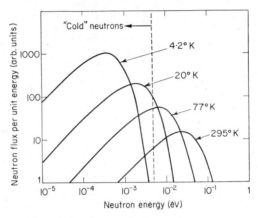

FIG. 4.3. Maxwell distributions for low moderator temperatures.

For experiments at neutron energies above 0·1 eV it would be desirable to have a high temperature moderator, operating at perhaps 1000–2000°C, and the design and performance of such sources has been discussed by Egelstaff, Moffitt and Saunderson (1964). The performance of a high temperature moderator can be estimated by the methods outlined in Section 4.10 for cold moderators. The theory used is in fact more applicable to a hot moderator for the assumption that the moderating atoms behave as heavy gas atoms is more pertinent. Applying equation (4.6) to the case of a 20 cm sphere of beryllium at 1100°C surrounded by a heavy water moderator yields an observable neutron beam temperature of 960°K. A 20 cm sphere of either graphite or beryllium oxide at 2400°C would on these theories yield a neutron temperature of 1600°K.

Figure 4.4 shows Maxwell distributions corresponding to 320°K, 960°K and 1600°K, merging into the same $1/E$ slowing down spectrum. The $1/E$ spectrum is assumed to fall rapidly to zero at 0·1 eV. The spectra shown in Fig. 4.4 can be represented by the equation

$$n_f(E)\mathrm{d}E = A\left[\frac{E}{(kT)^2}\,\mathrm{e}^{-\frac{E}{kT}} + \eta\cdot\frac{1}{E}\right]\mathrm{d}E \tag{4.4}$$

The value of η chosen is 0·0286 for $E>0·1$ eV and zero for $E<0·1$ eV, which is typical for a high flux beam hole in a reactor; A is an arbitrary constant. If a very large $1/E$ contribution is allowed the value of a hot neutron source is marginal, but in source positions where a very low background of $1/E$ neutrons exists the gain in using a hot neutron source can be much higher than shown in Fig. 4.4.

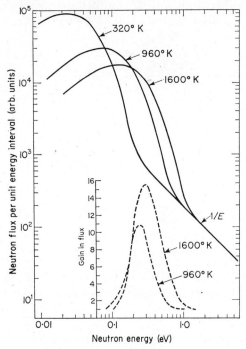

FIG. 4.4. Maxwell distributions for high moderator temperatures (Egelstaff, Moffitt and Saunderson, 1964). Insert shows ratio of 960°K and 1600°K spectra to 320°K.

The inset to Fig. 4.4 shows that the intensity gain over a moderator at room temperature which can be expected from a 960°K Maxwell distribution is a factor 11 at 0·25 eV, and that the 1600°K Maxwell distribution yields a maximum gain of 15 at 0·3 eV. After considering the moderating, physical and radiation damage properties of several materials, Egelstaff et al. (1964) conclude that a BeO moderator heated to 1400°C by the reactor's radiation is the most suitable hot moderator.

4.5 Pulsed Reactors

In applying the time-of-flight method short bursts of neutrons of about 10μ sec length, separated by periods of several milliseconds, are selected from a continuous beam of neutrons from a reactor. The continuous reactor flux is therefore very inefficiently used. Indeed the continuing neutron beam between bursts provides an unwanted background in the experiment. Rotating collimators, as used in the phased rotor apparatus described in Chapter 2, have essentially the purpose of switching off the reactor beam except when a burst is to be selected by the main neutron choppers. Clearly important advantages could be gained if the reactor itself were pulsed, the mean power level for the same flux in the pulses being reduced by a factor of perhaps 100 compared with continuously operating reactor. Further, the slow neutron burst, in passing over a short flight path, becomes separated in time from the burst of prompt fast neutrons and γ-rays.

Several thermal neutron reactors have been pulsed, though not specifically designed for pulsed operation. Due to the safety hazard associated with very short rise times of the reactivity and to the long life of the neutrons in thermal reactors, the pulses from such operation are long. McReynolds (1962) has summarized experience of pulsing thermal reactors and gives figures for the pulse width at half-height of 3·5 msec for the homogeneous uranyl sulphate solution reactor (KEWB), 15 msec for the swimming pool reactor with uranium–aluminium plates in light water (SPERT), and 10·5 msec for the solid homogeneous uranium zirconium hydride reactor (TRIGA). While the integrated neutron intensity in each pulse is very high ($\sim 10^{18}$ neutrons/pulse) the width of the pulse is too large for use with conventional time-of-flight apparatus. However, Maier-Leibnitz (1962) has suggested the use of a 100 m flight path with a pulsed TRIGA Mk II reactor to give a velocity resolution of 15 % with neutrons of 1000 m/sec (4Å). The pulse repetition rate is only several per hour so that electronic equipment for use with such infrequent intense neutron bursts would need special consideration. Pulsed thermal reactors have not been used for thermal neutron scattering experiments.

Pulses of thermal neutrons have, however, been produced using pulsed fast reactors, the neutrons being moderated to thermal energies outside the reactor core. The pulsed fast reactor IBR-1 at Dubna, U.S.S.R., is described by Blokhin et al. (1961). In this unique device, shown in layout in Figure 4·5, the reactor consists of a fixed core of plutonium rods in a cube of side about 20 cm and moving cores of uranium-235 mounted on two rotating disks. The two disks carry 7·4 % and 0·4 % of the reactivity of the whole reactor, which becomes supercritical when the two moving cores pass simultaneously through the fixed core. The disks are mechanically connected through a variable drive so that the smaller disk can be rotated at sub-multiples of the speed of the larger. In this way the period between pulses can be varied without changing the characteristics of each burst. Typical operation with the larger disk (diameter 1·10 m) rotated at 5000 rev/min yields neutron bursts with half width of 36 μsec. Operating with a mean power level of 1 kW the total neutron output is 5×10^{13} neutrons/sec. This reactor uses forced air cooling.

The application of IBR-1 as a thermal neutron source, has been described by Bondarenko *et al.* (1963). A slab of paraffin 5 cm thick placed close to the reactor core yields a burst of thermal neutrons of 135 μsec half width. A narrow burst is selected from this spectrum using a mechanical chopper phased with the reactor pulses. The velocity spectrum of neutrons

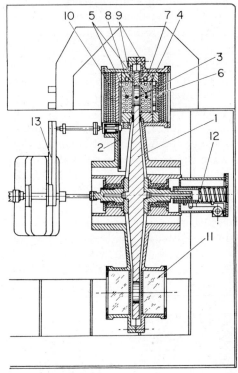

FIG. 4.5. The pulsed reactor at Dubna, U.S.S.R. (Blokhin *et al.*, 1961). (1) Rotating disc; (2) auxiliary disk; (3) main insert; (4) plutonium rods; (5) accident rod; (6) coarse control; (7) automatic control rod; (8) hand control rod; (9) side reflector; (10) end reflector; (11) safety glass; (12) safety mechanism for main insert; (13) reducing drive for the auxiliary insert.

after scattering from the sample placed after the chopper is measured by time-of-flight over a flight path which can be varied between 5 m and 45 m. Measurements using this machine by Bajorek *et al.* (1963) and Golikov *et al.* (1963) represent the first reported studies of the inelastic scattering of thermal neutrons using the pulsed reactor technique.

4.6 Electron Linear Accelerator Neutron Sources

Another pulsed neutron source is based on the electron linear accelerator (linac). Electron linacs produce neutrons in two stages. First the electrons are stopped by a target of high atomic number, lead, tungsten, or uranium, to make γ-rays. These γ-rays are then absorbed, often in the same target, to produce neutrons by (γ,n) or (γ,f) reactions. The target could in principle be simply a block of uranium to stop the electrons and produce γ-rays and the resulting neutrons. With the large power dissipation in the targets of the largest linacs, a more elaborate design becomes necessary. The electron beam of perhaps 30 MeV and 1 A in the pulse may have a cross-section less than 1 cm². Pulses of 5 μsec length with a repetition frequency of perhaps 200/sec require up to 30 kW mean power to be dissipated in a few cm³ of target. A stream of mercury or a rotating tungsten wheel have therefore been used to

TABLE 4.2

Linear accelerator	Pulse repetition frequency (per sec)	Electron energy (MeV)	Peak electron current (mA)	Pulse width (μsec)
Harwell, England	50–700	30	< 1000	0·25–2
Saclay, France	1–500	28	< 500	0·05–2
General Atomic, San Diego, U.S.A.	7·5–700	28	∼ 200	0·5–5
Rensselaer Institute, Troy, U.S.A	7·5–700	35	800	0·1–4·5

stop the electrons, and the γ-rays absorbed in a surrounding water-cooled uranium target to produce neutrons. The Harwell linac has a more complicated target. The electron target is surrounded by a subcritical assembly of ^{235}U (the "booster"), which provides, by cascade processes, a tenfold multiplication of the neutron output.

Electron lines have, to date, been employed as pulsed neutron sources principally for studies in the neutron energy range between 1 eV and 500 eV. Here the very short pulses allow high resolution measurements using the time of flight method. It has, however, been used for thermal neutron scattering experiments by McReynolds and Whittemore (1962).

The parameters of four electron linacs given in Table 4.2 are taken from a survey of electron linear accelerators by Bergere (1961) and from Gaerttner et al. (1962) for the Rensselaer instrument. As these accelerators are being developed, more recent operating conditions of electron energy and current may be higher than those given. For electron energies of 28 MeV or greater, the number of fast neutrons produced is approximately $2·5 \times 10^{15}$ neutrons/

sec per MW electron power. McReynolds and Whittemore (1962) have described experiments with the General Atomic linac using an electron beam of 28 MeV and peak current 80 mA; the peak neutron production is then $\sim 10^{16}$ neutrons/sec. They used 120 pulses/sec of 5 μsec width giving an average neutron production of 6×10^{12} neutrons/sec.

To slow down the primary neutrons of several MeV to energies below 1 eV, the target is surrounded by a moderator, usually a hydrogenous moderator such as polythene or water. The γ-ray background during the time that the

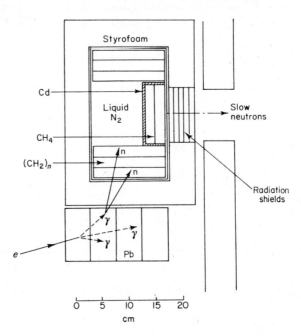

Fig. 4.6. The two-stage moderator for the linac neutron source (McReynolds and Whittemore, 1962).

electron burst is falling on the linac target will be severe. By using a moderator displaced laterally from the target, so that the detectors do not view the target directly, and by interposing massive shielding, the γ-ray background may be reduced somewhat, though at the expense of some neutron flux. However, it may be necessary to "pulse off" the neutron detectors during the linac electron pulse, so that they are insensitive to the γ-flash. Slow neutrons will arrive at the detectors some hundreds of microseconds after the γ-flash. If scintillation counters are used, added precautions must be taken, as the γ-flash may excite phosphorescence in the scintillators, lasting for several milliseconds.

Linacs produce very short pulses of fast neutrons but after moderation the pulses are inevitably broadened. In order to attain maximum thermal flux the target would be surrounded by a thick moderator, about 20 cm of water for example. The fast neutrons would then be moderated to thermal energies in about 20 μsec but the intensities would die slowly with a decay period of about 200 μsec. Use of a thin moderator reduces the decay period as neutrons have a shorter lifetime before they escape from the moderator; the number reaching thermal energy is then reduced, however. Most linacs installed are designed for work with neutrons of greater than 1 eV and have used thin moderators. Poole (1964) has suggested that a water target, 5 cm thick, yields only 9 % of the neutrons in a Maxwellian spectrum of thermal energies with a decay period of about 50 μsec.

McReynolds and Whittemore (1962) have devised the two-stage moderator shown in Fig. 4.6 which combines the advantages of a large moderator to reduce neutron leakage before thermalization and a small moderator to produce short pulses. The pulsed linac electron beam is directed at the outer lead block to produce the fast neutrons. These are slowed down to near 1 eV in about 1 μsec and can pass through the cadmium sheet into the smaller inner moderator where they are moderated to thermal energies with a few more collisions. Their life time as thermal neutrons in this moderator is short because of its small dimensions; the cadmium is a complete absorber for neutrons below $\sim$0·3 eV. Similarly, neutrons which spend many microseconds in the larger moderator and therefore attain thermal energies are prevented by the cadmium from broadening the output pulse at thermal energies. Pulse widths of about 20 μsec are achieved by this method. The introduction of liquid nitrogen to cool the moderator reduces the flux at energies above 0·05 eV but enhances the flux at low energies (see Section 4.4) typically by a factor 4 at 0·005 eV. The styrofoam insulation reduces the heat leak from the assembly. McReynolds and Whittemore (1962) have also used the linac installation to study moderation to low temperatures by water and liquid hydrogen using a simple cryostat to cool the moderator.

4.7 Comparison of Pulsed and Continuous Neutron Sources

The first important difference between these two sources is the efficiency of moderation of the primary fast neutrons to thermal energies. Moderation efficiency in continuous reactors approaches 100 % while for the pulsed sources the efficiency is low. In using the linear accelerator at the General Atomic Laboratory the moderator is placed at about 20 cm from the electron target. This geometrical arrangement allows the line of sight of the experiment to avoid the target so that the "γ-flash" does not cause undesirable background. Due to the size (20 cm side cube) of reactor core the moderator used at the Dubna pulsed reactor is at a comparable mean distance from the fast neutron source. The thin moderators used with these instruments moderate only about 10% of the primary neutrons to thermal energies. Thus the thermal flux at the moderators is given by

$$\text{thermal neutrons (neutrons cm}^{-2}\text{ sec}^{-1}) = 2 \times 10^{-5} \times \text{fast neutrons/sec}$$

This factor is used in deriving the thermal neutron fluxes given in Table 4.3. Table 4.3 also gives the width of thermal neutron bursts provided by the

TABLE 4.3

Source	Pulse repetition frequency (per sec)	Fast neutron pulse width (μsec)	Fast neutrons/sec		Thermal neutron flux (neutrons cm^{-2} sec^{-1})		Thermal neutron pulse width (μsec)
			Peak	Average	Peak	Average	
Dubna fast reactor	8·3	36	$1·5 \times 10^{17}$	$4·5 \times 10^{13}$	3×10^{12}	9×10^8	135
General Atomic linac	120	5	1×10^{16}	6×10^{12}	2×10^{11}	$1·2 \times 10^8$	20–50

sources. The long burst width of the pulsed reactor has been measured at the Dubna machine. The narrower burst width quoted here for the linac assumes the use of a special moderator as described in Section 4.6.

These sources have been combined with a flight path and phased rotor to select a narrow band of neutron velocities by Bondarenko et al. (1963) with the pulsed reactor, and by Whittemore and Danner (1963) with the linac. In this mode of operation the pulsed source may be compared, in principle, to the first chopper of a phased rotor system as described by Egelstaff et al. (1960). The thermal neutron pulse width of the chopper, 14 μsec, is however appreciably less than that of the pulsed sources (Table 4.3). In order to compare the beam intensities selected by the three instruments in similar experiments we must arrange the geometries of the instruments so that the angular divergence of the incident beams and the velocity ranges selected are similar. The second condition imposes a long flight path of 26 m for the pulsed reactor to give a velocity resolution equal to that achieved with the Chalk River phased rotor apparatus. The angular spread of the beam for the pulsed reactor instrument is then 0·7°. When the geometries of the instruments are arranged for equal angular and velocity resolutions, the two pulsed sources yield comparable intensities per cm² of selected beam and the phased rotor instrument gives about fifty times this intensity. The flight path from the scattering specimens to the detector for time-of-flight analysis of scattered neutrons must also be made longer for the broad pulsed instrument in order to retain the same velocity resolution as the phased chopper. The detector area required for acceptable detection intensity then becomes large (1000–2000 cm^2) and the provision of many detectors at different angles of scatter becomes cumbersome.

The discussion so far has related to neutrons which achieve thermal equilibrium with the moderator. The life time in the moderator of higher energy neutrons is smaller. Thus for these neutrons the burst widths will be shorter and the need for long flight paths correspondingly less. The shorter fast neutron burst ($\sim$1 μsec) available from the linac can here be used to advantage over the longer burst of the pulsed reactor (36 μsec). Thus in selecting neutrons in the energy region 0·1–1 eV the linac can be superior to the use of a continuous reactor. This point has been more fully discussed by Webb (1965). Further, the life time of neutrons with energies near 0·025 eV, which are in equilibrium with a moderator at room temperature, will fall if the moderator is cooled. Since the number of neutrons at this energy will also fall off as the moderator temperature is reduced, it follows that there is a moderator temperature which gives the greatest advantage for the use of the pulsed source at a given neutron energy. Thus the performance of a moderator may be optimized by choice of both its geometry and its temperature. Ribon and Michaudon (1961) have discussed the optimizing conditions for moderators used with linacs for neutron energies of 1 eV and above. No such studies have been reported for the energy region 0·005–1 eV. McReynolds and Whittemore (1962) have, however, discussed the properties of various materials for moderating neutrons to very low energies ($<$0·005 eV).

The technology and engineering of electron linear accelerators is progressing rapidly and also further developments of the pulsed reactor are to be expected. These advances combined with further experience of moderator design may make the pulsed sources competitive with the high flux conventional reactor over a wider range of low energy neutron studies. The pulsed sources have two potentially important advantages which result from the source being switched off between pulses. First the mean power dissipated in low temperature moderators, as discussed in this chapter, is lower than that required for an equivalent neutron flux in a continuous reactor by a factor of order one hundred. This yields valuable simplification in design and operation. Secondly, the background of fast neutrons at the time of arrival at the detectors of slow neutrons should be lower than for the continuous source. However, the average fast flux at the pulsed source (Table 4.3) is not markedly lower than that at a conventional reactor source block. It is therefore important to prevent these neutrons from being distributed in time by many reflections from surrounding materials.

4.8 Cold Neutron Moderators in Reactors

In Section 4.4 we mentioned the need to vary the temperature of the reactor neutron spectrum. So far the only extensive work which has been carried out on this subject has been concerned with lowering the neutron temperature in order to increase the flux of cold neutrons. We shall make some general remarks on several factors concerning cold moderator performance before proceeding to a discussion of particular results.

One important factor determining the efficiency of a cold neutron source is the disposition of the moderator relative to the core of the reactor. Three common arrangements of core and source block are shown in Fig. 4.7.

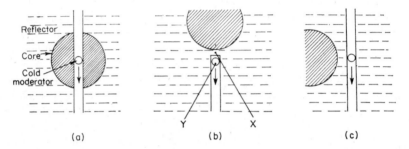

Fig. 4.7. The geometrical arrangements of reactor core and cold moderator.

In BEPO or BR1 the core surrounds the cold moderator (Fig. 4.7(a)) which is therefore immersed in an isotropic flux of thermal neutrons. A large proportion of the neutrons emerging from the reactor will have been scattered from the surface of the cold moderator, and suffered only one or two collisions; comparatively few will have been transmitted through the body of the cold moderator. Hence one would not expect the neutron beam to have a spectrum corresponding to perfect thermal equilibrium at the temperature of the cold moderator.

The arrangement of EL3 or DIDO is shown in Fig. 4.7(b). Here the most intense neutron flux is behind the cold moderator, so transmission through the chamber will be more important. If the chamber is thin the proportion of neutrons transmitted will be high, but moderation to low temperatures will not be complete; hence there will be an optimum thickness of chamber for maximum cold neutron output. One must remember that if the chamber were absent the neutron beam would come from a point X inside the heavy water tank. When the chamber is full of liquid hydrogen or other moderator the effective source of the neutron beam will be a point Y inside the chamber. Now the thermal neutron flux at Y may be only half that at X, as Y is further from the reactor core. In this case the cold moderator needs to double the cold neutron component of the spectrum before the cold neutron beam emerging from the reactor begins to exceed its intensity in the absence of a cold moderator. This fact explains why the gains of cold neutron flux observed in EL3 and DIDO tend to be smaller than those observed in BEPO (Fig. 4.11) with its more spherically symmetrical geometry. In addition the cold source area may be smaller than the source area viewed in the absence of a cold moderator.

The case of a tangential hole (Fig. 4.7(c)), as in BR2 or in a TRIGA, may involve both of the above factors, and the cold neutron flux will depend on the precise position of the moderator relative to the reactor core.

It is usual to specify the efficiency of a cold moderator by the ratio of the cold neutron flux obtained from the cold moderator to that obtained in the absence of the cold moderator. However, this ratio becomes meaningless when comparing the performance of cold moderators in different reactors with different reactor moderator temperatures. The flux of cold neutrons in a reactor spectrum is approximately inversely proportional to the square of the moderator temperature. In general the lower the temperature of the reactor moderator, the larger the *intensity* of cold neutrons which can be obtained by the use of a low temperature moderator. A larger *gain* of cold neutron flux may be measured when a low temperature moderator is inserted in a high temperature reactor; a low temperature moderator may be more necessary in such a reactor.

The effect of the material of the reactor moderator, graphite, heavy water or light water, on the observed efficiency of a cold neutron source is complex. The most useful reactor moderator would be one of heavy atoms with a high scattering cross section and negligible absorption cross-section. If such a moderator were available a cold neutron scattered out of the cold moderator would be reflected back with little gain of energy, and there would be little leakage of cold neutrons except through the collimators. No such ideal moderating material exists. In the case of a graphite moderated reactor, cold neutrons scattered out of the cold moderator back into the graphite suffer several collisions with graphite atoms before they return to thermal equilibrium at the temperature of the reactor. On the other hand graphite has a relatively small scattering cross-section, and cold neutrons from the cold moderator will travel considerable distances before being scattered by the reactor moderator, so that the chance of their being scattered back into the cold moderator is small. In a light water reactor the opposite is true; cold neutrons returning into the reactor moderator will be warmed up in a few collisions, but due to the high scattering cross-section of hydrogen they will be scattered many times in a short distance and stand a relatively high chance of being scattered back into the cold moderator. A heavy water moderator would be intermediate between these two cases. None of these materials forms a good reflector for a cold moderator. Light water has the additional disadvantage of an appreciable absorption cross-section, which will lead to a flux depression in the neighbourhood of the cold moderator due to the high absorption of cold neutrons.

The diameter of the cold moderator is limited by the size of the hole in the reactor, but there is considerable latitude in the detailed design of the chamber, its shape and thickness. Ideally a shape analogous to a "black body furnace" should be most efficient, a large sphere of cold moderating material in an isotropic flux of thermal neutrons, with a relatively narrow channel from its centre to convey out a beam of neutrons in thermal equilibrium at the low temperature. But in practical cases this ideal geometry cannot be achieved and one uses neutrons scattered off the surface or transmitted through the moderator.

4.9 Cold moderating materials

For a material to be an efficient low temperature moderator it needs to fulfil several stringent conditions. A low absorption cross-section is necessary; deuterium, beryllium and graphite are good, hydrogen is just tolerable. A high scattering cross-section is necessary as space is severely limited. Hence deuterium, beryllium and graphite have severe disadvantages. Low atomic mass is useful, as it reduces the amount of γ-ray heating, though in hydrogen there is additional fast neutron heating. Also there must be some mechanism for abstracting small amounts of neutron energy; for at low neutron energies the moderator atoms are more or less strongly bound and the neutron can lose energy only by exciting molecular vibrations or rotations, or lattice vibrations. The cross-section for exciting lattice vibrations of small energy is too small to be important, and the energies of molecular vibrations lie well above cold neutron energies. Molecular rotations are the most important means of achieving moderation to energies below 0·005 eV (Egelstaff, 1957); but the rotational cross-sections in the liquid and solid state have not been widely investigated for low temperature moderators, although the early experiments of Butterworth et al. (1957) on methane and methyl alcohol demonstrated their importance. Experiments on liquid hydrogen (Whittemore and Danner, 1963; Whittemore, 1963) at $E_0 \sim 0·05$ eV do not give a conclusive answer on this point. Egelstaff, Haywood, Webb and Baston (1964) have shown that rotational transitions can be observed by neutron scattering from liquid and solid hydrogen at temperatures as low as 12°K.

Some of the results of Van Dingenen's (1962) systematic study of a number of different organic moderating materials are summarized in Table 4.4. The moderating materials were kept at 78°K, and T_n deduced from the position of the maximum of the spectrum for each material. Values for the logarithmic decrement ξ_0 were calculated using equation (4.5) and compared with the specific heat per proton for each material—only mean specific heat values were available for most of the materials. There appears to be a correlation between the values of ξ_0 and the values of the specific heat, which is a measure of the freedom of motion of the hydrogen atoms. This again suggests that for a material to be a good low temperature moderator free rotations must be present to abstract small quantities of energy from the neutrons.

TABLE 4.4

Moderator	Relative cold neutron output	Neutron temperature T_n	Estimated log decrement ξ_0	Specific heat per proton C_H
CH_4	1·00	101	0·308	2·44
CH_3OH	0·81	115	0·205	1·83
C_2H_5OH	0·72	149	0·097	1·67
$C_2H_5OC_2H_5$	0·67	128	0·166	1·75
NH_3	0·66	142	0·094	1·53
H_2O	0·61	150	0·095	1·58
C_6H_6	0·46	164	0·128	1·59

Clearly an efficient low temperature moderating material must have a small neutron absorption cross-section, for not only does absorption reduce the total neutron flux observed, but as absorbers obey a $1/v$ law the lower energy neutrons are absorbed preferentially. Van Dingenen and Hautecler (1960) showed this very clearly in experiments using methyl alcohol at 78°K as moderator mixed with various amounts of trichloroethylene as an absorber. Experiments on liquid hydrogen moderators (Jacrot, 1962; Webb and Pearce, 1963) suggest that absorption may play some part in controlling the cold neutron output.

Cold neutron sources used so far are all based on liquid hydrogen as a moderator. The advantages of liquid hydrogen are several; it (together with methane) is the most efficient moderator in small volumes, it is its own coolant, its high latent heat and thermal conductivity make it a useful heat transfer medium, it has a low viscosity enabling it to be fed through narrow pipes to the reactor centre, radiation heating is smaller than for other moderators and it presents no radiation damage problem. This combination of advantages is unique to liquid hydrogen: the disadvantage is its relatively high neutron absorption cross-section, but because of the small sized holes available in most reactors this has not yet proved the dominant limitation.

7

4.10 Brief Theory of Cold Moderators

Very little theoretical work has been published on the subject of cold neutron sources. Most authors have contented themselves with general remarks on what properties would make a substance an efficient moderator at low temperatures. Scattering and absorption cross-sections, atomic weight, molecular binding, and the presence or absence of low-lying energy levels which could abstract small amounts of energy from slow neutrons have been considered. By making the sweeping assumptions that (i) the atoms of the moderator behave as if free with respect to colliding neutrons of all energies, and (ii) many small energy transfers occur before a neutron emerges from the cold moderator, the general behaviour of a cold moderator may be predicted.

Van Dingenen (1962) has derived a simple expression for the mean temperature of neutrons emerging from a cold moderator, starting from Cohen's (1955) treatment of epithermal neutrons in a reactor. If T_0 is the temperature of neutrons incident on a moderator of temperature T, the neutrons emerge with a temperature

$$T_n = T_0 \exp\left(-\sum_i n_i \xi_{0i} \left|1 - T/T_n\right|\right) \tag{4.5}$$

where n_i is the average number of collisions between a neutron and nuclei of kind i (that is $n_i = t(N_i \sigma_s)_i$ where t is the moderator thickness and N_i is the density of nuclei of type i). ξ_{0i} is the average logarithmic energy decrement, $\ln E_i/E_n$, at absolute zero of the moderator considering nuclei of kind i.

In a reactor the equilibrium temperature of the neutrons may be appreciably above the moderator temperature, as the thermal neutron distribution is a dynamic balance between fast neutrons feeding the moderator, and slow neutrons leaking out or being absorbed. Similarly if a cold moderator is fed with thermal neutrons with energies corresponding to the temperature of the reactor moderator, the temperature of neutrons leaving the cold moderator will depend on the amount of leakage from its surface, that is, whether neutrons spend long enough in the cold moderator and suffer enough collisions to reach thermal equilibrium. Assuming values of ξ_0 and σ_s independent of neutron energy Van Dingenen was able to calculate Maxwell distributions in general agreement with his experimental results (Fig. 4.12). However, the experimental curves depart from Maxwellian shape for the lowest moderator temperatures.

Another theoretical approach has been to consider the variation of the mean neutron temperature inside the cold moderator (Webb, 1961). This is based on the work of Kottwitz (1960), who derived expressions for the neutron flux distribution in the neighbourhood of a temperature discontinuity in a moderator. Schofield (1960) extended this work and produced a generalized expression for the mean neutron temperature.

The simplest geometry resembling an actual installation is a sphere of cold moderator surrounded by reactor moderator in an isotropic thermal neutron flux. Assuming neutrons emerging from the cold moderator were last scattered at a distance d inside the sphere, equal to the neutron mean free path in the cold moderator $(d = 1/\sum_Y)$, the mean neutron temperature T_n is

$$T_n = T_Y + (T_X - T_Y)\frac{R}{R-d}\exp\left[-\frac{\sqrt{6M_Y}}{(M_Y+1)}\right]\bigg/\left[\frac{\sum_x}{\sum_Y}\cdot\frac{Y-1}{X+1}+1\right] \quad (4.6)$$

T_X and T_Y are the temperatures, and $\sum_X$ and $\sum_Y$ the macroscopic scattering cross-sections of the reactor moderator and the cold moderator respectively and

$$X = R\sum_x\frac{\sqrt{6M_x}}{M_x+1}$$

$$Y = R\sum_Y\frac{\sqrt{6M_Y}}{M_Y+1}$$

M_X and M_Y being the atomic masses of reactor moderator and cold moderator.

This theory gives a pictorial explanation of many observed results, but the quantitative agreement must not be pushed too far. Kottwitz's treatment assumes scattering from a gas of heavy atoms, where energy transfers are small and scattering isotropic, not from liquid hydrogen which has light atoms weakly bound so that energy transfers may be considerable. Nor is it

TABLE 4.5

Moderator temperature	4	20	77	90°K
Experimental neutron temperature	65$\pm$8	75$\pm$6·5	134$\pm$7	137$\pm$5°K
Neutron temperature from equation (4·6)	73	87	132	144
Neutron temperature from equation (4·5)	41	57	107	117

accurate to assume spherical symmetry, as in a practical case the channel in a reactor is always larger in diameter than the cold moderator itself. However, the theory gives at least a qualitative guide to how the cold neutron flux may be altered by varying the temperature, size or material of the cold moderator. In Table 4.5 are shown the early results of Butterworth et al. (1957) on the mean temperatures of neutrons emerging from a methane moderator at temperatures from 4° to 90° K, compared to the theoretical results. These results vary in the same manner as the temperatures calculated from equation (4.6). The temperatures calculated from formula (4.5) also vary linearly with moderator temperature, but are somewhat lower.

In the absence of complete measurements of the differential scattering cross-section of liquid hydrogen or other low temperature moderators it was not profitable to pursue the theoretical approach further. Our present knowledge of neutron scattering by liquid hydrogen and methane is discussed at length in Chapter 8.

4.11 Liquid Hydrogen Moderators in Low Flux Reactors

The first cold moderator using liquid hydrogen (Butterworth *et al.*, 1957) was installed in the reactor BEPO at Harwell in 1956, and with various minor modifications and replacements it provided a source of cold neutrons for neutron scattering experiments until 1961. Similar systems, employing bulk liquid hydrogen as coolant, have been installed in BR1 at Mol and FiRI at Helsinki. The moderator chamber of the BEPO apparatus is shown in Figure 4.8. It consisted of an annular cooling chamber, through which liquid

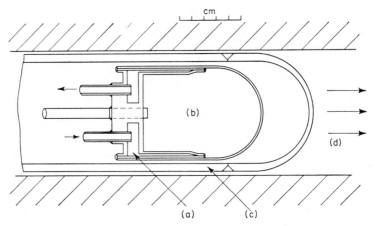

FIG. 4.8. The BEPO liquid hydrogen moderator chamber (Butterworth *et al.*, 1957). (a) Annular cooling chamber; (b) main moderator chamber; (c) vacuum case; (d) direction of neutrons leaving the reactor.

hydrogen was passed, partially surrounding the main volume which was filled with liquid hydrogen by condensation. The chamber was situated near the centre of the reactor, and was surrounded by a thick-walled vacuum case. Neutrons scattered out of the liquid in the direction (d) in Fig. 4.8 pass along a flight tube and through collimators to the scattering apparatus at the face of the reactor.

For experimental purposes the use of separate coolant and cold moderator systems, rather than using a single liquid hydrogen chamber, has considerable advantage. It is simple to vary either the coolant or the moderating material, and to investigate the moderating efficiencies of different substances at different temperatures. For everyday use as a cold neutron source the separate coolant and moderator have the advantage that the liquid hydrogen moderator can be kept under a pressure of a few atmospheres, so that the moderator chamber stays full of liquid hydrogen and free from bubbles. The only boiling takes place in the cooling space, which is comparatively small. Hence fluctuations of cold neutron flux are minimized.

The BR1 cold neutron source was similar to the BEPO design, but was installed in a vertical hole through the centre of the reactor, neutron scattering measurements being made in a shielded room underneath the reactor. The FiRI loop is situated in a tangent hole passing underneath the core of the TRIGA reactor. The holes in the three reactors were similar in size; BR1 was 8 cm in diameter, BEPO 10 cm and FiRI 15 cm. In no case did nuclear heating in the moderator chamber amount to more than 1 W, so most of the heat leakage was due to thermal radiation and conduction down supports. The consumption of liquid hydrogen in a low flux reactor installation should be 2 or 3 l/h, so the apparatus may be run for a day or more from a single 100-l storage vessel.

4.12 Liquid Hydrogen Moderators in High Flux Reactors

A liquid hydrogen moderator in a high flux reactor, such as EL3 at Saclay or DIDO at Harwell, presents an additional major problem, the problem of nuclear heating. This is caused by fast neutrons colliding with the hydrogen atoms, and by γ-rays absorbed in the liquid hydrogen and, more important, in the metal of its container. The amount of heating may vary widely depending on the location of the fuel elements in the reactor, which affect the fast neutron flux drastically; it is sometimes possible to shield the moderator chamber from some of the γ-ray flux. But nuclear heating will still perhaps account for 20 to 30 W, that is 3 or 4 l/h consumption of liquid hydrogen. It is inconvenient to provide such refrigeration from bulk liquid hydrogen, particularly since continuous running is a great advantage. So a self-contained refrigeration plant is required. For space and safety reasons this refrigeration plant is erected outside the reactor building, the long pipeline introducing, however, an additional refrigeration loss. In both EL3 and DIDO loops refrigeration has been provided by hydrogen liquefiers, though in principle helium refrigerators running at 20°K could be employed with consequent reduction of the safety problems.

The schematic layout of the DIDO liquid hydrogen loop (Webb, 1958) is shown in Fig. 4.9. A diaphragm compressor feeds high pressure hydrogen gas to a Joule-Thomson liquefier. The mixture of liquid and gaseous hydrogen from the expansion valve passes along a vacuum-insulated pipeline into the reactor building and the reactor. There it circulates round a coil in the moderator chamber and cools it to near 20°K. The hydrogen needed to fill the main volume of the moderator chamber is obtained from a separate cylinder. The shape of the chamber, similar to a hollow hemisphere is the nearest approach to a "black body furnace" that could be achieved within

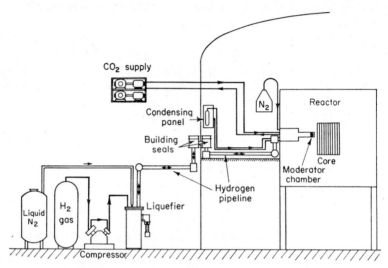

FIG. 4.9. Layout of the DIDO liquid hydrogen loop.

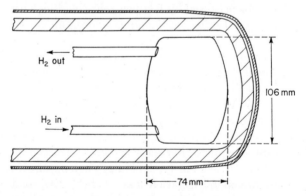

FIG. 4.10. The EL3 liquid hydrogen moderator chamber (Jacrot, 1962).

the limited dimensions. The vacuum case surrounding the moderator chamber is thick-walled to withstand any possible explosion. It also insulates the pipes supplying liquid hydrogen to the moderator chamber, and forms the first section of the neutron flight tube.

The DIDO cold neutron source has been designed to run continuously and only close down for maintenance when the reactor itself is closed down. It is provided with automatic controls where possible, and in the event of any fault it closes itself down safely.

A similar apparatus was installed in the EL3 reactor at Saclay (Jacrot, Lacaze and Weil, 1959), and since 1960 it has been in use as a source of cold neutrons. Its general layout is much the same as that of the DIDO loop. The moderator chamber (Fig. 4.10) is somewhat larger than the DIDO chamber, and only a single hydrogen system is used, the hydrogen liquefier filling the chamber directly. This single system has the virtue of simplicity, but it has the disadvantage that one is never quite sure how much liquid hydrogen is in the moderator chamber. If nuclear heating is too large the chamber will not be completely full of liquid hydrogen; it will reach an equilibrium level such that the nuclear heating in the metal of the chamber and in the liquid hydrogen just equals the refrigeration available in the chamber.

If liquid hydrogen cold neutron sources are to be employed in very high flux reactors, methods must be devised for removing much larger amounts of heat from the moderator chamber. While there is no particular difficulty in building a refrigeration plant with a capacity of a few kilowatts at 20°K, this amount of heat must be abstracted from a few hundred cubic centimetres of liquid hydrogen inside the reactor.

4.13 Increases in Cold Neutron Flux

The results for the liquid hydrogen moderator installed in BEPO at Harwell (Butterworth et al., 1957) are shown in Fig. 4.11. From a practical point of view the gains are very useful, though they do not approach the theoretical figures for complete thermal equilibrium at 20°K. The spectrum of neutrons scattered from the liquid hydrogen was measured with a slow chopper and time-of-flight technique, and compared with the flux obtained from a graphite source block at the reactor temperature in the same position. The spectrum was not a Maxwell distribution (equation (4.3)); the maximum remained at the reactor temperature, but there was a pronounced tail on the low energy side and it was this tail which led to the enhanced cold neutron flux. Further experiments (Webb, 1961) showed that the spectrum was unaltered by varying the para-hydrogen content of the moderator over the range 25–93 % and that an identical spectrum was obtained using hydrogen-deuteride instead of hydrogen. Cooling the hydrogen from 20°K down to 4°K with liquid helium resulted in only a small increase in cold neutron flux, about 15 % at 4 Å, decreasing to nothing beyond 8 Å. Solid methane at 77°K produced a gain of a factor 3 in the cold neutron flux from the reactor, though it is of limited practical use as a cold neutron source as decomposition under irradiation limits runs to a few hours.

Similar experiments have been made by Van Dingenen and Hautecler in an 8-cm vertical hole in the reactor BR1 at Mol (Van Dingenen and Hautecler, 1960; Van Dingenen, 1962). The spectrum of neutrons from methane was

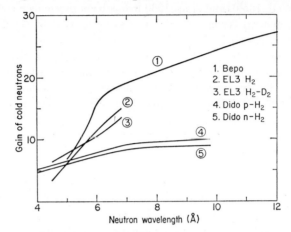

FIG. 4.11. Gains in cold neutron flux in BEPO, EL3 (hydrogen and hydrogen–deuterium mixtures) and DIDO (para-hydrogen and normal-hydrogen (75 % ortho))

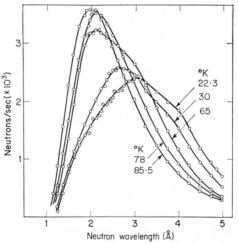

FIG. 4.12. Neutron spectra from methane at various temperatures (Van Dingenen, 1962).

measured with a crystal spectrometer at five different temperatures; the results are shown in Fig. 4.12. The spectra for the higher temperatures may be fitted by Maxwellian curves, but at the lowest temperature there are some deviations. Similar deviations from Maxwellian shape were observed using liquid hydrogen as moderator.

Measurements have been made with the EL3 cold neutron source using mixtures of liquid hydrogen and deuterium as the moderator (Jacrot, 1962). The gain in cold neutron flux at three wavelengths is shown in Fig. 4.13 as a function of the hydrogen-deuterium composition. Pure liquid hydrogen is the most effective moderator for long-wavelength neutrons, but for 4·5 Å neutrons the maximum flux is obtained with 60 % of deuterium in the chamber.

Measurements of the gain in cold neutron flux have been made using the DIDO liquid hydrogen source (Webb and Pearce, 1963); the results are shown in Fig. 4.11, compared with the result from the BEPO and EL3 sources.

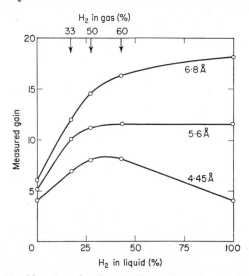

FIG. 4.13. Gains in cold neutron flux from hydrogen–deuterium mixtures (Jacrot, 1962).

The lower curve was obtained with the moderator chamber filled with normal hydrogen (75 % ortho). The gain varies from a factor 5 at 4 Å to 7·5 at longer wavelengths. With the chamber filled with para-hydrogen (containing perhaps 5 % ortho-hydrogen) the slightly higher values of the upper curve were obtained.

The gains shown for BEPO are notably higher than for either DIDO or EL3 in agreement with the remarks of Section 4.8. It is clear from these results that the geometry in which the source is placed has a considerable effect upon the gain factor.

4.14 Safety of Liquid Hydrogen Moderators

If liquid hydrogen is employed as the cold moderator or the coolant, there arises the question of safety. Mixtures ranging from 4 % to 74 % hydrogen gas in air are explosive, and owing to the high velocity of propagation of an explosion wave in a hydrogen–air mixture it is difficult to provide effective flame traps such as are commonly used in situations where other inflammable gases may be present. In addition liquid hydrogen has such a low temperature that if air leaked into the vacuum space it would condense on the cold parts of the apparatus and a large quantity of solid air might accumulate; such a situation is clearly dangerous. Two precautions seem adequate to meet this situation. First the part of the vacuum case inside the reactor is made strong enough to contain the explosion of the total amount of hydrogen present with the stoichiometric mixture of air. Secondly, by monitoring the vacuum system the amount of solid air which can accumulate and be involved in an explosion is limited, which automatically limits the explosion pressure which could build up. Thus the reactor is doubly protected.

Chemical combination of hydrogen–oxygen mixtures can occur by two processes:

(i) by smooth burning, usually referred to as normal explosion, which is controlled by chemical reaction rates and mixing processes and is characterized by a relatively low velocity of flame propagation;

(ii) by detonation which is characterized by a shock wave which travels through the unburnt gas at a velocity greater than that of sound.

The pressures which arise in a vessel due to normal explosion of a known mixture of hydrogen–air can be calculated easily (Lewis and Von Elbe, 1951). As an example we take the explosion of 100 ml of liquid hydrogen with its stoichiometric quantity of oxygen and the associated nitrogen in air in a vessel of volume 10 l. For 100 % efficient explosion and containment, the gases exert a pressure of 220 atm. This pressure would be relieved in a few tens of milliseconds by cooling of the gases or in practice by the bursting of a safety disk.

If detonation occurs, the pressure behind the shock wave is several times higher than the pressures calculated for normal explosion. The highest pressures are found at reflection of a shock wave from plane ends of a tube. Unfortunately, calculations are possible only under highly simplified assumptions. Further, the propagation of shock waves is strongly dependent on the geometry of the containing vessel. For example, shock waves are best propagated in long, narrow tubes and degenerate into normal explosion in tubes of expanding section. As a result of these complexities it becomes essential to conduct test explosions of hydrogen–air mixtures in vessels which closely simulate the intended vessel for the reactor installation. The results of such tests have been reported by Webb (1963) and by Ward et al. (1963). In each case a general rise of pressure lasting about 10 msec was found. Superimposed on this general pressure rise curve were sharper pressure peaks of less than 1 msec duration. Comparison of the measured average pressure levels with calculations of normal explosion pressures indicated an explosion efficiency of about 50 %. The shorter term pressure peaks were only 1·2–2·0 times greater than the general pressure levels observed. On the basis of such tests the DIDO vacuum case was constructed with walls (of magnesium alloy) $\frac{1}{4}$ in. thick.

4.15 General Properties of Thermal Neutron Detectors

All thermal neutron detectors are in fact detectors of secondary products arising from absorption of neutrons by nuclei. The reactions used are

(a) $^1n + {}^{10}B$ $\nearrow$ $^7Li^* + {}^4He \rightarrow {}^7Li + {}^4He + 0·48$ MeV γ-ray (93 %)
$\searrow$ $^7Li + {}^4He$ (7 %)

(b) $^1n + {}^6Li \rightarrow {}^3T + {}^4He$

(c) $^1n + {}^3He \rightarrow {}^1H + {}^3T$

The recoil particles are detected either by their ionization of a gas or by the light flash they produce in a scintillating material. The efficiency of detection of neutrons of energy E by a detector of thickness x, containing N atoms per cm³ of a neutron absorber for which the absorption cross-section is σ_a at the given neutron energy, may be expressed as

$$\text{Efficiency} = \epsilon[1 - \exp(-N\sigma_a x)] \qquad (4.7)$$

The term $[1 - \exp(-N\sigma_a x)]$ gives the fraction of incident neutrons which are absorbed in the detector and the factor ϵ is the fraction of these inter-actions which result in an output pulse from the detector. The neutron absorption cross-section for all the above reactions varies inversely with the neutron velocity in the thermal region. The values for neutrons of 2200 m/sec (0·025 eV) are given in Table 4.6.

In gas filled counters the factor ϵ is close to unity and the detection efficiency is limited by the number of absorbing nuclei in the path of the neutron through the detector. With solid scintillation detectors the density of absorber nuclei can be higher but in practice is limited by an associated fall-off in ϵ. As we shall discuss later, the range and energy of the recoil particles, given in Table 4.6, is then of importance in determining the value of ϵ. When ϵ is independent of the neutron energy, equation (4.7) may be used to calculate the detection efficiency at any neutron energy using the known absorber content. When ϵ varies with neutron energy (Section 4.18) the variation cannot be calculated with accuracy and an experimental calibration of the efficiency must be made at various neutron energies, usually by comparison with a detector of known efficiency variation.

The special requirements of detectors for thermal neutrons may be summarized as:

(i) a high detection efficiency for thermal neutrons,

(ii) a low detection efficiency for background radiation which usually consists of fast neutrons and γ-radiation,

(iii) a known variation of efficiency with energy.

In addition, for detectors used with time-of flight techniques, we add:

(iv) a physically thin detector to define the point of detection, and hence the flight path, accurately,

(v) a small time uncertainty in the detection of neutrons.

For extended detector arrays as discussed in Chapter 2, we add:

(vi) a large sensitive area.

(vii) a consistent performance between several detectors.

TABLE 4.6

Reaction	Cross-section (barns) for 0·025 eV neutrons	Particle	Energy (MeV)	Range† (mg/cm²)
$^{10}B+n$	3840	^{4}He	1·47	0·93
		^{7}Li	0·83	<0·1
^{6}Li+n	950	^{4}He	2·05	1·32
		^{3}T	2·74	7·80
^{3}He+n	5500	H	0·57	1·26
		^{3}T	0·20	0·26

† Measured in air.

The extent to which specific detectors satisfy these requirements are discussed in the sections which follow. Several preliminary remarks are, however, appropriate here. In certain detectors, notably the proportional counters (Sections 4.16 and 4.17), the amplitude of γ-ray induced pulses is considerably less than the amplitude of pulses from neutron detection. For these detectors the efficiency of detection of γ-rays can be made negligible using normal pulse height discrimination techniques. This valuable feature allows some freedom in the choice and disposition of material shielding the detector from background radiation, massive shielding needed to attenuate high energy γ-rays being minimized.

Scintillation detectors show a less favourable difference in pulse amplitudes from γ-ray and neutron events. The reduction of γ-radiation, particularly of high energy γ-rays, at the detector is then important and the shielding chosen includes high density materials such as steel-loaded or barytes concrete. Further, care is needed to prevent thermal neutron beams being absorbed in materials which yield high energy capture γ-rays. For this reason shielding containing boron (0·48 MeV capture γ-rays) is preferable to the use of cadmium (up to 7 MeV capture γ-rays).

In experimental areas at reactors and at particle accelerators, background in unshielded detectors from stray thermal neutrons and fast neutrons is usually of the order of thousands per minute. The shielding of the detectors is therefore required to reduce this background by about three orders of magnitude. A large decrease of background results from the removal of low energy neutrons by surrounding the detector with a thin (1 mm) sheet of cadmium; attenuation of the fast neutrons, however, is more troublesome. Usually the shielding required is about 30 cm thick and consists of a mixture of hydrogenous material to moderate the neutrons and boron containing compounds to absorb them. Paraffin wax, water, wood, polythene and resins have been applied as moderators and boron in the form of boric oxide, borax, boron carbide or amorphous boron is commonly used. Examples of detector shielding and the backgrounds achieved in experimental applications are given in the discussion of specific detectors. It should be remarked, however, that these backgrounds reflect the efficiency of the shielding as much as the intrinsic properties of the various detectors.

A useful criterion for the choice of optimum detection efficiency may be readily derived. Let us assume a scattered thermal neutron intensity S counts/min and background B counts/min. The total measuring time, τ min, will be shared between the time for measuring the sample with background and the time for measuring the background alone in the ratio which yields the minimum statistical error on S. Simple statistical arguments give the fractional error on S as,

$$\sqrt{\frac{2(S+2B)}{S^2\tau}} \qquad (4.8)$$

We now ask when a given change to the detector which increases both the sample count rate and the background rate represents a reduction in the fractional error on S for a fixed total measuring time τ. The answer clearly is that the best detector (or operating condition of a given detector) is that for which the ratio $S^2/(S+2B)$ is maximum. The region of a measured spectrum where optimum operating conditions are most important is where $S \ll 2B$, when the ratio to maximize will be $\approx S^2/B$. This criterion is useful, for example, in choosing the best background discrimination level for operating a scintillation detector which has a broad pulse height distribution.

We now apply this criterion to the case of a detector for which the detection efficiencies for thermal and fast neutrons are given by

$$S \propto (1 - e^{-N\sigma_{th}x}) \quad \text{and} \quad B \propto (1 - e^{-N\sigma_f x})$$

where σ_{th} and σ_f are the absorption cross-sections for the thermal neutrons of interest and the background fast neutrons respectively. Since $N\sigma_f x \ll 1$ may be assumed, we put $B \propto N\sigma_f x$,

whence
$$\frac{S^2}{B} \propto \frac{(1-e^{-N\sigma_{th}x})^2}{N\sigma_f x} \qquad (4.9)$$

If we examine the variation of S^2/B with Nx we find a maximum when

$$1-e^{-N\sigma_{th}x} = 0 \cdot 72 \qquad (4.10)$$

Thus the best choice of detector from this view-point is one which has absorption efficiency of 72 % for the thermal neutrons of interest. Higher efficiency increases the background sufficiently to give an overall deterioration of the statistical accuracy of the results. This conclusion is reached for the most exacting experimental condition, when $S \ll 2B$. If the required intensity S is larger than the background B the optimum efficiency would be nearer to 100 %. The condition given however is generally useful since the region where S is larger will always be more accurately determined.

Detectors employed for time-of flight analysis of scattered neutron spectra are required to define accurately the position and time of neutron detection. Flight paths used are at least one metre and neutron flight times are several hundred microseconds. Detectors having a thickness in the direction of the neutron path of less than about a centimetre and inherent timing errors less than one or two microseconds are needed. The use of many detectors and multi-input time analysers which record simultaneously neutrons scattered at different scattering angles has yielded an important increase in the overall efficiency of the time-of-flight method (Chapter 2).

When the scattering specimen is a single crystal, the angle of scatter relative to the incident beam and also the azimuthal angle (relative to axes which are fixed in the crystal) must be defined by the detector. Thus detectors of small dimensions, subtending a small angle, usually less than 1°, at the sample are needed. If instead the scattering specimen is a liquid, gas or polycrystalline solid, the second angle, the azimuthal angle, need not be defined. Only the angle of scatter of the neutrons relative to the incident beam need be defined by the detector which ideally would be a complete circle lying on the cone of constant angle of scatter. The cold neutron scattering apparatus of Harris *et al.* (1963a) has detectors for both types of experiment. An array of 24 scintillation detectors of 5 cm diameter (Section 4.18) with a flight path of 2·27 m is used for studies of single crystal specimens. For unoriented samples the detectors, several 30-cm long, tubular boron trifluoride filled counters (Section 4.16) are placed at 1·3 m from the sample and are arranged to conform to the cones of constant scatter angle at six different angles between 20° and 90°. Further examples of the use of multidetector arrays are given in the sections which follow.

4.16 Boron Trifluoride (BF₃) Filled Proportional Counters

The instrument most widely used for thermal neutron detection is the boron trifluoride filled proportional counter. Details of construction and operation are given in standard works by Allen (1960) or Curran and Craggs (1949) Here the recoil particles ionize the boron trifluoride gas and "gas amplification" is used to increase the output pulse size. The efficiency of detection of the recoil particles approaches 100 % and so the neutron detection efficiency is determined by the amount of boron-10 in the path of the neutron.

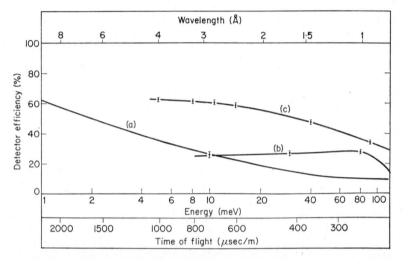

Fig. 4.14. The efficiency of three neutron detectors as a function of neutron energy. (a) A ¹⁰BF₃ filled counter of 10 cm path length and 70 cm Hg filling pressure. (b) A boron-10–zinc sulphide scintillator, see Section 4.18 (Harris, 1961). (c) A lithium-7–zinc sulphide scintillator, see Section 4.18 (Stedman, 1960).

Filling gas enriched to 96 % in the boron-10 isotope is readily available and cylindrical counters with filling pressures up to 2 atm, diameters up to 5 cm, and lengths up to 50 cm, are common. The calculated detection efficiency of a typical detector is shown in Fig. 4.14.

Boron trifluoride is a rather dense gas (2·99 g/l at S.T.P.); the ranges of the helium and lithium recoil particles in the gas at 1 atm pressure are 0·3 cm and 0·03 cm. Thus for a cylindrical counter of 2·5 cm diameter practically all of the reaction energy is used in producing ionization in the gas. The pulse size is therefore large compared to that produced by recoil electrons, from γ-rays which strike the walls or the gas filling, for which the range in the gas is about 10 times longer than the counter diameter. Thus it is easy to discriminate against the recording of γ-ray background and BF₃ counters can be regarded as insensitive to γ-radiation—a most important advantage.

Abson *et al.* (1958) report that pulses produced by 1 MeV γ-rays in a 2·5 cm diameter counter are about one-hundreth of the pulse size for neutron detection. They give the neutron pulse height distribution shown in Fig. 4.15.

Since BF_3 counters have been developed over several decades, standard production methods now yield robust, stable and reproducible detectors of several standard lengths and sizes but most commonly of cylindrical shape. From the known filling and dimensions of these counters one can calculate the detection efficiency as a function of neutron energy with sufficient accuracy for a wide range of experiments.

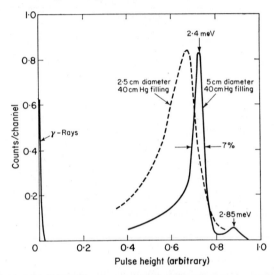

Fig. 4.15. Pulse height distribution from a boron trifluoride counter (Abson *et al.*, 1958).

The BF_3 counter thus has a formidable list of advantages as a thermal neutron detector. These have made it the universal choice for use with crystal spectrometers (see Chapter 3) where the length of the detector is usually unimportant so that a high detector efficiency is achieved with counters up to 30 cm long. The counters are arranged so that the neutrons pass along the length of the cylindrical counter. In this geometry, however, neutrons are absorbed in the small "dead" space inside the counter tube where the collecting wire is fixed. To reduce efficiency loss due to this "dead" space a low pressure in a long counter is often preferred to a short, high pressure counter.

For use with the time-of flight method the BF_3 counter has some disadvantages. The counter is usually arranged so that the neutrons pass parallel to a diameter of the counter. It is clear from Fig. 4.14 that one small diameter tube in this geometry can yield a rather low efficiency. Alternatively, counter dimensions chosen for high efficiency can become significant compared with the neutron flight path.

The variable collection time of ionization from events in different parts of the gas filling of BF_3 counters introduces an uncertainty in the neutron arrival time. This time uncertainty $\Delta\tau$ is given by Nicholson (1955) as

$$\Delta\tau = \frac{pc^2 \ln \dfrac{c}{a}}{2\,\alpha V} \tag{4.11}$$

where p is the filling pressure, a and c the radii of the wire and tube respectively, V is the applied voltage and α the electron mobility in the gas filling. Nicholson (1955) gives

$$\alpha = (1\cdot19 \pm 0\cdot06) \times 10^5 (\text{cm sec}^{-1})(\text{volt cm}^{-1})^{-1}(\text{cm of Hg pressure})$$

For a counter of 2·5 cm diameter filled to 1 atmosphere pressure and operated at 2400 V the time uncertainty is typically 1·0 μsec.

Where a large detector area was needed, attempts have been made to construct a single rectangular detector of large area, but the poor characteristics of such counters have severely limited their use. Usually a number of cylindrical counters are placed side by side and connected in parallel to afford a large detection area. In order to avoid reduced detection efficiency due to gaps between counters two or more staggered rows of parallel counters can be used to increase the efficiency. Without correction this gives a marked increase of error in flight path definition. Forte (1961) has, however, described a circuit to correct for the different flight times to such counter rows.

The triple axis crystal spectrometer of Brockhouse, which has been described fully in Chapter 3, uses BF_3 counters of 6·2 cm diameter and 25 cm length; the dead space at the end through which the neutrons pass is 3·7 cm. Counters of different filling pressures are used depending on the neutron energy range being studied; filling pressures of 5, 15, 30, 45 and 60 cm Hg are available.

In the time-of-flight method using the rotating crystal also developed by Brockhouse (Section 2.12) BF_3 counters are also used. The flight path is 330 cm and the BF_3 counters, used side on to the scattered neutrons, are 6·5 cm diameter and use filling pressures of 60 cm Hg or 73 cm Hg. Two detectors are used; the first is used for isotropic scatterers, liquids and polycrystals for example, and the second where high resolution in momentum space is needed, with single crystal studies for example. The first detector consists of two counters of 50 cm length. This detector defines the angles of scatter accepted by the detector to 2° horizontally and 9° vertically. The second detector must define the angle of scatter more closely (1° horizontally and 2° vertically); thus single counters of length 12 cm are used. These counter arrays are shielded by 2·5 cm of boron carbide (B_4C) close to the counters and 30 cm of a paraffin and boron mixture around the outside. For the first set of counters the background count rate is about 2 counts/min.

Boron trifluoride counters have also been used in the time-of-flight technique with the phased rotor apparatus at the M.T.R. reactor, Idaho (Section 2.10). The flight path here is 202 cm and counters of 2·5 cm diameter are used. The filling pressure is 167 cm Hg giving an efficiency of 40 % at 0·025 eV. At each scattering angle ten counters of 50 cm length are connected in parallel to cover a larger area for work with isotropic scatterers. The whole detecting system consists of ten such arrays and is enclosed in a shielded room whose walls of 30/70 wt % mixture of boric acid and paraffin wax are 30 cm thick. The background in a single array of ten detectors is of the order 20–50 counts/min.

4.17 Helium-3 Filled Proportional Counters

The use of helium-3 gas in a proportional counter has the attraction that high pressures of helium (at least 10 atm) can be used with modest voltages (less than 1500 V) on the electrode. Mills *et al.* (1962) found good plateaux for 2·5 cm diameter counters filled with 3 atm or 7 atm of helium-3. The neutron absorption of helium-3 is greater than for the same length and pressure of boron-10 trifluoride gas, being 75 % for helium-3 compared with 62 % for boron-10 trifluoride for 10 cm of each gas at 1 atm pressure with 0·025 eV neutrons. Since helium-3 filled proportional counters can be operated satisfactorily at several atmospheres pressure, counters of small diameter can be used with all the advantages of the usual boron trifluoride counters but with smaller flight path uncertainty. Helium-3 occurs naturally as only 1 part in 10^6 of natural helium. The isotope has, however, become available by irradiation of lithium-6 in reactors, the resulting tritium decaying with half-life 12·3 years to helium-3. Careful chemical separation of the helium from the parent tritium is needed to remove this source of background in counters using the gas. Helium-3 proportional counters have recently become widely available and their use in scattering experiments with thermal neutrons is expected to increase.

Their field of use is similar to that of the BF_3 counter. However due to the higher filling pressure and somewhat higher cross-section the efficiency for neutrons ∼0·1 eV can be 50 % for a thickness of 2·5 cm (4 atm ^{3}He). Consequently, they are supplanting the BF_3 counter for the time-of-flight instruments (described in Chapter 2) which cover this energy range.

4.18 Boron or Lithium (with Zinc Sulphide) Scintillation Detectors

The aim in this detector is to combine the neutron absorbing element intimately with a suitable scintillating phosphor so that the reaction products from neutron capture strike the phosphor producing a light flash. This light flash is then detected by a photomultiplier tube.

Silver activated zinc sulphide (abbreviated ZnS(Ag)) is well known to give a very high light output when struck by α-particles or charged light atoms. Several methods have been used to include finely powdered activated zinc sulphide in a transparent, boron containing medium. Palevsky et al. (1957) used ZnS(Ag) in fused boric oxide (B_2O_3) glass. Sun et al. (1956) avoided the high temperatures needed to fuse boric oxide and possible damage to the phosphor, by including the boron in a low melting point polymer. An improved boron containing polymer has been described by Wraight et al. (1965). This scintillator is prepared by heating 3·7 parts of ethylene glycol, 2·65 parts of n-butanol and 10 parts of boric acid (96 % enriched in boron-10) to 170°C for 3 minutes. The ZnS(Ag) is added to make a mixture 65 % by weight ZnS(Ag) and 35 % boron plastic. The mixture can be hot pressed onto a glass backing plate to give a detector containing 10 mg/cm² of boron-10 with total thickness about 0·5 mm.

The use of lithium-6 as the neutron absorber in association with ZnS phosphor has some important advantages. Despite a lower absorption cross for neutrons than boron-10 the energy of the recoil particles and the range of these particles is higher (Table 4.6). Stedman (1960) concluded from tests on boron polymer–ZnS(Ag) scintillators that the probability of a recoil particle from a neutron absorption event striking the ZnS(Ag) phosphor was considerably less than unity due to the short ranges (5×10^{-4} and $0\cdot5 \times 10^{-4}$ cm) of the particles. The potentially higher probability of the recoil particles from the lithium reaction (ranges 40×10^{-4} and 6×10^{-4} cm) striking the phosphor to produce a light flash was exploited by Stedman. Since lithium cannot readily be chemically combined in a clear glass-like medium Stedman's method was to hot press finely divided lithium fluoride and ZnS(Ag) powders together with Perspex (lucite) powder as a transparent bonding medium. The resulting detector is inert in air, unlike the boron plastic type which is hygroscopic and must be protected from the atmosphere.

Unfortunately, all of these methods produce a milky, translucent detector and several papers discuss the optimum sizes for the phosphor grains and the ratio of the components for highest efficiency for thermal neutrons. Stedman (1960) has demonstrated that the Perspex bonded detector can readily be corrugated to present a greater thickness of detector in the path of the incident neutrons while avoiding a thick detector in which the scintillation light is attenuated.

Harris (1961) has described the mounting of a 6 in. × 3 in. detector so that it is viewed by a 2-in. diameter photomultiplier placed 4 in. from the detector using a polished light guide (see Fig. 4.16). This optical system results in a reduction of pulse height by a factor of seven compared with that of a detector mounted directly on the photomultiplier but still gives pulses from neutron detection above the thermal noise of the phototube. The efficiency variation across this rather wide detector is satisfactory, falling at the edges to 75 % of the value at the centre. Stedman (1960) has described the mounting of a $4\frac{3}{4}$ in. side square detector on a photomultiplier with 5-in. diameter photosensitive face (see Fig. 4.17). Both of these large area detectors were mounted on $\frac{1}{2}$-in. glass blocks containing 62 % boric oxide. This block reduces

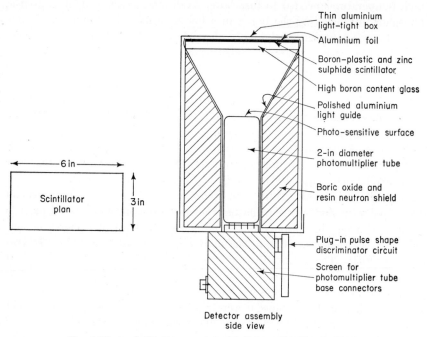

FIG. 4.16. A scintillation counter with light guide (Harris, 1961).

the background arising from stray neutrons arriving from the back of the detector and eliminates back-scattering of slow neutrons which have passed through the detector. The measured efficiencies for the boron containing detector of Harris and the lithium containing detector of Stedman are shown in Fig. 4.14. The efficiencies shown were measured by comparison with a boron trifluoride proportional counter of calculated efficiency. According to Wraight et al. (1965) such measurements are subject to errors of up to 20 % of the measured value.

The number of neutrons absorbed per unit thickness of the detector falls off exponentially through the detector (equation 4.7). Thus for those detectors which absorb a large fraction of the neutrons, most neutrons are absorbed on the side of the detector from which the neutrons arrive. The resulting light flashes must pass through the rest of the detector to reach the photosensitive face of the photomultiplier. For lower neutron energies (i.e. larger absorption cross-section) the mean position of interaction is further from the photo-sensitive surface. Thus the factor ϵ of equation (4.7), and so the overall detection efficiency also, falls off at lower neutron energy despite and, ironically, because of the increasing absorption cross-section of the absorber. This effect is seen for the boron containing detector in the Fig. 4.14. Clearly

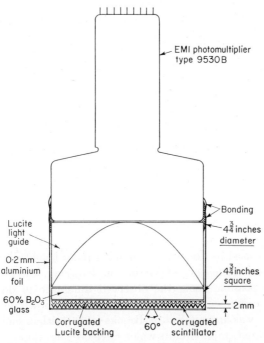

FIG. 4.17. A scintillation counter with light guide (Stedman, 1960). (The curved line on the lucite is due to the transition from a square scintillator to a circular phototube)

this can be avoided by decreasing the total thickness of the scintillator; indeed the thickness of scintillator can be optimized for a particular neutron energy range. The detectors described here are a compromise to give best efficiency for the energy range 0·01–0·1 eV. A further possibility, as yet not tried in practice, is to arrange to view the scintillator from the side from which the neutrons arrive. With these translucent detectors it is necessary to determine experimentally the detector efficiency as a function of neutron energy.

Harris *et al.* (1963b) report measurements on the response of ZnS(Ag) when bombarded by α-particles and by γ-rays. Using a very fast response oscillo-scope they show that, although the peak light output from the α-particles and recoil electrons are nearly equal, the principal component of the light output decays far more slowly for bombardment by α-particles. The decay times they observe are about 300 nsec and 20 nsec respectively. This result was confirmed in ZnS(Ag) containing scintillators when irradiated by neutrons and by γ-rays.

Usually, a ZnS(Ag) containing scintillator is used with associated circuitry having integration and differentiation time constants of about 100 nsec. The resulting output pulses are then larger for the neutron induced pulses than the γ-induced pulses. Scintillation detectors employing ZnS(Ag) have

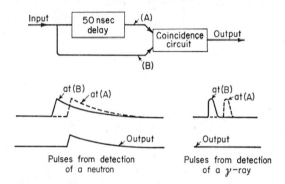

FIG. 4.18. The principle of the pulse shape discriminator circuit (Wraight *et al.*, 1965).

commonly been used in this way, employing pulse height discrimination to reduce the detection efficiency of γ-radiation. However, lower γ-ray detection efficiencies are possible using the observed difference in decay times for excitation by different particles. This method—known as pulse shape discrimination—was first applied by Brooks (1956) with organic scintillators. An account of three simple circuits which have been developed to differentiate between the different decay times of pulses from scintillation detectors has been given by Firk (1962).

Wraight (1961) has developed a delayed coincidence circuit for use with the ZnS(Ag) based scintillators. The principle of this circuit is shown in Fig. 4.18. Use of this circuit reduces both the γ-ray induced background in ZnS(Ag) containing detectors and also the background due to phototube noise. A factor of 10 reduction is quoted by Harris *et al.* (1963b). The detection efficiency for neutrons is also improved since the pulse height discriminator may be set to count smaller pulses without increasing the detection of γ-ray background and tube noise. Fast pulses which arise from γ-rays striking the phototube itself are also eliminated by the pulse shape discrimination method. Detectors in a γ-ray flux of 5 mR/h can be used without troublesome background. Figures 4.19 and 4.20 illustrate the clear discrimination between

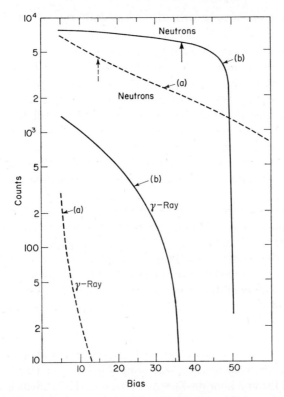

FIG. 4.19. Bias curves for a boron–ZnS (Ag) scintillator (Wraight *et al.*, 1965): (a) without pulse shape discriminator and (b) with pulse shape discriminator. The arrows indicate the operating points for low γ-ray sensitivity and demonstrate the higher efficiency obtained by using the discriminator.

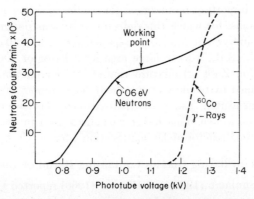

FIG. 4.20. Discrimination curve for a lithium–ZnS(Ag) detector using pulse shape discriminator (Harris *et al.*, 1963b).

neutron and γ-ray events with the boron–ZnS(Ag) and lithium–ZnS(Ag) scintillators using pulse shape discrimination.

The time uncertainty for ZnS(Ag) scintillators is increased by the presence of the hydrogenous material because the neutron may be scattered before being absorbed. While detailed calculations of this time broadening have not been made for the detector discussed it can be estimated that thermal neutrons may spend about 1 microsecond in the scintillator before being absorbed. This time uncertainty is usually not troublesome compared with the long flight times of thermal neutrons over a flight path of a few metres (cf. 454 μsec/m for 0·025 eV neutrons). The physical thickness of the detector, usually less than 1 mm, introduces negligible error in determining the flight path.

Three examples of the application of ZnS(Ag) based detectors in apparatus using the time-of-flight technique illustrate particularly the wide range of detection area to which these detectors can be adapted.

In recent development of the phased rotor apparatus at Chalk River (Section 2.9) the multidetector array employs up to 25 lithium fluoride–ZnS(Ag) detectors. Detectors of dimensions $4\frac{3}{4}$ in. $\times$ $4\frac{3}{4}$ in. and 6 in. $\times$ 3 in. are used at flight paths of 3, 2 and 1·3 m. The detectors are shielded immediately by several centimetres of boron loaded resins while 5 cm of paraffin wax and 30 cm of concrete shields the whole array. The detectors have mean efficiencies of 55 % at 0·025 eV and background rates of about 50 counts/min.

At Harwell the cold neutron scattering apparatus of Harris et al. (1963a) uses up to 24 lithium fluoride–ZnS(Ag) detectors. They are disposed at angles of scatter between 30° and 90° using a flight path of 2·27 m. The scintillators are 5-cm diameter disks with corrugated phosphor layers. These small detectors subtend angles of 0·57° at the specimen. Thus they define accurately the direction of the scattered neutrons which are detected. This is a particularly important requirement for studies of dispersion relations for phonons in crystals, for which this detector array was designed. The background rates of individual detectors range between 4 and 10 counts/min.

At Dubna, U.S.S.R., a very large area scintillator of 2000 cm^2 using a phosphor of boron–ZnS(Ag) mixture viewed by four photomultiplier tubes has been developed by Golikov et al. (1963). They report that an efficiency of 60 % was measured using thermalized neutrons from a polonium-beryllium neutron source. This detector has been used in scattering experiments at the pulsed reactor at Dubna (Section 4.5).

4.19 Scintillating Glasses Containing Boron or Lithium

Ginther and Shulman (1958) and Ginther (1960) reported the preparation of clear luminescent glasses. Boron or lithium oxides are included in these glasses which can therefore provide very valuable scintillation detectors for thermal neutrons. Similar glasses to those of Ginther have been made by Anderson *et al.* (1962) and Voitovetskii and Tomacheva (1961). Cerium has so far proved to be the most efficient activator but care must be taken in preparation to ensure that this is present in the Ce^{3+} state; Ce^{4+} ions tend to colour the glass.

Typical compositions (given as molar ratios) for two glasses containing boron and lithium respectively are:

Boron-containing glass (GL–55): $3 \cdot 0 B_2O_3$; $1 \cdot 0 Na_2O$; $1 \cdot 0 Al_2O_3$; $0 \cdot 10 Ce_2O_3$

Lithium-containing glass (GL–304): $3 \cdot 6 Li_2O$; $11 \cdot 0 SiO_3$; $0 \cdot 75 Al_2O_3$; $0 \cdot 10 Ce_2O_3$

The resulting densities of absorbers in these glasses is then respectively $35 \cdot 5$ mg/cm^2 and $11 \cdot 8$ mg/cm^2 per mm thickness of glass. The fraction of incident neutrons of energy $0 \cdot 025$ eV absorbed in 1 mm of these glasses is therefore $99 \cdot 9\%$ and 67% respectively. Thus very thin detectors are sufficient for efficient detection of thermal neutrons by each type of glass. Wraight *et al.* (1965) describe measurements of the absolute efficiency of these detectors, and suggest that they should be used as a standard for efficiency measurements.

A description of extensive tests on six boron-containing and six lithium-containing and one lithium plus boron-containing glass has been given by Bollinger *et al.* (1962) and the present data is taken largely from these authors and also from Harris *et al.* (1963b).

Bollinger and Thomas report that thin glass is effectively 100% transparent to its own scintillation light (wavelength 3800 Å). A pulse height distribution curve for scintillating glass therefore shows a well defined peak for detection of thermal neutrons in contrast to the broad distribution

TABLE 4.7

Detected counts per second due to cobalt-60 γ-rays (5mR/h at detector) for various glass thicknesses.

Thickness of glass (mm)	1·5	3	6	9
Count rate c/s	8	110	182	240

obtained with the translucent ZnS(Ag) containing scintillator. An example for a lithium containing glass is shown in Fig. 4.21. The abscissa of Fig. 4.21 "equivalent electron energy in glass" is the energy which an electron would need to expend in the glass to give a pulse height equal to the neutron pulse, 1590 keV for this lithium glass. The range of an electron of 1590 keV is about 3 mm in the glass so that only high energy electrons can dissipate enough energy in a detector of 1 mm thickness to cause a pulse which would be detected with the neutron pulses. Indeed the thinner the glass the fewer the recoil electrons which would be detected. Harris *et al.* (1963b) demonstrate this advantageous effect with the figures given in Table 4.7.

Thus the use of thin detectors (<2 mm) is of great benefit in reducing the detection of γ-rays. The pulse height for neutron detection in the boron containing glass is 7·65 times smaller than for the lithium glass. The "electron equivalent energy" for the boron glass is only 208 keV so that the detection

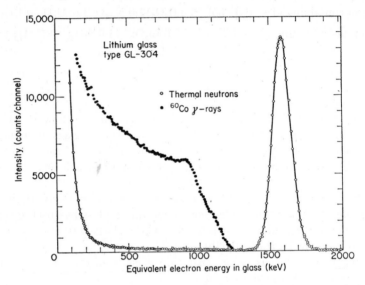

FIG. 4.21. Pulse height distribution for a lithium glass scintillator (Bollinger *et al.*, 1962).

of γ-rays for this glass is therefore more troublesome. The use of boron glass of about $\frac{1}{4}$ mm thickness might improve this situation. Unfortunately the measurements reported using γ-rays of mean energy 1·2 MeV from cobalt-60 give a rather optimistic view of performance of glass scintillator in experimental conditions. Compton recoil electrons from γ-rays of energy E_γ have energies up to E_e given by

$$E_e = \frac{E_\gamma}{1 + \dfrac{mc^2}{2E_\gamma}} \tag{4.12}$$

γ-rays in the vicinity of reactors have usually high energy components up to several MeV. The recoil electrons from these high energy γ-rays can therefore give larger scintillation pulses than those from cobalt-60 γ-rays. This explains why several observers have reported high background from γ-rays when glass scintillators have been used with reactor experiments.

From the data of Fig. 4.21 the resolution width is also obtained. The figure for the lithium glass, measured as the full width at half height of the neutron detection peak divided by the pulse height, is 9·5 %. Similar data for boron glass shows that it gives a poorer performance, the resolution width being 33 %.

This resolution width is important for two reasons. Firstly, the background recorded in a pulse height band set to accept the neutron capture events will be reduced if the band is narrow. Secondly, with a clearly defined peak from neutron capture it is possible to estimate accurately the fraction ϵ (near 100 % for the lithium glass) of those events producing pulses in the detector which are recorded above the discrimination level. Using the known absorber content of the glass one can thus calculate the absolute efficiency of the detector (equation (4.7)).

The decay times for neutron and γ-ray induced events have been examined by Bollinger and Thomas. They find a complex decay function for light pulses from boron or lithium glasses which cannot be represented by a single exponential decay. The characteristic times for the initial decay of the light were 43 nsec and 42 nsec respectively for neutron events with only a small difference for γ-ray events (55 nsec for the glass showing the most prominent difference). Thus the simple pulse shape discrimination circuits as already described cannot be applied to glasses described by these authors. However, the development of a lithium containing glass which shows a more marked difference in decay times, Coceva (1963), holds out hope of some development in this field.

In time-of-flight applications the life-time of neutrons in the detector before capture is of great importance. Bollinger and Thomas estimate that the mean life times of neutrons in boron and lithium detectors discussed here are 56 nsec and 406 nsec. For thermal neutrons these detection time uncertainties are not troublesome and represent an improvement over the other detectors discussed.

It is clear then that a glass detector, particularly lithium glass, offers the possibility of an outstanding thermal detector which can be made in large areas. However, they have not to date been used extensively in neutron scattering work. Three developments would help to change this situation.

(i) The discovery of a glass composition exhibiting marked pulse shape discrimination between neutron and γ-ray induced events.

(ii) The use of very thin glass scintillators (<1 mm thick).

(iii) Careful choice and placing of shielding to prevent high energy γ-rays striking the glass.

TABLE 4.8

| Detector | Reference to specific detector | Thickness x (and filling-pressure) | Density of absorber (atoms/barn) (Nx) | For 0·025 eV neutrons | | Ratio of pulse (c) heights for neutron and γ-ray detection | Detection Time Uncertainty |
				Fraction of neutrons absorbed ($1-e^{-N\sigma x}$)	Fraction of absorbed neutrons detected (ϵ)		
			Gas-filled proportional counters				
$B^{10}F_3$	—	10 cm (70 cm Hg)	$2·5\times10^{-4}$	62 %	>98 %	>10	∼1·0 μsec (for 2·5 cm diam. ctr)
$B^{10}F_3$	—	2·5 cm (140 cm Hg)	$1·25\times10^{-4}$	21 %	>98 %	>5	2·0 μsec (for 2·5 cm diam. ctr)
He^3	—	2·5 cm (280 cm Hg)	$2·5\times10^{-4}$	77 %	>90 %	>3	∼1 μsec

Scintillation counters

						Pulse-shape discrimination used (see 4.17)	
B⁰-ZnS(Ag)	Harris (1961)	0·5 mm	5×10^{-4}	85 %	75 %[a] 30% (average for whole detector)		1-2 μsec
Li⁶-ZnS(Ag)	Stedman (1960)	2 mm (with corrugations)	2×10^{-3}	85 %	80 %[a] 75 % (measured at centre of detector only)		1-2 μsec
Li⁶-glass	Bollinger *et al.* (1962)	1·0 mm	$1 \cdot 2 \times 10^{-3}$	68 %	>95 %[a]	1·5[b]	0·40 μsec
B¹⁰-glass	Bollinger *et al.* (1962)	0·25 mm	$4 \cdot 2 \times 10^{-4}$	80 %	>95 %[a]	0·2[b]	0·06 μsec
B¹⁰-liquid	Bollinger and Thomas (1957)	0·5 mm	$3 \cdot 0 \times 10^{-4}$	68 %	>95 %[a]	≲1	<0·1 μsec
Li⁶I-crystal	—	1·0 mm	$1 \cdot 84 \times 10^{-3}$	82 %	>95 %[a]	2·1[b]	0·1 μsec

[a] For scintillator mounted directly on the photomultiplier
[b] Measured with thick detector
[c] Maximum pulse height with detection of cobalt-60 γ-ray used

4.20 Other Detectors

Many luminescent liquids which incorporate boron have been suggested as neutron detectors. For example, Bollinger and Thomas (1957) have described a boron-10 containing scintillation counter in which boron in the form of trimethyl borate is added to a liquid scintillator (POPOP). Using a liquid thickness of only 0·5 millimetre this offers an efficient detector of thermal neutrons. It suffers from the low pulse height common to liquid scintillators and this feature has discouraged their use in slow neutron scattering experiments.

Lithium iodide is known to luminesce when it absorbs ionizing radiation and europium activated lithium-6 iodide crystals have been tested by Nicholson and Snelling (1954) and by Schenk and Heath (1952) as neutron detectors. The principal disadvantage reported is high γ-detection efficiency due largely to the presence of the high atomic number element iodine. However, when used as a thermal neutron detector the required thickness of crystal is small ($\sim$1 mm) so that pulse height discrimination against γ-detection may be employed as most recoil electrons would leave the scintillator without dissipating all of their energy, as already discussed in connection with the scintillating glasses. Thermal neutron detectors based on lithium-6 iodide are discussed by Haas et al. (1961).

4.21 Summary of Detector Performance

Important parameters of the detectors which have been discussed are summarized in Table 4.8.

The ready discrimination against γ-ray detection of the boron trifluoride filled detector together with its stable characteristics and availability has led to its great popularity. It is the universal choice in crystal spectrometer techniques. The helium-3 filled detector is less widely available; this situation is improving and its high detection efficiency per unit thickness recommends it for use with the time-of-flight technique.

The high detection efficiency in a very thin detector has led to the development of the scintillation counter. The zinc sulphide containing phosphors have proved the most successful, the application of the pulse shape discrimination method for reducing γ-detection having made a marked improvement in their performance. The disadvantages of these ZnS(Ag) phosphors are firstly, their broad pulse height distribution which makes necessary very stable associated circuitry and secondly, the need to calibrate experimentally the detection efficiency as a function of neutron energy.

Discrimination against γ-detection with other scintillators is substantially worse but the improved γ-discrimination available by using very thin detecting layers may make them useful in certain applications.

References

Abson, W., Salmon, P. G. and Pyrah, S. (1958). *Proc. Inst. elect. Engrs* **105B**, 357.

Allen, W. D. (1960). In "Neutron Detection". Newnes, London.

Anderson, D. G., Dracass, J., Flanagan, T. P. and Noe, E. N. (1962). BISRA Report A. 79.

Bajorek, A., Golikov, V. V., Zhukovskaya, I., Shapiro, F. L., Shkatula, A. and Janik, J. A. (1963). *In* "Inelastic Scattering of Neutrons in Solids and Liquids", Vol. I, p. 383. IAEA, Vienna.

Bergere, R. (1961). *In* "Neutron Time-of-Flight Methods", ed. by J. Spaepen, p. 329. Euratom, Brussels.

Blokhin, G. E. *et al.* (1961). *Atomnaya Energiya* **10**, No. 5, 437.

Bollinger, L. M. and Thomas, G. E. (1957). *Rev. sci. Instrum.* **28**, 489.

Bollinger, L. M., Thomas, G. E. and Ginther, R. J. (1962). *Nucl. Instrum. Methods* **17**, No. 1, 97.

Bondarenko, I. I., Liforov, V. G., Nikolaev, M. N., Orlov, V. V., Parfenov, V. A., Semenov, V. A., Smirnov, V. I. and Turchin, V. F. (1963). *In* "Inelastic Scattering of Neutrons in Solids and Liquids", Vol. I, p. 127. IAEA, Vienna.

Brooks, F. D. (1956). *Progr. nucl. Phys.* **5**, 252.

Butterworth, I., Egelstaff, P. A., London, H. and Webb, F. J. (1957). *Phil. Mag.* **2**, 917.

Christ, J. and Springer, T. (1962). *Nukleonik* **4**, 23.

Coceva, C. (1963). *Nucl. Instrum. Methods* **21**, No. 1, 93.

Cohen, E. R. (1955). USAEC Report NAA-SR.1127.

Curran, S. C. and Craggs, J. D. (1949). "Counting Tubes, Theory and Application". Butterworths, London.

Dyer, R. F., Low, G. G. E. and Lowde, R. D. (1959). Report AERE R.2981. H.M.S.O., London.

Egelstaff, P. A., London, H. and Webb, F. J. (1955). *In* "Conférence de Physique des Basses Températures", p. 375. Paris.

Egelstaff, P. A. (1957). Meeting "Use of Slow Neutrons to Investigate the Solid State". Swedish Atomic Energy Report, Stockholm.

Egelstaff, P. A., Cocking, S. J. and Alexander, T. K. (1960). AECL Report CRRP.1078.

Egelstaff, P. A., Haywood, B. C., Webb, F. J. and Baston, A. H. (1964). *Phys. Letters* **12**, 188.

Egelstaff, P. A., Moffitt, R. D. and Saunderson, D. H. (1964). Report AERE R.4289. H.M.S.O., London.

Forte, M. (1961). *In* "Neutron Time-of-Flight Methods", ed. by J. Spaepen, p. 457. Euratom, Brussels.

Firk, F. W. K. (1962). *In* "Fast Neutron Physics", Part II, p. 2237. Interscience, New York.

Gaerttner, E. R., Yeater, M. L. and Fullwood, R. R. (1962). *In* "Neutron Physics", ed. by M. L. Yeater, p. 263. Academic Press, New York.

Ginther, R. J. (1960). *IRE Trans. nucl. Sci.* NS-7, No. 2–3, p. 28.

Ginther, R. J. and Shulman, J. N. (1958). *IRE Trans. nucl. Sci.* NS-5, No. 3, p. 92.

Golikov, V. V., Shapiro, F. L., Shkatula, A. and Janik, J. A. (1963). *In* "Inelastic Scattering of Neutrons in Solids and Liquids", Vol. I, p. 119. IAEA, Vienna.

Golikov, V. V., Shimchak, G. F. and Shkatula, A. (1963). *Instrum. exp. Techn.* No. 2, p. 243.

Haas, R., Kley, W., Krebs, W. and Rubin, R. (1961). *In* "Neutron Time-of-Flight Methods", ed. by J. Spaepen, p. 289, Euratom, Brussels.

Harris, D. H. C. (1961). Report AERE R.3688. H.M.S.O., London.

Harris, D. H. C., Cocking, S. J., Egelstaff, P. A. and Webb, F. J. (1963a). *In* "Inelastic Scattering of Neutrons in Solids and Liquids, Vol. I, p. 107. IAEA, Vienna.

Harris, D. H. C., Duffill, C. and Wraight, L. A. (1963b). *In* "Inelastic Scattering of Neutrons in Solids and Liquids", Vol. I, p. 171. IAEA, Vienna.

Jacrot, B. (1962). "Pile Neutron Research in Physics", p. 393. IAEA, Vienna.

Jacrot, B., Lacaze, A. and Weil, L. (1959). 10th Congress of Institut International du Froid (Copenhagen).

Kottwitz, D. A. (1960). *Nucl. Sci. Engng* **7**, 345.

Kouts, H. (1963). *J. nucl. Energy*, **17**, Nos. 4/5, 153.

Lewis, B. and Von Elbe, G. (1951). "Combustion, Flames and Explosion of Gases". Academic Press, New York.

Maier-Leibnitz, H., (1962). General Atomic Inc. Report GA-3075.

Maier-Leibnitz, H. and Springer, T. (1963). *J. Nucl. Energy*, **17**, Nos. 4/5, 217.

McReynolds, A. W. (1962). *In* "Pile Neutron Research in Physics", p. 469. IAEA, Vienna.

McReynolds, A. W. and Whittemore, W. L. (1962). *In* "Inelastic Scattering of Neutrons in Solids and Liquids", p. 421. IAEA, Vienna.

McReynolds, A. W. and Whittemore, W. L. (1963). *In* "Inelastic Scattering of Neutrons in Solids and Liquids", Vol. I, p. 263. IAEA, Vienna.

Mills, W. R., Caldwell, R. L. and Morgan, I. R. (1962). *Rev. Sci. Instrum.* **33**, 866.

Møller, H. B., Passell, L. and Stecher-Rasmussen, F. (1963). *J. nucl. Energy* **17**, Nos. 4/5, 227.

Nicholson, K. P. (1955). Report AERE N/R.1639. H.M.S.O., London.

Nicholson, K. P. and Snelling, G. F. (1954). Report AERE EL/R.1350. H.M.S.O., London.

Palevsky, H., Otnes, K., Larsson, K. E., Pauli, R. and Stedman, R. (1957). *Phys. Rev.* **108**, 1346.

Poole, M. J. (1964). Private communication.

Ribon, P. and Michaudon, A. (1961). *In* "Neutron Time-of-Flight Methods", ed. J. Spaepen, p 357. Euratom, Brussels.

Schenck, J. and Heath, R. L. (1952). *Phys. Rev.* **85**, 923.

Schofield, P. (1960). Report AERE R.3400. H.M.S.O., London.

Stedman, R. (1960). AECL Report CRRP-931.

Sun, K. H., Malmberg, P. R. and Pecjak, F. A. (1956). *Nucleonics* **14**, No. 7, 46.

Van Dingenen, W. and Hautecler, S. (1960). CEN Report R.1888.

Van Dingenen, W. (1962). *Nucl. Instrum. Methods*, **16**, 116.

Voitovetskii, V. K. and Tomacheva, N. S. (1961). *Atomnaya Energiya* **10**, No. 5, 504.

Ward, D. L., Pearce, D. G. and Merrett, D. J. (1963). Report AERE R.4312. H.M.S.O., London.

Webb, F. J. (1958). Report AERE NP/R.2547. H.M.S.O., London.

Webb, F. J. (1961). *Nucl. Sci. Engng* **9**, 120.

Webb, F. J. (1963). *J. nucl. Energy* **17**, No. 4/5, 187.

Webb, F. J. (1965). Report AERE R.4263. H.M.S.O., London.

Webb, F. J. and Pearce, D. G. (1963). *In* "Inelastic Scattering of Neutrons in Solids and Liquids", Vol. I, p. 83. IAEA, Vienna.

Whittemore, W. L. (1963). General Atomic Inc., Report GA.4292.

Whittemore, W. L. and Danner, H. R. (1963). *In* "Inelastic Scattering of Neutrons in Solids and Liquids", Vol. I, p. 273. IAEA, Vienna.

Wraight, L. A. (1961). Report AERE M.833. H.M.S.O., London.

Wraight, L. A., Harris, D. H. C. and Egelstaff, P. A. (1965). *Nucl. Instrum. Methods* **33**, 181.

Zimmerman, R. L., Palevsky, H., Chrien, R. E., Olsen, W. C., Singh, P. P. and Westcott, C. H. (1961). *Nucl. Instrum. Methods* **13**, No. 1, 1.

CHAPTER 5

Thermal Vibrations of Crystal Lattices

G. DOLLING AND A. D. B. WOODS

Atomic Energy of Canada, Ltd., Chalk River, Ontario, Canada

5.1 Introduction.. 193
5.2 Metals and Alloys: Introduction..................................... 198
5.3 Face-centred Cubic Metals.. 201
5.4 Body-centred Cubic Metals.. 207
5.5 Other Metals and Alloys.. 212
5.6 Semiconductors: Introduction.. 216
5.7 Force Models for Semiconductors..................................... 219
5.8 Semiconductors: Comparison of Theory and Experiment................ 221
5.9 Determination of Polarization Vectors............................... 223
5.10 Ionic Crystals: Introduction.. 225
5.11 Shell Models for Alkali Halides..................................... 226
5.12 Longitudinal Optic Modes of Alkali Halides.......................... 229
5.13 Calcium Fluoride and Uranium Dioxide................................ 231
5.14 Strontium Titanate.. 233
5.15 Carbon... 235
5.16 Hydrogen Vibrations in Compounds.................................... 238
5.17 Anharmonic Effects.. 239
5.18 Summary.. 243
References... 244

List of Symbols

$C(\mathbf{q})$	Coulomb matrix elements	$\Delta(\mathbf{q}s\omega)$	Shift in phonon frequency due
K_F	Fermi radius		to anharmonicity
$R(\mathbf{q})$	Short-range (Born-von Kármán)	ϵ	Dielectric constant
	matrix elements	Φ_n	Interplanar force constant
$\Gamma(\mathbf{q}s\omega)$	Broadening of phonon frequency	$\Phi(\mathbf{q}s)$	Fourier transform of force con-
	due to anharmonicity		stant

5.1 Introduction

The possibility of obtaining information concerning the lattice dynamics of crystalline solids by means of inelastic scattering of slow neutrons was recognized independently by several physicists rather more than ten years ago (e.g. Placzek and Van Hove, 1954). The main purpose of the present chapter is to collect and summarize this work under the several headings which seem appropriate in view of the need not only to present existing results, but also to indicate current trends in this field. First, however, we shall make a few introductory remarks in order to establish a terminology and a framework within which the subsequent detailed discussion will be treated.

The cross-section for inelastic scattering of slow neutrons from a crystalline solid may be divided into two parts, a coherent and an incoherent part (see Chapter 1, equations (1.91)–(1.98)). Each part may itself be regarded as a sum of contributions arising from interactions between the neutron and the crystal involving one or more quanta of lattice vibrations (phonons). This description of the (assumed harmonic) vibrations of the nuclei in the crystal in terms of non-interacting lattice waves has been outlined in Chapter 1, and will be discussed in more detail in this chapter. Thus we may speak of "coherent two-phonon" scattering, "incoherent one-phonon" scattering, and so on. It is known (Placzek and Van Hove, 1954) that, from the point of view of the study of crystal dynamics, the most interesting and useful scattering processes are those involving one phonon. Scattering experiments utilizing such processes are thus designed to minimize the "background noise" of multiphonon processes as far as possible.

From coherent one-phonon scattering, it is possible to determine the frequencies (ν), wave vectors ($\mathbf{q}$) and polarization vectors ($\mathbf{V}_s^l$) of the normal modes of vibration of a crystal lattice.

The function $\nu_s(\mathbf{q})$, usually referred to as the phonon dispersion relation, may be measured by reason of the two δ-functions in equation (1.96) for the coherent one-phonon scattering cross-section, which express the fact that two conservation conditions, those of energy and "crystal momentum", must be satisfied for such scattering to occur:

$$E_0 - E \equiv \frac{\hbar}{2m}(k_0^2 - k^2) = +h\nu \tag{5.1}$$

$$\mathbf{k}_0 - \mathbf{k} \equiv \mathbf{Q} = 2\pi\boldsymbol{\tau} \pm \mathbf{q} \tag{5.2}$$

where E_0, E are the initial and final neutron energies, $\mathbf{k}_0$, $\mathbf{k}$ the corresponding neutron wave vectors, m the neutron mass, $\mathbf{Q}$ the momentum transfer vector, and $\boldsymbol{\tau}$ any reciprocal lattice vector. The $+(-)$ sign refers to phonon creation (annihilation) during the scattering process. Details of experimental methods for determining $\nu(\mathbf{q})$ by means of these equations are given in Chapters 2 and 3. The basic idea is quite straightforward; a monoenergetic beam of neutrons is allowed to fall upon the single crystal specimen. If the experimental conditions are such that the coherent one-phonon cross-section is large, then a well defined peak will be observed in the distribution of scattered neutrons. From the neutron energy corresponding to the centre of this peak, the energy $h\nu$ of the phonon concerned may be deduced, by means of equation (5.1) (the centre of the peak is generally taken to be the mid-point at half the maximum height). If, further, the specimen orientation and scattering angle are known, the phonon wave-vector may be obtained from equation (5.2). The importance of the third term in equation (1.96), usually called the "inelastic structure factor" or simply "the structure factor", should be emphasized:

$$F_{\tau s} = |\sum_l \bar{b}_l \exp(i\mathbf{Q} \cdot \boldsymbol{\rho}_l)\mathbf{Q} \cdot \mathbf{V}_s^l \, M_l^{-\frac{1}{2}} e^{-W_l}|^2 \qquad (5.3)$$

The occurrence of the polarization vectors $\mathbf{V}_s^l$ in this term permits, in principle at least, the determination of $\mathbf{V}_s^l$ by absolute measurements of the cross-section. A more detailed discussion of this point, together with appropriate experimental results for the particular case of germanium, will be given in Section 5.9.

Incoherent scattering, on the other hand, gives information concerning the frequency distribution function, $z(\nu)$, (or $z(f)$ where $f = 2\pi\nu$) of the normal modes. This follows at once from equation (1.106), which illustrates the very direct connection between the incoherent one-phonon scattering cross-section and $z(\nu)$, at least for simple crystals.

It should be emphasized that the above discussion rests upon two basic assumptions made in the conventional theory of lattice vibrations, namely, the *adiabatic* and *harmonic* approximations (Peierls, 1955; Ziman, 1960; Born and Huang, 1954; Chester, 1961; Leibfried and Ludwig, 1963). It may be possible, under suitable conditions, to detect the breakdown of either of these approximations by means of slow neutron scattering experiments. Some of the experiments to be described in the following sections, particularly Section 5.17, do in fact provide evidence for such breakdown.

Before entering into a discussion of the value, for lattice dynamics, of a knowledge of the functions $\nu_s(\mathbf{q})$, $\mathbf{V}_s^l(\mathbf{q})$ and $z(\nu)$, it would perhaps be in order to mention certain practical limitations to the application of these neutron scattering techniques. For example, there are two main points to be noted in connection with coherent one-phonon experiments. First, in order to perform such experiments, we require a *single crystal* specimen of high purity and crystalline perfection. Limited studies may be possible (see Section 5.15) with very poor specimens, but in general it is desirable for the crystals to have mosaic spreads less than about $\frac{1}{4}°$. Difficulties which may arise when the crystal mosaic spread is of this order or larger are discussed in Section 5.4. It is usually advantageous, in order to obtain adequate counting rates, to use quite large crystals, anywhere between 2 and 50 cm³ in volume, and this requirement seriously restricts, at the present time, the number of materials which may be studied in this way.

The second point, which is related to the first, concerns the absorption cross-section of the scattering material for slow neutrons. If this is high, then it is clearly necessary to employ a thin specimen in order that a reasonable proportion of the scattered neutrons may avoid being absorbed. Such a thin specimen will scatter relatively few neutrons and thus provide very low counting rates in the detectors. In practice, therefore, experiments are limited to those materials of not too high absorption cross-section (preferably less than 5 barns and certainly less than 100 barns). If much larger neutron fluxes become available in the future, it will of course become possible to study materials of increasingly unfavourable characteristics. It is also desirable that the specimen should have a very low or zero incoherent scattering cross-section, since incoherently scattered neutrons contribute to the "background" count rate, and may even, under certain circumstances (see Section 5.12) give rise to distributions resembling those from coherent scattering processes.

The relationships between the interatomic force constants and the frequencies, $\nu_s(\mathbf{q})$, of the normal modes of vibration in a crystal, have been expressed in terms of the *dynamical matrix*, $\boldsymbol{E}(\mathbf{q})$ (see Chapter 1, equations (1.81) and (1.84)). If there are L atoms per primitive unit cell, then $\boldsymbol{E}$ is of order $(3L \times 3L)$. For wave vectors in certain planes or directions of high symmetry in the crystal, it may be possible to factorize $\boldsymbol{E}$ into matrices of lower order. For example, in a mirror plane of symmetry, $\boldsymbol{E}$ factorizes into a $(2L \times 2L)$ matrix and a $(L \times L)$ matrix. The latter matrix refers to modes whose polarization vectors $\mathbf{V}_s^1$ are perpendicular to the mirror plane, and the former to modes with $\mathbf{V}_s^1$ lying *in* the plane. Further simplifications may be obtained, as, for example, in the $[\zeta\zeta\zeta]$ direction in a cubic crystal, where factorization into three $(L \times L)$ matrices occurs. The polarization vectors of the normal modes must, in this case, lie either parallel or perpendicular to the $[\zeta\zeta\zeta]$ direction, corresponding to strictly longitudinal or transverse vibrations, respectively. It should be emphasized that, in general, the normal modes are *not* strictly longitudinal or transverse, though it is often convenient to apply these labels rather loosely in order to identify the different modes.

Identification and classification of the normal modes are relatively straightforward for crystals having simple structures. In more complicated crystals, however, these problems require the application of the techniques of group theory for satisfactory solutions. The group theoretical notation used to indicate various directions in reciprocal space is given by Bouckaert *et al.* (1936) and Koster (1957). For example, in a cubic crystal, the $[00\zeta]$, $[\zeta\zeta0]$ and $[\zeta\zeta\zeta]$ directions are denoted by Δ, Σ and V respectively.

The significance of the above remarks from the theoretical point of view is clear: the analysis of normal mode frequencies, in terms of interatomic force constants, is very much simpler for $\mathbf{q}$ in directions of high symmetry than for some general value of $\mathbf{q}$. For a Bravais lattice ($L = 1$), the (3×3) dynamical matrix reduces immediately to three linear relations between the interatomic force constants and the squares of the phonon frequencies. For the diamond type structure ($L = 2$), one obtains three quadratic relations in place of the general (6×6) matrix. To a somewhat lesser degree, the same discussion applies to the treatment of experimental data in a mirror plane of symmetry.

In addition to these theoretical considerations, there are also substantial experimental advantages in performing experiments in mirror symmetry planes. We notice in equation (1.96) the occurrence of a factor $\mathbf{Q} . \mathbf{V}^l$ in the expression of the coherent one-phonon cross-section. Thus if $\mathbf{Q}$ and $\mathbf{V}^l_s$ are perpendicular for any particular mode, s, then no neutron scattering will be observed corresponding to that mode. If the experiments are arranged with $\mathbf{Q}$ always lying in a mirror plane of the crystal then no scattering can be observed for those modes polarized perpendicular to the plane. It is then much easier to observe clearly and identify unambiguously the remaining modes which do contribute to the scattered intensity. This technique is also very valuable in differentiating between these remaining modes, at least in those special directions where the orientations of the $\mathbf{V}^l_s$ are fixed by symmetry: it may be possible to choose experimental conditions such that scattering from transverse modes is prohibited $(\mathbf{Q} \perp \mathbf{V}^l(\text{trans.}))$ while that from longitudinal modes is a maximum $(\mathbf{Q} \| \mathbf{V}^l(\text{longit.}))$. Furthermore, the frequencies and polarization vectors will have *stationary* values along directions perpendicular to a mirror plane, and may therefore be expected to change relatively slowly in the vicinity of and perpendicular to that plane. This allows the experimentalist to relax his requirements of angular collimation of the incident and scattered neutron beams in this direction, thus obtaining higher counting rates without significant loss in accuracy of measurement.

As would be expected, the above considerations apply most effectively to the cases of crystals belonging to the highly symmetric groups, such as the cubic, hexagonal and tetragonal groups, and particularly to crystals in which the various atoms occupy special positions in the unit cell. It will not be surprising, therefore, to discover that almost all coherent one-phonon scattering experiments to date have been performed on simple crystals (usually cubic, and with only one or two atoms per unit cell), and have been concerned with the measurement of frequencies of phonons with wave vectors lying in mirror planes and, even more commonly, in high symmetry directions. These measurements of $\nu(\mathbf{q})$ have generally been analysed on the basis of various lattice dynamical models. That most often used is the Born-von Kármán model in which the (harmonic) interatomic forces are restricted only by the requirements of crystal symmetry (Chapter 1).

The subject divides most naturally into sections, each of which deals with materials of a particular type of interatomic binding and crystal structure. Subsequent sections are devoted to metals and alloys, diamond-type semiconductors, and ionic crystals; any remaining materials such as hydrogen containing compounds and graphite, which do not fit into the above categories are considered in separate "miscellaneous" sections. Experimental

results and theoretical work concerned with anharmonic effects in crystals
are briefly summarized in Section 5.17.

5.2 Metals and Alloys: Introduction

Neutron inelastic scattering has been applied more extensively to the study
of the lattice dynamics of metallic crystals than to any other type of material.
Coherent inelastic scattering from single crystals has been used to determine

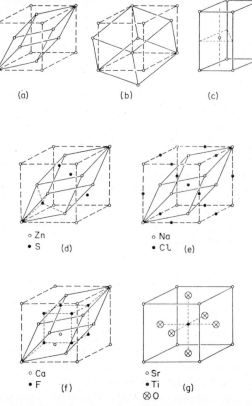

FIG. 5.1. Some simple crystal structures: (a) face-centred cubic, (b) body-centred cubic,
(c) hexagonal close-packed, (d) zinc blende, (e) sodium chloride, (f) fluorite (calcium fluoride),
(g) cubic perovskite (strontium titanate). The solid lines show the primitive unit cell in each
case.

the details of the dispersion curves in particular directions for many metals
(Al, Be, Cr, Cu, Fe, Mg, Mo, Na, Nb, Ni, Pb, Sn, Ta, W, Zn) and for the alloy
β-brass (CuZn). In addition the frequency distribution function ($z(f)$ or $z(\nu)$)
has been determined for various metals (V, Ni, Be, Ti) and alloys (Mn–Co,

Ti–Zr) using incoherent scattering from powdered specimens and other related techniques.

With the exception of tin, which is body-centred tetragonal, all of these metals belong to one of three simple crystal structures: face-centred cubic (f.c.c.), body-centred cubic (b.c.c.), and hexagonal close-packed (h.c.p.). The f.c.c. and b.c.c. structures have one atom per primitive unit cell, the h.c.p. two. These structures are illustrated in Fig. 5.1. The solid lines in each figure delineate the primitive unit cell. Application of the Born-von Kármán theory of lattice dynamics to these structures is straightforward. In most instances, however, interatomic forces of very long range have to be invoked to provide a satisfactory description of the observed dispersion relations, necessitating an inconveniently large number of disposable parameters. The conduction electrons play a significant part in determining the lattice dynamics, but their explicit inclusion into the dynamical equations is a very difficult problem, and has been attempted with success only for the case of sodium (Toya, 1958a); it is probably significant, however, that sodium is better described by a Born-von Kármán model with short range interactions than is any other metal studied to date. The electron–phonon interaction is particularly strong in such metals as lead, and may cause discontinuities in the slope of the dispersion curve at wave-vector values which bear a direct relationship to the Fermi surface. This effect was predicted by Kohn (1959) and will be discussed in more detail in connection with the lattice dynamics of lead (Section 5.3).

In the previous paragraph it was pointed out that even qualitative analysis of the $\nu(\mathbf{q})$ dispersion relation in terms of the Born-von Kármán theory of lattice dynamics could lead to some very interesting conclusions; this is true whether or not the Born-von Kármán force constants are physically significant in terms of direct two body interactions. A very convenient method of analysis which can be applied to simple substances is a Fourier series analysis (Foreman and Lomer, 1957) of the form

$$4\pi^2 M\nu^2 = \sum_{n=1}^{N} \Phi_n(1 - \cos n\pi q/q_{\max}) \qquad (5.4)$$

where $q_{\max}$ is the value of q beyond which that particular dispersion curve begins to repeat. In this equation, which is valid for dispersion curves in symmetry directions and for substances containing one atom per primitive unit cell, the Φ_n are linear combinations of the interatomic force constants, $G_{\mathbf{u}k\beta}^{\nu l\alpha}$ (see discussion following equation (1.76)). These Φ_n are known as the interplanar force constants, and it is instructive to consider them in this light without going through the detailed Born-von Kármán lattice dynamics for interactions out to very distant neighbours, for which the mathematics gets very cumbersome. Consider a face-centred cubic crystal with waves propagating along the cube edge ([00ζ] or Δ direction). Nearest neighbour *planes* contain first neighbour *atoms* (as well as many more distant neighbours), and hence, the leading interplanar force constant, Φ_1, for this direction will contain a *first* neighbour force constant, e.g. using the notation of Brockhouse *et al.* (1962),

$$\Phi_1 = 8\alpha_1 + 16\beta_3 + 8\beta_5 + \ldots \qquad (5.5)$$

for the Δ longitudinal branch. The closest neighbour in the third plane *in this direction* is the one at position (310), which is a fifth nearest neighbour. Thus the leading term in Φ_3 is a fifth neighbour force constant, and if the Fourier series for ν^2 in this direction requires three terms ($N = 3$), then the interatomic forces (on a Born-von Kármán model) extend to at least fifth neighbours. The Fourier series analysis of dispersion curves in symmetry directions thus provides a very simple, yet powerful, method for determining the range of the interatomic forces in a material with one atom per unit cell. The method also has limited applicability in several other more complicated situations. For lattice vibrations propagating along a direction *in* a mirror plane of symmetry, such a Fourier analysis may be performed directly upon the modes whose polarization vectors are perpendicular to that plane (transverse modes), and also upon the sums of the squares of the frequencies of the other two modes. Similarly, if there are two atoms in the unit cell, then the analysis can be applied, in symmetry directions, to the sum of the squares of the frequencies of the optic and acoustic branches. The usefulness of analysing sums of squares of frequencies is doubtful, however, as information about certain types of interactions is immediately discarded and, in addition, the presence of a high frequency branch will tend to swamp the information contained in the accompanying low frequency branch. This method of Fourier analysis has therefore been applied extensively to symmetry directions in simple crystals, but only rarely in other circumstances. An example of the Fourier analysis method as applied to lead is given in Section 5.3. Rosenstock (1963) has considered a related type of analysis involving the sums of squares of frequencies for a given **q**. Its limitations are similar to those encountered in all except the simple applications of the Fourier series method discussed above.

We now discuss briefly a method of dealing with the problem of the lattice dynamics of metals from first principles, in contrast to the phenomenological Born-von Kármán theory. The interatomic forces in a metal can be considered to consist of three parts: (1) a force due to the overlap of the electron shells of near neighbour ions; (2) a Coulomb interaction between the bare ions; and (3) interionic forces which act via the conduction electrons. The overlap potential is usually assumed to be of the Born-Mayer type

$$V(r) = A \exp\left(-r/\rho_0\right)$$

where A and ρ_0 are disposable parameters. This term may represent a large contribution to the cohesive energy, as is believed to be the case in copper, but in certain metals, for example sodium (Vosko, 1964), it is quite small and can be neglected. The Coulomb interaction can be calculated exactly with the help of Ewald lattice sums (Ewald, 1921), but, as would be expected on physical grounds, this contribution is largely cancelled by the screening effect of the conduction electron gas. The net effect of the near cancellation of these interactions can be very neatly described in terms of a weak pseudo-potential between the ions (see Ziman (1964) for a lucid discussion of this approach). The Fourier transform of the screened interionic potential is then modified by a dielectric function $\epsilon(Q)$, which has been evaluated by Bardeen (1937) for the case of a simple metal with a spherical Fermi surface of radius K_F:

$$\epsilon(Q) = 1 + \frac{4\pi e^2\, N(E_F)}{Q^2}\left\{1/2 + \frac{4K_F^2+Q^2}{8K_F\, Q}\ \ln\ \left|\frac{2K_F+Q}{2K_F-Q}\right|\right\}$$

where $N(E_F)$ is the electron density of states at the Fermi surface. The logarithmic singularity in $\epsilon(Q)$ at $Q = 2K_F$ gives rise to the Kohn effect which will be discussed in more detail in Section 5·3. The process of transforming this modified potential back into real space will clearly give rise to long range oscillations in the effective interionic potential. These can be shown to be of the form $r^{-3}\cos(2K_Fr+\phi)$ (ϕ is a complicated phase factor) and are analogous to the oscillations in the electron density at large distances from an impurity atom in a metal, first discussed by Friedel (1952, 1962). Koenig (1964) has emphasized the relation of corresponding oscillations of the interplanar force constants to the details of the Fermi surface. Although such oscillations have been observed (Sections 5.3 and 5.4) it is difficult to extract precise information concerning the Fermi surface from them for two reasons: (1) the oscillating function is not well-defined because of the small number of significant Fourier coefficients, and (2) this function may be the sum of several oscillations with different periods and different spatial dependence of amplitude. Nevertheless, the observation of such oscillatory behaviour in the interatomic potential provides evidence in favour of the existence of Kohn anomalies and the validity of the pseudopotential approach.

5.3 Face-centred Cubic Metals

The face-centred cubic metals were the first to be studied by coherent inelastic neutron scattering techniques. The dispersion relations for aluminium were first measured by Brockhouse and Stewart (1958), and by Carter et al. (1957), and latterly by Larsson et al. (1960), Stedman and Nilsson (1965), and Yarnell et al. (1965). Copper, lead, and nickel are the other face-centred cubic metals which have been investigated.

Most information in symmetry directions in face-centred cubic materials

8*

is obtained from scattering in the $(1\bar{1}0)$ plane of the crystal. With the crystal in this orientation measurements can be made of both longitudinal and transverse branches in the $[00\zeta]$ and $[\zeta\zeta\zeta]$ directions (both transverse branches are degenerate in these directions), and the longitudinal and one of the transverse branches (the one with polarization vector parallel to the cube edge, called T_2) in the $[\zeta\zeta0]$ direction. The $[\zeta\zeta0]$ transverse branch with its polarization vector parallel to the face diagonal (T_1) may be observed through scattering in the (001) plane. In this case modes with wave vector coordinates along the line $[1\zeta0]$ may also be observed. These modes are neither longitudinal nor transverse, but their polarization is determined from symmetry and hence the squares of their frequencies depend linearly upon the interatomic force constants. For f.c.c. crystals it is advantageous to continue measurements in the $[\zeta\zeta0]$ direction beyond the zone boundary (at $(0\cdot75, 0\cdot75, 0)$) to the point (1,1,0), beyond which the dispersion curve repeats. At this point, which is equivalent to the point (0,0,1), the $[\zeta\zeta0]L$ branch is degenerate with the $[00\zeta]T$ and the $[\zeta\zeta0]T_2$ is degenerate with the $[00\zeta]L$. These symmetry properties have been experimentally verified in all face-centred cubic materials so far studied. Similar considerations, involving different points in reciprocal space, hold for body-centred cubic structures.

Historically, aluminium was the first material for which the dispersion relations were measured. By present day standards the results were not very precise, but they were good enough to indicate that a theory based on near neighbour Born-von Kármán type interactions was not sufficient to represent the data accurately. More recent data have confirmed these early conclusions. Figure 5.2 shows the dispersion curves of aluminium for the $[00\zeta]$ and $[\zeta\zeta0]$ directions as measured by various groups of workers. Measurements by Walker (1956) using X-rays are also included. Detailed analysis by Squires (1963) has indicated that, within the Born-von Kármán theory, the data of Larsson et al. (1960) can only be fitted by assuming that interactions exist out to at least seventh nearest neighbours. Squires has noticed that the values of the interatomic force constants $(G_{uk\beta}^{v\,l\,\alpha})$ vary considerably ($\sim$5–10 %) as more distant neighbours are added. On the other hand the interplanar force constants, the Φ_n, remain remarkably constant ($\sim$1 %) when more distant planes are added to the Fourier fits. The physical significance of such long range direct interatomic forces in crystals, particularly metals, is open to question. Even when the measurements have been made at low temperatures, the anharmonic contributions from the zero point motion may be quite significant; more work needs to be done to clear up this point. In defence of the long range interatomic force constant fits, it may be said that they often constitute a very useful way of presenting the data and also provide what is probably a fairly accurate interpolation formula for calculating the frequencies of other modes and such quantities as $z(f)$, the frequency distribution function.

Some data on the dispersion relations in copper (Cribier *et al.*, 1961; Sosnowski and Kozubowski, 1962; Sinha and Squires, 1965) have been obtained. The results of neutron experiments are not consistent with each other, nor do they agree with the X-ray results of Jacobsen (1955). Toya (1958*b*) has performed calculations on copper similar to those for sodium. The two disposable parameters describing the Born-Mayer-type overlap potential

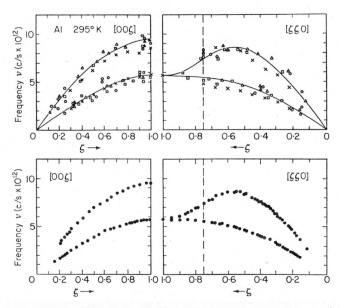

Fig. 5.2. The [00ζ]*L* and *T* and the [ζζ0]*L* and T_1 branches of the dispersion relation for aluminium as measured by various workers. The lower curve shows in detail the results of Yarnell *et al.* (1965) while the upper diagram shows the results of other workers (□—Brockhouse and Stewart, 1958; ○—Carter *et al.*, 1957; △—Larsson *et al.*, 1960; ×—Walker, 1956) compared with those of Yarnell *et al.* shown by the solid line.

between nearest neighbours in copper have been fitted (by Toya) to the zone boundary frequencies in the [ζζζ] direction as measured by X-rays. A more precise determination of the dispersion relations for copper would provide a useful test of this theory.

The dispersion relations for lead have been measured (Brockhouse *et al.*, 1962) very precisely and in this case the analysis indicates that Born-von Kármán-type forces are of extremely long range. The curves showed several interesting features. Local minima were observed in the [00ζ] direction at the zone boundary; these lead to extra critical points (Van Hove, 1953) in the frequency distribution function. The curves also showed sharp (within the resolution) discontinuities in slope (Brockhouse *et al.*, 1961a) which have been attributed to the Kohn effect.

The Kohn effect results from an abrupt change in the ability of the electrons to shield the ionic motions. The electrons cannot be scattered, with conservation of energy, with a wave vector transfer greater than an extremal distance across the Fermi surface. The force constants determining the ionic motions undergo an abrupt change when the phonon wave vector passes through the value determined by the relation

$$2K_F = |2\pi\tau+\mathbf{q}|, \qquad (5.6)$$

where K_F is the Fermi radius. The sign of the effect obeys the rule (Brockhouse *et al.*, 1962; Woll and Kohn, 1962) "as the phonon wave vector in the extended zone scheme exceeds the Fermi diameter, the abrupt decrease in

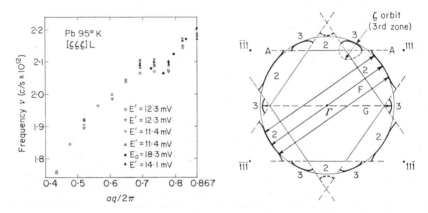

FIG. 5.3. The left hand side shows an expanded plot of the $[\zeta\zeta\zeta]L$ branch in lead at 100°K, showing the pronounced anomaly (believed to be caused by the Kohn effect) near $\zeta = 0.75$, for a series of measurements under different experimental conditions. The right hand side shows the relation of observed anomalies to the Fermi surface of lead. The arrow marked F corresponds to the anomaly shown on the left-hand side, that marked G to an observed anomaly on the $[\zeta\zeta0]L$ branch.

the shielding of the ions by the electrons causes the frequency to increase anomalously". Figure 5.3 shows an example of the observed effect in the $[\zeta\zeta\zeta]$ direction in lead and the influence of these measurements on the determination of the Fermi surface of lead. These dispersion curve anomalies in lead have been confirmed by X-ray measurements (Paskin and Weiss, 1962).

An example of the Fourier series analysis for the $[00\zeta]T$ branch of lead is shown in Fig. 5.4. The series $N = 2$ (see equation (5.4)) exhausts all contributions of interatomic forces out to and including fourth neighbours. The term $n = 3$ has fifth neighbour contributions, and $n = 4$ eighth neighbour contributions, as their respective leading force constants. The series $N = 2$ is clearly not a good fit to the data and hence at least fifth neighbour interatomic forces are required. The $[00\zeta]L$ branch indicates the necessity for even more terms in the series. The long range Fourier components in this case display oscillatory behaviour (Brockhouse *et al.*, 1962). These are very likely a direct consequence of the Kohn effect and correspond to the Friedel oscillations discussed above. Since the Fermi surface dimensions vary with direction, it is probably not physically realistic to attempt to fit a Born-von Kármán force model with interactions between distant neighbours to the

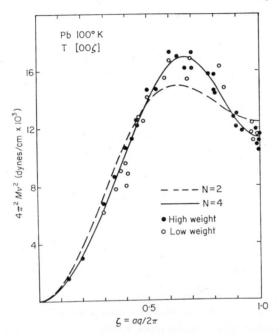

FIG. 5.4. Fourier analysis of $4\pi^2 M\nu^2$ for $[00\zeta]T$ branch in lead at 100°K. The series $N = 2$ exhausts all contributions from first and second neighbours. The necessity for the term $N = 4$ implies the necessity for including interactions out to at least eighth neighbours on a Born-von Kármán model.

experimental results; such a procedure might be more valid for those metals which have a spherical Fermi surface.

It is perhaps appropriate to conclude a discussion of experiments on lead with a description of an experimental difficulty which was particularly acute in that case. In neutron scattering experiments it is important to ensure that the scattered neutrons under observation do in fact result from coherent one-phonon processes, and to avoid confusion with other possible scattering processes: one such other process is that of coherent one-phonon scattering followed or preceded by elastic (Bragg) scattering in the specimen. (Compare this process with the double Bragg scattering process discussed in Chapter 1,

Section 1.8 and Chapter 3, Section 3.6.) The probability for the occurrence of this "double scattering" process depends upon the mosaic spread of the single crystal specimen, and may cause considerable difficulty in specimens with as little as $1/4°$ mosaic spread. One effect of this is to alter the effective cross-section for the simple one-phonon process under observation. Thus, for example, it may be possible by reason of the "double" process, to observe scattering involving a particular normal mode even when the experimental conditions have been specifically designed to eliminate such scattering (by making the wave vector transfer $\mathbf{Q}$ perpendicular to the polarization vector $\mathbf{V}_s^j$ of the normal mode). The incident neutron beam suffers a Bragg reflection in the specimen, and this reflected beam behaves as a secondary "incident beam", which may subsequently undergo one-phonon scattering exactly like the primary incident beam, except that the wave vector transfer $\mathbf{Q}$ will lie in a different direction. A similar argument applies to the reversed "double process" of one-phonon scattering, followed by Bragg reflection of the *scattered* neutron beam. Mathematically this can be seen by considering the conservation of "crystal momentum" equations (cf. equation (5.2)). In the following treatment $\mathbf{k}$ is the wave vector after the first scattering and $\mathbf{k}'$ the wave vector after the second scattering. We have

$$\mathbf{k}_0 - \mathbf{k} = 2\pi\boldsymbol{\tau}_1 + \mathbf{q}$$
$$\mathbf{k} - \mathbf{k}' = 2\pi\boldsymbol{\tau}_2,$$

hence
$$\mathbf{k}_0 - \mathbf{k}' = 2\pi(\boldsymbol{\tau}_1 + \boldsymbol{\tau}_2) + \mathbf{q}$$
$$= 2\pi\boldsymbol{\tau}_3 + \mathbf{q}, \tag{5.7}$$

since the sum of two reciprocal lattice vectors is itself a reciprocal lattice vector. These equations are completely symmetrical with respect to the order in which the elastic–inelastic processes occur.

Figure 5.5 shows neutron groups observed for lead which are thought to be due to this effect. Measurements were made on two different specimens. Specimen B was a sphere about 5 cm in diameter and had a mosaic spread of about $1·3°$. Specimen C was rectangular with dimensions $\sim 1·6$ cm $\times 3·5$ cm $\times 5$ cm; its mosaic spread was $\sim 1/4°$. The experiment was designed so that only the L mode at $(0,0,0·3)$ should appear. In specimen B, however, a strong neutron group with a frequency corresponding to the transverse mode at this point was observed. This anomalous group almost, but not quite, disappears in the specimen with the small mosaic spread.

The crystal dynamics of nickel have recently been studied by several techniques. The $\nu(\mathbf{q})$ dispersion relation has been determined (Birgeneau *et al.*, 1964) for the $[00\zeta]$, $[\zeta\zeta 0]$, $[\zeta\zeta\zeta]$ and $[1\zeta 0]$ directions and the results were fitted reasonably well by a fourth neighbour Born-von Kármán model. From this model the frequency distribution function $z(\nu)$, was calculated in a way similar to that described in Section 5.4. Several attempts to measure $z(\nu)$ directly have also been made. Two of these involved measurements of the total inelastic scattering from single crystal (Brugger, 1964) and powdered (Mozer et al., 1963) specimens of natural isotopic composition. Using a specimen of nickel with such an isotopic composition that the net coherent scattering length $\bar{b}$ was practically zero, Tchernoplekov et al. (1963) have determined $z(\nu)$ by direct measurement of the incoherent inelastic scattering.

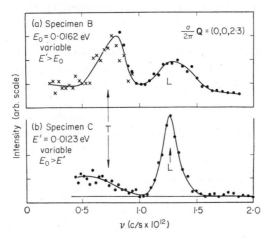

Fig. 5.5. Neutron groups observed in lead at the point $\mathbf{Q} = (0,0,2\cdot3)$ at which, by equation (5.3), only the longitudinal mode should be excited. The group with a frequency corresponding to that of the transverse mode is very strong in specimen B which had a larger mosaic spread than specimen C. (The crosses and filled circles in (a) refer to normalized scans with different counting times.)

Within their accuracy these various determinations of $z(\nu)$ agree with that calculated from the model which was fitted to the dispersion curve measurements. These direct measurements of $z(\nu)$ do not, however, have sufficient resolution to show up any critical points (Van Hove, 1953; Rosenstock, 1955), i.e. discontinuities in $dz/d\nu$ in the $z(\nu)$ curve.

5.4 Body-centred Cubic Metals

Sodium, iron, and the transition metals of the fifth and sixth columns of the periodic table compose the group of body-centred cubic metals which have been studied using the techniques of both coherent and incoherent one-phonon neutron scattering. With the exception of vanadium, for which the scattering cross-section is almost completely incoherent, these metals have been studied through measurements of $\nu(\mathbf{q})$ in symmetry directions using coherent neutron scattering.

The lattice dynamics of body-centred cubic materials has been discussed by several authors, sometimes with an attempt to include specifically the effect of the conduction electrons. Attempts to include the electronic effects in the lattice dynamics must be handled with care, however. The statement is often made that the electrons affect the longitudinal but not the transverse branches. Such a hypothesis may be applied when considering very long wavelength modes but is not applicable to short wavelength modes since, for example, at the zone boundary in the $[00\zeta]$ direction (i.e. the point $(0,0,1)$) the longitudinal and transverse modes are indistinguishable. This fact follows from the symmetry of the body-centred cubic lattice and must not be contradicted by the results deduced from over-simplified models.

The longitudinal and transverse modes are degenerate (by symmetry) not only at $(0,0,1)$ but also at $(\frac{1}{2},\frac{1}{2},\frac{1}{2})$. These symmetry properties are reproduced in all of the measurements made on body-centred cubic metals to date. Besides the $[00\zeta]$, $[\zeta\zeta0]$ and $[\zeta\zeta\zeta]$ directions, there are two other special lines in reciprocal space for which the polarization vectors are fixed by symmetry, and hence the squares of the frequencies amenable to linear analysis, viz., $[\zeta\zeta1]$ and $[\frac{1}{2}\frac{1}{2}\zeta]$.

The dispersion curves for iron have been measured in the $[00\zeta]$, $[\zeta\zeta0]$ and $[\zeta\zeta\zeta]$ directions by Low (1962) and, less extensively, by Iyengar et al. (1961). Low (1962) analysed his results using the Fourier series technique and deduced that third neighbour interactions at least were significant. The elastic constants of iron C_{12} and C_{44} differ by only about 20 % at room temperature and, hence, the forces might be thought to be essentially central. The relations between Low's force constants very nearly satisfy the central force conditions for a body-centred cubic crystal.

The dispersion relation for sodium has been determined (Woods et al., 1962a,b) with high precision, thus permitting a very detailed analysis of the results to be carried out. Measurements have been made at 90°K, along the symmetric lines $[00\zeta]$, $[\zeta\zeta0]$, $[\zeta\zeta\zeta]$, $[\zeta\zeta1]$ and $[\frac{1}{2}\frac{1}{2}\zeta]$. In addition, some measurements were made for several nonsymmetric modes in the $(1\bar{1}0)$ plane. The results were fitted, using the Fourier series method, to a Born-von Kármán model with interactions out to fifth neighbours. Central forces gave very nearly as good a fit as general forces. This is not particularly surprising, since the Cauchy relation fails by only about 15 % at 90°K. Second neighbour central forces gave a tolerably good fit to the data, but in this regard sodium represents an *exception* to the general run of metals, not the rule, as is often supposed in lattice dynamical calculations. Toya (1958a) has attempted to include the electron-phonon interaction in the calculations directly, using the Hartree-Fock self-consistent field method. His results for sodium agree with the experimental results quite well as shown in Fig. 5.6. There is probably a connection between this good fit and the facts that (1) the Kohn effect was not observed in sodium, and (2) near-neighbour central forces give a reasonably good fit to the data. On the other hand, the Kohn effect does appear explicitly in Toya's equations. However, calculation indicates that the effect will indeed be very small in this case. Cochran (1963) and Sham (1965) have interpreted these results using the pseudopotential method mentioned in Section 5.2 and find that this approach appears to be reasonable at least for the case of sodium.

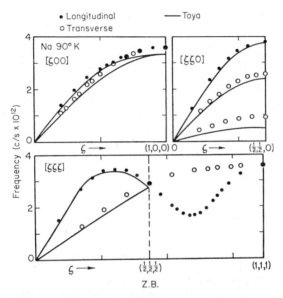

Fig. 5.6. The dispersion curves for sodium (Woods *et al.*, 1962a,b) compared with the theoretical calculations made by Toya. The large filled circles indicate superimposed L and T modes. At $(\frac{1}{2},\frac{1}{2},\frac{1}{2})$ and $(1,0,0)$ these modes are degenerate by symmetry.

The fifth neighbour force constant model has been used (Dixon *et al.*, 1963) to calculate frequencies at 180,441 points in the irreducible sector (1/48) of the Brillouin zone, resulting in a total of 24,576,000 frequencies; from these the frequency distribution function $z(\nu)$ has been determined. (A similar calculation using a more efficient sampling method has been carried out by Gilat and Dolling (1964) with similar results). The calculated $z(\nu)$ is reproduced in Fig. 5.7 and shows several critical points quite clearly; it is straightforward to identify many of these with features of the measured dispersion relation. This $z(\nu)$ leads to a temperature variation of the Debye characteristic temperature θ_D which agrees to within 2 % with experiment (Martin, 1960).

The body-centred cubic transition metals of columns V and VI of the periodic table form a system which has many interesting properties. The study of the crystal dynamics of these metals has revealed a pattern which may be correlated with other, particularly electronic, properties. The metals of column V (vanadium, niobium, and tantalum) have a very complicated interatomic force system, while the crystal dynamics of the metals of column VI (chromium, molybdenum, and tungsten) are, with the exception of certain striking features, reasonably well described by a Born-von Kármán theory with near neighbour interactions.

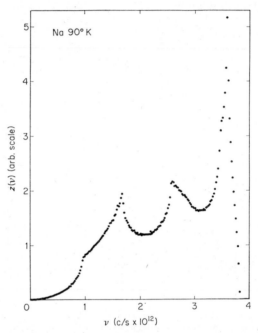

FIG. 5.7. $z(\nu)$ for sodium calculated from the fifth neighbour Born-von Kármán model which was fitted to the experimental $\nu(\mathbf{q})$ for directions of high symmetry.

Vanadium was the first of these metals to be studied. The coherent scattering cross-section for vanadium is only 0·048 barns, whereas the incoherent cross-section is 5·1 barns. This means that it is practically impossible to make use of coherent scattering to determine the frequency–wave vector dispersion relation. On the other hand its large incoherent cross-section makes vanadium a particularly favourable case in which to measure directly the density of phonon states or the frequency distribution function $z(\nu)$. There have been many attempts made to make such measurements (Stewart and Brockhouse, 1958; Eisenhauer et al., 1958; Turberfield and Egelstaff, 1962; Haas et al., 1963; Zemlyanov et al., 1963; Gläser et al., 1965) but none has been done with the precision necessary to locate the critical points of Van Hove (1953) or to give much detailed information about the interatomic forces in vanadium. The measured $z(\nu)$ for vanadium as determined by various groups is shown in Fig. 5.8.

More precise information concerning the interatomic forces in these metals can be obtained from dispersion curve measurements; such experiments have been carried out for chromium (Møller and Mackintosh, 1965), molybdenum (Woods and Chen, 1964), niobium (Nakagawa and Woods, 1963, 1965), tantalum (Woods, 1964) and tungsten (Chen and Brockhouse, 1964).

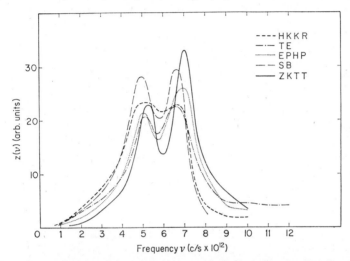

FIG. 5.8. The results of various experiments to measure $z(\nu)$ for vanadium by means of incoherent neutron scattering. The results of TE and HKKR (Turberfield and Egelstaff, 1962; Haas *et al.*, 1963) do not have any corrections for instrumental resolution. The effect of the instrumental resolution has been removed from the results of SB, EPHP and ZKTT (Stewart and Brockhouse, 1958; Eisenhauer *et al.*, 1958; Zemlyanov *et al.*, 1963).

Analysis shows (Woods, 1965) that the dispersion relations for niobium and tantalum are very similar to each other and it is likely that the measured $z(\nu)$ for vanadium is also consistent with this pattern. The dispersion curves for these metals have many peculiar features which cannot be even qualitatively explained on a Born-von Kármán model without invoking very long range interatomic forces. Although the chromium–molybdenum–tungsten results contain several features which require very long range forces to describe in detail, they can be qualitatively fitted using a model extending only to third nearest neighbours. The differences in the dispersion curves for niobium and molybdenum are shown in Fig. 5.9 for the [$\zeta\zeta\zeta$] L branch. Fourier analysis of $\nu(\mathbf{q})$ for these metals indicates that the long range forces are oscillatory and are therefore probably related to the Friedel oscillations discussed above. The differences in the Fermi surface for the metals of columns V and VI of the periodic table provides a mechanism for explaining the observed differences in $\nu(\mathbf{q})$ for these groups. Observed discontinuities in $\nu(\mathbf{q})$ for molybdenum, which are believed to be due to the Kohn effect are, in fact, consistent with the dimensions of the Fermi surface of molybdenum as deduced from theoretical considerations by Lomer (1962). This supports the contention that the differences in $\nu(\mathbf{q})$ between niobium and molybdenum are largely due to Fermi surface effects.

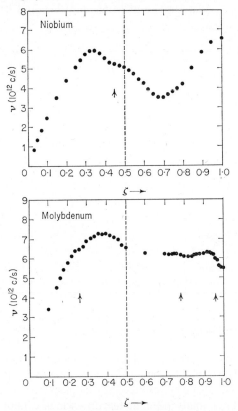

Fig. 5.9. Comparison of the longitudinal $[\zeta\zeta\zeta]$ branch for niobium and molybdenum at 296°K. The arrows indicate positions of suspected Kohn anomalies.

5.5 Other Metals and Alloys

In this section we discuss measurements of $\nu(\mathbf{q})$ and $z(\nu)$ for hexagonal close-packed metals (Be, Mg, Zn, and Ti), body-centred tetragonal (white) tin, and the alloys β-brass (CuZn), manganese–cobalt, nickel–palladium, and titanium–zirconium. (Koenig and Yarnell (1960) have made some preliminary measurements on bismuth, but a full account of this work has not yet been published.)

Since the primitive unit cell of the h.c.p. structure (see Fig. 5.1) contains two atoms, the dispersion relations display optic as well as acoustic modes. Structure factor considerations similar to those discussed here for germanium (see equation (5.3) and Section 5.9) and applied to hexagonal close-packed structures by Schmunk *et al.* (1962) and Iyengar *et al.* (1963) determine the intensities of the neutron groups, and hence aid in the identification of the branch

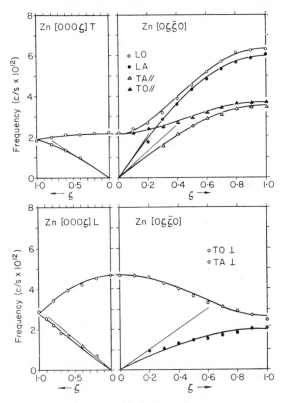

FIG. 5.10. The measured dispersion curves for zinc (Borgonovi *et al.*, 1963). The solid curves are calculated from a fourth neighbour Born-von Kármán model.

to which a particular phonon belongs. It should be re-emphasized that if the crystal has a finite mosaic spread, the double process of "phonon plus Bragg" scattering can occur; in this case the single phonon intensity formula (equation (1.96), Chapter 1) may no longer be applicable.

Measurements of the dispersion curves in various symmetry directions of magnesium have been made by three groups of workers: Collins (1962), Maliszewski *et al.* (1963), and Iyengar *et al.* (1963). Most of the measurements have been confined to the acoustic branches and each group has made measurements in two of the three directions $[\zeta\ \zeta\ \overline{2\zeta}\ 0]$, $[0\zeta\ \overline{\zeta}\ 0]$ and $[0\ 0\ 0\ \zeta]$, or, in group theory notation, along the lines T, Σ, and Δ, respectively. In general, the results are fairly consistent with one another. The analysis does not show much evidence for very strong long range forces such as observed for other metals.

Dispersion curves for zinc have been determined by Maliszewski *et al.* (1963, 1965) and by Borgonovi *et al.* (1963). The latter work is illustrated in Fig. 5.10. The results of Maliszewski *et al.* (1965) for the $[0\ \zeta\ \overline{\zeta}\ 0]$ transverse acoustic branch are in disagreement with the results of Borgonovi *et al.*; further study of this branch is needed.

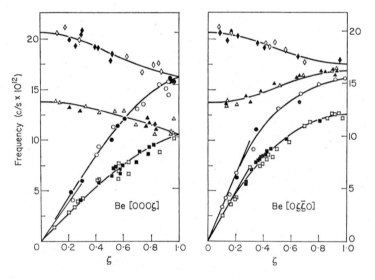

FIG. 5.11. The measured dispersion curves of beryllium (Schmunk *et al.*, 1962). The solid curves are merely a guide to the eye.

Beryllium forms a hexagonal close packed lattice with an unusually small spacing and tight binding. Fairly complete measurements have been made by Schmunk *et al.* (1962) for both optic and acoustic branches in the $[0\ 0\ 0\ \zeta]$ and $[0\ \zeta\overline{\zeta}\ 0]$ directions in beryllium. These are illustrated in Fig. 5.11. The curves show no outstanding qualitative features, but the models with short range interactions, used by those authors to try to fit their data, were completely inadequate. Once again the success of short range interatomic forces in metals to fit dispersion curve data seems to be the exception and not the rule, despite its widespread use in calculating many other properties of metals.

Sinclair (1963) and Schmunk (1964) have used "scattering law" techniques (Egelstaff and Cocking, 1961), correcting for the interference terms, to determine the $z(\nu)$ function for Be. The results do not show any sharp features or critical points, but the general shape of the curve is probably consistent with the results of Schmunk et al. (1962). In the same spirit Mozer et al. (1965) have measured the *total* inelastic scattering from titanium and titanium–zirconium alloys and have deduced functions which they believe are very similar to $z(\nu)$.

The frequency distribution function has also been measured (Stewart and Brockhouse, 1958) for an alloy of manganese and cobalt, described by the formula $Mn_{0.42}Co_{0.58}$, for which $\bar{b}$ was practically zero. In so far as the masses and interatomic forces of manganese and cobalt are similar, this alloy can be considered as a face-centred cubic material whose frequency distribution function may thus be determined directly from incoherent inelastic neutron scattering. The measured distribution function showed a single peak with no outstanding features.

The dispersion curves for the body-centred tetragonal (metallic) phase of tin have been measured in several laboratories (Borgonovi et al., 1965; Long-Price, 1965; Schmunk and Gavin, 1965; Rowe, Brockhouse and Svensson, 1965). The interest in white tin stems from the possible connection between the lattice vibrations and the phase transition to the semiconducting diamond structure (grey tin) just below room temperature. Several attempts to calculate the dispersion curves have been made (Wolfram et al., 1963; De Wames and Lehman, 1964; Musgrave, 1963), but these calculations are not in good agreement with the various measured $\nu(\mathbf{q})$ which, by and large, are consistent with one another.

The alloy β-brass has been studied in considerable detail in its ordered phase at 296°K and in less detail as a function of temperature, to temperatures above the order-disorder transition at about 730°K (Dolling and Gilat, 1964, 1965; Gilat and Dolling, 1965). The results at 296°K can be reasonably well fitted by a Born–von Kármán model with interactions out to fourth-nearest neighbours. Little change in the frequency of any mode was observed through the order–disorder transition temperature, although the widths of the neutron groups showed very interesting but unexplained behaviour.

We conclude these sections on metals with a short discussion of the effects of small amounts of other metals dissolved in the host lattice. These rise to "localized" modes in the case of a light atom impurity and "resonance" modes for the case of a heavy atom impurity. The localized modes have frequencies which lie outside $z(\nu)$ for the host lattice, or they may occur in a band gap in crystals with more complicated structures. The resonance modes have frequencies which occur within the frequency spectrum $z(\nu)$. Such effects have been discussed by Lifshitz (1944), by Brout and Visscher (1962), and more recently, by Elliott and Maradudin (1965). Attempts to measure defect modes have been made by Mozer *et al.* (1962) (see also Mozer and Otnes, 1963) for nickel–palladium alloys and by Rubin *et al.* (1965) for vanadium containing small amounts of hydrogen. The results are not readily interpretable, however, partly because of the large concentrations of impurity atom needed to detect any effect. Further experimental work in the study of localized and resonance modes in metals, particularly by means of coherent inelastic neutron scattering, would be very valuable. For the study of defects in non-metals, optical methods (e.g. infra-red absorption) enjoy distinct advantages over neutron spectrometry.

5.6 Semiconductors: Introduction

Semiconducting materials, such as silicon, germanium, and gallium arsenide have been the subject of intense study in recent years, since their properties, besides being of considerable intrinsic interest, have a very great commercial and technological importance. This importance is reflected in the fact that the major part of this study has been concerned with their electronic properties, an understanding of which is essential for progress in transistor technology. It is convenient to include a discussion of the case of diamond in these sections; it has the same structure as germanium and silicon, and comparison of their vibrational properties reveals some interesting features (Section 5.8).

These materials are also extremely interesting from the point of view of lattice dynamics, for the following reasons. Firstly, their structure, that of zinc blende (ZnS), is one of the simplest of those having more than one atom in the primitive unit cell (zinc blende has two). The normal vibrations thus display optic, as well as acoustic, modes. Secondly, the predominant interatomic forces are believed to be *covalent* in character, very different from those in metals, alkali halides or the "rare gas" solids, for example. Furthermore, the requirements for the application of the coherent one-phonon scattering method (see Section 5.1) are extremely well satisfied by both silicon and germanium, and to a lesser degree in gallium arsenide. Large, almost perfect, single crystals of very high purity are readily available; the absorption and incoherent scattering cross-sections are low; and most of the normal mode frequencies are of a suitable magnitude for measurement by conventional neutron spectrometers. (The situation in the case of diamond is very much less favourable, but coherent scattering experiments from a single crystal have nevertheless been carried out.)

The first experiments on germanium were performed by Brockhouse and Iyengar (1958). This paper emphasized the importance of the inelastic structure factor (see equation (5.3) and Section 5.9) for crystals with more than one atom in the unit cell, and demonstrated the value of neutron scattering experiments for the interpretation of infra-red absorption spectra. Other experimental work on germanium has been done by Hughes *et al.* (1959), and, more recently by Brockhouse *et al.* (1963). The latter work was directed primarily at the problem of the experimental determination of the *polarization vectors* of certain normal modes. Experiments on silicon have been performed by Brockhouse (1959b), by Hughes *et al.* (1959) and by Dolling (1961, 1963). Studies have been made of the lattice vibrational frequencies of gallium arsenide by Waugh and Dolling (1963) and Dolling and Waugh (1965) and of diamond by Yarnell *et al.* (1964) and Warren *et al.* (1965). Much theoretical effort has been expended upon the dynamics of the zinc blende and diamond structures. (Diamond is, of course, just a special case of the blende structure in which the two atoms in the unit cell are identical.) A comprehensive treatment of the diamond structure in terms of the Born-von Kármán theory has been given by Herman (1959): this paper contains references to earlier work in the same vein, notably the paper by Smith (1948). A somewhat different approach has been developed by Cochran (1959a). The Cochran treatment is derived essentially from a generalization of the Born-von Kármán theory, proposed originally by Mashkevitch and Tolpygo (1957), in which the potential energy of the vibrating crystal is expressed not only in terms of the displacements of the atoms from their equilibrium positions, but also in terms of the *electric dipole moments* induced at the lattice sites during a lattice vibration. Several superficially different variations upon this theme have been proposed by Hardy (1962), Tolpygo (1961), and Demidenko *et al.* (1962). Shell models for the zinc blende structure have been considered by Cochran *et al.* (1961), Cowley (1962a), Dolling (1961, 1963), Dolling and Waugh (1965), and by Kaplan and Sullivan (1963). The close connection, in essence, between these various treatments, has been demonstrated by Cowley *et al.* (1963).

We conclude this section with a brief discussion of the diamond lattice and its dynamical properties, within the framework of the Born-von Kármán theory. We have chosen to describe the diamond structure in detail, rather than that of zinc blende, in order to facilitate a discussion of results for the particular case of silicon, and comparison of these with the analogous results for diamond. The structure of diamond-type lattices is illustrated in Fig. 5.1; the cubic unit cell contains 8 atoms and has four times the volume of the primitive cell. The structure can be regarded as being made up of two identical, interpenetrating face-centred cubic sub-lattices; one sub-lattice has an "origin" atom at $(0,0,0)$, and the other has its "origin" atom at $(\frac{1}{4},\frac{1}{4},\frac{1}{4})$ (in units of the cubic unit cell side, a). There is a centre of inversion midway between each pair of adjacent atoms. (There is no such inversion centre in the zinc blende structure, since the two sub-lattices are not identical.)

A normal vibration with wave vector $\mathbf{q}$ in a mirror plane, e.g. $(0\bar{1}1)$, in reciprocal space must, by symmetry, have polarization vectors $\mathbf{V}$ either perpendicular or parallel to the plane. Both directions of highest symmetry, Δ and Λ, lie in the $(0\bar{1}1)$ plane. If $\mathbf{q}$ lies along either of these directions, then the vectors $\mathbf{V}$ must be perpendicular (transverse mode) or parallel (longitudinal) to $\mathbf{q}$.

The increased theoretical and experimental simplicity following from these symmetry restrictions, as mentioned in Section 5.1, has resulted in almost complete absence of information concerning wave vectors not in the $(0\bar{1}1)$ plane. In this plane, the (6×6) dynamical matrix factorizes into a (4×4) and a (2×2) matrix. The latter refers to the two modes, one optic and one acoustic, whose polarization vectors $\mathbf{V}$ are perpendicular (transverse) to the plane. The four other modes, two optic and two acoustic, are described by the (4×4) matrix. None of these latter modes is strictly longitudinal or transverse, except in the Δ and Λ directions, where complete factorization of the dynamical matrix into (2×2) matrices is possible. In this case, each pair of transverse modes becomes degenerate, and only four distinct "branches" of the dispersion relation exist.

In general, there are six such branches, which at $q = 0$ split into two groups of three degenerate modes each. One group has zero frequency of vibration (corresponding to a pure translation of the whole crystal) and represents the long wavelength limit of the ordinary acoustic (sound) waves in the crystal. The limiting slopes, $(\mathrm{d}\nu/\mathrm{d}q)_{q \to 0}$, of these three acoustic branches are governed (as usual) by the elastic constants of the material. The degeneracy of the other three (optic) modes at $q = 0$ leaves us with only one so-called "Raman frequency". We may note also that, at the point $\mathbf{q} = (0,0,2\pi/a)$ which is the zone boundary in the Δ direction, the two longitudinal modes are degenerate. In fact, longitudinal acoustic (LA) and optic (LO) modes in the Δ direction are *continuous* in the extended zone scheme. For this mode of vibration only, the unit cell in real space could be taken to be half-size, thus doubling the distance (in reciprocal space) to the zone boundary; from this viewpoint, there is really only one longitudinal mode (one "atom" per unit cell). Certain of the above degeneracies are split in the general zinc blende structure. These splittings are illustrated by Cochran *et al.* (1961) and Dolling and Waugh (1965) and we shall not describe them here.

All branches in the Δ and Λ directions (except the "LA/LO" branch along Δ) are required by symmetry to approach the respective zone boundaries with zero slope. The optic branches must also approach $q = 0$ with zero slope. All these features are illustrated in Fig. 5.12 which will be discussed below. In the directions Δ and Λ then, the relationships between the squares of the phonon frequencies (one longitudinal and two degenerate transverse) and the interatomic force constants, may be expressed by relatively simple quadratic equations. We may hope to be able to evaluate the force constants from the observed frequencies in these directions very much more simply than from any other frequencies.

5.7 Force Models for Semiconductors

The above-mentioned quadratic equations are listed by Herman (1959), for a Born-von Kármán model for the diamond structure involving general interatomic forces between an origin atom and its first through sixth nearest neighbours. In this paper, Herman attempts to fit the experimental results of Brockhouse and Iyengar (1958) on germanium, together with its elastic constants, on the basis of various models. He begins with simple ones having only first and second nearest neighbour interactions, and "adds in" extra neighbours step by step until a satisfactory fit is finally obtained. Owing to the non-linear character of the relations between the force constants and the normal mode frequencies, the evaluation of the force constants, even for fairly simple models, is subject to a certain ambiguity. In spite of this, Herman was able to show that *at least* fifth neighbour interactions were required to obtain a satisfactory fit to the data. His "fifth neighbour" model involves 15 adjustable parameters (the force constants), which are fitted to 19 pieces of experimental data (3 elastic constants and 16 phonon frequencies). It seems extremely likely that if this type of calculation were repeated, using the most recent experimental data, for either germanium or silicon, then even more distant neighbours, and many more force constants, would be required to obtain a satisfactory fit. It would then be extremely difficult to obtain sufficient independent experimental data to evaluate these force constants. It is probable that very similar considerations apply in the case of gallium arsenide, although an extensive test of the Born-von Kármán theory for this structure has not yet been carried out. The situation is somewhat different in the case of diamond itself. The experimental results of Warren *et al.* (1965) can be reasonably well-fitted by a Born-von Kármán model involving only first and second nearest neighbours, although there are indications that longer range forces would be necessary to achieve a fully satisfactory fit.

The implication is clear: there exist, in these structures, forces of a long-range character, which cannot be adequately treated in the Born-von Kármán theory. (This does not mean, of course, that the theory is in any sense "wrong"; it is merely too unwieldy, and its many parameters have lost the physical meanings which might be attributed to them if there were only short-range forces acting.)

It has been shown by Cochran (1959a) that these long-range forces are of *electrostatic* origin, and arise from the *polarizability* of the (neutral) atoms. This polarizability is represented pictorially, in Cochran's model, by regarding each atom (or, in general, each ion) to consist of a *core*, the nucleus and inner electrons, surrounded by a spherical *shell* of "outer" electrons. The core and shell are imagined to be coupled to each other with an isotropic force constant, and to neighbouring cores and shells by other force constants which represent the "short-range" forces of overlap repulsion, van der Waals attraction, etc. This kind of "shell model" was originally proposed by Dick and Overhauser (1958) in a paper dealing with the theory of the dielectric constants of alkali halides.

During a lattice vibration, the cores and shells may become relatively displaced, and the resultant electric dipoles then exert long-range electrostatic forces on each other. To find the net effect of these electrostatic forces, it is necessary, because of their extremely long range, to sum over all the induced dipoles throughout the crystal. A method for performing this summation by means of Ewald's (1921, 1938) theta-transformation has been described in detail by Kellermann (1940), in a paper on the dynamics of the sodium chloride lattice. The elements of the usual dynamical matrix E are split into two parts, one representing the short-range forces (i.e. the normal Born-von Kármán matrix elements) and the other the long-range electrostatic, or Coulomb, forces:

$$E_{\beta k}^{\alpha l}(\mathbf{q}) = R_{\beta k}^{\alpha l}(\mathbf{q}) + C_{\beta k}^{\alpha l}(\mathbf{q}) \tag{5.8}$$

The so-called "Coulomb coefficients" $C_{\beta k}^{\alpha l}(\mathbf{q})$ are computed by means of the theta-transformation, and added to the R matrix elements; the normal mode frequencies and polarization vectors are then found in the usual manner from E. Further discussion of Kellermann's model and the development of the shell model for alkali halides will be given in Section 5.11.

The way in which the mathematics is extended, in the shell model, to allow for the atomic polarizability, is simply to regard the cores and shells as distinct interacting entities. There are thus four such entities per diamond unit cell, rather than two as previously. The dynamical matrix E is now of order (12×12) instead of (6×6). We further assume that the *masses* of the electron shells are *zero*, and that, therefore, they follow the nuclear motions instantaneously. This assumption of zero shell mass is equivalent to the adiabatic approximation, which is believed to be extremely good for crystals such as pure silicon or germanium. E may now be reduced again to order (6×6), at the expense of making the individual elements rather more complicated in form. Another way of looking at this procedure is as follows: solution of the (12×12) matrix E would lead to the usual three acoustic modes, together with nine optic modes. Six of these optic modes will be of extremely high frequency (of order 10^{15} c/s) owing to the extremely small mass of the electron shells. The neutron scattering experiments are not capable of observing these "electronic" frequencies, which do not, in any case, form part of what we normally call the *lattice* vibrations. What the shell model does is to assign an effectively infinite value to these electronic frequencies, and then to concern itself only with the genuine "lattice vibrations".

The value of the shell model lies in the pictorial representation it provides of processes which are, of course, rather more complicated than the model implies. It also permits us to calculate the dispersion relation $\nu(\mathbf{q})$ in a rather simple manner, within the framework of the Born-von Kármán theory. It should be pointed out, however, that a quantum-mechanical justification can be given (see for example, Mashkevitch and Tolpygo (1957), Mashkevitch (1957), and more recently, Cowley (1962)) for the use of this simple shell model for an atom or ion with a closed electronic configuration. From this viewpoint, it becomes clear that the shell model is in fact a first approximation, which perhaps should be called a "dipole approximation", in a general theory involving an ascending series of electric multipole moments at the lattice sites. After all, whatever the distortion of the electronic configuration which *actually* occurs during a lattice vibration, we may clearly represent it by such a multipole expansion. In the shell, or dipole, model, this expansion is terminated after the dipole term. Whether or not this is a good approximation may perhaps be decided after comparing appropriate theoretical and experimental dispersion relations.

5.8 Semiconductors: Comparison of Theory and Experiment

The first comparison of this kind was made by Cochran (1959a), for the case of germanium. By means of a very simple shell model, involving short range forces between first nearest neighbours only, he was able to obtain quite good agreement with the then existing experimental data, of Brockhouse and Iyengar (1958). More detailed comparisons have been made by Dolling 1963), for both silicon and germanium, using more extensive and accurate experimental data, and a variety of different shell models: in particular, the effect of introducing second nearest neighbour short range forces has been investigated. Calculations of a similar nature have also been performed by Demidenko *et al.* (1962). Simple shell models (i.e. involving many approximations and hence a small number of parameters) have been proposed by Cochran *et al.* (1961) to describe their infra-red data for gallium arsenide. A more extensive study of this material has been made possible by the neutron scattering results of Dolling and Waugh (1965).

Figure 5.12 shows the dispersion relation $\nu(\mathbf{q})$ in three crystallographic directions Δ, Σ, and Λ, in silicon at room temperature, as determined by

Dolling (1963). Two sets of theoretical curves are given, representing two variations, A and B, of the basic Cochran shell model. Model A involves only first nearest neighbour short range forces and has 7 disposable parameters (force constants), while model B includes non-central second neighbour forces and has 11 disposable parameters. Model A provides a good qualitative fit to experiment, similar to that obtained by Cochran (1959a) for germanium, and is certainly a very marked improvement over simple Born-von Kármán models which do not allow for electrostatic forces. The

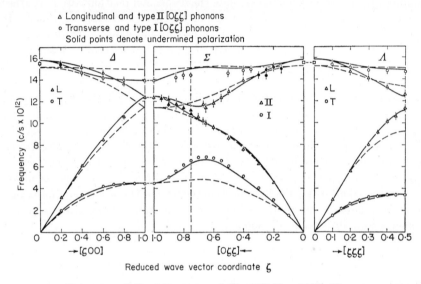

FIG. 5.12. The measured dispersion curves of silicon (Dolling, 1963). The curves represent various attempts to fit the data on the basis of the shell model.

fit displayed by model B is quantitatively satisfactory, but this agreement has only been achieved by employing a fairly large number of disposable parameters. While the *physical* meanings of some of the force constants in these complex models may be rather uncertain (see Section 5.11, where a similar situation exists), there is little doubt of the overall correctness of the introduction of electrostatic effects into force models for silicon and germanium. We should remember, however, that these shell models neglect all electrostatic interactions except those involving dipole moments, and it is possible that such interactions could, with advantage, be represented explicitly in future force models for the diamond structure. These conclusions concerning the validity of the shell model are applicable to germanium and gallium arsenide in addition to silicon. As mentioned in Section 5.7, the experimentally measured dispersion curves for diamond seem to be fairly well fitted by means of a simple Born-von Kármán force model. This implies that the atoms in diamond are much less polarizable than those in silicon and germanium. A thorough test of the dipole approximation model for diamond would nevertheless be of considerable interest.

It has been observed (Brockhouse, 1959a) that the ratio of any normal mode frequency for silicon to the analogous frequency for germanium is approximately 1.75; if the two materials were exactly homologous, this ratio would be that of their respective $(M^{-\frac{1}{2}}a^{-1})$ values, where M is the nuclear mass and a the cell side. For silicon and germanium this ratio is 1·675, which is significantly lower than the observed ratio. However, the remarkable constancy of this ratio for many different normal modes does explain the very similar conclusions which have been drawn concerning theoretical models for these two materials.

This kind of homologous relationship does not extend to the case of diamond. For example, the splitting of the TA and TO modes in the Δ-direction is so much less in diamond than in silicon or germanium, that the frequency of the TO mode at the zone boundary point (X) in diamond is *lower* than that of the LO mode, in contrast to the results shown in Fig. 5.12.

Information concerning the thermal vibrations of these materials may be obtained from various optical experiments. For example, it is possible to infer certain normal mode frequencies from infra-red absorption and reflection experiments, such as those by Macfarlane *et al.* (1959) on silicon and germanium. Although the frequencies measured by such methods are generally in good agreement with those found from the neutron scattering experiments, the assignment of polarization indices to the observed modes seems to be less reliable. For example, certain critical point frequencies in diamond have been measured by Hardy and Smith (1961), and polarization assignments made for the optic modes at the zone boundary by analogy with the case of silicon. Comparison with the neutron scattering results of Warren *et al.* (1965) shows that these assignments are probably incorrect, and re-emphasizes the value of neutron scattering experiments for checking the interpretation of optical measurements. Some neutron scattering measurements have been performed by Mitchell *et al.* (1963) on a powdered diamond specimen, with results which are roughly consistent with those of the single crystal experiments.

5.9 Determination of Polarization Vectors

The cross-section for the coherent one-phonon scattering of slow neutrons (equation (1.96)) is critically dependent on the polarization vectors $\mathbf{V}_s^j$. In most of the experiments described in this chapter, this dependence was exploited in order to identify the branch to which particular phonons belong. If a model for the interatomic forces in a crystal is postulated, then the V_s^l and hence the structure factor $F_{\tau s}$ (equation (5.3)) may be calculated for all $\mathbf{Q}$ and s. Such calculations are extremely useful for selecting regions of reciprocal space suitable for the observation of particular modes (see Brockhouse and Iyengar, 1958). Conversely, a measurement of the integrated intensity under a phonon peak can in principle be used to obtain information about the V_s^l, and hence the interatomic forces. The great advantage of such a determination of the V_s^l lies in the fact that, unlike the phonon frequencies, they are always *linear* functions of the dynamical matrix elements. The determination of force constants from an analysis of the observed V_s^l would thus be appreciably less hazardous than by the method of (non-linear) least-squares fitting to the observed frequencies.

In order to determine the V_s^l from the observed intensities, we must of course be able to insert values for the other terms in equation (1.96) such as k, k_0, ν_s, n, b_l, M_l, $\mathbf{Q}$, W_l, $\mathscr{J}_s$. The evaluation of $\mathscr{J}_s$ (eqn. (1.100)) is rather difficult, since it involves a knowledge of the *gradient* of ν_s with respect to $\mathbf{q}$. This difficulty may be avoided by means of the "constant-$\mathbf{Q}$" technique discussed in detail in Chapter 3. In this method, the vectors $\mathbf{Q}$, and hence also $\mathbf{q}$, are kept constant, while the energy difference $\hbar\omega$ between the incident and scattered neutrons is varied over a range in which the (constant) phonon frequency $\nu_s(\mathbf{q})$ is expected to lie. Referring to equation (1.96), we notice that if the value of $f(=2\pi\nu)$ in the first δ-function is kept constant, then, at least to first order in the resolution, $\mathscr{J}=1$. It is also possible to eliminate the factor (k/k_0) experimentally, by placing in the incident neutron beam a monitor detector having an efficiency inversely proportional to k_0 and by maintaining k constant. The signal counting time is controlled by the beam monitor counting rate, and the constant k factor is merely absorbed into the (constant) detector efficiency. It is now relatively straightforward to determine $F_{\tau s}$ for any values of s, $\mathbf{q}$, and $\boldsymbol{\tau}$. The only remaining problem is to extract the V_s^l from this data. In this connection, we note that the V_s^l satisfy certain orthonormality conditions (see Born and Huang, 1954, p. 298) and are subject to the requirements of crystal symmetry. Thus, for any particular $\mathbf{q}$, we may be able to measure the $F_{\tau s}$ for all s, at a variety of different $\mathbf{Q}$ values, and make use of conditions of the form

$$\sum_{l\alpha} V_s^{l\alpha}(\mathbf{q}) V_{s'}^{*l\alpha}(\mathbf{q}) = \delta_{ss'} \qquad (5.9)$$

If, in addition, $\mathbf{q}$ lies in a symmetry plane, or symmetry direction, then the V_s^l are further restricted by the symmetry and are therefore more readily determined.

In the case of germanium, the situation is further simplified, since the (real) quantities, b_l, M_l and W_l are independent of l (both atoms in the unit cell are the same) and may thus be taken outside the modulus signs in equation (5.3). It has been demonstrated by Brockhouse (1961) and by Brockhouse *et al.* (1963) that under these circumstances, at least, it is possible to determine reasonably accurate values of certain V_s^l in symmetry directions. Although attempts to extend the experiments to non-symmetry modes have so far been unsuccessful, it is clear that further efforts in this direction would be worthwhile. A note of caution, however, should be sounded at this point. The above discussion is based entirely upon the harmonic approximation. As we shall see in Section 5.17, the cross-section for neutron scattering from a real (anharmonic) crystal is somewhat more complicated. A scattered neutron group arising from a "one-phonon" process need not consist of a single peak, and it may be difficult to separate it from the "multiphonon" background. Some numerical calculations of these effects, based on a simple model of the anharmonic forces in strontium titanate, have been made by Cowley (1965b), and are discussed briefly in Section 5.17.

5.10 Ionic Crystals: Introduction

Ionic crystals have for many years been thought to be one of the best understood classes of solids. The reason for this is that the Coulomb interaction between the ions can be calculated exactly, and the resulting calculated binding energies, etc., are in excellent agreement with experiment (Seitz, 1940). Theoretical calculations of lattice vibration frequencies for these materials might therefore be expected to be easier and more reliable than for almost any other class of solid. The experimental determination of these frequencies, and subsequent comparison with theory, is thus of considerable and immediate interest. We shall first describe in some detail experimental and theoretical work on the lattice dynamics of alkali halides, and then briefly mention analogous results for ionic crystals of more complicated structure.

Experimentally, measurements of the dispersion relation for the three principal symmetry directions have been made for sodium iodide at 100°K (Woods *et al.*, 1960), and potassium bromide at 90°K (Woods *et al.*, 1963). Both these materials have the sodium chloride structure, consisting of two interpenetrating f.c.c. lattices, the sodium ions on one lattice, the chlorine ions on the other. The symmetry considerations discussed for f.c.c. crystals in Section 5.3 also apply to these materials. For example, the end point of the $[00\zeta]L$ branch (the point (0,0,1) or X) is degenerate with the end point of the $[\zeta\zeta0]T_2$ branch. Similarly $[\zeta\zeta0]T_1$, $[\zeta\zeta0]L$, and $[00\zeta]T$ branches are degenerate at this point. These considerations apply to both acoustic and optic modes. In the optic modes with zero wave vector, the lattice of positive ions moves rigidly against the lattice of negative ions. Another set of simple

9

modes are those at the point $(\frac{1}{2},\frac{1}{2},\frac{1}{2})$ or L. In the optic modes in NaI, for example, it is only the sodium ion which moves, second nearest neighbour ions vibrating against one another, while in the acoustic modes only the iodine ions move. Since there are two atoms per primitive unit cell the scattered neutron intensity depends upon the inelastic structure factor such as described for germanium in Section 5.9.

Various aspects of the lattice dynamics of ionic crystals and of alkali halides in particular have been treated extensively in the literature. Kellermann (1940) has calculated the frequencies of 48 independent modes of vibration of sodium chloride on the basis of the Born model (Born and Huang, 1954, pp. 33, 77) of ionic crystals. In this model each ion is treated as a unit point charge with electrostatic interaction throughout the whole crystal, and central forces are postulated to represent the "overlap repulsion" between nearest neighbour ions only. The one arbitrary parameter in this model was fitted to the bulk modulus (or an elastic constant), and the resulting frequencies lead to a fair description of the specific heat measurement and the infrared absorption frequency (the TO mode at $q = 0$).

The measured dispersion relations for KBr and NaI have been compared with calculations based on this model, and for the TO and acoustic branches the agreement between the calculations and experiment is fair except near the point (0,0,1). The calculated frequencies for the LO modes, on the other hand, lie $\sim$20 % above the measured values. This is not particularly surprising in view of the fact that the Born-Kellermann model (also known as the rigid ion model) takes no account of the polarizability of the ions. The optic modes, which depend to a large extent upon the electrical parameters of the system, are more sensitive to this neglect than are the acoustic modes.

5.11 Shell Models for Alkali Halides

The difficulties associated with including the polarizability of the ions into a lattice dynamical model have been largely overcome through the use of the shell model concept of Dick and Overhauser (1958). This model has previously been discussed in Section 5.7 for the case of semiconductors. Historically it was applied first to alkali halides (Cochran, 1959; Woods et al., 1960) and in this case the physical picture of electron shell coupled isotropically to rigid cores is more acceptable than in the case of semiconductors, although wave mechanical justifications (Mashkevitch and Tolpygo, 1957; Cowley, 1962) for its use exist in both cases. In the original calculations of the vibration frequencies in NaI (Woods et al., 1960), a simple version of the shell model was employed in which only the larger, negative iodine ion was considered to be polarizable. The vastly improved agreement between theory and experiment obtained in these calculations, and illustrated for KBr in

Fig. 5.13, is convincing evidence for the validity of the shell model as a representation of the ionic polarizability. As indicated in the previous section, the electronic distortions of the ions can be expanded in a series of electric multipoles of which the Born-Kellermann model is the leading monopole approximation and the shell model the dipole approximation. The introduction of higher multipole terms results in such a proliferation of parameters that the calculations become extremely unwieldy.

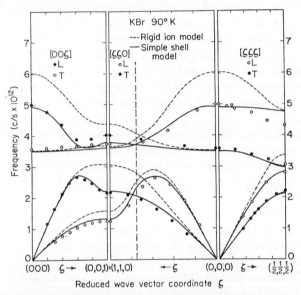

FIG. 5.13. The measured dispersion curves of potassium bromide (Woods *et al.*, 1963) showing the comparison of the data with the rigid ion and shell models.

Generally speaking, inelastic structure factors (equation (5.3) and Section 5.9) for neutron group intensities are not particularly sensitive to the details of the force model. However, in the case of sodium iodide, the structure factor for the longitudinal modes at the point (0,0,1) is quite different in the two models (the rigid ion model and the shell model). This difference was illustrated in a striking way during the earlier stages of the experimental determination of $v(\mathbf{q})$ for NaI, when only structure factor calculations for the Born-Kellermann model were available. Neutron groups corresponding to the mode (0,0,1)LA were sought for, and *not* found, at such points in reciprocal space that the Born-Kellermann calculations indicated would be favourable for this mode. Such neutron groups were found, however, at points indicated by the subsequent shell model calculations.

The shell model, or dipole approximation model, is very similar to that developed by Hardy (1962), and applied to the alkali halides by Karo and

Hardy (1963), and by Tolpygo and his co-workers (Tolpygo, 1961; Demidenko *et al.*, 1962). Several points of detail differ in the three models, but essentially they all recognize the fact that it is necessary to include polarization effects when making lattice dynamical calculations and that a multipole expansion of the electronic distortions is a simple and effective way to do this. The similarities and differences which are peculiar to one theoretical approach or another have been discussed by Cowley *et al.* (1963).

The simple shell model which takes into account central repulsive forces between nearest neighbours only and allows only the negative ion to be polarizable has three independent parameters and describes the dispersion relations for sodium iodide and potassium bromide tolerably well. It does not, however, fit the mode $(\frac{1}{2},\frac{1}{2},\frac{1}{2})$LO as can be seen in Fig. 5.13. A model (model VI of Cowley *et al.*, 1963) which takes into account second neighbour short range interactions, the polarizability of both ions, and the possibility of variable ionic charge is able to give a good description of the experimental results. This model has nine disposable parameters, some of which, however, have rather surprising values. In particular, the ionic charge is less than one, the electrical polarizability is shared more equally between the two ions than expected, and the short range polarizability (that induced by short range "overlap" forces) turns out to be negative for the positive ion, if it is assumed that all short range forces act through the shells. These results suggest that the picture of a rigid shell of electrons coupled isotropically to a rigid core is not completely realistic; once the simplest ideas of the shell model have been incorporated, it is perhaps more instructive to consider the general multipole expansion. In fact the nature of the mode $(\frac{1}{2},\frac{1}{2},\frac{1}{2})$ LO suggests a quadrupole type of distortion. The inclusion of quadrupole forces would not contribute significantly to our understanding of the problem at the present time, however, since a fit to the data can already be obtained without them.

The above-mentioned model VI, which was fitted to the results for the symmetry directions $(\varDelta, \varSigma$ and $\varLambda)$, was used to calculate $z(\nu)$ and the temperature variation of the Debye temperature $(\varTheta_D)$. The resulting $z(\nu)$ and $\varTheta_D(T)$ are shown for NaI in Fig. 5.14. The agreement between the calculated and experimental values of $\varTheta_D$ is well within the estimated errors.

Lyddane, Sachs and Teller (1941) have derived, for ionic crystals with two atoms per primitive unit cell, a fundamental relationship (hereafter referred to as the LST relation) between the frequencies of the optic modes at $q = 0$ ($q = 0$ implies a wavelength which is long compared with the cell size but short compared with either the dimensions of the crystal or the wavelength of light) and the dielectric constants, viz.

$$\left(\frac{\nu_{\text{LO}}}{\nu_{\text{TO}}}\right)_{q=0} = \left(\frac{\epsilon_0}{\epsilon_\infty}\right)^{\frac{1}{2}} \tag{5.10}$$

In this equation ν_{LO} and ν_{TO} are the longitudinal and transverse optic frequencies respectively, ϵ_0 the static dielectric constant, and ϵ_∞ the dielectric constant at frequencies above ionic frequencies but below electronic frequencies. This relation is independent of any particular lattice dynamical model and its derivation, as given in Born and Huang (1954), Chapter II, is based on electromagnetic theory. It is implicit in the Cochran shell model

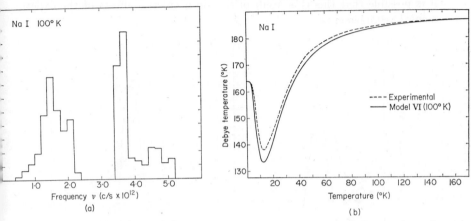

Fig. 5.14. (a) $z(\nu)$ for NaI calculated from the shell model "best fit" to the experimental $\nu(\mathbf{q})$. (b) The temperature variation of the Debye temperature of sodium iodide.

but is not properly accounted for in the rigid ion model (in which $\epsilon_\infty = 1$ and ϵ_0 has an unrealistic value). It has been verified to within the experimental error of a few percent for both NaI and KBr. It has also been verified for gallium arsenide (Waugh and Dolling, 1963) and for calcium fluoride (Section 5.13).

5.12 Longitudinal Optic Modes of Alkali Halides

The lattice dynamics of the alkali halide crystals has the appearance of being well understood if the good fit of the dipole approximation model to the experimental results is a valid criterion. On the other hand, the difficulties associated with the measurements of the longitudinal optic modes have not yet been explained completely. In Section 5.17, it is shown that for typical metals (the only materials on which extensive work has been done) broadening of the neutron groups becomes appreciable at temperatures of the order of 40 % of the melting temperature. In KBr (melting point 1003°K), the acoustic modes show no apparent broadening at 400°K, while the TO modes display, at the same temperature, a broadening in energy of a few percent of the phonon energy. The overall picture of phonon energy widths given by these measurements is, however, at variance with observations of the LO modes. Even at 200°K, the increase in width for the mode (0·1,0·1, 0·1)LO from that observed at 8°K, is quite apparent, and the change in width for the mode (0·64,0·64,0·64)LO between sample temperatures of 90°K and 400°K is also very marked, as shown in Fig. 5.15. In addition, it seems that even at 90°K, the width of the neutron distribution increases with decreasing values of $|\mathbf{q}|$. At $q = 0$, the width is anomalously large, but it is possible that this is a result of certain geometric effects of the experimental arrangements.

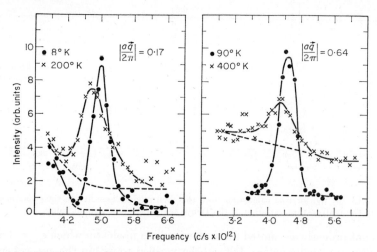

FIG. 5.15. Neutron groups scattered from potassium bromide at various temperatures. The dashed lines under the peaks represent the background which will preserve the temperature corrected integrated intensities.

Even more surprising is that the shape of the neutron distributions appears to be specimen dependent. Two different specimens of sodium iodide were used in the experiments. One of them had a mosaic spread of ~1·3°, the other a mosaic spread ~0·1°. The crystal with the large mosaic spread gave satisfactory results for the TO and acoustic branches, but the only indication of LO modes was a "bump" on the high frequency side of a peak resulting from incoherent scattering processes (this incoherent scattering will be further discussed below). The frequency represented by this bump was ~4·8 × 10^12 c/s and did not vary appreciably with changes in $\mathbf{q}$. The specimen with the mosaic spread of 0·1°, on the other hand, gave neutron groups for the LO modes similar to those obtained for KBr.

It should be emphasized that the experimental results for the TO and acoustic modes measured using the two specimens of NaI were in good agreement with each other. It has not been established precisely how these results vary with specimen history, and how much of the temperature variation is independent of the history. In spite of the obvious necessity for more experimental work to elucidate these points, it is likely from the work of Cowley (1963a) that at least part of the anomalous behaviour of the LO modes is not specimen-dependent, and almost certainly arises from anharmonic interactions between the ions (see Section 5.17). The specimen-dependent effects may be associated with defects in the crystal which limit the effective crystallite size. It is well known (Fröhlich, 1949) that in a crystal of finite size the LO and TO modes at $q = 0$ are degenerate. The large effective fields which accompany the LO modes may be strongly perturbed by electronic defects, with resultant damping and hence broadening of the LO modes.

An experimental difficulty encountered during the measurements on NaI should be mentioned at this point. The incoherent scattering cross-section of sodium is large, and there is a pronounced peak in the frequency distribution function for NaI at about $3 \cdot 6 \times 10^{12}$ c/s. Reference to equation (1.106) shows that these two facts will combine to produce more or less well-defined peaks in the scattered neutron energy distribution, and it turns out that the intensity of these peaks is comparable with those due to coherent one-phonon scattering processes. (Strictly speaking, equation (1.106) is applicable only to crystals with one atom per unit cell. For NaI, this equation must be modulated by an inelastic structure factor analogous to equation (5.3)). Thus the observation of coherent scattering involving optic modes of frequencies near $3 \cdot 6 \times 10^{12}$ c/s is considerably obscured by this incoherent scattering. This kind of effect is liable to occur whenever one is studying a material with an appreciable incoherent scattering cross-section.

5.13 Calcium Fluoride and Uranium Dioxide

Calcium fluoride and uranium dioxide have the same structure, usually referred to as the fluorite structure (Fig. 5.1). It consists of three interpenetrating face-centred cubic lattices, the calcium ions lying on one and the fluorine ions on the other two. Each calcium ion occupies a centre of symmetry and is surrounded by eight fluorine ions situated at the corners of a cube of side $a/2$ (a is the lattice constant). The primitive unit cell, outlined in Fig. 5.1, contains three ions, and hence the dispersion relation displays nine branches, of which three are acoustic and six optic in character. These are subject to symmetry conditions rather similar to those described for alkali halides in Section 5.10. Models of the interatomic forces may likewise be constructed for the fluorite structure in a similar manner to those discussed for alkali halides in Section 5.11.

The dispersion curves have been determined by means of coherent one-phonon scattering studies for CaF_2 by Cribier et al. (1963) and for UO_2 by

Woods *et al.* (1965). In both cases, the results can be described by means of rigid ion models of the interatomic forces. Such models have been proposed for CaF_2 by Ganesan and Shrinivasan (1962) and for UO_2 by Woods *et al.* (1965). If short range forces extending to second nearest neighbour ions are postulated, and the effective ionic charge is allowed to vary from its "nominal" value (+2 for Ca, +4 for U) then surprisingly good qualitative agreement with the neutron results is obtained in both cases. This is illustrated for CaF_2 in Fig. 5.16. Improved agreement may be obtained if the ionic polarizabilities are taken into account.

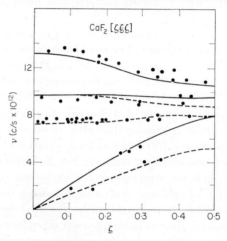

Fig. 5.16. The measured dispersion curves for the $[\zeta\zeta\zeta]$ direction of calcium fluoride (Cribier *et al.*, 1963) compared with the calculations of Ganesan and Shrinivasan (1962).

Of particular interest for CaF_2 is the verification of the Lyddane, Sachs and Teller (LST) relation described in Sections 5.11 and 5.14. It might be thought that the generalized form of this relation, equation (5.11), could be tested in CaF_2 in view of the existence of more than one LO mode at zero wave vector. (In the case of alkali halides and other materials with diatomic unit cells having only one such LO mode, it is clear that only the special case of the LST relation, equation (5.10), may be tested.) However, the high symmetry of CaF_2 requires the degeneracy of the three optic modes in which the two fluorine sub-lattices vibrate against each other while the calcium ions remain stationary, and so the LST relation reduces once more to equation (5.10). Cribier *et al.* (1963) find, for CaF_2, that the LST relation is verified to within the experimental accuracy (a few per cent). From the appropriate optic mode frequencies in UO_2, together with the known high frequency dielectric constant, Woods *et al.* (1965) have calculated the static dielectric constant assuming the validity of the LST relation for this material.

In certain alkali halide crystals in which the two ions have very different masses (e.g. NaI), it is known that there is a gap in frequency between the optic and acoustic modes. In view of the large ratio of the mass of uranium to that of oxygen, a similar frequency gap might be expected in the case of UO_2. The behaviour of the Δ_2' branch demonstrates, however, that no such gap exists.

5.14 Strontium Titanate

The ferroelectric or antiferroelectric character of several crystals having the perovskite structure (see Fig. 5.1) has been widely studied for many years. The special nature of such materials, for example, barium titanate, lead zirconate, and strontium titanate, is difficult to define precisely, but each displays peculiarities in the behaviour of its static dielectric constant ϵ_0 as a function of temperature T. For a review of the general properties and phenomenological theories of ferroelectrics see, for example, Kittel (1956) or Kanzig (1957).

It has recently been proposed by Cochran (1960), that the phenomenon of ferroelectricity is intimately associated with certain characteristic features of the lattice vibration spectrum of the material concerned. He suggested specifically that the function $\epsilon_0(T)$ observed in ferroelectrics is directly correlated with the anomalous behaviour of certain transverse optic (TO) modes of vibration of the lattice. These ideas are illustrated by the following argument, which is based on the LST relation (equation (5.10)).

This relation has been generalized by Cochran (1960) and Cochran and Cowley (1962) to apply to more complex crystals having n atoms per unit cell, and hence $3(n-1)$ optic modes:

$$\frac{\epsilon_0}{\epsilon_\infty} = \Pi_i \left(\frac{\nu_{Li}}{\nu_{Ti}}\right)^2 \tag{5.11}$$

where ν_{Ti}, ν_{Li}, are the frequencies of the ith TO and LO modes as $q \to 0$ and the product is taken over all such optic modes. If ϵ_0 follows a Curie law in the paraelectric phase,

$$\epsilon_0 = C/(T-T_c) \tag{5.12}$$

where T_c is the Curie temperature, and C a constant and if, in addition, only one particular mode, TO_1, is appreciably *temperature dependent*, then it follows that a relation of the type

$$\nu_1^2 = \text{Constant} \times (T-T_c) \tag{5.13}$$

will govern its temperature dependence. Thus we expect that the frequency, ν_1, of a certain TO mode near $q = 0$ will *fall* with temperature, while the other normal mode frequencies may remain more or less constant. When ν_1 becomes

9*

zero, the crystal becomes *unstable* against a lattice vibration in this mode, and the crystal structure must then change to a more stable form. The nature of this change may be predicted from a knowledge of the atomic polarization

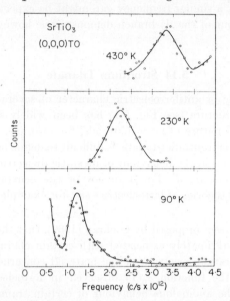

Fig. 5.17. The temperature dependence of the frequency of a TO mode at $q = 0$ in $SrTiO_3$. The width variation probably reflects the wavelength dependent resolution of the spectrometer.

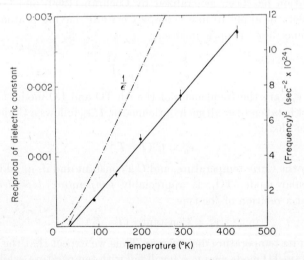

Fig. 5.18. The temperature dependence of the frequency of a TO mode at $q = 0$ compared with the temperature dependence of the reciprocal of the dielectric constant (ϵ).

vectors associated with the temperature dependent TO mode. This type of behaviour has in fact been observed by Cowley (1963b) for the case of $SrTiO_3$. The neutron groups corresponding to ν_1 at three different temperatures are shown in Fig. 5.17 and the variation of ν_1^2 with temperature is shown in Fig. 5.18. The intercept on the temperature axis gives a Curie temperature (32°K) which is in excellent agreement with values obtained from measurements of dielectric constant (Mitsui and Westphal, 1961) and dielectric loss (Rupprecht and Bell, 1962) In the same series of experiments, measurements of the longitudinal mode frequencies for the $\varDelta$ direction in $SrTiO_3$ were also made. The success of these initial experiments in helping to substantiate the Cochran theory of ferroelectricity is an excellent example of the use of slow neutron scattering techniques in the study of the solid state. It would be of considerable interest to perform similar experiments on other materials with "ferroelectric character", though the interpretation and analysis of results would become extremely difficult for materials with structures more complex than that of $SrTiO_3$. Even in the latter case, the frequencies of lattice vibrations along directions of high symmetry are eigenvalues of a (5×5) dynamical matrix. The experimental determination of eigenvectors described in Section 5.9 would be especially valuable in such cases, although the complications which arise (at least for $SrTiO_3$, see Section 5.17) from the anharmonicity of the normal vibrations may restrict its usefulness.

5.15 Carbon

The crystalline forms of carbon, diamond and graphite, constitute two of the most interesting materials for the solid state physicist. As regards the study of their lattice dynamics by means of slow neutron scattering, the main obstacle has been the lack of single crystal specimens of sufficient size and availability. This difficulty has been overcome, in the case of diamond, by Warren et al. (1965), who performed their experiments with a synthetic industrial diamond weighing 48 g. Their results have been discussed in Section 5.8. It has not yet been possible to manufacture large single crystals of graphite, and the only naturally occurring specimens are very small. Thus the lattice dynamics of graphite have been studied mainly with polycrystalline specimens which have a special interest for reactor technology. Recently, however, the production has been achieved of large specimens of a form of graphite, known as pyrolytic graphite, which displays certain single crystal characteristics (Klein et al., 1962). The carbon atoms in graphite are arranged hexagonally in two-dimensional "sheets": in pyrolytic graphite these sheets are stacked so as to have a common normal, the hexagonal axis, but are otherwise randomly oriented. This is illustrated schematically in Fig. 5.19(a), while the arrangement of the atoms within each sheet is shown in Fig. 5.19(b). The distinctive physical properties of graphite can be understood, at least qualitatively, by assuming that the forces between neighbouring atoms within the same sheet are very much greater than those between different sheets or planes. For example, the use of graphite as a lubricant arises from the ease with which different sheets of atoms may slide over each other.

An unambiguous determination of the dispersion relation for graphite, using pyrolytic graphite specimens, is restricted to lattice waves propagating along the unique hexagonal axis, since in all other directions the material is

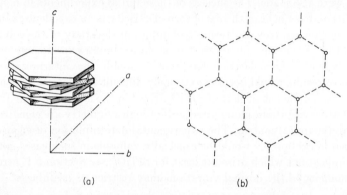

(a)   (b)

FIG. 5.19. The structure of pyrolytic graphite showing (a) the stacking of the planes and (b) the atomic arrangement in a single plane.

effectively polycrystalline. From a study of such waves, information concerning only the *interplanar* forces in graphite may be obtained. Slow neutron scattering experiments have been performed on pyrolytic graphite by Dolling and Brockhouse (1962), Fig. 5.20 shows, for example, the dispersion curve for longitudinally polarized lattice waves propagating along the hexagonal axis. In this mode of vibration, entire atomic layers move as essentially rigid units in a direction normal to themselves: the forces involved are therefore those which control the interplanar spacing. Fourier analysis of this curve (almost a pure sine curve) leads to the not unexpected result that these interplanar forces in graphite are almost entirely between nearest neighbour planes. Some information concerning the "shearing" forces between different planes was also obtained (Dolling and Brockhouse, 1962); it is clear, however, that a really definitive study of the lattice vibrations of graphite must await the production of true single crystal specimens.

It is of interest at this point to consider what information may be obtained from polycrystalline graphite specimens. Since the crystal structure of graphite is not simple (there are four atoms in the primitive hexagonal unit cell) and since the scattering cross-section of carbon is almost entirely coherent, the determination of the frequency distribution function $z(\nu)$ cannot be carried out in the direct manner described in Section 5.2 for the case of vanadium. Egelstaff and Cocking (1961) have developed a method for obtaining an approximate $z(\nu)$ (about 10 % accuracy in favourable cases) from the differential scattering cross-section over a wide range of neutron energy and momentum transfers observed for coherent scattering materials. Using this technique, Haywood and Thorson (1963) have obtained the distribution function for polycrystalline graphite at room temperature. An

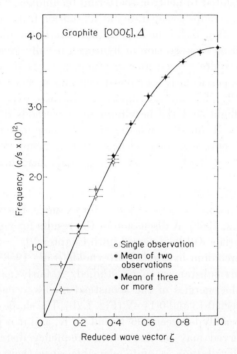

FIG. 5.20. The dispersion curve for longitudinal waves travelling along the normal to the hexagonal planes in pyrolytic graphite. The solid curve is the best fitting sine wave to the results.

interesting feature of their result is an abrupt change in the slope of the distribution function at an energy $\approx 0\cdot016$ eV. This corresponds closely to the maximum frequency ($\nu = 3\cdot83 \times 10^{12}$ c/s) of the longitudinal branch shown in Fig. 5.20. The appearance of a critical point in $z(\nu)$ at this energy is thus to be expected; the agreement between the two kinds of experiment in this region is gratifying. Some features of the high-frequency region of the distribution function for graphite at 950°C have been determined by Egelstaff and Harris (1963) from observations of the energy distribution of (initially very slow) neutrons scattered by a polycrystalline specimen. This distribution shows three peaks which are qualitatively similar to predictions of Yoshimori and Kitano (1956), and also to more detailed calculations of Young and Koppel (1965).

5.16 Hydrogen Vibrations in Compounds

The study of the vibrations of hydrogen atoms in various compounds is particularly well suited to neutron scattering techniques. The small mass of the hydrogen atoms helps to separate out its motion from that of the rest of the lattice, very often resulting in a rather flat optic branch. The large incoherent scattering cross-section of hydrogen usually gives rise to intense peaks which give quite a good average frequency of vibration throughout the Brillouin zone, particularly for a powder specimen. Since the resolution in Q-space is generally of secondary importance in these experiments, the cold neutron time-of-flight and the beryllium filter methods (Chapters 2 and 3 respectively) are well suited to investigations of these materials. Some of the compounds of this nature which have been studied include several metal hydrides (McReynolds *et al.*, 1958; Pelah *et al.*, 1957; Bergsma and Goedkoop, 1961; Saunderson and Cocking, 1963; Woods *et al.*, 1961a), ammonium halides (Woods *et al.*, 1961a; Mikke and Kroh, 1963; Venkataraman *et al.*, 1963; Palevsky, 1962), and many organic solids, for example, the so-called globular compounds (Becka, 1963). A discussion of the results for ammonium halides and organic materials will be deferred until Chapter 10.

Historically, zirconium hydride (McReynolds *et al.*, 1958) was the first of these hydrogenous substances to be studied. A fairly narrow peak, well separated from the energies of the acoustical modes, occurs in the energy distribution between 0·13 and 0·14 eV (Fig. 1.2b). The shape of this peak does not change appreciably between 296°K and 95°K, and it is possible that the finite width observed may be due to the frequency distribution of optic modes. Such a distribution is quite plausible since there is no reason to believe that transverse and longitudinal optic modes have the same frequency, or that their frequencies are independent of wave vector. Analysis of the titanium hydride results (Sanderson and Cocking, 1963) reinforces the conclusion that the hydrogen vibrations cannot be adequately represented by a single Einstein oscillator. A detailed discussion of these results is given in Chapter 10.

Lithium hydride and sodium hydride are both ionic in character. This manifests itself as a double peak (the separation of longitudinal and transverse optic branches) in the scattered neutron distribution (Woods *et al.*, 1961a). No detailed analysis of these results has been made and more precise data are probably necessary if any conclusions are to be significant.

5.17 Anharmonic Effects

Reference was made in section 5.1 to certain fundamental approximations, particularly the harmonic approximation, commonly employed in the theory of lattice vibrations, approximations which have been implicit in much of the discussion of Sections 5.2 through 5.16. Recently, however, considerable attention has been paid to the effects of the higher order terms in the expansion of the potential energy of a crystal, terms which are neglected in the harmonic approximation (Van Hove, 1959; Baym, 1961; Kashcheev and Krivoglaz, 1961; Kokkedee, 1962; Hahn, 1963; Maradudin and Fein, 1962; Cowley, 1963a, 1965a; Ambegaokar et al., 1965). The theoretical and experimental study of anharmonic effects in crystals is still at an early stage, and it should be emphasized that the following brief description of phonon lifetimes and frequency shifts does scant justice to the importance of this rapidly developing field of study.

The inclusion of the "anharmonic" or higher order terms in the potential as small *perturbations* of the harmonic problem leads to the concept of a "phonon–phonon" interaction, and allows transitions in which one phonon decays into two other phonons (or more). Such a decay can be characterized by a "phonon lifetime" and hence, through the uncertainty principle, by a spread in phonon energy or frequency. There are of course other phenomena, such as phonon scattering by electrons and by lattice imperfections, which may complicate the experimental investigation of the phonon–phonon interactions. This spread in phonon frequency manifests itself in the neutron scattering experiments as a broadening of the neutron group associated with any coherent one-phonon scattering process. Neglecting the finite resolving power of the instrument, these neutron groups should, according to equation (1.96), be δ-functions. An associated effect of the higher order terms is to alter the normal mode frequencies from their "harmonic" values. The situation is analogous to that of a resonant system, having a single resonant frequency f in the undamped condition: when damping is applied, the resonant frequency is altered as well as broadened into a band. In fact, certain theoretical treatments of phonon lifetimes have been proposed which merely apply a phenomenological damping factor $\exp(-\gamma t)$ to the harmonic vibrations $\exp(ift)$ (Butterworth and Marshall, 1957; Brockhouse et al., 1961b).

The most recent treatments of this problem have used either simple perturbation theory or more sophisticated methods involving Green's functions and the concept of "diagrams". Although a full description of these developments is beyond the scope of this book, it is worthwhile to mention some of the theoretical results which have been obtained, so that comparison with the analogous harmonic expressions derived in Chapter 1 may be made. The expression (equation (1.76)) for the crystal potential energy is extended to include cubic and quartic terms; the fifth and sixth order terms belong to the next higher order approximation and are neglected here. For example, the cubic term may be written

$$\tfrac{1}{6} \sum_{\mathbf{v}l\alpha} \sum_{\mathbf{u}k\beta} \sum_{\mathbf{w}m\gamma} G^{\mathbf{v}l\alpha}_{\mathbf{u}k\beta\ \mathbf{w}m\gamma}\, u^{\alpha}_{\mathbf{v}l}\, u^{\beta}_{\mathbf{u}k}\, u^{\gamma}_{\mathbf{w}m} \tag{5.14}$$

A function $\Phi(^{\mathbf{q}_1\mathbf{q}_2\mathbf{q}_3}_{s_1 s_2 s_3})$, analogous to the dynamical matrix $\mathbf{E}$, can be defined as the Fourier transform of (5.14) (cf. Born and Huang, 1954, p. 305). The quartic term can be expressed in a similar manner.

It is assumed that these higher order terms are small enough for the application of perturbation theory; in practice this restricts the theory to temperatures substantially below the melting point (T_m) of the solid, where the energy broadening of the phonons is small compared to their energies. To the lowest non-vanishing order in the anharmonic terms, the differential coherent scattering cross-section for processes in which an incident neutron creates one phonon (of mode $\mathbf{q}s$) in a simple Bravais crystal is expressed, according to Maradudin and Fein (1962), in terms of the shift $\varDelta(\mathbf{q}s\ )$ and broadening $\varGamma(\mathbf{q}s\omega)$ of the phonon frequency, $f_{\mathbf{q}s}$

$$\frac{\mathrm{d}^2\sigma^{\mathrm{coh}}}{\mathrm{d}\varOmega\mathrm{d}E} = \frac{N\bar{b}^{2}}{2\pi M} \cdot \frac{k}{k_0}\left[1-\mathrm{e}^{-\frac{\hbar\omega}{kT}}\right]^{-1} \mathrm{e}^{-2W}\frac{(\mathbf{Q}\cdot\mathbf{V}_s)^2}{f_{\mathbf{q}s}}\,\delta(\mathbf{Q}-\mathbf{q}-2\pi\boldsymbol{\tau})\times$$

$$\left[\frac{\varGamma(\mathbf{q}s\omega)}{[\omega-f_{\mathbf{q}s}-\varDelta(\mathbf{q}s\omega)]^2+\varGamma^2(\mathbf{q}s\omega)} + \frac{\varGamma(\mathbf{q}s\omega)}{[\omega+f_{\mathbf{q}s}+\varDelta(\mathbf{q}s\omega)]^2+\varGamma^2(\mathbf{q}s\omega)}\right] \tag{5.15}$$

where

$$\varDelta(\mathbf{q}s\omega) = \frac{h}{8Nf_{\mathbf{q}s}} \sum_{\mathbf{q}_1 s_1} \frac{\Phi(^{-\mathbf{q}\ \mathbf{q}\ \mathbf{q}_1\ -\mathbf{q}_1}_{\ s\ s\ s_1\ \ s_1})}{f_{\mathbf{q}_1 s_1}}\,(2n_1+1)+$$

$$\frac{h}{16Nf_{\mathbf{q}s}} \sum_{\substack{\mathbf{q}_1 s_1 \\ \mathbf{q}_2 s_2}} \delta(-\mathbf{q}+\mathbf{q}_1+\mathbf{q}_2)\frac{|\Phi(^{-\mathbf{q}\ \mathbf{q}_1\ \mathbf{q}_2}_{\ s\ \ s_1\ s_2})|^2}{f_{\mathbf{q}_1 s_1}f_{\mathbf{q}_2 s_2}}\times$$

$$\left[-\frac{n_1+n_2+1}{(\omega+f_1+f_2)} + \frac{n_1+n_2+1}{(\omega-f_1-f_2)_p} - \frac{n_1-n_2}{(\omega-f_1+f_2)_p} + \frac{n_1-n_2}{(\omega+f_1-f_2)_p}\right]$$

$$\varGamma(\mathbf{q}s\omega) = \frac{\pi h}{16Nf_{\mathbf{q}s}} \sum_{\substack{\mathbf{q}_1 s_1 \\ \mathbf{q}_2 s_2}} \delta(-\mathbf{q}+\mathbf{q}_1+\mathbf{q}_2)\frac{|\Phi(^{-\mathbf{q}\ \mathbf{q}_1\ \mathbf{q}_2}_{\ s\ \ s_1\ s_2})|^2}{f_{\mathbf{q}_1 s_1}f_{\mathbf{q}_2 s_2}}\times$$

$$[-(n_1+n_2+1)\,\delta\,(\omega+f_1+f_2)+(n_1+n_2+1)\,\delta\,(\omega-f_1-f_2)-$$

$$(n_1-n_2)\,\delta\,(\omega-f_1+f_2)+(n_1-n_2)\,\delta\,(\omega+f_1-f_2)].$$

The phonon occupation numbers n_i are given by $\left[\exp\left(\dfrac{\hbar f_{\mathbf{q}_i s_i}}{kT}\right)-1\right]^{-1}$, $\delta(-\mathbf{q}+\mathbf{q}_1+\mathbf{q}_2)$ expresses conservation of "crystal" momentum, ω is the "applied" frequency corresponding the neutron energy transfer, and p denotes the principal value, which may be written:

$$\frac{1}{(\omega)_p} = \lim_{t \to \infty} \frac{1}{\omega}\left(1 - \frac{\sin \omega t}{\omega t}\right)$$

Finally, we note that e^{-2W} is the well-known Debye-Waller factor, suitably corrected for anharmonic effects. Reference to equation (1.95) shows that the δ-function peaks of the harmonic theory have become, in the (weakly) anharmonic case, approximately Lorentzian peaks having frequency dependent shifts and widths. We notice that both cubic and quartic terms contribute to the phonon frequency shift $\varDelta(\mathbf{q}s\omega)$ but that (in this approximation) the broadening $\varGamma(\mathbf{q}s\omega)$, and hence the phonon lifetime, depends only on the cubic term. The temperature dependence of $\varDelta$ and $\varGamma$ is dominated by the phonon occupation numbers n_i. For temperatures T higher than the Debye temperature, $\varTheta_D$, the n_i are proportional to T. Thus we expect the frequency shifts and widths to be linear functions of temperature over the range $\varTheta_D \ll T \ll T_m$. This result forms the basis of Hahn's suggestion (Hahn, 1963) (see also Leibfried and Ludwig (1963)) that the shift of the phonon frequency, from the value it would have in the absence of the anharmonic terms, may be determined experimentally by extrapolation back to 0°K of phonon frequencies observed over the temperature range of "linear behaviour". (The extent of this linear behaviour may however be rather small and difficult to determine in many practical cases.)

As the temperature of the crystal increases, the phonon frequencies usually decrease and the phonon lifetimes get shorter. The frequency changes are quite often of the order of a few percent and may in many cases be detected without difficulty. The observations of changes in width of the neutron groups (related through the uncertainty principle to the phonon lifetimes) show up qualitatively in many cases, but extracting quantitative information is usually extremely difficult. The background scattering generally shows a large increase with increasing temperature. This in itself makes the attainment of adequate statistical accuracy more difficult, but the chief problem is in determining just what this background level is. Since the line width at high temperatures is similar to a Lorentzian function, a considerable part of the phonon intensity resides in the broad wings of the distribution. The technique generally employed is to assume that the one phonon intensity formula (equation (1.96), Chapter 1) holds even at high temperatures, and to calculate just what intensity is expected compared with the intensity observed at very low temperatures. This calculation allows a (featureless) background line to be drawn under the observed "one-phonon" neutron group, and hence, the half-width to be measured. (In fact the multi-phonon component of the background under such peaks does contain structure, but an adequate calculation of this background shape is very difficult, and the experimental accuracy usually attained does not as yet warrant such subtleties.) This half-width, of course, contains the resolution function for the spectrometer, a variable quantity since it is also a function of the particular phonon being measured. If sufficient information about the dispersion relation for the crystal is available, the spectrometer resolution function could, in principle, be calculated for each phonon, and the observed neutron group line shape appropriately corrected. However, in view of the difficulties associated with such calculations, the use of the low temperature neutron group as the resolution function of the instrument seems much to be preferred at the present time.

In spite of these difficulties some results have been obtained for metals and for alkali halides. The broadening of the neutron groups has been studied by Larsson *et al.* (1960) and Stedman and Nilsson (1965) in aluminium and by Brockhouse *et al.* (1961b) in lead. Similar broadening has been observed in sodium, Woods *et al.* (1961b) but the details are even more obscure in this case, since the incoherent cross-section contributes a very large amount of inelastic scattering to the background under the peaks. The results for metals show that even at modest temperatures ($T \approx \frac{2}{3}$ of melting temperature) lifetimes of phonons near the zone boundary are of the order of one vibrational period.

Some of the theoretical treatments referred to above have been carried to the point of making comparisons between theory and experiment. Thus Maradudin and Fein (1962) have applied their theory to lead and have calculated, for example, the effect of the phonon–phonon interaction on the energy widths of the neutron groups scattered at high temperatures. They employed an over-simplified force-model (nearest neighbour central forces only) and, in addition, neglected the electron–phonon interaction; nevertheless they obtained order of magnitude agreement with the experimental measurements (Brockhouse *et al.*, 1961b).

Potassium bromide has also been studied (Woods *et al.*, 1963) as a function of temperature. In this case the broadening of phonon peaks does not seem to be as large as for metals at the corresponding temperature, except in the case of the longitudinal optical (LO) modes. These modes have been discussed in Section 5.12. Cowley (1963a) has employed methods similar to those of Maradudin and Fein (1962) to the calculation of many anharmonic properties of both potassium bromide and sodium iodide. From the analysis of appropriate dispersion curves in terms of the "shell model" (Cowley *et al.*, 1963), a simple exponential form for the interatomic potential function was devised in order to fit the short range force constants. From this function, cubic and quartic contributions to the crystal potential energy were calculated, from which Cowley succeeded in calculating quantities such as the thermal expansion and the shapes of scattered neutron groups as a function of temperature. One result of this work was that even at low temperatures ($\sim$100°K) the anharmonic contributions to the measured frequencies, for example, were significantly larger than the estimated errors in the experimental determinations. Of particular interest is the result that the calculated line shape associated with the LO mode of zero wave vector, for both NaI and KBr, displays a complicated structure even at 90°K. When allowance is made for the smoothing effect of the instrumental resolution, an extremely broad neutron group is predicted for NaI at room temperature. The line shape for the TO mode is by contrast very simple, consisting of a single narrow peak. This difference in behaviour arises because the "damping" function $\Gamma(\mathbf{q}s\omega)$ is strongly peaked near the LO mode frequency, owing to the large number of possible two-phonon combinations whose frequency sum has this value. Calculations of the line shapes of neutron groups appropriate to the three transverse optic modes of zero wave vector in strontium titanate have also been made by Cowley (1965b). As in the cases of potassium bromide and sodium iodide, the calculations are based on a dipole approximation model fitted to the observed dispersion relation, and extended in a simple manner to include anharmonic interactions, in this case between nearest neighbour titanium-oxygen ions. Although the anharmonic interactions assumed by Cowley are not large in an absolute sense, the existence of the low frequency TO mode associated with the ferroelectric behaviour (see Section 5.14) produces some very anomalous effects. The situation is further complicated by the fact that the polarization vectors of the three TO modes are not completely determined by the crystal symmetry; in such a situation, the peak position of a neutron group corresponding to a particular phonon is not necessarily the same for observations made with respect to different reciprocal lattice points.

It should be emphasized that although the various theoretical calculations mentioned above are based on over-simplified models of anharmonic forces, they nevertheless exhibit reasonable overall agreement with the existing experimental data, and should provide a powerful stimulus to further quantitative experimental tests.

5.18 Summary

The experiments discussed in this chapter demonstrate the power of the method of inelastic scattering in the study of atomic vibrations in crystals. The most important achievement of the method so far has been the direct determination of the frequency/wave vector dispersion relation for the normal modes of vibration of a crystal, from which information concerning the interatomic force system in that crystal may be deduced. We may expect further advances in the study of more complex crystals and of anharmonic properties as experimental and theoretical techniques improve. The close connection between important quantities, such as specific heat, thermal conductivity, thermal expansion, infrared absorption, etc., and the information obtained by neutron spectrometry, has yet to be fully exploited.

Acknowledgment

The authors are particularly grateful to Professor B. N. Brockhouse for valuable discussions and for his helpful comments on the manuscript.

References

Ambegaokar, V., Conway, J. M. and Baym, G. (1965). *In* "Lattice Dynamics", ed. by R. F. Wallis, p. 261. Pergamon Press, London.

Bardeen, J. (1937). *Phys. Rev.* **52**, 688.

Baym, G. (1961). *Phys. Rev.* **121**, 741.

Becka, L. N. (1963). *J. chem. Phys.* **38**, 1685.

Birgeneau, R. J., Cordes, J., Dolling, G. and Woods, A. D. B. (1964). *Phys. Rev.* **136**, A1359.

Bergsma, J. and Goedkoop, J. A. (1961). *In* "Inelastic Scattering of Neutrons in Solids and Liquids", p. 501. IAEA, Vienna.

Borgonovi, G., Caglioti, G. and Antal, J. J. (1963). *Phys. Rev.* **132**, 683.

Borgonovi, G., Caglioti, G. and Antonini, M. (1965). *In* "Inelastic Scattering of Neutrons" Vol. I, p. 117. IAEA, Vienna.

Born, M. and Huang, K. (1954). "Dynamical Theory of Crystal Lattices". Clarendon Press, Oxford.

Bouckaert, L. P., Smoluchowski, R. and Wigner, E. (1936). *Phys. Rev.* **50**, 58.

Brockhouse, B. N. (1959a). *Phys. Rev. Letters*, **2**, 256.

Brockhouse, B. N. (1959b). *J. Phys. Chem. Solids*, **8**, 400.

Brockhouse, B. N. (1961). *J. phys. Soc. Japan*, **17**, Suppl. B-II, 363.

Brockhouse, B. N. and Iyengar, P. K. (1958). *Phys. Rev.* **111**, 747.

Brockhouse, B. N. and Stewart, A. T. (1958). *Rev. mod. Phys.* **30**, 236.

Brockhouse, B. N., Rao, K. R. and Woods, A. D. B. (1961a). *Phys. Rev. Letters*, **7**, 93.

Brockhouse, B. N., Arase, T., Caglioti, G., Rao, K. R. and Woods, A. D. B. (1962). *Phys. Rev.* **128**, 1099.

Brockhouse, B. N., Arase, T., Caglioti, G., Sakamoto, M., Sinclair, R. N. and Woods, A. D. B. (1961b). *In* "Inelastic Scattering of Neutrons in Solids and Liquids", p. 531. IAEA, Vienna.

Brockhouse, B. N., Becka, L. N., Rao, K. R. and Woods, A. D. B. (1963). *In* "Inelastic Scattering of Neutrons in Solids and Liquids", Vol. II, p. 23. IAEA, Vienna.

Brout, R. and Visscher, W. (1962). *Phys. Rev. Letters* **9**, 54.

Brugger, R. M. (1964), AERE Report R4562. H.M.S.O. (London).

Butterworth, I. and Marshall, W. (1957). Proceedings of the Meeting on the Use of Slow Neutrons to Investigate the Solid State, Stockholm, October 1957.

Carter, R. S., Palevsky, H. and Hughes, D. J. (1957). *Phys. Rev.* **106**, 1168.

Chen, S. H. and Brockhouse, B. N. (1964). *Solid State Commun.* **2**, 73.

Chester, G. V. (1961). *Advanc. Phys.* **10**, 357.

Cochran, W. (1959). *Phys. Rev. Letters* **2**, 495.

Cochran, W. (1959a). *Proc. roy. Soc.* **A253**, 260.

Cochran, W. (1960). *Advanc. Phys.* **9**, 387; (1961). **10**, 401.

Cochran, W. (1963). *Proc. roy. Soc.* **A276**, 308.

Cochran, W. and Cowley, R. A. (1962). *J. Phys. Chem. Solids* **23**, 447.

Cochran, W., Fray, S. J., Johnson, F. A. and Quarrington, J. E. (1961). *J. Appl. Phys.* **32**, 2102.

Collins, M. F. (1962). *Proc. phys. Soc.* **80**, 362.

Cowley, R. A. (1962). *Proc. roy. Soc.* **A268**, 109.

Cowley, R. A. (1962a). *Proc. roy. Soc.* **A268**, 121.

Cowley, R. A. (1963a). *Advanc. Phys.* **12**, 421.

Cowley, R. A. (1963b). *In* "Inelastic Scattering of Neutrons in Solids and Liquids", Vol. II, p. 229. IAEA, Vienna and *Phys. Rev. Letters* **9**, 159.

Cowley, R. A. (1965a). *In* "Lattice Dynamics", ed. by R. F. Wallis, p. 295. Pergamon Press, London.

Cowley, R. A. (1965b). *In* "Inelastic Scattering of Neutrons", Vol. I, p. 297. IAEA, Vienna.

Cowley, R. A., Cochran, W., Brockhouse, B. N. and Woods, A. D. B. (1963). *Phys. Rev.* **131**, 1030.

Cribier, D., Farnoux, B. and Jacrot, B. (1963). *In* "Inelastic Scattering of Neutrons in Solids and Liquids", Vol. II, p. 225. IAEA, Vienna.

Cribier, D., Jacrot, B., and Saint-James, D. (1961). *In* "Inelastic Scattering of Neutrons in Solids and Liquids", p. 549. IAEA, Vienna.

Demidenko, Z. A., Kucher, T. I. and Tolpygo, K. B. (1962). *Sov. Phys. Solid State* **3**, 1803 (translation from *Fiz. Tverdoga Tela* **3**, 2482 (1961)).

De Wames, R. E. and Lehman, G. W. (1964). *Phys. Rev.* **135**, A170.

Dick, B. G. and Overhauser, A. W. (1958). *Phys. Rev.* **112**, 90.

Dixon, A. E., Woods, A. D. B. and Brockhouse, B. N. (1963). *Proc. phys. Soc.* **81**, 973.

Dolling, G. (1961). *In* "Inelastic Scattering of Neutrons in Solids and Liquids", p. 563. IAEA, Vienna.

Dolling, G. (1963). *In* "Inelastic Scattering of Neutrons in Solids and Liquids", Vol. II, p. 37. IAEA, Vienna.

Dolling, G. and Brockhouse, B. N. (1962). *Phys. Rev.* **128**, 1120.

Dolling, G. and Gilat, G. (1964). *Solid State Commun.* **2**, 79.

Dolling, G. and Gilat, (1965). *In* "Inelastic Scattering of Neutrons", Vol. I, p. 343. IAEA, Vienna.

Dolling, G. and Waugh, J. L. T. (1965). *In* "Lattice Dynamics", ed. by R. F. Wallis, p. 19. Pergamon Press, London.

Egelstaff, P. A. and Cocking, S. J. (1961). *In* "Inelastic Scattering of Neutrons", p. 569. IAEA, Vienna.

Egelstaff, P. A. and Harris, D. H. C. (1963). *Phys. Letters* **7**, 220.

Eisenhauer, C. M., Pelah, I., Hughes, D. J. and Palevsky, H. (1958). *Phys. Rev.* **109**, 1046.

Elliott, R. J. and Maradudin, A. A. (1965). *In* "Inelastic Scattering of Neutrons in Solids and Liquids", Vol. I, p. 231. IAEA, Vienna.

Ewald, P. P. (1921). *Ann. d. Phys.*, **64**, 253; (1938). *Nach. Ges. Wiss. Gottingen* 55.

Foreman, A. J. E. and Lomer, W. M. (1957). *Proc. phys. Soc.* **B70**, 1143.

Friedel, J. (1952). *Phil. Mag.* **43**, 153.

Friedel, J. (1962). *J. Phys. Radium* **23**, 692.

Fröhlich, H. (1949). "Theory of Dielectrics". Clarendon Press, Oxford.

Ganesan, S. and Shrinivasan, R. (1962). *Canad. J. Phys.* **40**, 74.

Gilat, G. and Dolling, G. (1964). *Phys. Letters* **8**, 304.

Gilat, G. and Dolling, G. (1965). *Phys. Rev.* **138**, A1053.

Gläser, W., Carvalho, F. and Ehret, G. (1965). *In* "Inelastic Scattering of Neutrons",
    Vol. I, p. 99. IAEA, Vienna.

Haas, R., Kley, W., Krebs, K. H. and Rubin, R. (1963). *In* "Inelastic Scattering of
    Neutrons in Solids and Liquids", Vol. II, p. 145. IAEA, Vienna.

Hahn, H. (1963). *In* "Inelastic Scattering of Neutrons in Solids and Liquids", Vol. I,
    p. 37. IAEA, Vienna.

Hardy, J. R. (1962). *Phil. Mag.* **7**, 315.

Hardy, J. R., and Smith, S. D. (1961). *Phil. Mag.* **6**, 1163.

Haywood, B. C. and Thorson, I. M. (1963). *In* "Inelastic Scattering of Neutrons in
    Solids and Liquids", Vol. II, p. 111. IAEA, Vienna.

Herman, F. (1959). *J. Phys. Chem. Solids* **8**, 405.

Hughes, D. J., Palevsky, H., Ghose, A., Pelah, I. and Eisenhauer, C. M. (1959). *Phys.
    Rev.* **113**, 49.

Iyengar, P. K., Satya Murthy, N. S. and Dasannacharya, B. A. (1961). *In* "Inelastic
    Scattering of Neutrons in Solids and Liquids", p. 555. IAEA, Vienna.

Iyengar, P. K., Venkataraman, G., Rao, K. R., Vijayaraghavan, P. R. and Roy, A. P.
    (1963). *In* "Inelastic Scattering of Neutrons in Solids and Liquids", Vol. II, p. 99.
    IAEA, Vienna.

Jacobsen, E. H. (1955). *Phys. Rev.* **97**, 654.

Kanzig, W. (1957). *In* "Solid State Physics", ed. by F. Seitz and D. Turnbull, Vol. IV,
    p. 1. Academic Press, New York.

Kaplan, H. and Sullivan, J. J. (1963). *Phys. Rev.* **130**, 120.

Karo, A. M. and Hardy, J. R. (1963). *Phys. Rev.* **129**, 2024.

Kashcheev, V. N. and Krivoglaz, M. A. (1961). *Sov. Phys. Solid State* **3**, 1107 (translation
    from *Fiz. Tverdogo Tela* **3**, 1528 (1961)).

Kellermann, E. W. (1940). *Phil. Trans.* **A238**, 513.

Kittel, C. (1956). *In* "Introduction to Solid State Physics", 2nd Ed. Wiley, New York.

Klein, C. A., Straub, W. D. and Diefendorf, R. J. (1962). *Phys. Rev.* **125**, 468.

Koenig, S. H. (1964). *Phys. Rev.* **135**, A1693.

Koenig, S. H. and Yarnell, J. L. (1960). *Bull. Amer. phys. Soc.* **5**, 198.

Kohn, W. (1959). *Phys. Rev. Letters* **2**, 393.

Kokkedee, J. J. J. (1962). *Physica*, **28**, 374; (1963). *In* "Inelastic Scattering of Neutrons
    in Solids and Liquids", Vol. I, p. 15. IAEA, Vienna.

Koster, G. F. (1957). *In* "Solid State Physics", ed. by F. Seitz and D. Turnbull, Vol. V,
    p. 173. Academic Press, New York.

Larsson, K. E., Dahlborg, U. and Holmryd, S. (1960). *Ark. Fys.* **17**, 369.

Leibfried, G. and Ludwig, W. (1963). *In* "Solid State Physics", ed. by F. Seitz and D.
    Turnbull, Vol. 12. Academic Press, New York.

Lifshitz, I. M. (1944) *J. Phys. USSR* **8**, 89.

Lomer, W. M. (1962). *Proc. phys. Soc.* **80**, 489.

Long-Price, D. (1965). *In* "Inelastic Scattering of Neutrons", Vol. I, p. 109. IAEA,
    Vienna.

Low, G. G. E. (1962). *Proc. phys. Soc.* **79**, 479.

Lyddane, R. H., Sachs, R. G. and Teller, E. (1941). *Phys. Rev.* **59**, 673.

Macfarlane, G. G., McLean, T. P., Quarrington, J. E. and Roberts, V. (1959). *J. Phys.
    Chem. Solids*, **8**, 388.

McReynolds, A. W., Nelkin, M. A., Rosenbluth, M. N. and Whittemore, W. L. (1958). Proc. 2nd U.N. Int. Conf. PUAE, Vol. 16, p. 297.

Maliszewski, E., Rosolowski, J. H. and Sledziewska, D. (1965). In "Lattice Dynamics", ed. by R. F. Wallis, p. 33. Pergamon Press, London.

Maliszewski, E., Sosnowski, J., Blinowski, K., Kozubowski, J., Padlo, I. and Sledziewska, D. (1963). In "Inelastic Scattering of Neutrons in Solids and Liquids," Vol. II, p. 87. IAEA, Vienna.

Maradudin, A. A. and Fein, A. E. (1962). Phys. Rev. 128, 2589.

Martin, D. L. (1960). Proc. Roy. Soc. A254, 433.

Mashkevitch, V. S. (1957). Sov. Phys., J.E.T.P. 5, 707. (translation from Zh. eksp. teoret. Fiz. 32, 866 (1957)).

Mashkevitch, V. S. and Tolpygo, K. B. (1957). Sov. Phys., J.E.T.P. 5, 435 (translation from Zh. eksp. teoret. Fiz. 32, 520 (1957)).

Mikke, K. and Kroh, A. (1963). In "Inelastic Scattering of Neutrons in Solids and Liquids", Vol. II, p. 237. IAEA, Vienna.

Mitchell, E. W. J., Hardy, J. R. and Saunderson, D. H. (1963). In "Inelastic Scattering of Neutrons in Solids and Liquids", Vol. II, p. 49. IAEA, Vienna.

Mitsui, T. and Westphal, W. B. (1961). Phys. Rev. 124, 1354.

Möller, H. B. and Mackintosh, A. R. (1965). In "Inelastic Scattering of Neutrons in Solids and Liquids", Vol. I, p. 95. IAEA, Vienna.

Mozer, B. and Otnes, K. (1963); In "Inelastic Scattering of Neutrons in Solids and Liquids", Vol. II, p. 167. IAEA, Vienna.

Mozer, B., Otnes, K. and Myers, V. W. (1962). Phys. Rev. Letters 8, 278.

Mozer, B., Otnes, K. and Palevsky, H. (1965). In "Lattice Dynamics", ed. by R. F. Wallis, p. 63. Pergamon Press, London.

Musgrave, M. J. P. (1963). Proc. roy. Soc. A272, 503.

Nakagawa, Y. and Woods, A. D. B. (1963). Phys. Rev. Letters 11, 271.

Nakagawa, Y. and Woods, A. D. B. (1965). In "Lattice Dynamics", ed. R. F. Wallis, p. 39. Pergamon Press, London.

Palevsky, H. (1962). J. phys. Soc. Japan, 17, Suppl. B-II, 367.

Paskin, A. and Weiss, R. J. (1962). Phys. Rev. Letters, 9, 199.

Peierls, R. E. (1955). "Quantum Theory of Solids". Clarendon Press, Oxford.

Pelah, I., Eisenhauer, C. M., Hughes, D. J. and Palevsky, H. (1957). Phys. Rev. 108, 1091.

Placzek, G. and Van Hove, L. (1954). Phys. Rev. 93, 1207.

Rosenstock, H. B. (1955). Phys. Rev. 97, 290.

Rosenstock, H. B. (1963). Phys. Rev. 129, 1959.

Rowe, J. M., Brockhouse, B. N. and Svensson, E. C. (1965). Phys. Rev. Letters 14, 554.

Rubin, R., Peretti, J., Verdan, G. and Kley, W. (1965). Phys. Letters 14, 100.

Rupprecht, G. and Bell, R. O. (1962). Phys. Rev. 125, 1915.

Saunderson, D. H. and Cocking, S. J. (1963). In "Inelastic Scattering of Neutrons in Solids and Liquids", Vol. II, p. 265. IAEA, Vienna.

Schmunk, R. E. (1964). Phys. Rev. 136, A1303.

Schmunk, R. E., Brugger, R. M., Randolph, P. D. and Strong, K. A. (1962). Phys. Rev. 128, 562.

Schmunk, R. E. and Gavin, W. R. (1965). Phys. Rev. Letters 14, 44.

Seitz, F. (1940). "Modern Theory of Solids". McGraw-Hill, New York.

Sham, L. J. (1965). Proc. roy. Soc. A283, 33.

Sinclair, R. N. (1963). In "Inelastic Scattering of Neutrons in Solids and Liquids", Vol. II, p. 199. IAEA, Vienna.

Sinha, S. K. and Squires, G. L. (1965). *In* "Lattice Dynamics", ed. by R. F. Wallis, p. 53. Pergamon Press, London.

Smith, H. M. J. (1948). *Phil. Trans.* **241**, 105.

Sosnowski, J. and Kozubowski, J. (1962). *J. Phys. Chem. Solids*, **23**, 1021.

Squires, G. L. (1963). *In* "Inelastic Scattering of Neutrons in Solids and Liquids", Vol. II, p. 55. IAEA, Vienna.

Stedman, R. and Nilsson, G. (1965). *In* "Inelastic Scattering of Neutrons", Vol. I, p. 211. IAEA, Vienna.

Stewart, A. T. and Brockhouse, B. N. (1958). *Rev. mod. Phys.* **30**, 250.

Tchernoplekov, N. A., Zemlyanov, M. G., Tchetserin, A. G. and Lyashtchenko, B. G. (1963). *In* "Inelastic Scattering of Neutrons in Solids and Liquids", Vol. II, p. 159, IAEA, Vienna.

Tolpygo, K. B. (1961). *Sov. Phys. Solid State* **3**, 685 (translation from *Fiz. Tverdoga Tela,* **3**, 943 (1961)).

Toya, T. (1958a). *J. Res. Inst. Catalysis, Hokkaido Univ.* **6**, p. 183.

Toya, T. (1958b). *Progr. theor. Phys.* **20**, 974.

Turberfield, K. C. and Egelstaff, P. A. (1962). *Phys. Rev.* **127**, 1017.

Van Hove, L. (1953). *Phys. Rev.* **89**, 1189.

Van Hove, L. (1959). Technical Report No. 11, Solid State and Molecular Theory Group, Massachusetts Institute of Technology, Cambridge, Massachusetts.

Venkataraman, G., Usha, K., Iyengar, P. K., Vijayaraghavan, P. R. and Roy, A. P. (1963). *In* "Inelastic Scattering of Neutrons in Solids and Liquids", Vol. II, p. 253. IAEA, Vienna.

Vosko, S. H. (1964). *Phys. Letters* **13**, 97.

Walker, C. B. (1956). *Phys. Rev.* **103**, 547.

Warren, J. L., Wenzel, R. G. and Yarnell, J. L. (1965). *In* "Inelastic Scattering of Neutrons", Vol. I, p. 361. IAEA, Vienna.

Waugh, J. L. T. and Dolling, G. (1963). *Phys. Rev.* **132**, 2410.

Wolfram, T., Lehman, G. W. and De Wames, R. E. (1963). *Phys. Rev.* **129**, 2483.

Woll, E. J. and Kohn, W. (1962). *Phys. Rev.* **126**, 1693.

Woods, A. D. B. (1964a). *Phys. Rev.* **136**, A781.

Woods, A. D. B. (1965). *In* "Inelastic Scattering of Neutrons", Vol. I, p. 87. IAEA, Vienna.

Woods, A. D. B. and Chen, S. H. (1964). *Solid State Commun.* **2**, 233.

Woods, A. D. B., Dolling, G. and Cowley, R. A. (1965). *In* "Inelastic Scattering of Neutrons ", Vol. I, p. 373. IAEA, Vienna.

Woods, A. D. B., Brockhouse, B. N., March, R. H. and Bowers, R. (1962a). *Proc. phys. Soc.* **79**, 440.

Woods, A. D. B., Brockhouse, B. N., March, R. H., Stewart, A. T. and Bowers, R. (1962b). *Phys. Rev.* **128**, 1112.

Woods, A. D. B., Brockhouse, B. N., March, R. H. and Bowers, R. (1961b). *Bull. Amer. phys. Soc.* **6**, 261.

Woods, A. D. B., Brockhouse, B. N., Cowley, R. A. and Cochran, W. (1963). *Phys. Rev.* **131**, 1025.

Woods, A. D. B., Brockhouse, B. N., Sakamoto, M. and Sinclair, R. N. (1961a). *In* "Inelastic Scattering of Neutrons in Solids and Liquids", p. 487. IAEA, Vienna.

Woods, A. D. B., Cochran, W. and Brockhouse, B. N. (1960). *Phys. Rev.* **119**, 980.

Yarnell, J. L., Warren, J. L. and Wenzel, R. G. (1964). *Phys. Rev. Letters* **13**, 13.

Yarnell, J. L., Warren, J. L. and Koenig, S. H. (1965). *In* "Lattice Dynamics", ed. by R. F. Wallis, p. 57. Pergamon Press, London.

Yoshimori, A. and Kitano, Y. (1956). *J. phys. Soc. Japan* **11**, 352.

Young, J. A. and Koppel, J. U. (1965). *J. chem. Phys.* **42**, 357.

Zemlyanov, M. G., Kagan, Yu. M., Tchernoplekov, N. A. and Tchetserin, A. G. (1963). *In* "Inelastic Scattering of Neutrons in Solids and Liquids", Vol. II, p. 125. IAEA, Vienna.

Ziman, J. M. (1960). "Electrons and Phonons". Clarendon Press, Oxford.

Ziman, J. M. (1964). *Advanc. Phys.* **13**, 89.

CHAPTER 6

Magnetic Inelastic Scattering of Neutrons

B. Jacrot

Centre d'Études Nucléaires de Saclay, France

T. Riste

Institutt for Atomenergi, Kjeller, Norway

6.1 General Remarks on Magnetism and Neutron Scattering.................. 251
6.2 Uncoupled Ions; Paramagnetic Scattering at High Temperature........... 253
6.3 Coupled Ions... 256
6.4 Experimental Results on Coupled Systems............................. 259
6.5 Magnetic Inelastic Scattering at Low Temperatures.................... 261
6.6 Methods for Distinguishing Spin Wave Scattering from Other Inelastic
    Components... 264
6.7 Experimentally Observed Dispersion Curves........................... 267
6.8 The Effect of Temperature on the Spin Wave Dispersion Curve and Line Width 272
6.9 Conclusions from Spin Wave Experiments.............................. 275
6.10 The Theory of Critical Scattering.................................. 277
6.11 Experimental Results on Critical Scattering in Iron and Nickel....... 281
6.12 Critical Scattering in Antiferromagnetic and Ferrimagnetic Substances..... 286
6.13 Conclusions... 288
References... 288

List of Symbols

a	Lattice constant	T_c	Curie temperature
C	Curie constant	T_N	Néel temperature
$D(T)$	Constant in magnon dispersion law, $f = Dq^2$	α	Angle between $\mathbf{Q}$ and $\boldsymbol{\mu}$
		ζ	Coefficient in formula for $D(T)$
f	Magnon frequency	θ_w	Curie-Weiss constant
g	Landé splitting factor	Λ	Spin diffusion constant
H	Magnetic field strength	μ_J	Total magnetic moment
$J_{ij}(\mathbf{Q})$	Fourier transform of exchange integral, J_{ij}	ρ	Radius of scattering surface
		τ_q	Relaxation time for spin fluctuations
M	Magnetization		

6.1 General Remarks on Magnetism and Neutron Scattering

By definition we call a substance magnetic if it has a macroscopic magnetic moment M when put in a magnetic field H. The magnetic properties of the substance may be discussed in macroscopic terms and similarly looked for by measurements on its macroscopic moment.

However, great interest is attached to microscopic, or rather atomic, magnetism. In our discussion we shall usually adopt an atomic description. This is natural when discussing neutron scattering, because the neutron with its magnetic moment provides us with a magnetic probe which is small enough to investigate the atomic magnets. These tiny magnets are the real origin of the magnetism observed macroscopically. The cross-sections for magnetic scattering of neutrons were discussed in Chapter 1, Sections 1.15 to 1.18.

It is well known that an atomic moment is due to the spin and the orbital motion of the electrons, when neglecting the small contribution from the nucleus. We shall discuss only the cases where the moment is due to an un-filled internal electron shell, and there are three groups of elements which have such an unfilled shell, i.e.:—

the iron group ($3d$ shell),
the rare earth group ($4f$ shell),
the actinide group.

We shall be dealing only with the former two of these.

In an isolated ion or atom the spins of the electrons in the unfilled shell add, according to Hund's rule, to form a total spin $\mathbf{S}$ of the atom. Similarly a total orbital momentum $\mathbf{L}$ is formed. Then by spin-orbit coupling $\mathbf{S}$ and $\mathbf{L}$ may combine to form a total angular momentum $\mathbf{J} = \mathbf{L} + \mathbf{S}$. The values of S, L and J are known from spectroscopic measurements, because such measurements are performed under conditions which correspond very well to that of isolated ions or atoms.

It is expected that corresponding to $\mathbf{J}$ the atom has a resultant magnetic moment given by $\mu_J = g[J(J+1)]^{\frac{1}{2}}$ Bohr magnetons, where g is the Landé splitting factor depending on S, L and J. Such moment values are observed in susceptibility measurements on rare earth salts. In salts of the iron group, however, such measurements yield moment values which agree better with the assumption that only the spins contribute to the magnetic moment.

Susceptibility measurements have to be performed on a large collection of atoms, as do the neutron scattering experiments. By a suitable choice of sample materials, however, such measurements may give information on the magnetic moments and the energy level structure both of isolated, uncoupled atoms and of coupled ones.

A great deal of information on magnetic moment values has been ob-tained in the past 10 or 15 years by elastic neutron scattering experiments. Some information, but to a much smaller extent, has in the same period been obtained on energy level structures in magnets by inelastic neutron scattering. In fact, almost all the experiments performed to date in the latter field will be mentioned in the present review. These experiments have been conducted with unpolarized neutrons, for reasons of intensity. However polarized neutrons have proved very useful in experiments on magnetic form factors and spin configurations. Their main merit is to enhance magnetic diffraction components so as to make them discernible in the presence of strong nuclear components. One can expect that polarized neutrons for the same reason will prove equally useful in the study of dynamic effects, especially in the low temperature region. The theory has been given by Saenz (1960), Maleev (1961) and Izyumov and Maleev (1961, 1962), and has been verified by experiments on Fe_2O_4 by Ferguson and Saenz (1962) and by Samuelsen *et al.* (1963).

Several reviews of this field have appeared and we mention that of De Gennes (1963) for a theoretical account and Lowde (1965) for spin wave scattering.

6.2 Uncoupled Ions; Paramagnetic Scattering at High Temperature

When magnetic ions are far from each other (for instance when they are present only dilutely in a non-magnetic salt) there is essentially no interaction between them, or this interaction is at most small in comparison with other interactions of the magnetic ion with its non-magnetic neighbours. The substance is then paramagnetic at all but the lowest temperatures. For an ideal paramagnet the susceptibility $\chi = M/H$ is then given by the Curie law

$$\chi = \frac{C}{T} \qquad (6.1)$$

containing the Curie constant C.

The physical problem with which we are concerned is the behaviour of such a magnetic ion in the crystalline electric field from the neighbouring ions. By neutron inelastic scattering one aims at finding the energies of the different states that can be formed by combination of the quantum numbers L and S. The cross-sections were discussed at the end of Section 1.15. Such data may supplement those obtained by susceptibility measurements and by the electron resonance technique. For our purpose, a system of uncoupled ions is best approximated by the high temperature state of a substance having a low Curie point, and we shall consider room temperature scattering by substances having Curie points $\approx 1°K$. If, on the other hand, the substance has a Curie point $\approx 100°K$, the interactions are no longer negligible. In Section 6.3 below we consider neutron scattering from such substances at room temperature. The data are representative of a system of coupled ions in the paramagnetic state.

First assume that no other forces, either of electric or magnetic origin, are acting on the ions. The ground state then has a total degeneracy of $(2L+1)$ $(2S+1)$. If a spin-orbit coupling exists, we have seen that **L** and **S** combine to form a total angular momentum **J**. The degeneracy is then reduced to $(2J+1)$. If furthermore one makes allowance for the electric field due to the nonmagnetic neighbours. the degeneracy is lifted and $2J+1$ equally spaced energy levels are formed. Hence we see that two effects may reduce the degeneracy of the energy states in a system of uncoupled ions:

(1) the L–S coupling;
(2) the electric field due to nonmagnetic neighbours.

The two effects have different importance for the rare earth group and the iron group.

Let us consider first the rare earth group of elements. The unfilled $4f$ shell has a small radius and lies rather deep inside the ion. It is partly shielded from the electric field of its neighbours by the $5s$ and $5p$ electrons. Thus the crystalline electric field is too weak to break up the L–S coupling. J is a good quantum number and the typical distance between the levels of different J is 1 eV. The crystalline electric field gives sublevels within each J-state which are separated by 10^{-3} to 10^{-1} eV. This splitting falls in the range of the neutron technique and in principle the measurements give information about the symmetry and strength of the crystalline field.

Table 6.1

Ho$_2$O$_3$				
at Saclay*		25	76	365
at Chalk River †	10·5	22	80	360
Er$_2$O$_3$				
At Saclay*	10	40·5	81	420
at Chalk River†	14·5	40	81	

The values are in optical units (cm^{-1}); refer to conversion chart for other units.

* Cribier and Jacrot (1960).
† Brockhouse et al. (1962).

Some information on the splitting of the lowest J state by the crystalline field has been obtained for Ho$_2$O$_3$ and Er$_2$O$_3$ by two groups of experimenters (Cribier and Jacrot, 1960; Brockhouse et al., 1962). A typical result for Ho$_2$O$_3$ is given in Fig. 6.1(a). Verification of the magnetic character of the lines was made in two ways: by comparing the spectrum with that obtained from a nonmagnetic substance, very similar to the one under study, and by measuring the angular variation of the intensity of the energy group. In the latter case the variation must exhibit the characteristic of a form factor curve. The transitions observed are given in Table 6.1.

These transitions are just a few among a large number possible and the theoretical analysis of the results is difficult. Similar measurements could with advantage be carried out with a rare earth ion of a lower J value, like Ce^{3+}.

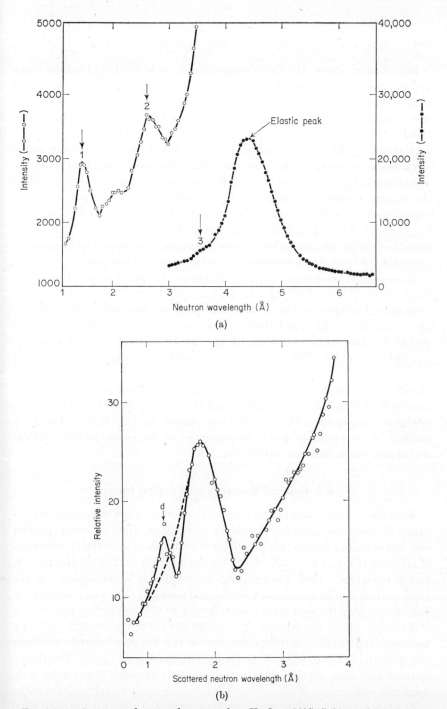

Fig. 6.1. (a) Spectrum of scattered neutrons from Ho_2O_3 at 30°C (Cribier and Jacrot, 1960) (arrows mark peaks listed in Table 6.1). (b) Inelastic peak due to a magnetic transition in $FeCl_2$ (Hautecler *et al.*, 1962); the peak marked "d" is probably due to non-magnetic effects and the expected behaviour of the magnetic scattering is shown by the dotted line.

In the cases above, the Curie temperatures are in the liquid helium range and the coupling between the ions is weak. Some degree of coupling does of course exist and must lead to some broadening of the lines. The theory of the broadening due to exchange coupling has been given by Saint-James (1961).

Contrary to the case that we have just discussed, the magnetically active electrons in an atom of the iron group are only weakly shielded from the crystalline field by an outer $4s$ shell. In the ionic state the $3d$ shell is in fact the outermost shell and thus directly exposed to the electric field from the neighbouring ions. This has the effect of (largely) breaking up the L–S coupling. Furthermore the state belonging to a certain L is split by the crystalline field into $2L+1$ sublevels, and in most cases this again leads to partial or complete quenching of the orbital contribution to the magnetic moment.

According to theoretical work by Kanamori (1958), Yamada (1960) and Saint-James (1961), $FeCl_2$ should offer a simple problem for the neutron technique. In this case the orbital multiplets are too widely separated to give any detectable contribution and the only detectable transition should be due to a splitting of the lowest orbital doublet into five equidistant doublets. The latter splitting should arise from a weak spin-orbit coupling and be of magnitude 100–200 cm^{-1}. Hence a single line of this energy should appear in the neutron spectrum. Just one magnetic line was observed by Hautecler et al. (1962), and the energy of 165 cm^{-1} was of the predicted magnitude. Their results are shown in Fig. 6.1(b). The peak marked "d" is probably due to uncertainties in the corrections for nuclear scattering, which has been subtracted.

6.3 General Remarks on Coupled Ions

With the possible exception of very large dilution, some interaction always exists between the magnetic moments of the ions. Here we shall consider only the exchange interaction, which gives a contribution to the Hamiltonian of the system equal to $-2J_{ij}\,\mathbf{S}_i\cdot\mathbf{S}_j$ for the interaction between the spins $\mathbf{S}_i$ and $\mathbf{S}_j$ (equation 1.130). The exchange interaction is a consequence of the Pauli exclusion principle and has no classical analogue (e.g. Van Vleck, 1955). Notice that only the spin gives a contribution to this interaction and that S_i is the total spin of the ith ion. J_{ij} is called the exchange integral and is an unknown and possibly intricate function of the distance between the ions, but is related to the overlap of the charge distributions of i and j. The charge distributions may overlap directly or indirectly through intervening non-magnetic ions.

As a consequence of the exchange interactions, the spins (or the associated magnetic moments) line up in an orderly manner at low temperatures.

Ferromagnetism, in which all the spins are parallel, is the simplest one of the ordered states. Other ordered arrangements are possible: antiferro-magnetism, ferrimagnetism, helimagnetism, etc. These arrangements can be determined by elastic scattering of neutrons as described by Bacon (1962).

In a specimen of any of the ordered materials, e.g. a ferromagnetic one, the direction along which the moments are ordered is not the same throughout the whole specimen. Instead the specimen is composed of domains within each of which the direction of magnetization is the same. In the absence of an external magnetic field the total magnetization of a ferromagnetic body may be zero, due to the random orientation of the domain magnetizations. When an external field is applied, the domain magnetizations line up in the direction of the field and a macroscopic moment is observed.

The ordered spin arrangement within a domain, i.e. the spontaneous magnetization, may be observed with neutron scattering even if no external field is applied. The coherent elastic magnetic scattering described by (1.120) is due to scattering by such an ordered spin assembly. At low temperatures ($kT \ll J$) there is little disorder in the spin alignment within a domain. The small disorder that exists may be considered in terms of spin waves, as shown in Chapter 1. The energy level structure of the spin system, as given by the spin wave theory, can be observed by inelastic neutron scattering experiments.

As the temperature is increased, the spin disorder and thus the excitation of spin waves, increases. The coherent elastic magnetic scattering, which is proportional to the square of the spontaneous magnetization, will then decrease. At the same time the spin wave scattering increases. The increasing temperature also has the effect of increasing the interaction between the spin waves and thus reducing their energy and lifetime. The latter two effects are both observed by neutron scattering.

At very high temperatures ($kT \gg J$), in the paramagnetic region, the spin system is completely disordered. The exchange interactions expressed by J still exist, but are too weak to introduce an order in competition with the disordering effect due to the thermal energy kT supplied to the system. Even though the system is different from an ideal paramagnet of uncoupled ions, the susceptibility behaves very nearly as described by (6.1). More correctly it is expressed by the Curie-Weiss law

$$\chi = \frac{C}{T-\theta}. \tag{6.2}$$

θ, the paramagnetic Curie Temperature, can be positive or negative, and expresses the effect of the exchange coupling. At the transition temperature*

---

* In antiferromagnetic substances it is often denoted by T_N and called the Néel temperature.

10

T_c the spin system transforms from an ordered to a disordered state, or vice versa. It is one of the best examples of a second order phase transition and has much similarity with the order-disorder transition in an alloy like β-brass. A significant difference, however, is due to the greater mobility of spin orientation than of atomic position. Hence the kinetics of the two transitions are quite different.

At the Curie point there is compensation between the tendency to order due to the exchange interaction and the tendency to disorder due to the thermal motion. This gives some freedom to the system to take up either an ordered or a disordered arrangement. In fact it subdivides into regions or cells which are more or less ordered. In any cell the total spin or magnetization goes through large fluctuations. Also, at temperatures above or below the Curie point the system is free to fluctuate, but to a smaller degree. At $T > T_c$ the magnetization within the cell fluctuates around a vanishing mean value. At $T < T_c$ the domain magnetization fluctuates around a mean value given by the magnetization. This mean value is observable as an elastic neutron diffraction peak, as explained above. The fluctuations give rise to inelastic diffuse peaks which thus are of maximum intensity in the critical region, i.e. close to the Curie point. At lower temperatures, spin waves constitute a certain part of the fluctuations. They are the fluctuations of the transverse (x,y) spin components around their vanishing mean values.

For simplicity we shall now, unless otherwise mentioned, be considering only substances in which there is no orbital contribution to the magnetic moment. As mentioned in the previous section, this remains a reasonable assumption as long as we consider ions of the iron group.

The theory of inelastic scattering by an assembly of exchange-coupled ions in the paramagnetic temperature region was first given by van Vleck (1939) and later improved by de Gennes (1958). Here we shall give only a general outline of this theory.

At a high temperature $(T \gg T_c)$ the spin disorder is perfect. This means that

$$\langle \mathbf{S}_i(0)\mathbf{S}_j(\tau)\rangle = 0 \tag{6.3}$$

for $i \neq j$. If we disturb the state of a spin at time zero, the disturbance will propagate due to the exchange coupling of the spins, and in the region of temperatures not too high

$$\langle \mathbf{S}_i(0)\mathbf{S}_j(\tau)\rangle \neq 0 \tag{6.4}$$

Now we refer to equation (1.152) which gives the cross-section as the Fourier transform of the correlation function in equation (6.4). As a consequence of the general properties of Fourier transforms, the cross-section at very large angles or scattering vectors $\mathbf{Q}$ derives only from the self term $\langle \mathbf{S}_i(0)\mathbf{S}_i(\tau)\rangle$ of the correlation function. This correlation function is gaussian, since a spin is located in the random field created by its neighbours. The differential cross-section will then also be a gaussian. Hence an initially monoenergetic beam should have a gaussian energy distribution after scattering with a second moment which, in the case of a polycrystal, is found to be

$$\overline{\omega^2} = \frac{2}{3}\frac{1}{\hbar}S(S+1)\sum_j z_j(2J_{ij})^2 \tag{6.5}$$

The energy change is $\hbar\omega$. J_{ij} is the exchange integral with the z_j neighbours of type j. This result was obtained by van Vleck (1939) and we note that $\overline{\omega^2}$ is independent of Q, because only the self correlation is taken into account. De Gennes (1958) later showed that it was valid only when $Qa \gg \pi$, a denoting the lattice constant. For scattering with a smaller momentum transfer, the time dependent correlation between different spins has to be considered. This is naturally connected with the motion of spin density over large distances, a motion which is thought to be well described by a diffusion process. If Λ denotes the diffusion constant, the cross-section is a Lorentzian given by

$$\frac{d^2\sigma}{d\Omega d\omega} = \left(1\cdot91\frac{e^2}{m_e c^2}\right)\frac{1}{3\pi}\frac{k}{k_0}|f(Q)|^2 S(S+1)\frac{2\Lambda Q^2}{\omega^2+(\Lambda Q^2)^2}\frac{1}{r_1^2(K_1^2+Q^2)} \tag{6.6}$$

An expression of this form was first given by Van Hove (1954) for the case of critical scattering, a subject to be discussed later. The formula is strictly valid at small momentum transfers when $Qa \ll \pi$, and if $Q \to 0$ the energy change goes to zero, as it should. In that case the scattering is due to the sample as a whole, which of course has a constant spin density.

Concerning the diffusion constant Λ, De Gennes (1958) using a moment method of calculation has given the following expression for it at high temperatures:

$$\Lambda = \frac{2\pi}{27} a^2 [S(S+1)]^{\frac{1}{2}}\frac{2J}{\hbar} \tag{6.7}$$

This formula is valid for a simple cubic structure with distance a between interacting neighbours.

6.4 Experimental Results on Coupled Systems

The first attempt to observe indirectly the inelasticity in scattering by coupled ions was made by Bendt (1953). By comparing the angular distribution of scattered neutrons for different incident neutron energies he was able to get some information on $\overline{\omega^2}$. Direct information was obtained for the first time by Brockhouse (1959) in experiments on Mn_2O_3. The values $T_c = 80°K$ and $\theta = -176°K$ of its physical parameters are large enough that the ions are exchange coupled even at room temperature. In the same series of experiments $MnSO_4$ was studied. This substance has the values $<14°K$ and $-24°K$ for these parameters respectively and can thus be expected to exhibit the character of a system of uncoupled ions. The experimental results of Fig. 6.2 show the expected behaviour. The broadening of the neutron spectrum observed for Mn_2O_3 is of the right order of magnitude; in $MnSO_4$ no broadening is visible.

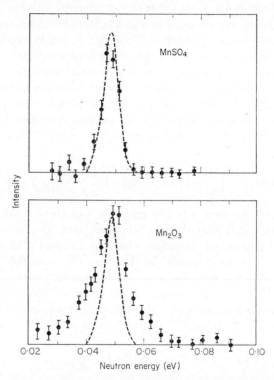

Fig. 6.2. Neutron scattering in $MnSO_4$ and Mn_2O_3 for 0·05 eV incident energy and angle of 11°20′. The incident spectrum is drawn as a dotted line. (Brockhouse, 1959.)

In the experiment just mentioned the scattering vector was too large to observe the narrowing of the spectrum predicted by equation (6.6). The same was the case for MnO, for which Iyengar and Brockhouse (1958) encountered some difficulty in interpreting the data due to a significant short range ordering of spins at temperatures well above the Curie point. New experiments have been made on MnO by Deniz et al. (1964), and their results cannot be analysed in the simple theory of de Gennes (1958). This is due to the importance of short range order; the results seem to indicate the existence of excitations of the spin wave type in this substance in the paramagnetic region.

In experiments on MnF_2, however, Cribier and coworkers (Cribier *et al.*, 1959; Cribier and Jacrot, 1963) were able to test the applicability of formulae (6.5) to (6.7). Using the cold neutron technique, described in Chapter 2, they were able to work in the range of small scattering vectors. The width of the scattered neutron spectrum has the predicted behaviour, as shown by Fig. 6.3. At high angles, the width is constant and the Gaussian character of the line was established with a high degree of accuracy. Using formulae (6.5) and (6.7) consistent values of the predominant exchange integral could be obtained.

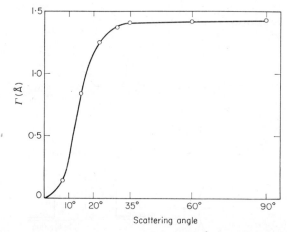

FIG. 6.3. The width Γ of the energy spectrum of 4·5 Å neutrons scattered by MnF_2 at different angles. Corrections have been made for the width of the incident spectrum. (Cribier *et al.*, 1959.)

Formula (6.5) expresses the second moment as a sum over the exchange integrals that are significant. Additional information about the same sum is obtained from the value of the paramagnetic Curie temperature θ. If only two exchange integrals are important, they can be determined from such data. Making such an assumption for MnF_2, it was found that the antiferromagnetic coupling of an ion to eight of its surrounding ions is more than twenty times stronger than the ferromagnetic coupling to six neighbours which are at a comparable distance. By using a single crystal instead of a polycrystalline sample, further information on the exchange interactions may be obtained. Further discussion of MnF_2 is given in Section 6.7.

6.5 Magnetic Inelastic Scattering at Low Temperatures

We now consider the low temperature range, which in this context means $T \ll T_c$. The spin system then exhibits a high degree of order and the deviation from perfect ordering can be analysed in terms of spin waves. If, within each domain, the direction of magnetization is chosen as the z-axis, the spin waves will describe the fluctuation of the transverse (i.e. x and y) spin components. As the temperature increases and approaches T_c, fluctuations of the longitudinal (z) components become important. As mentioned under Section 6.3, the latter fluctuations reach a maximum at T_c and give rise to critical scattering, to be discussed in Section 6.10. Except for temperatures close to T_c, transverse fluctuations are by far the most important ones.

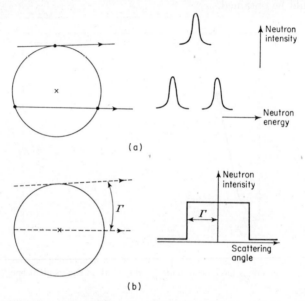

FIG. 6.4. Schematic representation of experimental methods used in neutron inelastic scattering when studying spin waves. The spherical scattering surface on the left is investigated by (a) the energy analysis technique or (b) the diffraction technique under the assumption of ideal resolution.

In the spin wave approximation the transverse fluctuations are described as a coherent spin motion of a wavelike character. The fundamentals of the spin wave theory and its connection with neutron inelastic scattering have been outlined in Chapter 1. An early spin wave scattering cross-section for the case of a ferromagnetic crystal was given by Lowde (1954) who observed the corresponding magnon scattering from iron.

Spin waves are characterized by dispersion relations giving the connection between their frequencies and wave vectors. A complete picture of the dispersion relation, and thus the spin waves, is obtained by plotting iso-frequency or constant-energy surfaces of spin waves in the reciprocal lattice. We shall show now that the constant energy surfaces are directly related to the scattering surfaces that may be observed in neutron scattering experiments.

Let us consider the case of a ferro- or ferrimagnet, in which the dispersion relation is expected to be $hf \propto q^2$ for small energies. If anisotropy effects are neglected, one expects scattering surfaces in the form of spheres, as shown previously by equation (1.142). Thus a scattering surface may be regarded as a conformal mapping of a constant energy (E_0) surface of spin waves. Equation (1.140) shows that the centre of the scattering surface is displaced from the reciprocal lattice point by a distance which is small compared to its radius.

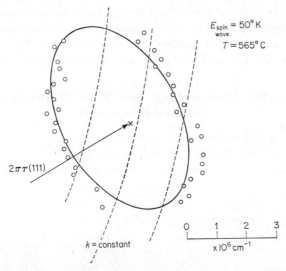

Fig. 6.5. Constant energy surface of spin waves in Fe_3O_4 as measured by the method of Fig. 6.4(a). The non-spherical shape is due to instrumental resolution effects. (Cribier *et al.*, 1963.)

This means that the energy parameter E_0 defining a scattering surface is given by the distance from the reciprocal lattice point to the sphere of reflection. Consequently, in an experiment where the crystal is kept fixed, the locus of the outgoing k corresponds to a constant energy surface of spin waves with energy parameter determined by the crystal setting. Equation (1.142) also shows that the radius of the sphere depends on the exchange integral and, of course, on E_0. In typical cases the radius is small, corresponding to an angular width of say five degrees. In forward scattering (around the 000 lattice point), this angular width is even smaller, of the order of 1° or less. This implies that a good resolution is required, both as concerns energy and momentum.

The radii of the scattering surfaces or, what amounts to the same, of the constant energy surfaces of spin waves, may be measured in two different ways, as demonstrated by Fig. 6.4. In Fig. 6.4 (a) the energy of the scattered neutrons is measured directly. If the direction of observation is tangential to the sphere, then only one peak will be observed, otherwise one observes two peaks. When observing in a direction which cuts through the centre, the distance between the peaks corresponds to the diameter of the sphere. In the second method, demonstrated by Fig. 6.4(b), one simply takes the profile of the diffuse peak and its angular width is again a measure of the sphere (see e.g. Lowde, 1954).

Both methods have been used and have given consistent results. If the neutron flux is sufficient for a direct energy analysis to be made, then that method is preferable. In Fig. 6.5 a constant energy surface has been traced out for spin waves in Fe_2O_4, using the latter technique. The sphere is distorted by the experimental resolution and the resulting curve is elliptic.

6.6 Methods for Distinguishing Spin Wave Scattering from Other Inelastic Components

There is no problem involved in distinguishing spin wave scattering from elastic components. Elastic coherent scattering gives rise to the sharp diffraction peaks which may be observed only under conditions where

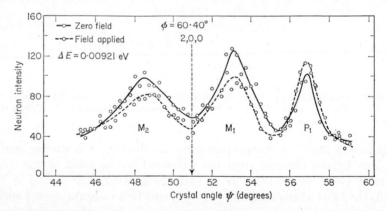

FIG. 6.6. Identification of magnon and phonon peaks in $Co_{0.92}Fe_{0.08}$ by their different response to a magnetic field. When applying a field perpendicular to the scattering vector the magnon peaks decrease as expected. The simultaneous increase of the phonon peaks is due to a strong contribution of magneto-vibrational scattering. (Sinclair and Brockhouse, 1960.)

crystal and counter settings satisfy the Bragg relation. Also an incoherent component gives an isotropic angular distribution and is easily separable from the diffuse diffraction peaks due to spin waves.

It may sometimes be difficult, however, to distinguish spin wave scattering from other inelastic components, such as vibrational scattering. In some cases (such as method 6.4b) one may base such a separation merely on the difference in angular distribution. This is particularly true when the Curie or Néel temperature T_c is higher than the Debye temperature, in which case the angular width of the magnon peaks is much smaller than for the phonon peaks of the same energy. In the energy analysis technique one then expects to find the magnon and phonon groups well separated in the energy diagram.

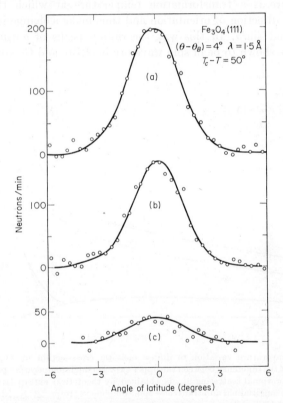

FIG. 6.7. Decomposition of a diffuse peak (a) from Fe_3O_4 into contributions from transverse (b) and longitudinal fluctuations (c) by the method explained in the text (Riste $et\ al.$, 1959).

The best method in separating phonon and magnon scattering is provided by their different response to an external magnetic field. According to formula (1.137) the spin wave cross-section is proportional to $(1+\cos^2\alpha)$. This factor changes by $+50\%$ or -25% on going from an unmagnetized crystal to the cases of a magnetic field parallel to or normal to the scattering vector, respectively. The same changes in the magnetic

10*

field leave the nuclear vibrational scattering unchanged. Magneto-vibrational scattering (see Section 1.17), on the other hand, will have its intensity changes determined by the factor $\sin^2\alpha$. Thus this component changes by -100% or $+50\%$ respectively under the conditions above. Figure 6.6 gives an example of a case where magnon and phonon peaks have been identified by this method (Sinclair and Brockhouse, 1960).

In the case of an antiferromagnet there is little or no orientation effect on the magnetic moments when applying an external field. In some antiferromagnets there is a transformation temperature at which the moments change their direction of orientation and thus make a change in the factors $(1 + \cos^2\alpha)$ and $\sin^2\alpha$. In this way the diffuse peaks of antiferromagnetic $\alpha\text{-}Fe_2O_3$ were shown to be of spin wave origin (Riste and Goedkoop, 1960).

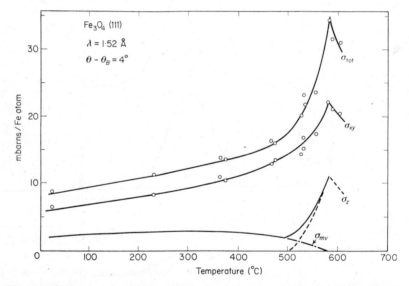

Fig. 6.8. Temperature variation of diffuse inelastic cross-section in Fe_3O_4. The lower curves represent the difference between the upper two. The high temperature part of the curve for magneto-vibrational scattering σ_{mv} is obtained by theoretical extrapolation. Subscripts z and xy refer to longitudinal and transverse spin components, respectively (Riste et al., 1959).

An additional inelastic component grows into the diffraction pattern as the critical temperature is approached from below. This is the scattering due to fluctuations in the longitudinal (i.e. z-) components of the spins (Elliot and Marshall, 1958; de Gennes and Villain, 1960). Its response to a magnetic field is given by $\sin^2\alpha$ and thus the intensity components due to transverse and longitudinal fluctuations respond oppositely under the influence of an external field. The longitudinal component increases strongly as the temperature increases and the resultant effect of an external field on the magnetic inelastic component vanishes, as it must, above T_c. In Fig. 6.7, a diffuse magnetic inelastic peak in Fe_3O_4 has been decomposed into its two constituents by taking two peak profiles with the diffraction technique (Riste *et al.*, 1959) under conditions $\sin^2\alpha = 0$ and $\sin^2\alpha = 2/3$. These measurements were performed over a wide range of temperature and in this way the cross section, integrated over the scattering surface, has been decomposed to give Fig. 6.8.

In small angle scattering experiments (eg. Fig. 6.4(b)) elastic refraction-type scattering may be disturbing, but only at extremely small angles. The main disturbance in the experiments is thus due to other inelastic components which may be separated out by the field effect just described.

6.7 Experimentally Observed Dispersion Curves

Spin wave dispersion curves have been measured by neutron scattering in a few favourable cases. By the energy analysis method of Fig. 6.4(a), Sinclair and Brockhouse (1960) have measured the dispersion curve for ferromagnetic face-centered cubic $Co_{0.92}Fe_{0.08}$ shown in Fig. 6.6. In this case the dispersion curve (for the [111] direction) was fitted to the equation:

$$\hbar\omega = C + 12\,JS\left[\,1 - \cos\left(\frac{qa}{\sqrt{3}}\right)\right]$$

in order to find the value of JS. Here, a is the lattice parameter and C is a constant related to the anisotropy and the applied field. (See, e.g. Herring and Kittel, 1951.) A value of $JS = 14 \cdot 7 + 1 \cdot 5$ meV was obtained, which with $S \simeq 0.92$ finally gave $J = 16$ meV. This value may be compared to independent values of $24 \cdot 2$ and $11 \cdot 2$ meV derived from magnetization and other data.

In more complicated lattices one expects several branches in the spin wave spectrum. In the case of Fe_3O_4 the primitive unit cell has six iron ions which belong to sublattices A and B. Within each sublattice the spins are parallel, but spins on A are aligned antiparallel to those on B. Kaplan (1958) has predicted that this must lead to six branches in the spin wave spectrum. One branch is "acoustical" with $hf \propto q^2$, and the other branches are "optical" with finite energies at $q = 0$. By the energy analysis method Brockhouse and Watanabe (1963) have found the complete acoustical branch and part of an optical branch, as shown in Fig. 6.10. In this way the AB and BB interactions could be determined. If one of the branches sensitive to the AA interactions could be measured, one would have a complete set of values for the exchange integrals. The measurement of an optical branch meets with certain difficulties, however. The magnetic form factor $f(Q)$, which enters the cross-section formulae, makes it necessary to measure at small momentum transfers the rather large energy changes which are involved in scattering by an optical branch.

In Fe_7S_8, Wanic (1964) has measured the spin wave dispersion relation both by the energy analysis and by the diffraction method. He finds an acoustical branch which is almost linear, but becoming quadratic at very

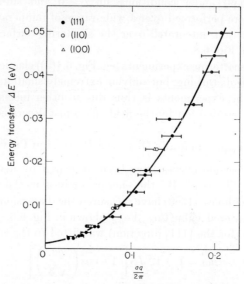

FIG. 6.9. Dispersion curve of spin waves in $Co_{0.92}Fe_{0.08}$ as measured by neutron scattering experiments. The propagation direction of the spin waves is indicated. (Sinclair and Brockhouse, 1960.)

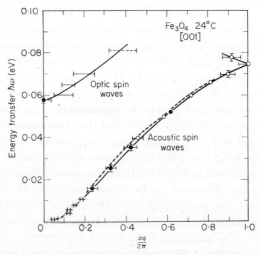

FIG. 6.10. Experimental dispersion curve for spin waves in Fe_3O_4 at room temperature. The dashed curve gives the results before correction for resolution. (Brockhouse and Watanabe, 1963.)

small q's. This is indeed what may be expected for an antiferromagnet with vacancies on one of the sub-lattices, as is the case for this substance. The experimental results are given in Fig. 6.11. The triangular points are due to spin waves propagating in the base plane of the hexagonal structure; they fall below the other points which are due to spin waves having q-vectors out of this plane. Ψ denotes the angle between the propagation direction and the base plane. The directional dependence of q thus observed gives information

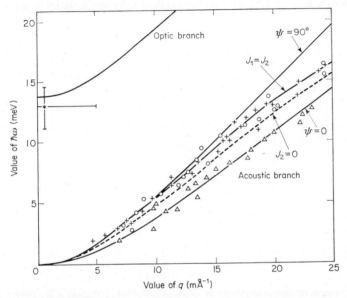

FIG. 6.11. Dispersion curve of spin waves in Fe_7S_8. Various theoretical curves are also given (see text). (Wanic, 1965.)

on the ratio between the two most important exchange interactions J_1 and J_2 of this substance. As seen in the figure, some evidence for an optical branch was also found.

In antiferromagnets, with sufficiently low anisotropy, the dispersion relation is expected to be linear in the region of small q. This has been verified by measurements with the diffraction method (Riste and Goedkoop, 1960). The slope of the dispersion curve gives directly the velocity of antiferromagnetic magnons. In α-Fe_2O_3, Riste and Goedkoop (1960) found a value of $3 \cdot 8 \times 10^6$ cm sec^{-1}. The magnon velocity gives one equation for the exchange integrals that may be active. A direct experiment has been performed by Okazaki, Turberfield and Stevenson on MnF_2 (Okazaki et al., 1964). The dispersion curve is shown on Fig. 6.12. This shows the important energy gap at $q = 0$, due to anisotropy field. The dispersion in MnF_2 can be attributed essentially to the effect of four parameters: J_1, J_2 and J_3 for the exchange integrals between an atom and its first, second and third neighbours, and H_A for the anisotropy field. J_1 and J_3 operate between atoms on the same sublattice, while J_2 is effective between sublattices. J_2/k and H_A/k can be determined from the perpendicular susceptibility and from spin-wave resonance to be respectively $-1.76°K$ and $1.06°K$. Using these figures the neutron data yield $J_1/k = 0.32°K$ and $|J_3|/k < 0.05°K$. Applying now the result for $|J_3|$ to the earlier data of Cribier and Jacrot (see Section 6.4) their paramagnetic scattering yields $J_2/k = -1.75 + 0.02°K$, in excellent agreement with the input value.

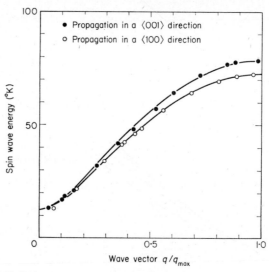

FIG. 6.12. Dispersion curve of spin waves in MnF_2 (Okazaki et al., 1964).

A similar experiment has been performed on MnO by Collins (1964).

The diffraction method (Fig. 6.4(b)) has also been used in small angle scattering experiments by Lowde and Umakantha (1960) and Hatherly et al. (1964). As mentioned above, the scattering surface around (000) is very narrow and the scattered intensity is confined to a cone of half-angle given by the ratio ρ/k_0 between the radius of the scattering surface and the wave vector of the incident neutron. But ρ is found to be proportional to k_0 which means that a white beam technique may be used in order to enhance the intensity. Using a well collimated beam, these authors measured angular distributions of rectangular shape in iron (Lowde and Umakantha, 1960), nickel and iron–nickel alloys (Hatherly et al., 1964). The cut-off angle is proportional to $(JS)^{-1}$. Their results are analysed in terms of the exchange coupling parameter expressed as a function of interatomic separation. Among the interesting results obtained we mention especially that the "exchange integral" between Fe–Fe pairs on a f.c.c. lattice is found to have the negative value -9 ± 2.6 meV. In the b.c.c. lattice it was concluded that the Fe–Ni interaction appears to change sign as a function of distance. The method of analysis in small angle scattering technique has to take into account the effect of dipole-dipole terms, anisotropy and the applied field. Better results should be obtained if one uses monochromatic neutrons.

An important feature of the small angle scattering technique is that powder samples may be used. Another advantage is that the scattering by phonons is weak or completely absent in the region of small angles. The

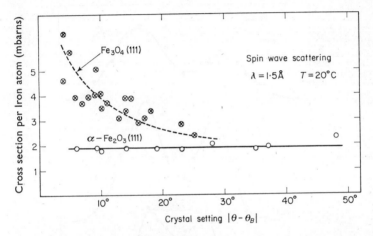

Fig. 6.13. Neutron scattering cross-section for spin waves in Fe_3O_4 and α-Fe_2O_3. The intensification at small values of $|\theta - \theta_B|$ is characteristic of a quadratic dispersion relation. (Riste *et al.*, 1959; Riste and Goedkoop, 1960.)

method has on the other hand some disadvantages compared with experiments using $\tau \neq 0$. In the latter case one can alter the energy selection of the scattered neutrons by changing the crystal setting, and in addition antiferromagnetic substances may be studied.

Some information on the dispersion relation may be obtained from the intensity distribution as a function of the crystal angle. At low q the dispersion relation of ferromagnetic spin waves has a constant and a quadratic term. In some cases the constant may be neglected and the dispersion relation is quadratic; then the intensity integrated over the scattering surface is strongest at small crystal mis-settings from the Bragg position. The curves of Fig. 6.13 show the predicted behaviour; no intensification occurs when the dispersion relation is linear. In small angle scattering this means that the predominant contribution to the scattered intensity comes from spin waves of very low energies, i.e. where the quadratic dispersion relation is valid.

6.8 The Effect of Temperature on the Spin Wave Dispersion Curve and Line Width

In connection with Fig. 6.8 one may ask, what is the upper limit of the spin wave approximation? The early theoretical work in this field gave an upper limit $\approx 0 \cdot 1\ T_c$. At higher temperatures the whole picture was expected to break down due to mutual interactions between the spin waves. Later theoretical work has suggested, however, that the effect of the interactions had been overestimated (Dyson, 1956; Oguchi, 1960). Some recent work in

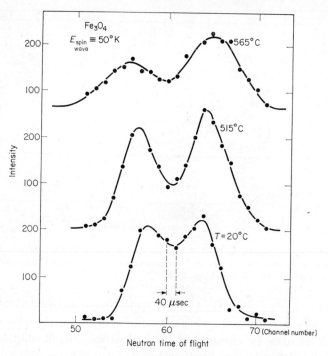

FIG. 6.14. Temperature behaviour of constant energy surface of spin waves in Fe_3O_4, as explained in the text. Neutron energy given on a time of flight scale (Riste, 1962).

this field has given the result that at increasing temperatures the spin wave frequency, corresponding to a definite wave vector, would decrease because of these interactions (Keffer and Loudon, 1961; Bloch, 1962; Nakamura and Bloch, 1963) and go to zero as the magnetization vanishes at T_c (Brout and Haken, 1960; Englert, 1960).

The situation has been elucidated by neutron scattering experiments. Figure 6.14 shows the temperature behaviour of the scattering or constant energy surface of spin waves of an energy 50°K (Riste, 1962; Jacrot and

Cribier, 1962) in Fe_3O_4. The increasing distance between the two peaks in the energy diagram shows that the surface expands: this means that the wave vector of the spin wave has to increase in order to preserve its energy. If experiments had been done with the "constant-Q" method one would have seen a decreasing spin wave frequency. The upper curve in the figure shows that discrete peaks, i.e. coherent excitations, exist even close to T_c. The finite width of the surface observed above T_c shows that the frequencies remain finite even after the magnetization has vanished (Riste *et al.*, 1959; Riste, 1962). From these measurements we can obtain the values of D in the relation $f = Dq^2$, assuming that this relation remains valid for small q at all temperatures.

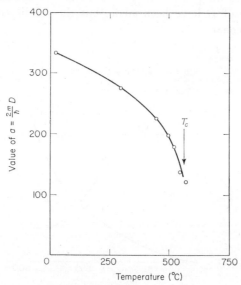

FIG. 6.15. Variation of exchange constant, given by inelastic peak separation, as in Fig. 6.14, with temperature. (Jacrot and Cribier, 1962.)

However, it is important to realize that the frequencies remain non-zero above T_c only for non-zero q; Hatherly *et al.* (1964) used the small angle technique to study the temperature dependence of spin wave energies of very small q and found that the modes in nickel disappeared at the Curie temperature. Figure 6.15 shows results, obtained in the way described above, by Jacrot and Cribier (1962). Similar, but less extensive, results have been obtained by Brockhouse and Watanabe (1963). The results fit formula (6.8) below.

A detailed study by Turberfield *et al.* (1965) on the changes in the magnetic excitation spectra in MnF_2 has shown that for this antiferromagnet the spin wave approximation is extremely good up to $0.9\ T_N$ if one takes into account the interactions between spin waves. Above this temperature, well defined spin waves are no longer recognizable in the observed spectra, but the observed dependence of the spectra on crystal setting at temperatures up to $1 \cdot 2 T_N$ indicates that excitation spectra continue to display properties which depend on the magnetic ordering of the antiferromagnetic phase.

Keffer and Loudon (1961) derive the formula,

$$D(T) = D(0)\left[1 - \zeta\left(\frac{T}{T_c}\right)^{5/2}\right]$$ (6.8)

and the coefficient ζ has been given by Tannenwald (1962), who used the spin wave resonance technique. A variety of attempts to examine the temperature dependence of D have been made, but the validity of equation (6.8) remains controversial.

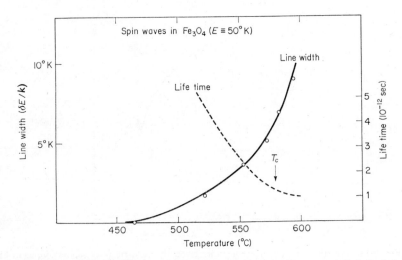

FIG. 6.16. Temperature variation of linewidth and lifetime of magnons, as derived from data of the type illustrated at Fig. 6.14. The linewidth at room temperature has been taken to represent the instrumental resolution (Riste, 1962).

In experiments of rather poor resolution using the diffraction technique on Fe_3O_4 the expansion of the scattering surface was found to be different at different spin wave frequencies (Riste, 1961). Wanic (1965) in more accurate experiments does not find this behaviour. This phenomenon should perhaps be studied more closely by the energy analysis method before making any definite conclusions, but such behaviour is found by Nakamura and Bloch (1963) for a simple model of a ferrimagnet.

Figure 6.14 reveals an additional phenomenon. The two peaks of the top curve are seen to be wider than the lower ones. There is a pronounced increase of the line width as T_c is approached from below, and the experimental data are summarized in Fig. 6.16. This evidently corresponds to a decrease of the lifetime and of the mean free path of the magnons. In the same figure the behaviour of the lifetime, as derived from the line width by means of the Heisenberg uncertainty relation, has been plotted. The magnon line widths were observed to behave in the same way by Okazaki et al. (1964) for MnF_2.

Information on lifetimes may also be obtained from experiments with the diffraction technique. Even if the angular resolution is good, the cut-off angle is sharp only if the lifetime of the spin waves is long. In the iron–nickel

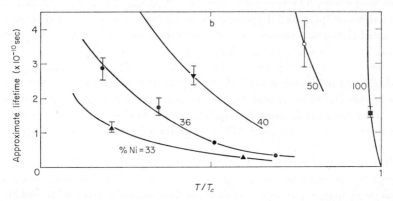

FIG. 6.17. Approximate lifetimes of long wavelength spin waves in nickel–iron alloys (Hatherly et al., 1964).

experiments (Lowde and Umkantha, 1960) the energy spread and the lifetime of long wavelength spin waves was estimated by means of the slope of the intensity distribution at the cut-off angle. The results are given in Fig. 6.17; they show a general tendency towards shorter lifetimes in the alloys of smaller effective exchange integrals. It should be remembered that the lifetime measured is in this case that of magnons which contribute to the intensity at the cut-off angle. The contributing wavelength is dependent upon the temperature and the alloy composition, but is in all cases above 100 Å.

6.9 Conclusions from Spin Wave Experiments

The neutron scattering experiments have established the existence of spin waves in ionic ferrimagnets and antiferromagnets. Where the anisotropy is small the respective dispersion relations are quadratic or linear in the low energy region, as predicted by theory. The spin waves exist also at temperatures approaching T_c, but with lowered frequencies and lifetimes. The frequency drop is less than that predicted by the random phase approximation according to which the frequencies should renormalize with the magnetization and vanish at T_c. Spin wave like excitations exist even above T_c, indicating that the regions of local order are sufficiently large so that coherent excitations of a finite range may propagate.

The experiments on metals and alloys have so far been restricted to ferromagnets. The results give definite support to the spin wave theory and disagree with the predictions of the Stoner collective electron theory. Marshall (1962) has pointed out that the strong temperature dependence of $D(T)$ observed in nickel implies that the exchange interaction in this material is of long range. The spin wave should in this case be thought of as an extended region of reduced spin propagating with a wavevector $\mathbf{q}$. Low and Okazaki (1963) have given some consideration as to how the spatial extent of such a region could be measured.

Even though the experimental results on nickel (and their interpretation just referred to) favour a band-theoretical picture for this metal, they should not be considered as an evidence for the correctness of this model. According to recent theoretical work by Izuyama et al. (1963), the influence of non-localized magnetic electrons will become manifest only in subtle details in the neutron scattering.

In the indirect model of ferromagnetic metals, conduction electrons play a role in the magnetic coupling between localized d- or f-electrons. The associated magnon–conduction electron interaction gives rise to enhanced linewidths and a distorted dispersion relation at certain magnon wave-vectors. Frikkee and Riste (1962, 1964) have reported an anomaly in the dispersion relation of f.c.c. Co and tentatively attributed it to such an effect.

According to modern band theory the Stoner continuum of one electron states is at low q-values well separated from the otherwise normal acoustical spin wave branch. At $q = 0$ this energy gap is equal to the band splitting, i.e. of the order of 1 eV or somewhat less. Hence the total internal magnetic energy of a metal should not deviate much from that of a Heisenberg magnet. Lowde (1965) has made use of this fact and attempted to exhibit the band properties of $3d$-alloys by a systematic measurement of D in several alloy compositions. This constant, often referred to as the exchange stiffness constant, was measured in spin wave experiments by the small angle technique. When plotting D as a function of the electron-to-atom ratio, he obtained a curve which bears a striking resemblance to that of the internal magnetic energy plotted against the same ratio. The magnetic energy was calculated from the density-of-states curve by Shimizu and Katsuki (1964).

In spite of the promise that these latter results hold, it seems fair to say that a conclusive experiment on spin waves in metals has not been performed so far. In insulators, the interpretation of the experiments is on the other hand straightforward and additional experiments should increase our knowledge of exchange parameters.

6.10 The Theory of Critical Scattering

So far we have been dealing mainly with cases where the sample is well above or below the Curie point. In our introductory discussion on systems of coupled ions we mentioned, however, that large fluctuations of spins (or magnetization) appear close to T_c. This phenomenon and the neutron scattering which follows, the 'critical scattering', is the subject for the rest of this chapter.

The main features of the scattering are predictable already from a qualitative discussion of the spin fluctuations. The enhanced scattering close to T_c is due to an increase of the coherent (and in general inelastic) cross-section which may be written as the four-dimensional space-time Fourier transform of the correlation function of spins, as shown by formula (1.155). The ultimate reason for the critical scattering must therefore be changes of the spin correlations.

Concerning the static spin correlations, we know that $\langle \mathbf{S}_i(0)\mathbf{S}_j(0)\rangle = \delta_{ij}S(S+1)$ at very high temperatures. As the temperature is lowered towards T_c, short range correlations appear and $\langle \mathbf{S}_i(0)\,\mathbf{S}_j(0)\rangle \neq 0$. This in turn implies coherent magnetic scattering of small q in the vicinity of the angles at which magnetic diffraction peaks appear for $T<T_c$. The probability for formation of large regions of correlated spins, i.e. regions of coherence, increases strongly near T_c, hence the maxima in the angular distribution get more pronounced.

The configuration or ordering of spins is also time dependent. Changes of the spatial part of the correlation function in the critical temperature region are accompanied by changes in the time dependence. Outside this temperature region there is a strong preference for the spin system to be either ordered ($T<T_c$) or disordered ($T>T_c$). If at $T>T_c$ an ordered spin configuration has been established through a fluctuation, there are strong restoring forces tending to re-establish the disorder. In such a case the spin system has a short relaxation time. In the critical region the ordered and disordered phases are almost equally stable and only weak restoring forces are involved. Hence the evolution of the fluctuations is slow and the critical scattering is in general weakly inelastic.

We summarize the situation at T_c: the fluctuations extend to their maximum range and have their maximum relaxation time; the angular distribution of scattered neutrons is more strongly peaked than at any higher temperature and the inelasticity of the scattering is a minimum.

The qualitative considerations above can be put on a more quantitative basis. The static part of the correlation function, and hence the angular distribution of the scattering, has been calculated from thermodynamic fluctuation theory (van Hove, 1954; de Gennes and Villain, 1960; Krivoglaz, 1958). This is a macroscopic approach which expresses the scattering in terms of phenomenological coefficients. More detailed calculations may be given for systems of localized ionic spins, and the scattering is then expressed by parameters determined by the exchange integrals and the lattice constant. Two different methods have been used, the cluster model method (Elliott and Marshall, 1958) and the local molecular field method (de Gennes, 1959; de Gennes and Villain, 1960; Villain, 1963). We outline below some of the calculations using the latter method by de Gennes and Villain. To simplify the discussion, we consider an ionic ferromagnet at $T \gg T_c$.

First we define a new concept, the wavelength-dependent susceptibility $\chi(\mathbf{Q})$. If one applies to the spin system a small static external field, sinusoidal in space, the response of the system is also sinusoidal with the same wavelength. $\chi(\mathbf{Q})$ is then the ratio between the induced magnetization and the applied field. For $\mathbf{Q} = 0$, $\chi(\mathbf{Q})$ reduces to the conventional susceptibility χ. In the absence of exchange interactions, χ is denoted by χ_0. Next we recall that χ is proportional to the fluctuation of the square of the magnetization, i.e. to the spin correlations, as remarked in the discussion following (1.154). From this it follows that,* for classical spins:

$$S(S+1)\frac{\chi(\mathbf{Q})}{\chi_0} = \sum_R \langle \mathbf{S}_0 \mathbf{S}_R \rangle \, e^{i\mathbf{Q}\mathbf{R}} \tag{6.9}$$

This gives immediately:

$$\frac{d\sigma}{d\Omega} = \frac{2}{3}\left[1 \cdot 91\,\frac{e^2}{m_e c^2}f(Q)\right]^2 S(S+1)\frac{\chi(\mathbf{Q})}{\chi_0} \tag{6.10}$$

The problem is now changed to a calculation of $\chi(\mathbf{Q})$. This is done using the molecular field method, according to which the moment at position $\mathbf{R}$ is in equilibrium under the action of an external field ($\mathbf{H}$) and the molecular field due to interacting neighbours:

$$\boldsymbol{\mu}_R = \frac{S(S+1)}{3kT}\,(g^2\mu_B^2\mathbf{H}_R + \sum_{R'} 2J_{RR'}\,\boldsymbol{\mu}_{R'}) \tag{6.11}$$

which has the Fourier transform

$$\boldsymbol{\mu}_R e^{i\mathbf{Q}\mathbf{R}} = \frac{S(S+1)}{3kT}\,(g^2\mu_B^2\mathbf{H}_R e^{i\mathbf{Q}\mathbf{R}} + \sum_{R'} 2J_{RR'}e^{i\mathbf{Q}(\mathbf{R}-\mathbf{R'})}\boldsymbol{\mu}_{R'}e^{i\mathbf{Q}\mathbf{R'}}) \tag{6.11a}$$

---

* A proof of this relation is given by de Gennes (1959).

Making use of the definition of $\chi(\mathbf{Q})$, this gives

$$\frac{1}{\chi(\mathbf{Q})} = \frac{1}{\sum_{R'}\chi_{RR'}(0)e^{i\mathbf{Q}(\mathbf{R}-\mathbf{R'})}} = \frac{1}{g^2\mu_B^2}\left[\frac{3kT}{S(S+1)} - 2J(\mathbf{Q})\right] \tag{6.12}$$

where $J(\mathbf{Q})$ denotes the Fourier transform of the exchange integral $J_{RR'}$. Using the relations

$$\chi = \frac{C}{T-T_c}$$

with

$$C = \frac{g^2\mu_B^2 S(S+1)}{3k}$$

(6.12) may be written as

$$\frac{1}{\chi(\mathbf{Q})} = \frac{2}{g^2\mu_B^2}\left[J(0)\frac{T}{T_c} - J(\mathbf{Q})\right] \tag{6.13}$$

Due to the periodicity of $J(\mathbf{Q})$ this shows that the critical scattering has a maximum when $\mathbf{Q}$ is equal to zero or one of the reciprocal lattice vectors $2\pi\boldsymbol{\tau}$. If in addition T approaches T_c, the intensity goes to infinity. For a cubic crystal $J(\mathbf{Q})$ may be expanded to give the following cross-section for neutrons scattered with momentum transfer $\hbar\mathbf{Q}$

$$\frac{d\sigma}{d\Omega} \approx f^2(Q)[A_0 + \sum_i A_i \cos \mathbf{Q}\mathbf{R}_i]^{-1} \tag{6.14}$$

A_i contains the exchange interaction between an ion and its ith neighbour.

Introducing $\mathbf{q} = \mathbf{Q} - 2\pi\boldsymbol{\tau}$ and expanding in powers of q, we get

$$\frac{d\sigma}{d\Omega} = \left[1\cdot 91\frac{e}{\hbar c}f(Q)\right]^2\frac{2kTV}{\dfrac{V}{\chi} + Aq^2 + Bq^4 + \ldots} \tag{6.15}$$

The cross-section is relative to a volume V.

In the first calculations on critical scattering by van Hove (1954) the expansion in the denominator was carried out only up to the second power in q (see equation (1.159)). The constant K_1^{-1}, the range of the fluctuations, used in van Hove's formula (see 1.157) is related to A by

$$A = \frac{V}{\chi}\frac{1}{K_1^2} \tag{6.16}$$

It can be seen that (6.15) is a general formula which gets rid of the asymptotic approximation. It can also be derived by means of a thermodynamic theory, using Landau's expansion of the thermodynamic potential (de Gennes, 1963; Landau and Lifshitz, 1960). Hence the formula is valid also for metals.

In the case of an ionic solid, the molecular field derivation relates the co-efficients in the expansion of the denominator to the interaction constants. It follows from both derivations that an expansion up to second power in q^2 is sufficient only for short range interactions. Deviation from the corresponding cross-section formula should be interpreted as an indication of a finite interaction between distant neighbours.

The molecular field treatment has been generalized to include the cases of antiferromagnets (de Gennes, 1958) and ferrimagnets (de Gennes and Villain, 1960). In the antiferromagnetic case there is no fluctuation of the total magnetization, which is zero, but only of the magnetization of each sublattice. It leads to critical scattering around the positions where magnetic reflections are found at $T < T_c$. For a true antiferromagnet there is no singularity in the forward direction. Exceptions to this rule are known for complicated substances like $FeCl_2$ (Wilkinson et al., 1959; Heap, 1962).

Next we turn to the relaxation or time dependence of the fluctuations at $T \geqslant T_c$. This phenomenon and its effect on the degree of inelasticity of the critical scattering was first treated by van Hove (1954) by means of the theory of irreversible processes. At small $\mathbf{q}$ (long wavelength), the motion of the magnetization in a ferromagnet is supposed to be well described as a macroscopic spin diffusion process. It leads to a Lorentzian energy distribution of the scattered neutrons, as given by formula (6.6). The relaxation time is given by $(\Lambda q^2)^{-1}$ and is thus very long for small q. This is a *kinematic* effect due to the conservation of the total spin (de Gennes and Villain, 1960). The slow relaxation in the critical region, which has been described qualitatively at the beginning of the present section, is a *thermodynamic* effect which, according to de Gennes and Villain (1960) and Elliott and Marshall (1958), should take place even in antiferromagnets. In ferromagnets at small q's (and for certain q's in a ferrimagnet (de Gennes and Villain, 1960)) the kinematic and thermodynamic effects are both active. This makes Λ decrease as $(T - T_c)$ decreases and vanish at T_c.

Mori and Kawasaki (1962) have given a more detailed treatment of a slow relaxation process of either kinematic or thermodynamic origin. In the case of a ferromagnet they find, as before, a relaxation time τ_q given by

$$\frac{1}{\tau_q} = \Lambda_q q^2 \tag{6.17}$$

But instead of de Gennes' expression

$$\Lambda = 2Ja^2 \frac{T - T_c}{T_c} \tag{6.18}$$

they find

$$\Lambda_q = D\left(\frac{V}{\chi}\frac{1}{\Lambda} + q^2 + \ldots\right) \tag{6.19}$$

D is a factor independent of q and the expression in the brackets is the denominator of (6.15) divided by A. The final form of the scattering cross-section for a ferromagnet is thus

$$\frac{\mathrm{d}^2\sigma}{\mathrm{d}\Omega\mathrm{d}\omega} = \left(1 \cdot 91 \frac{e}{\hbar c}\right)^2 f^2(Q) \frac{2}{\pi} \frac{kTV}{\frac{V}{\chi} + Aq^2 + Bq^4 + \ldots} \frac{\Lambda_q q^2}{\omega^2 - \Lambda_q^2 q^4} \qquad (6.20)$$

By integrating over ω and assuming q constant during the integration (6.15) is rederived.

In the case of an antiferromagnet they find, instead of (6.17)

$$\frac{1}{\tau_q} = \Lambda_q B \qquad (6.21)$$

with Λ_q given by (6.19). There is no factor q^2 on the right hand side because there is no kinematic braking of the relaxation.

Our review of the theory of critical scattering has been limited to $T \geqslant T_c$. Some predictions are also found in the literature for the space dependence (Elliott and Marshall, 1958; de Gennes and Villain, 1960; de Gennes, 1959) and the time dependence (de Gennes, 1959; Mori and Kawasaki, 1962; Kocinski, 1963) of the fluctuations when $T < T_c$. In general the longitudinal fluctuations behave very similarly to fluctuations at $T > T_c$.

As a result of the spin-lattice coupling a weak additional nuclear scattering may develop in the critical region. This effect has been treated by Krivoglaz (1958). The latter author also discussed the effect of an external field on the scattering. We have earlier seen that at $T < T_c$ the cross-section may be changed when the direction of the field relative to the scattering vector is changed. In the critical region, however, the susceptibility gets very large and the size and range of the fluctuations may be reduced by the field. A more detailed treatment of this effect has been given by Villain (1963).

6.11 Experimental Results on Critical Scattering in Iron and Nickel

As explained in the preceding paragraph the critical scattering has two aspects. The first one concerns the range of the spin correlations. Information about this is obtained from the angular distribution, as seen from equation (6.15), as long as the static approximation is valid. The obvious criterion for the validity of this approximation is that the relaxation time τ_q of the correlation is much larger than the time spent by a neutron within the range of this correlation. For a neutron of 4 Å and a correlation range of 10 Å the time spent by the neutron is 10^{-12} sec. All the experiments give a diffusion constant between 10^{-3} and 10^{-2} cm^2 sec^{-1} so that neutrons of 4 Å scattered at 1° this corresponds to τ_q between 10^{-11} and 10^{-10} sec, which is larger than 10^{-12} sec found above. But for scattering at a somewhat larger angle the relaxation time will be of the same order as the time spent by the neutron. In this case precautions have to be taken for experiments where the angular distribution only, is measured.

The second aspect of critical scattering to be considered is the relaxation time of the correlated spin arrangements. This is evaluated from measurements of $d^2\sigma/d\Omega d\omega$, but as τ_q is large the observable effect is small. In order to derive τ_q, a well defined line spectrum of neutrons is allowed to fall upon the specimen, and the broadening in energy of this line as a function of scattering angle is measured.

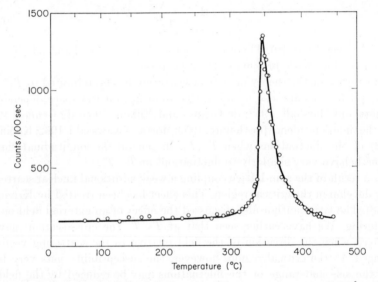

Fig. 6.18. Critical scattering by nickel. The curve gives the total intensity of 4·75 Å neutrons scattered at 2° (Cribier et al., 1962).

The intensity of 4·75 Å neutrons scattered by nickel at 2° is shown in Fig. 6.18. This figure reveals the intensity peak characteristic of critical scattering. In an experiment on iron (Jacrot et al., 1963), a variation of the scattered intensity by 30 % for a relative variation of 10^{-3} in the temperature has been measured. This implies that the temperature of the sample must be extremely well defined for accurate measurements to be made.

Several experiments (Palevsky and Hughes, 1954; Squires, 1954; Wilkinson and Shull, 1956; Lowde, 1958; Ericson and Jacrot, 1960) have been made on iron which was the first case where critical scattering was observed. An experiment has also been made on nickel (Cribier et al., 1962) but some of the above experiments are incomplete. In nickel and in iron (Jacrot et al., 1963) an attempt has been made to measure the differential cross-section

$d^2\sigma/d\Omega d\omega$ and make a determination of all the parameters involved. A similar experiment has also been made on iron by Passel *et al.* (1964).

The correlation range is in general not well defined. By convention we use the inverse of K_1 defined by equation (6.16). This is an obvious choice when one reduces the correlation function to the asymptotic form $\dfrac{1}{r}\exp(-K_1 r)$, in which case the cross-section (6.15) reduces to terms in q^2. In the general case where higher terms in q appear, this quantity still is a good measure of

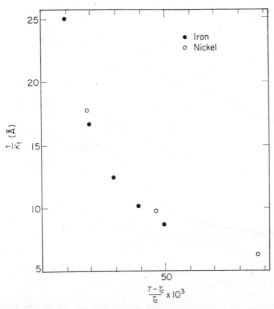

FIG. 6.19. Comparison between the measured values of the correlation range in iron and nickel, on a reduced temperature scale (Jacrot *et al.*, 1963).

the range of the correlations. By measuring the angular distribution at small q in the forward direction the correlation lengths of iron (Jacrot *et al.*, 1963) and nickel (Cribier *et al.*, 1962) were derived; the results are given in Fig. 6.19. At T_c the data give a minimum value of 140 Å for the correlation range in iron. In general the range observed is a factor two larger than calculated from simple molecular field theory.

Even though iron and nickel from the data on K_1 seem very similar, there is a significant difference between the interaction forces in these two metals. This shows up in the importance of the q^4 term, which in neither case is negligible, but which for nickel is four times higher than for iron. This means that the exchange forces of nickel have a very long range, in gratifying agreement with the spin wave results (Hatherly *et al.*, 1964) quoted earlier.

Some of the data on iron which led to Fig. 6.19 are shown in Fig. 6.20. The lower curve has the expected behaviour and the other curves too in the immediate neighbourhood of T_c. The unusual appearance of the curves at lower temperatures is due to the characteristics of the spin wave scattering and the associated scattering surface. When this surface expands over the temperature region shown, the intensity scattered into a narrow detector decreases with temperature, even though the intensity integrated over the

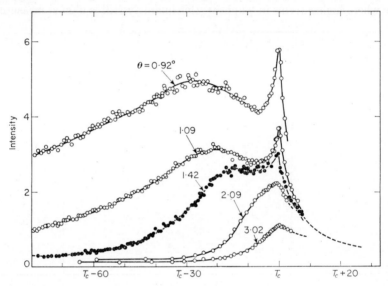

FIG. 6.20. Intensity scattered by iron in the critical temperature range for different scattering angles (Jacrot *et al.*, 1963).

scattering surfaces is increasing. By applying an external field to the iron sample it was found that the broad bump in the curves was indeed due to spin waves. The same experiment served to verify the predictions by Villain concerning the effect on the critical scattering of applying a field. As seen from Fig. 6.21 the correlation range and the intensity of the fluctuations decrease as the field is applied such as to give the predicted intensity changes.

An interesting aspect of the results on the correlation range K_1 lies in the relation (6.16) of this quantity with the susceptibility χ. Calculations of Gammel *et al.* (1963) predict a $\frac{3}{4}$ power law of variation of $1/\chi$ with $(T-T_c)$. This point has been verified for iron by Jacrot *et al.* (1963), Passel *et al.* (1964) and Gordon (1965). More accurate data are needed to specify accurately the exponent of $(T-T_c)$, and the exact behaviour very close to T_c, $(T-T_c<1$ deg. C).

The most complete data on the relaxation time have so far been obtained for iron (Jacrot *et al.*, 1963; Passel *et al.*, 1964). Figure 6.22 shows the incident and scattered energy spectrum of neutrons for 9° scattering angle at T_c. A detailed analysis of the scattered spectrum shows that it has indeed the form obtained when folding the incident spectrum with a Lorentzian cross-section, as given

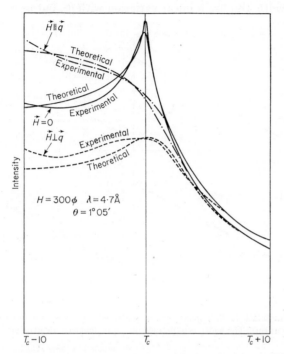

Fig. 6.21. The critical scattering in iron and the effect of applying an external field of 300 oersteds to the sample. (Villain, 1963.)

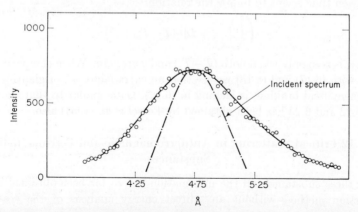

Fig. 6.22. The energy spectrum of neutrons scattered at 9° at the Curie point. The incident spectrum is shown for comparison (Jacrot *et al.*, 1963).

by (6.20). The width at half maximum of the experimental curve varies linearly with θ^2 (i.e. q^2), as shown by Fig. 6.23. The slope of the line gives the diffusion constant which at T_c has the value $\Lambda = 3 \cdot 6 \times 10^{-3}$ c.g.s. At $15°$ and $30°$ above T_c the halfwidth also has a linear variation with θ^2, but as $\theta \to 0$ it does not

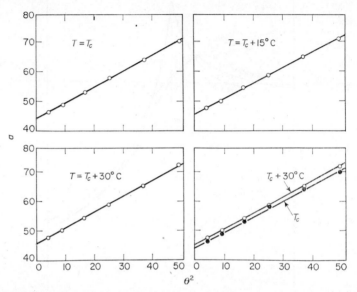

FIG. 6.23. The width at half maximum of scattered neutrons as a function of scattering angle and temperature. The width is expressed on a wavelength scale in arbitrary units. (Jacrot et al., 1963.)

extrapolate to the width of the incident spectrum as it does at T_c. Thus the relaxation time seems to follow the relation

$$\left(\frac{1}{\tau_q}\right)_{exp} = D[a(T - T_c) + q^2] \tag{6.22}$$

and $1/\tau_q$ is zero only when both $(T - T_c)$ and q are zero. When comparing this result with (6.17) and (6.18) we see that an extra factor q^2, originating from the kinematical braking, is lacking in (6.22). Data similar to that shown in Figs 6.22 and 6.23 has been obtained by Passel et al. (1964) also.

6.12 Critical Scattering in Antiferromagnetic and Ferrimagnetic Substances

For these substances all the information has so far been obtained by the diffraction method without any direct energy analysis of the scattered neutrons. Consequently, the data mostly concern the space dependence of the spin correlations.

In antiferromagnetic CoO, McReynolds and Riste (1959) observed critical scattering at the (111) superlattice position. By a Fourier transform of the observed angular distribution, the static part of the correlation function, i.e. $\langle S(0)S(R)\rangle$, was derived. The results are given in Fig. 6.24. It is seen that as the temperature approaches T_c, the correlation between distant spins increases.

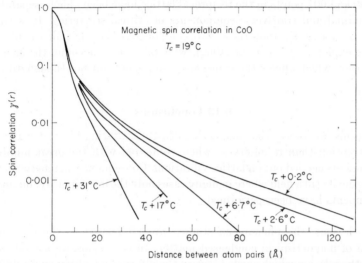

FIG. 6.24. Spin correlations in CoO (McReynolds and Riste, 1959). $\left[\gamma(R) = \dfrac{\langle S(0)S(R)\rangle}{S(S+1)}\right]$.

Other antiferromagnetic substances which have been studied are $\alpha\text{-Fe}_2\text{O}_3$ (Riste and Wanic, 1961) and Cr_2O_3 (Krasnicki et al., 1963). These substances are crystallographically isomorphous, but have different spin structures. In $\alpha\text{-Fe}_2\text{O}_3$ the intensity and range of the spin correlations are quantitatively in agreement with molecular field calculations for $T \geqslant T_c$. At T_c the minimum value of the correlation range is 100 Å. Below T_c there is qualitative agreement with the theory. In Cr_2O_3 it was expected that the correlation range should be greater than in $\alpha\text{-Fe}_2\text{O}_3$ as a result of interaction between more closely spaced neighbours. This was indeed found and the range is greater than can be accounted for by molecular field theory. In both cases the intensity follows a q^{-2} dependence, which according to our previous discussions is indicative of short range interactions.

In ferrimagnetic Fe_3O_4 Riste (1961) found that, when approaching T_c from below, the longitudinal fluctuations increased in a way determined by the decrease of the spontaneous magnetization. This is in agreement with a confident theoretical prediction (van Hove, 1954; Elliott and Marshall, 1958; de Gennes and Villain, 1960). The intensity distribution is again indicative of short range interactions, but the correlation range is longer than can be accounted for theoretically. In this case an attempt was made also to obtain some information on the relaxation processes. It was tentatively concluded that the diffusion constant is very nearly the same as for iron and nickel but the thermodynamic braking process could not be detected.

In MnF_2 Turberfield et al. (1965) by observing the critical scattering around the 100 and 001 points in the reciprocal lattice have been able to separate the longitudinal and transverse components of critical scattering. It is only at about 5° above T_N that these two components become indistinguishable. This is explained by Tomita (1962), who takes into account the magnetic anisotropy which affects the transverse component but not the longtitudinal one.

6.13 Conclusions

It seems fair to say that magnetic inelastic scattering has so far attracted less attention than it deserves, when compared with the great number of experiments carried out on lattice vibrations. Consequently magnetic inelastic scattering is still a field where in many cases only the introductory, qualitative experiments have been performed.

If we exclude the experiments dealing with the spectroscopy of paramagnetic ions, the phenomena studied are all related to the cooperative nature of magnetism in condensed matter. In conclusion we should like to stress the relation which exists between the information obtained for different temperature regions in the latter case. The kinetics of the spin arrangements may vary, from the spin waves found in the low temperature region to the diffusive motion at high temperatures. Still the phenomena are all the time governed by the magnetic interaction forces, mainly of the exchange type. The experiments should in principle enable one to tell what the range and strength of these forces are and how they change with temperature. Information of this kind obtained from elastic scattering data is much less direct, because these experiments give the static configuration of spins only.

The temperature region near the Curie point is attractive to the experimentalist because of the great magnitude of the cross-section. There is also a great physical interest attached to the critical fluctuations, in regard to both thermodynamics and statistical physics. Neutrons provide us with a unique tool for studying the way in which information (correlation) is transmitted over large distances in the substance.

References

Bacon, G. (1962). "Neutron Diffraction". Oxford University Press, London.
Bendt, P. J. (1953). Phys. Rev. **89**, 561.
Bloch, M. (1962). Phys. Rev. Letters **9**, 286.

Brockhouse, B. N. (1959). *Phys. Rev.* **99**, 601.

Brockhouse, B. N. and Watanabe, H. (1963). *In* "Inelastic Scattering of Neutrons in Solids and Liquids", Vol. II, p. 297. IAEA, Vienna.

Brockhouse, B. N., Becka, L. N., Rao, L. R. and Woods, A. D. B. (1962). *J. phys. Soc. Japan* **17**, Suppl. B–III, 63.

Brout, R. and Haken, K. (1960). *Bull. Amer. phys. Soc.* **5**, 148.

Collins, M. F. (1964). Proc. Int. Conf. Magnetism, Nottingham, p. 319 (Inst. Phys. and Phys. Soc. London).

Cribier, D., Jacrot, B. and Riste, T. (1963). Unpublished.

Cribier, D. and Jacrot, B. (1960). *C.R. Acad. Sci., Paris* **250**, 2871.

Cribier, D. and Jacrot, B. (1963). *In* "Inelastic Scattering of Neutrons in Solids and Liquids", Vol. II, p. 309. IAEA, Vienna.

Cribier, D., Jacrot, B. and Parette, G. (1962). *J. phys. Soc. Japan* **17**, Suppl. B-III, 67.

Cribier, D., Ericson, M., Jacrot, B. and Sarma, G. (1959). *C.R. Acad. Sci., Paris* **248**, 1631.

de Gennes, P. G. (1958). *J. Phys. Chem. Solids* **4**, 223.

de Gennes, P. G. (1959a). *J. Phys. Chem. Solids* **6**, 43.

de Gennes, P. G. (1959b). Contribution a l'étude de la diffusion magnétique des neutrons. Presses Universitaire de France, Paris.

de Gennes, P. G. (1963). *In* "Magnetism", ed. by G. T. Rado and H. Suhl, Academic Press, New York.

de Gennes, P. G. and Villain, J. (1960). *J. Phys. Chem. Solids* **13**, 10.

Usha Deniz, K., Venkataraman, G., Satyamurthy, N. S., Dasannacharya, B. A. and Iyengar, P. K. (1964). Proc. Int. Conf. on Magnetism, Nottingham, p. 322 (Inst. Phys and Phys. Soc. London).

Dyson, F. J. (1956). *Phys. Rev.* **102**, 1217, 1230.

Elliott, R. J. and Marshall, W. (1958). *Rev. mod. Phys.* **30**, 75.

Englert, F. (1960). *Phys. Rev. Letters* **5**, 102.

Ericson, M. and Jacrot, B. (1960). *J. Phys. Chem. Solids* **13**, 235.

Ferguson, G. A. and Saenz, A. W. (1962). *J. Phys. Chem. Solids* **23**, 117.

Frikkee, E. and Riste, T. (1964). Proceedings of the International Conference on Magnetism, Nottingham, p. 299. Institute of Physics and Physical Society, London.

Gammel, J., Marshall, W. C. and Morgan, L. (1963). *Proc. roy. Soc.* **A275**, 257.

Gordon, A. (1965). Private communication.

Hatherly, M., Hirakawa, K., Lowde, R. D., Mallett, J. F., Stringfellow, M. W. and Torrie, B. H. (1964). *Proc. phys. Soc.* **84**, 55.

Hautecler, S., Konstantinovic, J., Cribier, D. and Jacrot, B. (1962). *C.R. Acad. Sci., Paris* **254**, 1026.

Heap, B. R. (1962). *Proc. roy. Soc.* **80**, 248.

Herring, C. and Kittel, C. (1951). *Phys. Rev.* **81**, 869.

Iyengar, P. K. and Brockhouse, B. N. (1958). *Bull. Amer. phys. Soc.* II, **3**, 195.

Izuyama, T., Kim, D. J. and Kubo, R. (1963). *J. phys. Soc. Japan* **18**, 1025.

Izyumov, Yu. A. and Maleev, S. V. (1961). *Zh. eksper. teoret. Fiz.* **41**, 1644; (1962). *Soviet Physics JETP* **14**, 1168.

Jacrot, B. and Cribier, D. (1962). *J. Phys. Radium* **23**, 494.

Jacrot, B., Konstantinovic, J., Parette, G. and Cribier, D. (1963). *In* "Inelastic Scattering of Neutrons in Solids and Liquids", Vol. II, p. 317. IAEA, Vienna.

Kanamori, J. (1958). *Progr. theoret. Phys.* **20**, 890.

Kaplan, T. A. (1958). *Phys. Rev.* **109**, 782.

Keffer, F. and Loudon, R. (1961). *J. Appl. Phys.* **32**, 2S.

Kocinski, J. (1963). *Phys. Letters* **4**, 184.

Krasnicki, S., Murasik, A., Riste, T., Wala, K. and Wanic, A. (1963). *In* "Inelastic Scattering of Neutrons in Solids and Liquids", Vol. II, p. 327. IAEA, Vienna.

Krivoglaz, M. A. (1958). *Dokl. Akad. Nauk SSSR* **118**, 51; *Soviet Phys. Dokl.* **3**, 61.

Landau, L. D. and Lifshitz, E. M. (1960). "Electrodynamics of Continuous Media". Pergamon Press, London.

Lowde, R. D. (1954). *Proc. roy. Soc.* **A221**, 206.

Lowde, R. D. (1958). *Rev. mod. Phys.* **30**, 69.

Lowde, R. D. (1965). *J. appl. Phys.* **36**, 884.

Lowde, R. D. and Umakantha, R. H. (1960). *Phys. Rev. Letters* **4**, 452.

Low, G. G. E. and Okazaki, A. (1963). AERE—R4299. H.M.S.O., London.

McReynolds, A. W. and Riste, T. (1959). *J. phys. Radium* **20**, 111.

Maleev, S. V. (1961). *Zh. eksper. teoret. Fiz.* **40**, 1224; (1962). *Soviet Physics JETP* **14**, 1168.

Marshall, W. C. (1963). "Proceedings of the Eighth International Conference on Low Temperature Physics, 1962." Butterworths Scientific Publications Ltd., London.

Mori, H. and Kawasaki, K. (1962). *Progr. theoret. Phys.* **27**, 529.

Murasik, A., Ruta-Wala, K. and Wanic, A. (1961). *Physica* **27**, 883.

Nakamura, T. and Bloch, M. (1963). *Phys. Rev.* **132**, 2518.

Oguchi, T. (1960). *Phys. Rev.* **117**, 117.

Okazaki, A., Turberfield, K. C. and Stevenson, R. W. H. (1964). *Phys. Letters* **8**, 9.

Palevsky, H. and Hughes, D. J. (1954). *Phys. Rev.* **92**, 202.

Passel, L., Blinowski, K., Brun, T. and Nielsen, P. (1964). *J. appl. Phys.* **35**, 933.

Riste, T. (1961). *J. Phys. Chem. Solids* **17**, 308.

Riste, T. (1962). *J. phys. Soc. Japan* **17**, Suppl. B-III, 60.

Riste, T. and Goedkoop, J. A. (1960). *Nature, Lond.* **185**, 450.

Riste, T. and Wanic, A. (1961). *J. Phys. Chem. Solids* **17**, 318.

Riste, T., Blinowski, K. and Janik, J. (1959). *J. Phys. Chem. Solids* **9**, 153.

Saenz, A. W. (1960). *Phys. Rev.* **119**, 1542.

Saint-James, D. (1961). Thesis, Paris.

Samulesen, E. J., Riste, T. and Steinvoll, O. (1963). *Phys. Letters* **6**, 47.

Shimizu, M. and Katzuki, A. (1964). Proceedings of the International Conference on Magnetism, Nottingham, p. 182. Institute of Physics and Physical Society, London.

Sinclair, R. N. and Brockhouse, B. N. (1960). *Phys. Rev.* **120**, 1638.

Squires, G. L. (1954). *Proc. phys. Soc.* **67**, 248.

Tannenwald, P. E. (1962). *J. phys. Soc. Japan* **17**, Suppl. B-I, 592.

Tomita, K. (1962). *J. phys. Soc. Jap. Suppl.* B1, **17**, 71; private communication.

Turberfield, K. C., Okazaki, A. and Stevenson, R. W. H. (1965). *Proc. phys. Soc.* **85**, 1.

van Hove, L. (1954). *Phys. Rev.* **95**, 249, 1374.

van Vleck, J. H. (1939). *Phys. Rev.* **55**, 924.

van Vleck, J. H. (1955). "The Theory of Electric and Magnetic Susceptibilities", p. 316. Oxford University Press, London.

Villain, J. (1963). *J. Phys. Radium* **24**, 622.

Wanic, A. (1964). *J. Phys. Paris* **25**, 627.

Wanic, A. (1965). Private communication.

Wilkinson, M. K. and Shull, C. G. (1956). *Phys. Rev.* **103**, 516.

Wilkinson, M. K., Cable, J. W., Wollan, E. O. and Koehler, W. C. (1959). *Phys. Rev.* **113**, 497.

Yamada, Y. (1960). *J. phys. Soc. Japan* **15**, 429.

CHAPTER 7

Theory of Neutron Scattering by Liquids

ALF SJÖLANDER

Institute of Theoretical Physics, Gothenburg, Sweden

7.1	Introduction	291
7.2	Van Hove Correlation Functions	294
7.3	Moment Relations	298
7.4	Fluctuation-dissipation Theorem	301
7.5	Scattering by Harmonic Solids	303
7.6	Scattering by Anharmonic Solids	306
7.7	General Discussion of Classical Liquids	309
7.8	Interference Effects	320
7.9	Gaussian Approximation	326
7.10	Introduction of the Velocity Frequency Function	328
7.11	Discussion of Various Explicit Dynamical Models	331
7.12	Concluding Remarks	341
	References	342

List of Symbols

a_1, a_2, b_1, b_2	Coefficients in expansion of $I(\mathbf{Q}, \tau)$ and $I_s(\mathbf{Q}, \tau)$	$\mathbf{R}(\tau)$	Position of atom at time τ
a	Relative weight	v_a	Volume per atom
C_P, C_V	Principal specific heats	$\mathbf{v}(\tau)$	Velocity of atom at time τ
c	Velocity of sound	$w_D(\tau)$	Contribution to width function due to diffusion
D	Diffusion constant		
D_0	Diffusion constant for centre of vibrations in Oskotskii model	$w_B(\tau)$	Contribution to width function due to other effects
D_T	Thermal diffusion coefficient	α	Coefficient of thermal expansion
$\mathbf{F}(\tau)$	Stochastic driving force	β	$1/kT$
f_D	Debye frequency	Γ	Generalized damping constant
f'	Limiting frequency for diffusive modes	$\gamma(\mathbf{Q})$	Space Fourier transform of pair-distribution function, $g(\mathbf{r})$
f_0	Natural frequency of atoms	ζ	Frictional coefficient
$g(f, \tau)$	Weighting factor	ζ_0	Frictional coefficient for diffusive modes only
$I^{(n)}$	nth order time-derivative of I		
l	Jump-distance	$K(\tau)$	Actual force on atom
$M(\mathbf{r}, t)$	Width-function matrix	$\xi_s(\tau)$	Displacement of atom due to mode s
$p(\mathbf{Q})$	Parameter in jump-diffusion model	τ_0	Average vibration time of atom
		τ_1	Average wandering time of atom
R_g	Radius of globule	χ_S	Adiabatic compressibility
		χ_T	Isothermal compressibility

7.1 Introduction

The use of neutron scattering as a tool for studying lattice vibrations in solids has proved very successful (see Chapter 5). Through these experiments one has gained detailed information on phonon dispersion curves and life times which was hardly possible by any other means available at present. There are certain requirements on neutron energies to be used and also on the samples to be studied in order to reveal the dynamics in detail. The magnitude of the energy transfers involved is of the order 10^{-4}–10^{-2} eV and in order to resolve these small energy changes one is often forced to use very slow neutrons. However, the intensities obtained from the reactors, even when using cold moderators, drop rapidly for longer wavelengths and one has to make a compromise between intensity and energy. Fortunately, 4–6 Å turns out to be a convenient wavelength region both from this point of view as well as for other reasons.

In many cases only polycrystalline samples are available and these can indeed be used to obtain some information on dispersion curves but the most detailed information is obtained only when using single crystal samples, where sharp resonance peaks appear in the scattering corresponding to creation or absorption of single phonons. The position of these peaks and their widths give very directly the frequency and life time of single phonons. In a polycrystal these peaks are washed out due to the random orientation of the microcrystals forming the polycrystals. There remains, however, certain characteristic effects which produce a sharp rise in the energy distribution of the scattered neutrons and the position of this rise can be used to determine approximate single phonon frequencies. However, the life time of the phonons cannot be obtained in this way.

The applicability of neutron scattering is not restricted to solids and quite naturally it has been used to study the atomic motions in liquids as well. This field is in many respects more challenging for both the experimentalists and theorists. Due to absence of lattice ordering in liquids we cannot get such a direct observation of the motions here as in single crystals. One should in this respect rather compare liquids with polycrystals. The magnitude of the energy changes involved and the convenient neutron wavelengths to be used are the same as in solids. For solids one has a detailed theory of lattice vibrations on which to base the interpretations of the the experimental data. There the aim has mainly been to determine experimentally the force constants in Born-von Kármán's theory, for instance, and also the constants entering in the anharmonic terms. For liquids no theory exists which is sufficient to form the basis for a general interpretation of the scattering data.

The study of the liquid state aims at giving decisive knowledge of the general character of the rapid atomic motions, which are responsible for the thermodynamic properties and transport properties of liquids. There are strong indications that liquids on an atomistic scale are much more similar to a solid than their macroscopic behaviour indicates. On the other hand one can point out many dissimilarities too and the basic problem at present is to throw light on this point. There exists in liquids both collective and single particle motions. The hydrodynamic equations and the equation for heat diffusion are two examples of collective equations valid, however, only for the very long wavelength and low frequency region. The single particle motions show up, for instance, in measurements on light emitted from single atoms and emission of γ-rays from the nuclei as a line-broadening. In neutron scattering both the collective and the single particle aspects can be revealed conveniently by varying scattering angle and incident energy. A basic problem is to find out how far into the short wavelength region the collective motions remain distinct and how and in which sense the single particle and collective aspects merge into each other for very short wavelengths. To the theorists is given the task to first introduce and precisely define quantities which are suitable to describe such correlated motions as may occur on an atomistic scale in liquids. The aim is, of course, to find equations of motion which should serve the same purpose as Born-von Kármán's equations for solids. We believe that the goal cannot be stretched much further at the moment.

Even though basic research on liquid dynamics using neutron scattering began only a few years ago decisive results have been obtained and will be described in detail in this chapter and in Chapter 8. Parallel to the experimental research important theoretical work has been carried out both on the general formalism and on the question of finding models which should describe approximately the actual atomic motions and be used for analysing the experimental data.

In this chapter a general presentation of the theory underlying neutron scattering in liquids will be given. The first three sections are of a general character valid for any system and not relying on any particular dynamical model. Perhaps this makes the presentation somewhat formal and, therefore, we begin each section with a more descriptive survey in order to make the reading easier. Even though scattering in harmonic as well as anharmonic solids lies outside the scope of this review we find it convenient to illustrate the general results of the first three sections by these simpler systems. In particular, recent investigations on weakly anharmonic solids have some bearing on liquids as well. In the following sections we give a review of approximations which are currently made and in the final section various explicit models are discussed, which have been used in the interpretation of the experiments. The closing section contains the essential conclusions which can be drawn from present experimental and theoretical work and some remarks are made on remaining basic questions.

Shorter reviews of this field have been given earlier by Nelkin (1961), Schofield (1962), Sjölander (1964) and Egelstaff (1965). A recent monograph by Turchin (1963) covers part of the material presented here also.

7.2 Van Hove Correlation Functions

The analysis of slow neutron scattering in liquids has almost without exception been based on the space-time formulation of Van Hove* (1954). A brief discussion of this approach was given by Lomer and Low in Chapter 1. We shall go into more details of this formulation here. For the derivation of the general expression for the scattering cross-section we refer to the original papers of Van Hove (1954, 1958) where he discusses thoroughly the classical interpretation of the correlation functions he introduces. Here we shall stress those points which are of conceptual interest or special importance for the applications and lay less emphasis on purely mathematical details for which reference to the literature will be given.

Van Hove found that formally a great similarity could be established between X-ray diffraction and slow neutron scattering. In X-ray diffraction one observes in liquids the instantaneous positions of the atoms and the information obtained is precisely the static pair distribution function. The intensity of the scattered X-rays is simply the space Fourier transform of this function where the variable is the momentum transfer. Van Hove made a generalization by introducing a time dependent correlation function, which for zero time describes the instantaneous location of an atom at the origin surrounded by other atoms for which the distribution is given by the static pair-distribution function. As the time develops the correlation function changes and Van Hove found that the coherent neutron scattering is determined by the four-dimensional Fourier transform in space and time of this correlation function. The variables are the momentum transfer and the energy transfer both of which can be controlled in the experiments. For the incoherent scattering he found a similar relation. Here, however, only that part of the above correlation function enters which describes the motion of the particular atom located at the origin for zero time. Precise definitions of these correlation functions were given by Van Hove and the problem is to calculate them for particular systems based on the equations of motion for the atoms. It is obvious that this is not possible in practice except for some few very idealized cases. One tries, therefore, in various ways to get some insight without really solving the whole problem. Some general conclusions can be drawn fairly easily whereas other results cannot be obtained without unmanageable calculations. One finds it often more convenient to discuss the space Fourier transformed correlation function, the so called "intermediate scattering function", rather than the original Van Hove correlation function. These latter functions are, however, more easily interpreted in physical terms and play for that reason an essential role in clarifying the physics behind the formalism.

---

* Essentially the same formulation was developed simultaneously by R. J. Glauber 1955) for application to harmonic solids.

The two space-time correlation functions of Van Hove, usually denoted by $G(\mathbf{r},\tau)$ and $G_s(\mathbf{r},\tau)$, are mathematically defined as follows (see Chapter 1, equations (1.24, 1.26)):

$$G(\mathbf{r},\tau) = \frac{1}{N} \sum_{mn} \int d\mathbf{r}' \; \overline{\delta(\mathbf{r}+\mathbf{R}_n(0)-\mathbf{r}')\delta(\mathbf{r}'-\mathbf{R}_m(\tau))}, \tag{7.1a}$$

$$G_s(\mathbf{r},\tau) = \frac{1}{N} \sum_{n} \int d\mathbf{r}' \; \overline{\delta(\mathbf{r}+\mathbf{R}_n(0)-\mathbf{r}')\delta(\mathbf{r}'-\mathbf{R}_n(\tau))}, \tag{7.1b}$$

where $\delta(...)$ is a Dirac δ-function. $\mathbf{R}_n(0)$ and $\mathbf{R}_m(\tau)$ are the position vectors, considered as Heisenberg observables, of the nth atom at time zero and the mth atom at time τ. The summation in (7.1a) extends over all atoms m and an averaging, $(1/N)\sum_n$, is performed over the atoms. N is the total number of atoms in the system. In equation (7.1b) $n = m$ and the summation means an averaging over the atoms. $\overline{(.....)}$ denotes a statistical average corresponding to equilibrium conditions at a temperature T. Hence

$$\overline{(.....)} = Tr\{e^{-\beta H} ...\}/Tr\{e^{-\beta H}\}, \tag{7.2}$$

$e^{-\beta H}$ being the ordinary Boltzmann statistical weight factor, where H is the Hamiltonian of the total system and $\beta = 1/kT$, k being the Boltzmann constant.

For the sake of simplicity, we shall restrict ourselves to monatomic liquids. If surface effects are neglected, all the atoms are equivalent and we can drop the averaging $(1/N)\sum_n$. In the classical limit the operators can be permuted at will, and the space integrations in equations (7.1a,b) lead to

$$G(\mathbf{r},\tau) = \sum_n \overline{\delta[\mathbf{r}+\mathbf{R}_0(0)-\mathbf{R}_n(\tau)]}, \tag{7.3a}$$

$$G_s(\mathbf{r},\tau) = \overline{\delta[\mathbf{r}+\mathbf{R}_0(0)-\mathbf{R}_0(\tau)]}. \tag{7.3b}$$

The atom which is given the zero index is, of course, arbitrary.

A direct consequence of the definition is that

$$G_s(\mathbf{r},0) = \delta(\mathbf{r}) \quad \text{and} \quad G(\mathbf{r},0) = \delta(\mathbf{r})+g(\mathbf{r}), \tag{7.4}$$

where $g(\mathbf{r})$ is the static pair-distribution function, which gives the average particle density around a given particle. Thus $G(\mathbf{r},0)$ tends for $\mathbf{r}\to\infty$ to the macroscopic density ρ. For $\tau\to\infty$, $\mathbf{R}_n(\tau)$ is expected to be completely uncorrelated to $\mathbf{R}_0(0)$ on the average, and this leads to

$$G_s(\mathbf{r}, \infty) = 0, \; G(\mathbf{r},\infty) = \rho. \tag{7.5}$$

In other words, the two correlation functions, which for zero time show strong local structure, are smoothed out as the time develops. The classical interpretation of $G_s(\mathbf{r},\tau)$ and $G(\mathbf{r},\tau)$ was formulated by Van Hove, based on equations (7.3a,b), as follows.

Given a particle at the origin at time zero $G_s(\mathbf{r},\tau)$ gives the probability of finding that particle at position $\mathbf{r}$ after a time τ has elapsed. $G(\mathbf{r},\tau)$ gives the probability of finding any particle at position $\mathbf{r}$ at time τ under the same initial condition.

$G_s(\mathbf{r},\tau)$ is thus related to self-diffusion in the liquid. Even if the interpretation above does cover the essential properties of the G-functions it has been somewhat misleading by ignoring certain essential aspects, which are inherent in the exact definitions in equations (7.1a,b) but are lost in the classical definitions. It should also be noted that the interpretation above stresses the single particle aspects of the motion of the liquid, which is not always preferable.

By introducing the microscopic particle density

$$\rho(\mathbf{r},\tau) = \sum_n \delta[\mathbf{r}-\mathbf{R}_n(\tau)], \tag{7.6}$$

which is classically zero everywhere except where the particles are actually sitting, we can write $G(\mathbf{r},\tau)$ in the following form:

$$G(\mathbf{r},\tau) = \overline{\rho(0,0)\rho(\mathbf{r},\tau)}/\rho. \tag{7.7}$$

This gives the correlation between the densities at two different positions and times. Here we stress the collective aspects and we may expect the sound waves, which we know give rise to density fluctuations in the liquid, to play an important role for long wavelengths.

The exact correlation functions are in general complex, contrary to what one may expect from their classical interpretations, and the imaginary part is often, somewhat confusingly, referred to as a quantum correction. The first direct physical interpretation of the imaginary part was given by Van Hove (1958). All these points will be discussed in detail in the following sections.

The scattering cross-section for a system of N atoms, separated into the coherent and incoherent scattering,* is, except for some trivial factors, the four-dimensional Fourier transform of the correlation functions above (see equations (1.29) and (1.30)):

$$\frac{\mathrm{d}^2\sigma^{\mathrm{coh}}}{\mathrm{d}\Omega \mathrm{d}\omega} = N\frac{\bar{b}^2}{2\pi}\frac{k}{k_0}\int e^{i(\mathbf{Q}\cdot\mathbf{r}-\omega\tau)}G(\mathbf{r},\tau)\mathrm{d}\mathbf{r}\mathrm{d}\tau, \tag{7.8a}$$

$$\frac{\mathrm{d}^2\sigma^{\mathrm{inc}}}{\mathrm{d}\Omega \mathrm{d}\omega} = N\frac{\overline{b^2}-\bar{b}^2}{2\pi}\frac{k}{k_0}\int e^{i(\mathbf{Q}\cdot\mathbf{r}-\omega\tau)}G_s(\mathbf{r},\tau)\mathrm{d}\mathbf{r}\mathrm{d}\tau. \tag{7.8b}$$

$\hbar\mathbf{Q}$ and $\hbar\omega$ denote the momentum and energy transfers in the collision between the neutron and the scatterer and through the relations

$$\mathbf{Q} = \mathbf{k}_0-\mathbf{k}, \quad \omega = \frac{\hbar k_0^2}{2m} - \frac{\hbar k^2}{2m}, \tag{7.9}$$

---

* The meaning of coherent and incoherent scattering has been clarified in Chapter 1.

(m being the neutron mass), are expressed in terms of the initial and final wave vectors $\mathbf{k}_0$ and $\mathbf{k}$. $\overline{b}^2$ and $(\overline{b^2 - \overline{b}^2})$ are, respectively, the squares of the coherent and incoherent scattering lengths introduced in Chapter 1.

The spatial integrations in equations (7.8a,b) can be performed, using the definitions in equations (7.1a,b), and lead to *

$$I(\mathbf{Q},\tau) = \sum_n \overline{\exp\left[-i\mathbf{Q}.\mathbf{R}_0(0)\right]\exp\left[i\mathbf{Q}.\mathbf{R}_n(\tau)\right]}, \qquad (7.10a)$$

$$I_s(\mathbf{Q},\tau) = \overline{\exp\left[-i\mathbf{Q}.\mathbf{R}_0(0)\right]\exp\left[i\mathbf{Q}.\mathbf{R}_0(\tau)\right]}. \qquad (7.10b)$$

which are often called "intermediate scattering functions". The cross-section is thus given by the time transforms of these, and we shall for convenience introduce the notations

$$S^{\mathrm{coh}}(\mathbf{Q},\omega) = \frac{1}{2\pi}\int_{-\infty}^{\infty} e^{-i\omega\tau}I(\mathbf{Q},\tau)\mathrm{d}\tau, \qquad (7.11a)$$

$$S^{\mathrm{inc}}(\mathbf{Q},\omega) = \frac{1}{2\pi}\int_{-\infty}^{\infty} e^{-i\omega\tau}I_s(\mathbf{Q},\tau)\mathrm{d}\tau, \qquad (7.11b)$$

which are sometimes termed "scattering laws".

By measuring the energy and angular distribution of the scattered neutrons, assuming a monochromatic and well collimated incident beam, one can experimentally determine the Van Hove functions directly, at least in principle. One then considers the Fourier inversion of (7.8a,b). Such a procedure has indeed been undertaken by Brockhouse and co-workers (1963) and more recently by Dasannacharya and Rao (1965). However, due to practical difficulties in applying this method, one often makes use of more indirect procedures. $G(\mathbf{r},\tau)$ and $G_s(\mathbf{r},\tau)$ are assumed to have some reasonable form with adjustable parameters built in and one tries to get as good fit as possible to the experimental data on the differential scattering cross-sections. It is obvious that in such an approach one must know beforehand the essential features of the Van Hove correlation functions and these are determined by the dynamics of the system. We have at present no possibility of calculating these functions from first principles except in some idealized cases—ideal gas, purely harmonic solid, etc.

The same correlation functions as above appear in the theory of the scattering of X-rays and electrons and also in the theory of infrared absorption and Mandel'shtam-Brillouin scattering of light. Particularly Mandel'shtam-Brillouin scattering is analogous to neutron scattering; the main difference lies in the much shorter wavelengths used in the latter case. In X-ray

---

* The averaging $\dfrac{1}{N}\sum_n$ has been dropped when neglecting surface effects.

scattering, only the value of $G(\mathbf{r},\tau)$ for $\tau = 0$ enters and, as is well known, X-ray diffraction is a powerful means for determining experimentally the pair-distribution function $g(\mathbf{r})$. It should also be mentioned that resonance absorption of γ-rays is formally analogous to neutron scattering (see e.g. Fraunfelder, 1962).

7.3 Moment Relations

Even though the detailed shape of $S(\mathbf{Q},\omega)$ is not easily calculated, some general conclusions could be drawn from a knowledge of its frequency width. In fact, knowing all the moments $\int \omega^n S(\mathbf{Q},\omega)\mathrm{d}\omega$, one can under fairly general conditions find the exact form of the function. This is, however, not feasible but some of the lower moments can be calculated exactly and, if $S(\mathbf{Q},\omega)$ should be a smooth function of the frequency, Gaussian-like, for instance, these moments would determine $S(\mathbf{Q},\omega)$ to a fair degree of accuracy. If $S(\mathbf{Q},\omega)$ contains structure, which is indeed the case, less information is gained from the low order moments but it is still of interest to make as much use as possible of these exactly calculable quantities. By adjusting the experimental variables in a suitable way one can experimentally measure the frequency distribution for fixed $\mathbf{Q}$, and a special technique for such measurements has been developed by Brockhouse (1961) and was discussed in Chapter 3. In this way one can establish a contact between theory and experiment which does not suffer from uncertainties in approximations made. In fact, one rather gets a test on the accuracy of the experiments. These general relations, which go under the name of "moment relations" are a direct mathematical consequence of the fact that $S(\mathbf{Q},\omega)$ is a Fourier integral of a certain function $I(\mathbf{Q},\tau)$. Apart from the physical meaning one finds generally that the calculation of the moments corresponds to an expansion of the above function in powers of the variable τ. It turns out that the first moment, which physically gives the "mean energy transfer" for fixed $\mathbf{Q}$ in the scattering, is determined by the coefficient before the first power of τ in the expansion of $I(\mathbf{Q},\tau)$. This coefficient depends only on the mass of the atoms and is independent of the particular interaction between the atoms. In other words, the mean energy transfer is independent of the interaction in the system and is thus the same in a liquid as in an ideal gas. Other conclusions can be drawn from the relations for the higher moments. One important general result was obtained by De Gennes (1959) who showed that the energy spread in the coherent cross-section should vary in a characteristic oscillatory manner, determined essentially by the Fourier transform of the static pair distribution function, and that this should not occur for the incoherent cross-section. This has been confirmed experimentally (e.g. Brockhouse and Pope, 1959).

From equations (7.11a,b) we find that

$$\int_{-\infty}^{\infty} S^{\text{inc}}(\mathbf{Q},\omega)d\omega = I_s(\mathbf{Q},0) \text{ and } \int_{-\infty}^{\infty} S^{\text{coh}}(\mathbf{Q},\omega)d\omega = I(\mathbf{Q},0) \qquad (7.12)$$

and using equation (7.4) we further get

$$I_s(\mathbf{Q},0) = 1, \quad I(\mathbf{Q},0) = 1+\gamma(Q), \qquad (7.13)$$

where $\gamma(Q)$ denotes the space Fourier transform of the pair-distribution function. This quantity is directly measurable by X-ray diffraction and is known with fair accuracy for a large number of liquids (e.g. Gingrich 1943, Furukawa 1962). By inverting equations (7.11a,b) and afterwards differentiating with respect to time, we obtain the following set of relations

$$\int_{-\infty}^{\infty} \omega^n S^{\text{inc}}(\mathbf{Q},\omega)d\omega = (-i)^n I_s^{(n)}(\mathbf{Q},0), \qquad (7.14a)$$

$$\int_{-\infty}^{\infty} \omega^n S^{\text{coh}}(\mathbf{Q},\omega)d\omega = (-i)^n I^{(n)}(\mathbf{Q},0), \qquad (7.14b)$$

where $I_s^{(n)}$ stands for the nth order time derivative of I_s, and similarly for I.

Explicit calculations of the time derivatives were first carried out by Placzek up to the fourth for the self term and the third for the coherent term (1952) and later such calculations were made for the fourth coherent term by De Gennes (1959) who, however, neglected all "quantum" corrections, particularly recoil effects. More recent discussions of this point are given by de Gennes (1961), Nelkin (1961), Rahman et al. (1962), Schofield (1961) and Summerfield and Zweifel (1963) where the quantum corrections to the results of De Gennes are found. It is notable that in the low order moment relations above only measurable quantities appear and they can thus in principle be used as a check on the consistency of the experimental results.

For $n = 1$ we have

$$I_s^{(1)}(\mathbf{Q},0) = \frac{\hbar Q^2}{2M}, \quad I^{(1)}(\mathbf{Q},0) = \frac{\hbar Q^2}{2M}, \qquad (7.15)$$

where M is the atomic mass. We notice that the result is independent of the interaction in the system and is the same for both the coherent and incoherent cases. The higher derivatives depend explicitly on the interaction potential and get more and more involved as we go to higher order and are, therefore, of less practical interest. We shall here consider only the case $n = 2$ and state the approximate expressions obtained by De Gennes (1959), valid only for high temperatures,

$$I_s^{(2)}(\mathbf{Q},0) = \frac{-Q^2}{M\beta}, \qquad I^{(2)}(\mathbf{Q},0) = \frac{-Q^2}{M\beta}, \qquad (7.16)$$

where as before $\beta = 1/kT$. The normalized coherent second moment below, where the fact that the area under $S^{coh}(\mathbf{Q},\omega)$ varies with Q is taken into account,

$$\int_{-\infty}^{\infty}\omega^2 S^{coh}(\mathbf{Q},\omega)\mathrm{d}\omega \Big/ \int_{-\infty}^{\infty} S^{coh}(\mathbf{Q},\omega)\mathrm{d}\omega = Q^2/M\beta(1+\gamma(Q)), \qquad (7.17)$$

tells us that the energy spread in the coherent cross-section depends on Q and is considerably narrowed for peak values of $\gamma(Q)$. Such an effect has, indeed, been found experimentally (see Chapter 8). De Gennes showed also by considering the ratio of the fourth moment to the square of the second moment that the energy distribution should be more peaked for Q-values

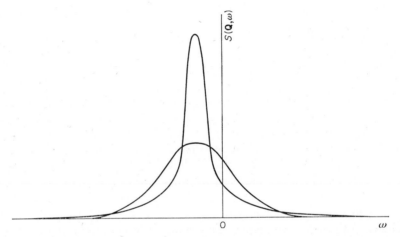

FIG. 7.1. Two different curves are given which have the same zero, first and second moments.

where $\gamma(Q)$ has its maximum, than for other Q-values. It is known that for sufficiently large values of Q, where $\gamma(Q)\rightarrow 0$, $S(\mathbf{Q},\omega)$ has a Gaussian shape in the frequency.* De Gennes, therefore, suggests that a Lorentzian shape may be more appropriate for Q-values where $\gamma(Q)$ is close to its maximum. As an illustration two curves are drawn in Fig. 7.1 for which first and second moments are the same but which have different higher moments.

It should be stressed that the low-order moments give only the behaviour of $I(\mathbf{Q},\tau)$ and $I_s(\mathbf{Q},\tau)$ for small times. We cannot, therefore, draw any conclusion about the long time behaviour. As will be shown in the following the characteristic structure in the energy spectrum depends sensitively on the long and intermediate time behaviour.

* See, for instance, Rahman et al. (1962).

7.4 Fluctuation-dissipation Theorem

The Van Hove correlations functions are in general complex. So, the real part of $G(\mathbf{r},\tau)$, defined as in (7.7), is given by the symmetrical product

$$\operatorname{Re} G(\mathbf{r},\tau) = \frac{1}{2\rho} \overline{\{\rho(0,0)\rho(\mathbf{r},\tau) + \rho(\mathbf{r},\tau)\rho(0,0)\}}, \qquad (7.18\text{a})$$

and the imaginary part by the antisymmetrical product

$$\operatorname{Im} G(\mathbf{r},\tau) = \frac{1}{2i\rho} \overline{\{\rho(0,0)\rho(\mathbf{r},\tau) - \rho(\mathbf{r},\tau)\rho(0,0)\}}. \qquad (7.18\text{b})$$

In a purely classical calculation the density operators are c-numbers and then the imaginary part vanishes. The physical interpretation of the Van Hove correlation functions, stated earlier, applies only to the real part. The imaginary part of $G(\mathbf{r},\tau)$ was shown by Van Hove (1958) to be connected with the density change in the system induced by the incident neutron. More generally, if a space and time dependent external potential $V(\mathbf{r},t)$ is applied to the system the local density will vary in space and time and is on the average given by (see Van Hove, 1958; Ruijgrok, 1963):

$$\overline{\rho(\mathbf{r},t)} = \rho - \rho \int\limits_{-\infty}^{t} dt' \int dr' \left\{ \frac{2}{\hbar} \operatorname{Im} \{G(\mathbf{r}-\mathbf{r}', t-t')\} V(\mathbf{r}',t') \right\}, \qquad (7.19)$$

considering only effects linear in $V(\mathbf{r},t)$. The first term on the right side is the static mean density for no external disturbance. $2/\hbar \operatorname{Im} G(\mathbf{r},\tau)$ describes how the disturbance propagates through the medium and has a unique classical counterpart. We note that $\operatorname{Im} G(\mathbf{r},\tau)$ is an odd function of τ whereas $\operatorname{Re} G(\mathbf{r},\tau)$ is even.

Schofield (1960) was, however, the first to state the real physical significance of the imaginary part to the scattering problem. When the scattered particles are in thermal equilibrium with the surrounding medium the number of particles scattered into and out of a certain energy region should be the same and this is known under the *condition of detailed balance*. Mathematically this can be stated as the following condition on the "scattering law"

$$S(\mathbf{Q},-\omega) = e^{-\beta\hbar\omega} S(\mathbf{Q},\omega), \quad \beta = 1/kT. \qquad (7.20)$$

Schofield found that this implies a definite relation between the real and imaginary parts of the Van Hove correlation functions. It is most simply expressed for their time Fourier transforms and for $G(\mathbf{r},\tau)$ we have *

$$\int\limits_{-\infty}^{\infty} e^{-i\omega\tau} \operatorname{Im} G(\mathbf{r},\tau) d\tau = -i \tanh\left(\tfrac{1}{2}\beta\hbar\omega\right) \int\limits_{-\infty}^{\infty} e^{-i\omega\tau} \operatorname{Re} G(\mathbf{r},\tau) d\tau \qquad (7.21)$$

---

* For a simple proof see, for instance, Singwi and Sjölander (1960b).

and similarly for $G_s(\mathbf{r},\tau)$. Later formulations of the scattering cross-section have been determined largely by the efforts to take properly into account both the "condition of detailed balance" and the low order moments, discussed in the last section.

Such relations as above are well known in the theories of irreversible processes and go under the name of fluctuation-dissipation theorems * and play an essential role in the calculations of transport quantities. Equation (7.21) can also be written in the following equivalent form.

$$\mathrm{Im}\, G(\mathbf{r},\tau) = -\tanh\left(\tfrac{1}{2}\beta\hbar\frac{\partial}{\partial t}\right)\mathrm{Re}\, G(\mathbf{r},\tau), \qquad (7.22)$$

where tanh (. . .) stands for an infinite sum of time differentiations obtained by expanding in a power series. By simply making a Fourier transformation of equation (7.22) one comes back to (7.21). In the classical limit, $\hbar \to 0$, we have

$$\frac{1}{\hbar}\mathrm{Im}\, G(\mathbf{r},\tau) = -\tfrac{1}{2}\beta\frac{\partial}{\partial t}\mathrm{Re}\, G(\mathbf{r},\tau). \qquad (7.23)$$

The condition imposed by (7.21) or (7.22) is in a form which is often unsuitable for direct applications. Schofield noted that the fluctuation-dissipation theorem imposes the condition that $G(\mathbf{r},\tau+i\beta\hbar/2)$ should be a real and even function of τ.†) We shall introduce a special notation for that real function;

$$G\left(\mathbf{r},\tau+\frac{i\beta\hbar}{2}\right) = \tilde{G}(\mathbf{r},\tau). \qquad (7.24)$$

The "scattering law" $S(\mathbf{Q},\omega)$ is then given by

$$S(\mathbf{Q},\omega) = \frac{1}{2\pi}\int\limits_{-\infty}^{\infty} e^{i(\mathbf{Q}\cdot\mathbf{r}-\omega\tau)}\tilde{G}\left(\mathbf{r},\tau-\frac{i\beta\hbar}{2}\right)\mathrm{d}\mathbf{r}\,\mathrm{d}\tau, \qquad (7.25)$$

where we have replaced $G(\mathbf{r},\tau)$ by the equivalent function $\tilde{G}(\mathbf{r},\tau-i\beta\hbar/2)$, and we can, after a change of time variable $\tau' = \tau-i\beta\hbar/2$, write it in the following form.

$$S(\mathbf{Q},\omega) = e^{\beta\hbar\omega/2}\frac{1}{2\pi}\int\limits_{-\infty}^{\infty} e^{i(\mathbf{Q}\cdot\mathbf{r}-\omega\tau')}\tilde{G}(\mathbf{r},\tau')\mathrm{d}\mathbf{r}\,\mathrm{d}\tau'. \qquad (7.26)$$

Due to the fact that $\tilde{G}(\mathbf{r},\tau)$ is an even function of τ, the Fourier transform

---

* See, for example, Bernard and Callen (1959); Callen (1962); Callen and Welton (1951); Kubo (1957, 1962).

† This was known earlier in the general theory of many-body systems and enters, for instance, in the formulation of the many-body theory by Martin and Schwinger (1959).

becomes even in ω and hence the condition of detailed balance is automatically fulfilled. The above arguments apply equally well to $G_s(\mathbf{r},\tau)$.

In an early attempt to calculate the incoherent scattering in liquids Vineyard (1958) proposed using the classical self-diffusion function, obtained from the macroscopic diffusion equation or Langevin's equation. An obvious shortcoming was that $G(\mathbf{r},\tau)$ becomes even in τ and hence does not fulfil the requirements in equation (7.21). All recoil effects are then discarded and this prohibits, for instance, the slowing down of fast neutrons in the scattering process. Schofield, therefore, made a slight change of the Vineyard proposal by substituting the classical self-diffusion function for $\tilde{G}(\mathbf{r},\tau)$, and noted that this should give results accurate to the first order in $\hbar$. Later papers (Aamodt et al., 1962, Turner, 1961, and Rosenbaum and Zweifel, 1965) have shown explicitly that in the Schofield procedure one takes properly into account quantum corrections in $G_s(\mathbf{r},\tau)$ linear in $\hbar$ but neglects higher order corrections. It was at first concluded by Turner (1961) that one had obtained a recipe which should hold very good for all classical systems, but this was corrected later (Kosaly and Turner, 1962). One finds that for an ideal classical gas the recipe above does not lead to the exact result and the missing terms are important for large momentum transfer. Great efforts have been made to make improvements and some of these will be discussed in later sections.

7.5 Scattering by Harmonic Solids

A harmonic crystal is one of the few examples where a more explicit calculation of the Van Hove correlation functions can be carried out and detailed numerical calculations on neutron scattering have also been performed in this case.[*] The underlying theory is the Born-von Kármán equations for the lattice vibrations. There the atomic motion is considered as a superposition of plane wave disturbances, the so called "phonons".

We shall here restrict ourselves to cubic symmetric Bravais lattices and in this case we have (Van Hove, 1954)

$$G_s(\mathbf{r},\tau) = [4\pi w(\tau)]^{-3/2} \exp\left[-r^2/4w(\tau)\right] \tag{7.27}$$

and

$$G(\mathbf{r},\tau) = \sum_{\mathbf{R}} [64\pi^3/\mathrm{Det}\,\{M^{-1}(\mathbf{R},\tau)\}]^{-1/2} \exp\{-\tfrac{1}{4}(\mathbf{r}-\mathbf{R})\,.\,M^{-1}(\mathbf{R},\tau)\,.\,(\mathbf{r}-\mathbf{R})\}, \tag{7.28}$$

where the summation extends over all lattice points. $G_s(\mathbf{r},\tau)$ gives a Gaussian distribution around the origin with the width given by the function $w(\tau)$. $G(\mathbf{r},\tau)$, on the other hand, gives a non-spherical Gaussian particle distribution around each lattice point and the width in the various directions is

---

[*] See, for example, Kothari and Singwi (1959) and Sjölander (1958).

determined by the components of a matrix $M^{-1}(\mathbf{R},\tau)$. [For convenience we have introduced the inverse of a matrix $M(\mathbf{R},\tau)$.] Due to the symmetry of the crystal we have for $R = 0$

$$M_{xx}(0,\tau) = M_{yy}(0,\tau) = M_{zz}(0,\tau) \quad \text{and} \quad M_{xy}(0,\tau) = 0, \text{ etc.,} \qquad (7.29)$$

and in equation (7.27) $w(\tau)$ stands for one of the diagonal elements of $M(0,\tau)$. The intermediate scattering functions have a somewhat simpler form;

$$I_s(\mathbf{Q},\tau) = \exp\left[-Q^2 w(\tau)\right], \qquad (7.30)$$

$$I(\mathbf{Q},\tau) = \sum_{\mathbf{R}} e^{i\mathbf{Q}\cdot\mathbf{R}} \exp\left[-\mathbf{Q}\cdot M(\mathbf{R},\tau)\cdot\mathbf{Q}\right]. \qquad (7.31)$$

We notice the very simple $\mathbf{Q}$-dependence. This is a consequence of the assumption on harmonic forces between the atoms but it seems to hold approximately under much more general conditions.

The width function $M(\mathbf{R},\tau)$ is most often written in terms of running waves, the phonons, characterized by the wave vector $\mathbf{q}$, the frequency $f_{\mathbf{q}}$ and the polarization direction $\mathbf{V}_{\mathbf{q}}(|\mathbf{V}_q| = 1)$. We have

$$M_{xy}(\mathbf{R},\tau) = \frac{1}{N}\sum_{s}\{g(f_s,0)-g(f_s,\tau)\,e^{i\mathbf{q}\cdot\mathbf{R}}\}\,V_{sx}V_{sy}, \qquad (7.32)$$

where

$$g(f,\tau) = \frac{\hbar}{2Mf}\left\{\frac{1}{e^{\beta\hbar f}-1}\,e^{-if\tau}+\left(\frac{1}{e^{\beta\hbar f}-1}+1\right)e^{if\tau}\right\}, \qquad (7.33)$$

and the summation extends over all phonon wave vectors and polarization directions. The strict periodicity of the lattice points means that the phonon wave vectors are restricted to the first Brillouin zone. The lattice vibrations are in a sense periodic in the reciprocal space. This is not so for amorphous solids where the equilibrium positions are more or less randomly distributed.

The above expression is for $\mathbf{R} = 0$ considerably simplified if one introduces the phonon frequency distribution $z(f)$, here normalized to make

$$\int_0^\infty z(f)\mathrm{d}f = 1, \qquad (7.34)$$

which gives the relative number of "modes" per frequency interval. We then get the following expression for the width function $w(\tau)$:

$$w(\tau) = \int_0^\infty [g(f,0)-g(f,\tau)]z(f)\mathrm{d}f, \qquad (7.35)$$

where for a Debye crystal

$$z(f) = 3f^2/f_D^3, f<f_D \\ = 0 \qquad ,f>f_D, \qquad (7.36)$$

f_D being the maximum frequency.

For harmonic crystals the motion of the system is completely described in terms of these phonons propagating with a definite frequency for each wave vector and polarization direction. The phonon distribution function $z(f)$ has a sharp cut-off and the corresponding wave vector is determined by the lattice parameter.

If expanding $w(\tau)$ in equation (7.35) in a power series of τ and using (7.34) we get for high temperatures ($\beta \hbar f_D < 1$)

$$w(\tau) = -\frac{i\hbar}{2M}\tau + \frac{1}{2M\beta}\tau^2 + \dots, \tag{7.37}$$

which is consistent with the moment relations in equations (7.15, 16). The corresponding expansion for $M(\mathbf{R},\tau)$ is

$$M_{xy}(\mathbf{R},\tau) = M_{xy}(\mathbf{R},0) - \delta_{xy}\frac{i\hbar}{2M}\tau + \delta_{xy}\frac{1}{2M\beta}\tau^2 + \dots, \tag{7.38}$$

where

$$M_{xy}(\mathbf{R},0) = \frac{1}{NM\beta}\sum_s \frac{1}{f_s^2}(1 - e^{i\mathbf{q}\cdot\mathbf{R}})V_{sx}V_{sy}, \tag{7.39}$$

and δ_{xy} is the ordinary Kronecker symbol ($\delta_{xx} = 1$, $\delta_{xy} = 0$ for $x \neq y$). The coefficients in equations (7.37, 38) could have been obtained from the first few moments of $S(\mathbf{Q},\omega)$ and in more complex systems, where the equations of motions cannot be solved, one is forced to use the moment relations. In a similar way the imaginary part of equation (7.33) follows from the real part, if using the fluctuation-dissipation theorem. From a proper theory this should come out automatically as it indeed does in this harmonic case.

$M(\mathbf{R},\tau)$ can also be expressed in terms of the displacement vectors $\mathbf{u}(\mathbf{R},\tau)$ of the atoms relative to their equilibrium lattice positions as follows :

$$M(\mathbf{R},\tau) = \overline{\mathbf{u}(0,0)\mathbf{u}(0,0)} - \overline{\mathbf{u}(0,0)\mathbf{u}(\mathbf{R},\tau)}, \tag{7.40}$$

where as before $\overline{(\dots\dots)}$ denotes the equilibrium statistical average. This latter formulation, which does not explicitly refer to any phonons, has a more general validity than that in (7.32).

As can be seen from (7.32) the width function $M(\mathbf{R},\tau)$ stays finite for $\tau \to \infty$ and this leads to a $\delta(\omega)$-singularity in both $S^{\text{inc}}(\mathbf{Q},\omega)$ and $S^{\text{coh}}(\mathbf{Q},\omega)$. A finite fraction of the scattering occurs with no energy change, known for many years as Bragg scattering. The intensity of the elastic peak is governed by the Debye-Waller factor $\exp[-Q^2 w(\infty)]$. This is certainly not consistent with the general properties of the Van Hove functions stated in equation (7.5) and it is due to neglect of diffusion. However small this may be it should make $w(\tau)$ tend to infinity for large times and this makes the Bragg scattering not exactly elastic. The broadening is, however, too small to be observed in neutron scattering but has indeed been found in Mössbauer experiments on solids at high temperatures (Boyle et al., 1961).

7.6 Scattering by Anharmonic Solids

In going beyond the harmonic approximation for the lattice vibrations the computational difficulties increase considerably and only recently have more detailed calculations on anharmonic motions been carried out and their application to neutron scattering considered (Ambegaokar et al., 1965; Baym, 1961; Elliot and Stern, 1961; Hahn, 1961, 1963; Van Hove et al., 1961; Kashchev and Krivoglaz, 1961; Kokkedee, 1962, 1963; Krivoglaz, 1962; Lax, 1964; Maradudin and Fein, 1962; Thomson, 1963).

Due to the anharmonic effects a single phonon in a solid has a finite life time, which manifests itself in an ill-defined phonon frequency for a given wave vector. The spread in the phonon frequency is a direct measure of the life time. The formulation of the neutron scattering is essentially the same as in the harmonic case and we shall write the expression for the coherent function (cf. equation (7.31));

$$I(\mathbf{Q},\tau) = \sum_R e^{i\mathbf{Q}\cdot\mathbf{R}} \exp\{-\mathbf{Q}\cdot\mathbf{M}(\mathbf{R},\tau)\cdot\mathbf{Q} + \ldots\}, \qquad (7.41)$$

where for the width function $M(\mathbf{R},\tau)$ we can still use the expression in (7.40)

$$M(\mathbf{R},\tau) = \overline{\mathbf{u}(0,0)\mathbf{u}(0,0)} - \overline{\mathbf{u}(0,0)\mathbf{u}(\mathbf{R},\tau)}. \qquad (7.42)$$

The atoms are assumed to vibrate in an anharmonic manner around fixed lattice positions and this makes sure that the concept of regular lattice points and regular reciprocal lattice points remains unchanged. As a consequence the phonon wave vectors are still restricted to the first Brillouin zone.

The first change we get from the harmonic result is that the form

$$\exp\{-\mathbf{Q}\cdot\mathbf{M}(\mathbf{R},\tau)\cdot\mathbf{Q}\}$$

is no longer exactly valid but correction terms appear and are in equation (7.41) denoted by dots. These correction terms contain products of three or more displacement vectors and, therefore, should be small for low temperatures, where the displacements are on average small. Another effect arising from the anharmonicity is that the numerical value of the width function in equation (7.42) deviates from the harmonic value. Numerical results presented by Ambegaokar and Maradudin (1964), have given a clear indication that the anharmonic terms which were denoted by dots in equation (7.41) are much less important than the anharmonic corrections appearing in $M(\mathbf{R},\tau)$ and can, therefore, be neglected.

It is conventional to define mathematically and also experimentally the phonons through the Fourier transform of the displacement auto-correlation function appearing in equation (7.42). As a matter of fact the neutron scattering experiments make a Fourier analysis of the Van Hove space–time correlation functions and for one-phonon processes this means a Fourier analysis of the above displacement correlation function. Formally we can define a spectral tensor function $P(\mathbf{q},\omega)$ through (cf. equation (7.32)) the following equation:

$$M(\mathbf{R},\tau) = \frac{1}{N} \sum_{\mathbf{q}} \int_0^\infty [g(f,0) - g(f,\tau)\, e^{i\mathbf{q}\cdot\mathbf{R}}]\, P(q,f)\mathrm{d}f \qquad (7.43)$$

In order to keep the similarity to the harmonic case we write the expression as a sum over discrete wave vectors, which certainly is appropriate for a finite system. For a macroscopic system, however, this sum goes over into an integration over the first Brillouin zone, which is also the case for harmonic solids. The function $g(f,\tau)$ is the same as in equation (7.33) and its appearance in this case also is mainly a consequence of the fluctuation-dissipation theorem.

If we compare equation (7.32) with the formal expression above we find that if $P(\mathbf{q},f)$ is chosen to be

$$P(\mathbf{q},f) = \sum_{j=1}^{3} V_{qj} V_{qj} \delta(f - f_{qj}) \qquad (7.44)$$

the frequency integration above leads exactly to the harmonic result for $M(\mathbf{R},\tau)$. In this case $P(\mathbf{q},f)$ is a sum of three δ-functions for a fixed wave vector $\mathbf{q}$, one for each of the three polarization directions. In other words, each phonon corresponding to a given wave vector gives rise to a peak in the spectral function $P(\mathbf{q},f)$. If the phonons have a long life time one should expect that this result remains essentially unchanged except for some broadening of the δ-functions.

The explicit form of $P(\mathbf{q},f)$ depends on the dynamics of the atomic motion and cannot be obtained without detailed calculations. From its definition the following properties of the matrix $P(\mathbf{q},f)$ follow generally and independently of the physical interpretation:

(a) $P(\mathbf{q},f)$ is a positive definite matrix; (7.45a)

(b) $P(\mathbf{q},f)$ is an even function of f; (7.45b)

(c) $\int_0^\infty P(\mathbf{q},f)\mathrm{d}f = 1.$ (7.45c)

The first two statements follow quite directly from the definition and the third statement follows from the commutation rules for positions and momenta of the atoms. The statement under (c) should be compared with the normalization condition of the frequency spectrum $z(f)$ in the harmonic case (7.34).

The moment relations give uniquely the first few terms in the time expansion of $M(\mathbf{R},\tau)$. We have, for high temperatures,

$$M_{xy}(\mathbf{R},\tau) = M_{xy}(\mathbf{R},0) - \delta_{xy}\frac{i\hbar}{2M}\tau + \delta_{xy}\frac{1}{2M\beta}\tau^2 + \ldots, \qquad (7.46)$$

where

$$M_{xy}(\mathbf{R},0) = \frac{1}{NM\beta}\sum_{\mathbf{q}}\int_0^{\infty}\frac{1}{f^2}(1-e^{i\mathbf{q}\cdot\mathbf{R}})P_{xy}(\mathbf{q},f)\mathrm{d}f, \qquad (7.47)$$

which should be compared with the corresponding expressions in equations (7.38) and (7.39) for a harmonic solid.

As one determines experimentally in the harmonic case the single phonon frequencies and the polarization directions one determines in the anharmonic case the spectral function $P(\mathbf{q},f)$. Due to the fact that fairly distinct phonon peaks appear for solids at quite high temperatures one is justified in interpreting these as arising from single phonons, which are frequency broadened due to finite life times. One has indeed in this way gained valuable information on the dynamics in some solids up to the melting point. The theoretical calculations by the authors referred to above have lead to approximate expressions for the single phonon frequencies and life times as a function of temperature. The computations are based on low order perturbation techniques and this makes the results obtained strictly valid only for fairly low temperatures, where the anharmonic effects should not be too large. So for instance, diffusion effects in solids are completely discarded in these calculations.

In addition to the auto-correlation function for the displacement vectors, higher order correlation functions, denoted by dots in equation (7.41), enter in the expression for the scattering cross-section. It has been stressed by several authors that this may cause some difficulties when interpreting the experimental peaks in the so called "one-phonon scattering" in terms of real phonons of the crystal. A mixing of other effects should occur and this gives rise to a distortion of the phonon peak. This is certainly an important point but recent numerical computations of Ambegaoker and Maradudin (1964) show that this effect is small and is at present beyond experimental observation. It can therefore be concluded that one is justified in using the standard procedure of interpreting the experimental peak as arising from single phonons. This may not be the case some time in the future if the Mössbauer technique can be used for such measurements. It should be stressed here that the difficulty of separating the single phonon peaks from the more or less smooth background due to multiphonon effects has nothing in common with the effect discussed above. The multiphonon terms originate from expanding the exponential $\exp\{-\mathbf{Q} \cdot M(\mathbf{R},\tau) \cdot \mathbf{Q}\}$ in a power series as is conventional in the harmonic case.

7.7 General Discussion of Classical Liquids

No real theory of the atomic motions in liquids exists at present and one has, therefore, to take recourse to very simplified models. In this section we shall summarize some of the most essential properties of liquids and briefly discuss some various aspects of the atomic motion. Recent reviews of the atomic theories of liquids have been given by Cole (1956) and Fisher (1962). For more comprehensive presentations of the field we refer to books by Frenkel (1946), Green (1952), and Prigogine (1957) among others.

In general the problem has been approached from two different directions. Born and H. S. Green gave a general derivation of the hydrodynamic equations from which they arrived at formal expressions for the transport coefficients (see Green, 1952). In their treatment they approach the liquid phase essentially from the condensed gas side. Lennard-Jones and Devonshire, on the other hand, developed a cell model for liquids (see Barker, 1963; Prigogine, 1957). The atoms are assumed here to be trapped in a potential well formed by the surrounding atoms similar to what happens in a solid.

A third approach was introduced by Kirkwood (1946) and later developed further by M. S. Green (1952) and Mori (1958), who express the transport coefficients in terms of certain time correlation functions. Kirkwood derived a modified Boltzmann equation, where the collision term is that corresponding to a Brownian motion. This makes his treatment valid only if the collisions occur with small momentum exchange. Rice and collaborators (Alnatt and Rice, 1961; Davis et al., 1961; Rice and Alnatt, 1961) have removed this limitation by treating separately the strong repulsive interaction and the more smooth attractive interaction, for which the Kirkwood treatment should be approximately valid.

Thermodynamic quantities as energy, pressure, etc. can easily be calculated if the static pair-distribution function is known, assuming a two-particle interatomic interaction potential $V(r)$. Thus we have the following expression for the total energy and pressure, respectively:

$$E/N = \tfrac{3}{2}kT + \tfrac{1}{2}\int V(r)g(\mathbf{r})d\mathbf{r}, \tag{7.48}$$

$$p = \rho kT - \tfrac{1}{6}\rho \int r\frac{dV(r)}{dr} g(\mathbf{r})d\mathbf{r}, \tag{7.49}$$

where ρ is the macroscopic density and N is the total number of atoms in the system.* For the isothermal compressibility X_T we have†

$$\rho kTX_T = 1+\int(g(\mathbf{r})-\rho)d\mathbf{r}. \qquad (7.50)$$

This leads to the following relation for $\gamma(Q)$, introduced in equation (7.13):

$$1+\gamma(Q)\to\rho\, kTX_T, \quad \text{as} \quad Q\to0. \qquad (7.51)$$

Several approximate equations for the pair-distribution function have been derived (Born and Green, 1946; Kirkwood and Boggs, 1942; Van Leeuwen *et al.*, 1959; Percus and Yevick, 1958) and they have been used for extensive numerical calculations (Kahn, 1964; Kirkwood *et al.*, 1950, 1952). As mentioned before the pair-distribution function can also be obtained experimentally from X-ray diffracton. In Fig. 7.2 are plotted $g(r)$ and $\gamma(Q)$ in a typical

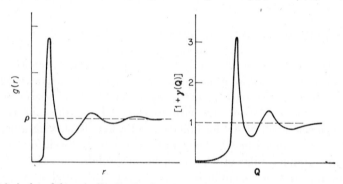

Fig. 7.2. A plot of the pair-distribution function and its Fourier transform for a typical case liquid argon).

case. There is a strong peak at approximately the mean distance between neighbouring atoms and subsidiary more diffuse peaks at larger distance. This indicates a fairly strong local ordering. On the other hand, long range order as in crystals disappears suddenly at the melting point. In substances like glass, where no crystalline structure exists, the transition from the solid to the liquid phase occurs smoothly without any sharp melting point. It has been argued that the local structure in crystals should remain essentially unchanged on melting. From the shape of the pair-distribution function one concludes, however, that above the melting point we should have large fluctuations in the number of nearest neighbours.

Some experimental data are summarized in the following tables. The list is incomplete and should be considered as an illustration of some typical cases.

* Notice that by definition $g(r)\to\rho$ for $r\to\infty$.

† Landau, L. D., and Lifshitz, E. M. (1958). "Statistical Physics", p. 365. Pergamon Press, London.

Density

Table 7.1 presents data on the density of some liquids just above the melting point and also on the density of a few solids just below the melting point. The melting and boiling temperatures are also given. For the inert gases there is a change of about 15 % in the density on melting (Domb, 1958). We notice that no drastic change occurs when crystals melt and consequently the interatomic interaction is of the same order in the liquid as in the solid phase.

TABLE 7.1

	T_b (°K)	T_m (°K)	ρ^* liquid (g/cm³)	ρ^* solid (g/cm³)	Structure in the solid phase	Reference
A	87·5	84·0	1·42			a, b
Kr	120·3	116·6	2·45			a
Xe	166·1	161·2	3·05			a
CH₄	111·6	90·6	0·42			b
Li	1610	459			b.c.c.	b
Na	1150	371	0·93	0·95	b.c.c.	b
K	1030	335	0·83	0·85	b.c.c.	b
Cu	2610	1356	8·22		f.c.c.	b
Ag	2220	1234	9·51		f.c.c.	b
Al	2330	933	2·38		f.c.c.	b
Pb	1890	600	10·6	11·0	f.c.c.	b
Zn	1180	693	6·5		h.c.p.	b
Hg	630	234	13·7	14·2		a, b

a = American Institute of Physics Handbook, 2nd Ed., McGraw-Hill (1963).
b = Handbook of Chemistry and Physics, 41st Ed., Chem. Rubber Pub. Co. (1960).
* The values for the densities are in some cases very approximate.

Specific heat

The specific heat at constant volume C_V is $3R$ for a harmonic crystal and in an ideal gas $\frac{3}{2}R$. In the latter case there is no potential contribution. The specific heat at constant pressure C_P is given by

$$C_P - C_V = VT\alpha^2/\chi_T, \qquad (7.52)$$

where α is the coefficient of thermal expansion and χ_T is the isothermal compressibility. For a monatomic ideal gas $C_P - C_V = R$ whereas $C_P = C_V$ in a harmonic solid. Table 7.2 gives the specific heats for some liquids at the melting point. The data are presented in the form KR, where the factor K is tabulated below. We find, in many cases, no drastic change in C_V from the solid value.

Compressibility

For an ideal gas the isothermal and adiabatic compressibilities are given by

$$\chi_T = \frac{1}{\rho k T}, \qquad \chi_S = \frac{C_V}{C_P}\chi_T, \tag{7.53}$$

where $C_P/C_V = 5/3$ for a monatomic gas. The compressibility increases both in the liquid and the solid phase approximately linearly with temperature,

TABLE 7.2

	$\frac{C_P}{K}$	$\frac{C_V{}^*}{K}$	Reference
A	5·0	2·3	Rowlinson (1959)
CH_4	6·4	4·0	Rowlinson (1959)
Na	3·8	3·4	Landolt-Börnstein (1961)
K	3·9	3·5	Landolt-Börnstein (1961)
Pb	3·7	3·1	Landolt-Börnstein (1961)
Zn	3·9	3·2	Landolt-Börnstein (1961)
Hg	3·4	3·1	Landolt-Börnstein (1961)

* Calculated using equation (7.52).

TABLE 7.3

	Liquid phase		Solid phase		Reference
	$\chi_S \times 10^{12}$ (cm²/dyne)	$\chi_T \times 10^{12}$ (cm²/dyne)	$\chi_S \times 10^{12}$ (cm²/dyne)	$\chi_T \times 10^{12}$ (cm²/dyne)	
A*	95†	200	62	67	Barker and Dobbs (1955) Itterbeck *et al.* (1959) Rowlinson (1959)
CH_4*	89†	140		>75	Rowlinson (1959) Stewart (1959)
Na	17	19	~15	~16·5	Beecroft and Swenson (1961) Pochapsky (1951)
K	36	40		>36	Kleppa (1950)
Pb	2·9	3·5		~2·8	Kleppa (1950)
Zn	2·0	2·4		>1·7	Kleppa (1950)
Hg	3·4†	3·8†			Bett *et al.* (1954)

* The values are for vapour pressure.
† Extrapolated value.

with a discontinuous increase at the melting point. Table 7.3 gives the experimental values of χ_T and χ_S for some substances on both sides of the melting point. We recall that at absolute zero temperature $\chi_S = \chi_T$.

Viscosity

There is a definite difference in the temperature dependence of the viscosity for a gas and a liquid. In a gas the atomic collisions occur more frequently at higher temperatures and, therefore, the viscosity increases with temperature and is found to go approximately as $T^{\frac{1}{2}}$ at constant density. In a liquid, on the other hand, the viscosity decreases with increasing temperature due to a decrease of the effective interatomic interaction. One finds that, at least within a limited temperature range, the viscosity varies according to the Andrade formula

$$\eta = A \, e^{B/T} \tag{7.54}$$

where A and B are approximately constant. In Table 7.4 some experimental values for A and B/T_m are given.

TABLE 7.4

	A $\times 10^3$ (poise)	B/T_m	Reference
A	0·114	3·22	Zhdanova (1957)
Li	1·39	1·47	Andrade and Dobbs (1952)
Na	0·82	2·16	Liquid Metals Handbook (1954)
K	1·00	1·67	Andrade and Dobbs (1952)
Cu	7·7	1·53	Gebhardt et al. (1952)
Ag	5·7	1·91	Gebhardt and Wörwag (1951)
Al	2·8	1·49	Gebhardt and Detering (1959)
Pb	4·2	1·91	Landolt-Börnstein (1961)
			Liquid Metals Handbook (1954)
Zn	5·6	1·74	Gebhardt and Detering (1959)
Hg	5·1	1·40	Landolt-Börnstein (1961)

A remarkable exception is liquid helium, for which the viscosity decreases with decreasing temperature below 3·5°K and differs drastically from other liquids also at higher temperatures. However, the interatomic distance is exceptionally large and the attractive interaction small, which is why liquid helium is closer to a condensed gas than the other liquids. Furthermore the quantum effects are significant in this case.

Self-diffusion

Self-diffusion shows differences for the gas and the liquid states similar to those found for the viscosity. In a gas the temperature variation goes approximately as $T^{\frac{1}{2}}$ at constant density. In a liquid the diffusion increases more rapidly and the temperature variation is reasonably well reproduced by the expression

$$D = C\, e^{-W/T} \tag{7.55}$$

with C and W constant, at least over a limited temperature range. The same formula holds also for a solid with a change of the values for C and W. Some experimental values for C and W/T_m are given in Table 7.5. Liquid helium is again an exception from the normal behaviour of liquids. In solids the activation energies are 4–7 times larger than for liquids. This makes the diffusion constants drop from a value of the order 10^{-5} cm²/sec just above the melting point to 10^{-9} cm²/sec just below the melting point.

TABLE 7.5

	C $\times 10^4$ (cm²/sec)	W/T_m	Reference
A*	6·1	3·74	Cini–Castagnoli and Ricci (1960)
Kr*	5·1	3·47	Naghizadeh and Rice (1962)
Xe*	7·3	3·75	Naghizadeh and Rice (1962)
CH₄*	19·4	4·60	Naghizadeh and Rice (1962)
Na	11·0	3·33	Meyer and Nachtrieb (1955)
Ag	7·1	3·32	Yang et al. (1958)
Pb	9·2	3·73	Rothman and Hall (1956)
Zn	12	4·07	Lange et al. (1959)
Hg	1·26	2·49	Hoffman (1952)

* The values are extrapolated to 1 atm from measurements at higher pressure.

Acoustic Attenuation

The theoretical calculations of propagation and attenuation of sound waves are based on Navier-Stoke's equations and the agreement with experiments is good except for very high frequencies (Hertzfeld and Litovitz, 1959). The sound velocity for low frequencies is independent of the frequency f and the absorption varies as f^2. For very high frequencies both the velocity and the absorption should go as $f^{\frac{1}{2}}$. In glycerol, for instance, the high frequency region has been studied experimentally by using ultrasonic waves. The transition from the low to the high frequency region occurs around

10^8 periods per sec at $-14°C$. One has found a large discrepancy from the theoretical predictions. The sound velocity saturates at a certain value which is only 50 % higher than the low frequency value. Also the absorption stays finite. In many other cases—water is one—the difference between the high and low frequency values of the sound velocity is even smaller. The reason for this discrepancy is essentially structural relaxation effects. At low frequencies the molecules have time to relax to local equilibrium whereas at high frequencies this is not the case. Similar effects are found in liquid CS_2 but here the cause is assumed to be non-instantaneous energy transfer to internal motion of the molecules (Kneser liquids).

For ordinary monatomic liquids the transition to the high frequency region occurs at frequencies that cannot be reached by ultrasonic technique. It is, therefore, fortunate that inelastic scattering of light, so called Mandel'shtam-Brillouin scattering, gives similar information. Due to long wavelength density fluctuations, which are sound waves of frequencies much higher than used in ultrasonic experiments, light is scattered inelastically. One finds two energy displaced lines, one on each side of the elastic line. The magnitude of the energy shift gives the sound velocity and the width of the peaks give information on the attenuation of the sound waves. By this technique one can conveniently reach frequencies of the order 10^{10} periods per sec. The theory was first given by Landau and Placzek (1934)* based on Navier-Stoke's equations. They showed that the ratio of the intensity of the undisplaced elastic peak to the intensity of the two displaced peaks should be equal to (C_P/C_V-1). Experimentally one finds in many cases a considerably larger ratio. Furthermore, a weak continuous background extending beyond the Mandel'shtam-Brillouin components has been found (Fabelinskii, 1956; Rytov, 1958). Due to the very high frequencies considered in these experiments it should not be surprising if the hydrodynamic equations cease to be valid. Rytov (1958) has modified the theory by basing the calculations on a model for a visco-elastic medium. He is able to explain the essential features of the experimental results. The smooth background is according to him mainly due to shear dispersion. He finds that for very high frequencies even liquids, which normally have a low viscosity, have a finite shear modulus which rapidly drops to zero below some characteristic frequency $1/\tau$, where for benzol the number $\tau \approx 3 \times 10^{-12}$ sec is mentioned. Ginzburg (1958) has criticized Rytov for ignoring several sources of scattering and this may make his theory quantitatively doubtful but should not cast any doubt on the qualitative features.†

* Landau, L. D. and Lifshitz, E. M. (1960). "Electrodynamics of Continuous Media", p. 387. Pergamon Press, London.

† In this context we want to draw the attention to the section on shear elasticity in liquids in Green, H. S. (1959). "Handbuch der Physik", Band X, p. 69. See also Hertzfeld and Litovitz (1959), Ch. XII.

The electronic properties of liquid metals have recently been reviewed by Cusack (1963). The conclusion one may draw from the data presented above is that there are remarkable similarities between solids and liquids, particularly near the melting point. There are, however, drastic changes in viscosity and diffusion. One might at first be tempted to strongly favour such an approach as the Lennard-Jones cell model. It has been stressed by Barker (1963) that this model is really a model only for the solid phase in spite of its success in explaining many thermodynamic properties above the melting point. We should not ignore the fact that there is a first order phase transition between the solid and liquid phases with a discontinuous change in the thermodynamic quantities.

So far we have mainly been concerned with bulk properties of liquids. In neutron scattering the motion of the *individual* atoms are partly seen. A single atom moves on a very erratic path and can be successfully described only on a statistical basis. A frequently used model is that for a Brownian motion based on Langevin's equation;*

$$M\ddot{\mathbf{r}} + M\zeta\dot{\mathbf{r}} = \mathbf{F}(t). \tag{7.56}$$

The force acting on the atom is a friction force, $-M\zeta\dot{\mathbf{r}}$, and a rapidly varying stochastic force $\mathbf{F}(t)$. The velocity auto-correlation function one obtains from the above equation has the following very simple form:

$$\overline{\mathbf{v}(0) \cdot \mathbf{v}(\tau)} = \frac{3}{M\beta}\, e^{-\zeta\tau}, \quad \tau > 0. \tag{7.57}$$

ζ is related to the macroscopic self-diffusion constant through

$$D = \tfrac{1}{3}\int_0^\infty \overline{\mathbf{v}(0) \cdot \mathbf{v}(\tau)}\mathrm{d}\tau = \frac{1}{M\zeta\beta}. \tag{7.58}$$

Kirkwood (1946) has also given the following relation:

$$\zeta = \frac{\beta}{3M}\int_0^\infty \overline{\mathbf{K}(0) \cdot \mathbf{K}(\tau)}\mathrm{d}\tau, \tag{7.59}$$

where $\overline{\mathbf{K}(0) \cdot \mathbf{K}(\tau)}$ is the auto-correlation function for the actual force on the atom. Equation (7.56) was originally proposed for the motion of a heavy particle suspended in a fluid and it was proved to give the adequate description in that case. For the motion of a single atom the validity of Langevin's equation may seem doubtful.

---

* See articles by Chandrasekhar, S., Uhlenbeck, G. E., and Ornstein, L. S., and by Wang, M. C. and Uhlenbeck, G. E. (1954) in "Selected Papers on Noise and Stochastic Processes", ed. by N. Wax. Dover, New York.

The following pictorial description of the motion of an atom may give a basis for understanding equation (7.56) and also illustrate where modifications have to be made. Consider a system in statistical equilibrium and select a group of atoms which at a certain time, say $\tau = 0$, have the same velocity vector $\mathbf{v}_0$. We shall assume these marked atoms to be far from each other so that they can be considered to move independently of each other. The

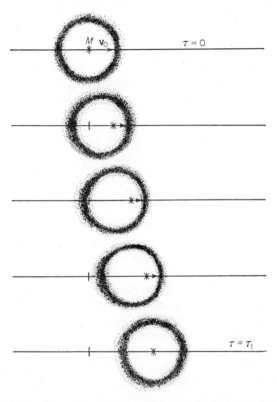

FIG. 7.3. A schematic outline of how the density around a marked * atom changes with time on the average. The broad line indicates the position of the maximum of the density of the neighbouring atoms.

actual force on an atom depends strongly on its immediate surroundings but on the average there is no force acting on the marked atoms at $\tau = 0$. This follows from the fact that the equilibrium distribution function for the system separates in the classical case into a purely velocity and purely position dependent part and the latter part gives on the average a spherically symmetric density distribution around each marked atom. Therefore, the atoms will at first move with constant velocity $\mathbf{v}_0$ (Fig. 7.3). A distortion of the surroundings is thereby induced and this in turn leads to a force reacting back on the marked atom. Consequently it will be slowed down and come to rest after some microscopic time τ_1. The surroundings then become spherically symmetric again. This is, however, only the average behaviour. There are deviations for each individual atom which can be described in terms of a probability distribution function. The origin of these fluctuations are forces which on the average are essentially uncorrelated to the position and velocity of the considered atom. So, for instance, the fluctuating forces make the mean kinetic energy of a single particle tend to the value $\frac{3}{2}kT$ instead of zero.

When using Langevin's equation one assumes the correlated force to be proportional to the velocity of the particle and one also assumes that the fluctuating force varies much more rapidly than the correlated one. This should certainly be valid for a heavy particle moving in a medium of light particles. It should presumably hold good also for an atom in a monatomic medium if only small momenta are exchanged in the collisions. We can, however, expect that a large fraction of the collisions occur with fairly large momentum transfer and that the strong short range repulsive interaction between the atoms is partly responsible for this, especially at higher temperatures. The value one gets from (7.58) for τ_1, is of the order 10^{-13}–10^{-14} sec ($D \sim 10^{-5}$ cm^2/sec). When compared with the periods of lattice vibrations, which are of the order 10^{-13} sec, the relaxation time obtained above seems to be far too small. One may expect the atoms to make some oscillatory motions before they are slowed down to rest; the oscillatory motion being similar to that observed in a solid. In a solid the atom is oscillating around the same equilibrium position for a very long time which certainly is not true for a liquid. Recent machine computations by Wainwright and Alder (1958) and Rahman (1964) have indeed given a strong evidence for these oscillatory motions in liquids.

We should also like to draw the attention to a recent investigation by Rubin (1960; 1961) on the motion of a single atom bound in a harmonic lattice. He finds in the one-dimensional case that the velocity auto-correlation function is exactly that in equation (7.57) if the mass of the atom is large compared to the mass of the other atoms in the lattice. For equal masses it is known, assuming only nearest neighbour interaction, that

$$\overline{\mathbf{v}(0) \cdot \mathbf{v}(\tau)} = \frac{3}{M\beta} J_0(2f_0\tau), \qquad (7.60)$$

where J_0 is the zero order Bessel function, which shows an oscillatory behaviour. It should be noted that the one-dimensional lattice is really a model for a condensed gas. It gives, for instance, a large diffusion constant. In the three-dimensional case similar results are obtained. For equal masses the correlation function is oscillatory but the atom is bound to a fixed equilibrium position. For a large mass, Rubin got the same auto-correlation functions as obtained from Langevin's equation for a harmonic oscillator

$$M\ddot{\mathbf{r}} + M\zeta\dot{\mathbf{r}} + Mf_0^2\mathbf{r} = \mathbf{F}(t),\qquad(7.61)$$

where $Mf_0^2\mathbf{r}$ is the harmonic restoring force. The velocity auto-correlation function is in this case

$$\overline{\mathbf{v}(0)\cdot\mathbf{v}(\tau)} = \frac{3}{M\beta}\left(\cos f_1\tau - \frac{\zeta}{2f_1}\sin f_1\tau\right)e^{-\zeta\tau/2}\qquad(7.62)$$

where $f_1^2 = f_0^2 - \dfrac{\zeta^2}{4}$.

One can indeed derive from Liouville's equation an approximate single particle equation (A. Sjölander, unpublished):

$$\dot{\mathbf{v}}(t) + \frac{\beta}{3M}\int_0^t \overline{\mathbf{K}(t)\cdot\mathbf{K}(t')}\mathbf{v}(t')\mathrm{d}t' = \frac{1}{M}\mathbf{F}(t),\qquad(7.63)$$

where the correlation function under the integral sign is the same as in (7.59) and $\mathbf{F}(t)$ is some unknown stochastic force which does not depend on the coordinates of the particle considered. If the velocity should vary slowly over the relaxation time for the force auto-correlation function we get Langevin's equation (7.56) with the Kirkwood friction term (7.59). On the other hand, if the correlation function should vary slowly compared to the velocity we get the harmonic oscillator equation * (see equation (7.61))

$$\ddot{\mathbf{r}} + f_0^2\mathbf{r} = 0,\qquad(7.64)$$

with $f_0^2 = \dfrac{1}{3M}\beta\overline{\mathbf{K}(0)\cdot\mathbf{K}(0)} = \dfrac{1}{3M}\int \nabla^2 V(r)g(\mathbf{r})\mathrm{d}\mathbf{r}$, $V(r)$ being the two-particle interaction potential. This is the result obtained, for instance, from the cell model in the harmonic limit.

A proper atomistic theory should, of course, give both the single particle aspect and the *collective* aspect of the motion. Let us consider the density correlation function $\overline{\rho(0,0)\rho(\mathbf{r},\tau)}$ which enters in the coherent scattering cross-section. We can write generally

$$\overline{\rho(0,0)\rho(\mathbf{r},\tau)} = \frac{\rho}{(2\pi)^3}\int S^{\mathrm{coh}}(\mathbf{Q},\omega)\,e^{-i(\mathbf{Q}\cdot\mathbf{r}-\omega\tau)}\mathrm{d}\mathbf{Q}\mathrm{d}\omega,\qquad(7.65)$$

where the notations are the same as used earlier—see equations (7.7, 7.10, 7.11). Long wavelength and slow motions, corresponding to small $\mathbf{Q}$ and ω, should be governed by Navier-Stoke's equations. For purely adiabatic

---

* If the friction term is neglected one should also neglect the stochastic force for consistency.

processes the Fourier coefficient above can be found from Landau and Lifshitz.* We have

$$S^{coh}(\mathbf{Q},\omega) = \rho kT\chi_S \frac{1}{\pi} \frac{\Gamma_S c^2 Q^4}{(\omega^2 - c^2 Q^2)^2 + (\Gamma_S \omega Q^2)^2},\qquad(7.66)$$

where χ_S is the adiabatic compressibility, $c = (M\rho\chi_S)^{-\frac{1}{2}}$ is the sound velocity and $\Gamma_S = (\zeta + \frac{4}{3}\eta)/M\rho$, where η and ζ are the coefficients of viscosity.

This expression shows strong peaks at $\omega = \pm cQ$ and the width of the peaks is determined by the coefficients of viscosity. The space correlation function takes the form

$$\overline{\rho(0,0)\rho(\mathbf{r},0)} = \rho^2 kT\chi_S \,\delta(\mathbf{r}) + \rho^2 \,\dagger\qquad(7.67)$$

We recall that the exact result is (equation (7.4))

$$\overline{\rho(0,0)\rho(\mathbf{r},0)} = \rho[\delta(\mathbf{r}) + g(r) - \rho] + \rho^2\qquad(7.68)$$

As expected the local ordering for small $\mathbf{r}$ is not exhibited in the macroscopic theory and it cannot, therefore, give the correct $S^{coh}(\mathbf{Q},\omega)$ for large $\mathbf{Q}$.

Comparing the result from (7.66) after integration over ω,

$$I(\mathbf{Q},0) = \int_{-\infty}^{\infty} S^{coh}(\mathbf{Q},\omega)d\omega = \rho kT\chi_S,\qquad(7.69)$$

with the exact one obtained from (7.68),

$$I(\mathbf{Q},0) = 1 + \gamma(\mathbf{Q}) \to \rho kT\chi_T \quad \text{for} \quad \mathbf{Q} \to 0,\qquad(7.70)$$

we conclude that not even for $\mathbf{Q} \to 0$ have we obtained the complete correlation function. There are fluctuations of a different kind from sound waves. For small $\mathbf{Q}$ these are governed by the equation for heat diffusion. The local temperature can fluctuate giving a local density change without pressure variation, which may be obtained from the hydrodynamic and thermodynamic equations if one does not restrict oneself to purely adiabatic or purely isothermal processes.

In a harmonic solid the fluctuations are completely described by sound waves but here both longitudinal and transverse waves exist.

The single particle aspect is lost in the macroscopic theory but appears in the microscopic one in the broadening of $\delta(\mathbf{r})$ in equation (7.68).

7.8 Interference Effects

In order to make any quantitative predictions from the general theory one has to make several simplifying approximations. Depending on the values

---

* See Landau, L. D., and Lifshitz, E. M. (1959). "Fluid Mechanics." Pergamon Press, London. For a more complete presentation see Kadanoff and Martin (1963).

† The constant term ρ^2 gives rise only to forward scattering and is, therefore, not included in (7.66).

of the two nuclear scattering lengths the relative importance of the incoherent and coherent scattering varies from substance to substance. In the incoherent scattering the neutron waves scattered from different nuclei do not interfere and this makes the cross-section additive over the nuclei. In the coherent scattering this is not the case and interference effects can be very significant. In a solid these are responsible for the sharp resonance peaks in the scattered neutron spectrum, which are used to determine the phonon dispersion curves and life times. No such resonance effect occurs in the incoherent scattering—there is no conservation rule for momentum in the incoherent case—and for that reason we get only information on the number of phonons in each frequency range. In liquids significant effects such as those found for single crystals do not appear and either one has ignored interference effects or tried to correct for them. It turns out to be difficult to do that and the interference effects in liquids are at present fairly poorly understood. Recently attention has been turned more seriously to the interference effects in order to extract from them information on local collective motions in liquids, which it is not possible to obtain from the incoherent scattering or in the incoherent approximation of the coherent scattering. In the following we shall describe two different ways of correcting for the interference effects and at the end shall very briefly discuss the most recent attempts to utilize these effects in a positive direction.

We recall the classical interpretation of $G(\mathbf{r},\tau)$. It gives the probability of finding a particle at position $\mathbf{r}$ at time τ under the condition that one particle was at the origin at $\tau = 0$. This latter particle reaches the position $\mathbf{r}$ with the probability $G_s(\mathbf{r},\tau)$ and the probability for another particle reaching $\mathbf{r}$ at time τ is given by the difference $(G(\mathbf{r},\tau) - G_s(\mathbf{r},\tau))$. We further know that the pair-distribution function $g(\mathbf{r})$ gives the particle density around the origin at $\tau = 0$. Vineyard (1958) made the following assumption:

$$G(\mathbf{r},\tau) = G_s(\mathbf{r},\tau) + \int G_s(\mathbf{r}-\mathbf{r}',\tau)g(\mathbf{r}')d\mathbf{r}', \qquad (7.71)$$

known as the "convolution approximation".

He assumed a particle to move from $\mathbf{r}'$ to $\mathbf{r}$ without any knowledge of the particle at the origin at $\tau = 0$. Obviously this cannot be fully correct. If, for instance, one atom has moved to the positon $\mathbf{r}$ it will prevent other atoms approaching it and hence depress their probability of reaching $\mathbf{r}$. Nevertheless, this approximation has often been used and it leads to considerable simplifications.

For the intermediate scattering function one gets

$$I(\mathbf{Q},\tau) = (1+\gamma(Q))I_s(\mathbf{Q},\tau), \qquad (7.72)$$

where the term $\gamma(Q)I_s(\mathbf{Q},\tau)$ is due to interference effects. We can immediately see one consequence of the above approximation. Expanding both sides of (7.72) in powers of τ we find that the moment relations in (7.14, 15, 16) are not fulfilled. The first and second moments should be the same for $I(\mathbf{Q},\tau)$ and $I_s(\mathbf{Q},\tau)$ which does not follow from (7.72). It has been argued that the approximation should be good for small momentum and energy transfers which are connected with motions over large distance and time. If so, the failure to satisfy the moment relations should not be taken too seriously. These give, namely, only the short time behaviour. However, as shown by De Gennes (1959) and later by Singwi and Sjölander (1964) in connection with scattering of light in liquids one does not even get the essential features correct in the limit of very small momentum and energy transfer. In that case the correlation functions are obtained from general thermodynamic arguments (see the end of the last section). The validity of the convolution approximation is, therefore, at present an open question.*

In order to improve the interference corrections and make them consistent with the exact moment relations as well as the fluctuation-dissipation theorem Egelstaff (1961 and 1963) proposed a modification of the Vineyard approximation.

He first noticed that in order to satisfy the fluctuation–dissipation theorem it is convenient to express the time dependent correlation functions in terms of a quantity which itself becomes real when making the Schofield time substitution $\tau \rightarrow \tau + i\hbar\beta/2$ (see the comments following equation (7.23)). The most simple choice is

$$y^2 = (\tau^2 - i\beta\hbar\tau). \tag{7.73}$$

Inserting the complex time $(\tau + i\hbar\beta/2)$ we get the real quantity $y^2 = (\tau^2 + \beta^2\hbar/4)$. In order to discuss how to satisfy the first few moment relations we expand the intermediate scattering functions in powers of y. We recall the statement in Section 7.4 that after inserting the complex time $(\tau + i\hbar\beta/2)$ the correlation function should become a real and even function of τ. This means that the expansion in y should contain only even powers and furthermore that all the expansion coefficients should be real numbers. In other words, we must have

$$I_s(\mathbf{Q},\tau) = 1 + a_1 y^2 + a_2 y^4 \ldots, \tag{7.74a}$$

$$I(\mathbf{Q},\tau) = (1 + \gamma(Q)) + b_1 y^2 + b_2 y^4 + \ldots, \tag{7.74b}$$

where $a_1, a_2, \ldots$ and $b_1, b_2, \ldots$ are real. The first term in both expansions follows from the zero moment relations (7.13). The first moment should be the same for $I_s(\mathbf{Q},\tau)$ and $I(\mathbf{Q},\tau)$ and this means that the coefficients before the linear terms in τ are equal in the two cases, which implies $a_1 = b_1$, and we get the value

$$a_1 = b_1 = -\frac{Q^2}{2M\beta}. \tag{7.75}$$

* See the discussion in "Inelastic Scattering of Neutrons in Solids and Liquids", Vol. I, p. 248. IAEA, Vienna, 1963.

By using the higher order moment relations one can successively determine the other expansion coefficients. For that purpose we reorder the terms in equations (7.74a,b) to get the expansions in powers of τ;

$$I_s(\mathbf{Q},\tau) = 1 + i\frac{\hbar Q^2}{2M}\tau - \left(\frac{Q^2}{2M\beta} + \beta^2\hbar^2 a_2\right)\tau^2 + \dots,\qquad(7.76a)$$

$$I(\mathbf{Q},\tau) = (1+\gamma(Q)) + i\frac{\hbar Q^2}{2M}\tau - \left(\frac{Q^2}{2M\beta} + \beta^2\hbar^2 b_2\right)\tau^2 + \dots.\qquad(7.76b)$$

The second moments are exactly known (Placzek, 1952; Schofield, 1961; Rahman et al., 1962) and they determine the coefficients before the τ^2-terms and hence the coefficients a_2 and b_2. We notice that for high temperatures where $\beta\to0$—we can let $\hbar$ tend to zero instead if we want—the second moments are the same in the coherent and incoherent cases as has already been stated in equation (7.16). The coefficients a_2 and b_2 are obtained from the quantum corrections to these classical values. We are only interested in the difference between $I(\mathbf{Q},\tau)$ and $I_s(\mathbf{Q},\tau)$ and we state the approximate final expression given by Egelstaff (1961):

$$b_2 - a_2 = -Q^2\gamma(Q)\frac{1}{3M\hbar^2\beta^2}\left(\tfrac{1}{2}Mv^2 - \frac{3}{2\beta}\right)\qquad(7.77)$$

$$= -CQ^2\gamma(Q),$$

where the constant C is obtained from the first line. The bracket gives the quantum correction to the mean kinetic energy of an atom. A rough estimate of the constant above is obtained by considering the liquid as a Debye solid with a proper Debye temperature $\hbar\omega_D/k$. One then finds

$$C = \omega_D^2/40M\beta.\qquad(7.78)$$

Returning to equations (7.74a,b) we can now write

$$I(\mathbf{Q},\tau) - I_s(\mathbf{Q},\tau) = \gamma(Q) - CQ^2\gamma(Q)y^4 + \dots.\qquad(7.79)$$

For large times Egelstaff assumes that the convolution approximation is appropriate and he combines the results in equation (7.79) and equation (7.72) in the form

$$I(\mathbf{Q},\tau) - I_s(\mathbf{Q},\tau) = \gamma(Q)\exp\left[-Q^2 p(y)\right],\qquad(7.80)$$

where $p(y)$ should be a suitable function which for small times goes as Cy^4 and for large times should make $\exp[-Q^2 p(y)]$ equal to $I_s(\mathbf{Q},\tau)$. In fact, he also writes $I_s(\mathbf{Q},\tau)$ as an exponential. An explicit suggestion for $p(y)$ is given by Egelstaff (1963).

Comparing equation (7.72) with (7.80) we see that the modification of the convolution approximation is to replace $G_s(\mathbf{r},\tau)$ under the integral sign in (7.71) by another function which should be more proper for small times. Even though this reduces the interference corrections Egelstaff (1963) still finds the corrections come out too large for inelastic scattering. Both in (7.72) and (7.80) the interference term is written as a product of the oscillatory factor $\gamma(Q)$ and a function smooth in Q. In the harmonic solid case we know that the interference effects are most pronounced for the elastic scattering, Bragg scattering, somewhat less for the one-phonon scattering, which shows a δ-singularity in the energy distribution only, and definitely much less for the higher phonon scattering. In the above approximations we get a similar interference correction for the inelastic as for the elastic scattering through the factor $\gamma(Q)$.

For large momentum transfer, $1/Q$ much smaller than the interatomic distance, the interference effects are negligible and the cross-section is governed by $G_s(\mathbf{r},\tau)$, which gives only the single particle motion. This is, indeed, consistent with equations (7.72, 7.80). In the opposite case, $1/Q$ much larger than the interatomic distance, the collective behaviour dominates.

The correlation function:

$$G(\mathbf{r},\tau) = \overline{\rho(0,0)\rho(\mathbf{r},\tau)}/\rho \tag{7.81}$$

at the extreme long wavelength and low frequency region is obtained from the macroscopic hydrodynamic and thermodynamic equations (see the end of the last section). In this case we have (Kadanoff and Martin, 1963, equation 87a).*

$$S^{\text{coh}}(\mathbf{Q},\omega) = \rho k T \chi_S \left[(C_P/C_V - 1) \frac{1}{\pi} \frac{D_T Q^2}{\omega^2 + (D_T Q^2)^2} \right. +$$
$$\left. \frac{1}{\pi} \frac{\Gamma c^2 Q^4}{(\omega^2 - c^2 Q^2)^2 + (\Gamma \omega Q^2)^2} - (C_P/C_V - 1)\frac{1}{\pi} \frac{D_T Q^2 (\omega^2 - c^2 Q^2)}{(\omega^2 - c^2 Q^2)^2 + (\Gamma \omega Q^2)^2} \right]. \tag{7.82}$$

Here D_T is the heat diffusion constant and

$$\Gamma = D_T(C_P/C_V - 1) + (\zeta + \tfrac{4}{3}\eta)/M\rho. \tag{7.83}$$

We notice that the integrated intensity is correctly given by $\rho k T \chi_T$.

Due to the fact that ω is connected to $\mathbf{Q}$ through the relations (see equation (7.9)):

$$\mathbf{k}_0 - \mathbf{k} = \mathbf{Q} \quad \text{and} \quad \hbar k_0^2/2m - \hbar k^2/2m = \omega \tag{7.84}$$

it is not obvious that the resonance condition $\omega = \pm cQ$ can be satisfied. As a matter of fact, for incident neutron velocities smaller than the sound velocity, which is normally the case, the resonance condition will never be satisfied for processes where the neutrons lose energy. In energy gain processes the condition is satisfied only for quite large momentum transfers, but

---

* $\chi''_{nn}(k,\omega)$ used by Kadanoff and Martin is the Fourier transform of the imaginary part of the density auto-correlation function. In order to get the real part the fluctuation-dissipation theorem is applied in the classical limit.

then (7.82) is not applicable. We do not expect, therefore, to get two displaced peaks and a central peak as for scattering of light but possibly two central peaks with different widths. If the life time of the sound waves is large, i.e. $\Gamma \to 0$, we get no contribution from the second term in (7.82) whereas if the life time is small, i.e. Γ large, the second term becomes appreciable, giving a broad spectrum. We notice that the central peak disappears if $C_P = C_V$.

The case $\Gamma \to 0$ is analogous to that of a solid at low temperature. There no coherent scattering occurs for zero reciprocal lattice vector, if the neutron velocity is smaller than the sound velocity. A difference is that no coherent quasi-elastic scattering appears in the solid case. We may in this respect compare with Mandel'shtam-Brillouin scattering in solids and liquids.

Egelstaff (1965) has recently interpreted some experimental data on liquids along these lines. He made appropriate modifications in equation (7.82) in order to satisfy the first and second moment relations. This, for instance, automatically introduces dispersion effects for small wavelengths. Some similar ideas were also put forward by Ruijgrok (1963).

It should be noted that for $\mathbf{Q}$ and ω tending to zero, higher phonon terms do not appear. This is also the case for a harmonic solid. The intensity for two- and higher phonon scattering goes to zero for $\mathbf{Q}$ and ω tending to zero, a result which follows quite directly from equation (7.28) together with equations (7.32) and (7.33).

Yip and Nelkin (1964) have recently calculated density fluctuations in gases based on a simplified Boltzmann equation, assuming a single relaxation time. They find a significant deviation from the hydrodynamic equations for wavelengths of the order of a mean free path and smaller, and the sound waves seem to persist for wavelengths not much larger than one mean free path. Thus, the Fourier transformed density auto-correlation function shows a quite clear peak corresponding to these sound waves. Similar calculations for $G_s(\mathbf{r}, \tau)$ have been carried out by Nelkin and Ghatak (1964).

In conclusion we shall briefly discuss some interesting recent results from experiments on liquid tin, lead and aluminium, described in Chapter 8. In a single crystal the one-phonon scattering peaks are obtained from the energy and momentum conservation rules; ·

$$\left. \begin{array}{c} \mathbf{k_0 - k = q} + 2\pi\boldsymbol{\tau} \\[2mm] \dfrac{\hbar k_0^2}{2m} - \dfrac{\hbar k^2}{2m} = \pm f_{\mathbf{q}} \end{array} \right\} , \tag{7.85}$$

where $\mathbf{q}$ and $f_{\mathbf{q}}$ are the wave vector and frequency, respectively, of the phonon involved and $\boldsymbol{\tau}$ is a reciprocal lattice vector. In a polycrystalline material the direction of $\boldsymbol{\tau}$ is randomly distributed, giving a broad energy spectrum instead of a sharp peak. The momentum conservation rule ensures that for a fixed reciprocal lattice vector only those phonons contribute for which

$$|\mathbf{Q}| - |\mathbf{q}| \leqslant 2\pi|\boldsymbol{\tau}| \leqslant |\mathbf{Q}| + |\mathbf{q}|, \qquad (7.86)$$

where as before $\mathbf{Q} = \mathbf{k_0} - \mathbf{k}$. The intensity has a sharp fall for

$$|\mathbf{Q}| + |\mathbf{q}| = 2\pi|\boldsymbol{\tau}| \quad \text{and} \quad |\mathbf{Q}| - |\mathbf{q}| = 2\pi|\tau| \qquad (7.87)$$

Experiments on polycrystals indeed show sharp breaks in the energy spectrum and the positions of these breaks can be used to determine an average frequency corresponding to a given wave number $|\mathbf{q}|$. Similar results are found for the liquid state and can be used to determine an average dispersion curve in the liquid (see Section 8.5). These experiments indicate that in a liquid we have similar conservation rules. Both Cocking and Guner (1963) and Larsson et al. (1965) analyse their data using essentially a polycrystalline model after Egelstaff (1962a).

More recently, Singwi (1964) and Singwi and Feldman (1965) have extended this model and carried out extensive numerical calculations. They show clearly how the oscillatory variations of the width of the coherent quasi-elastic scattering for increasing momentum transfer, pointed out earlier by De Gennes, enters through the strong peak in $\gamma(Q)$. For the same reason the variation of $S^{\mathrm{coh}}(Q,\omega)$ for a fixed value of ω shows a strong maximum given essentially by the factor $(1+\gamma(Q))$ when the energy transfer is fairly small, but this maximum is smoothed out for larger energy transfers. This behaviour has recently been demonstrated by Randolph (1964) in experiments on liquid sodium.

Work done in recent years shows that important information on the atomic motions seem to be hidden in the interference effects for liquids. Further experimental work has to be done and theoretically only very preliminary results have been obtained so far. We shall now leave the interference effect aside and concentrate our attention on the incoherent scattering.

7.9 Gaussian Approximation

In most calculations on incoherent scattering, simplifying assumptions have been made on the self-correlation function $G_s(\mathbf{r},\tau)$. Vineyard (1958) noted in his early work on scattering by liquids that in many of the idealized models of interest, which could be treated exactly, $G_s(\mathbf{r},\tau)$ is Gaussian in space. It is so for a harmonic solid, for an ideal gas and for a particle which diffuses according to the simple diffusion equation or Langevin's equation. He proposed, therefore, to use the Gaussian form also in more general cases;

$$G_s(\mathbf{r},\tau) = [4\pi w(\tau)]^{-3/2} \exp\left[-r^2/4w(\tau)\right], \qquad (7.88)$$

where $w(\tau)$ is so far an unknown width function varying with time. Now we know that this seems to be the appropriate form also for a weakly anharmonic solid (see Section 7.6). There is experimental evidence that (7.88) should hold reasonably well also for liquids.*

Assuming the "Gaussian approximation" above, it is found that $w(\tau)$ is uniquely determined by the velocity correlation function as follows (De Gennes, 1959; Schofield, 1961; Rahman $et\ al.$, 1962)

$$w(\tau) = -i\hbar\tau/2M + \tfrac{1}{3}\int_0^\tau (\tau-\tau')\overline{\mathbf{v}(0)\cdot\mathbf{v}(\tau')}\mathrm{d}\tau'. \tag{7.89}$$

We recall that a correlation function $\overline{\mathbf{v}(0)\cdot\mathbf{v}(\tau)}$ is in general complex and that the real and imaginary parts are related to each other as in equations (7.21) and (7.22). Expanding the width function in powers of τ,

$$w(\tau) = -i\hbar\tau/2M + \tfrac{1}{6}\overline{v^2}\tau^2 + \cdots, \tag{7.90}$$

where classically $\overline{v^2} = 3/M\beta$, and inserting this in equation (7.88) gives automatically the first and second moments correctly. We also notice that for large times

$$w(\tau) \to D|\tau| + \text{const.}, \tag{7.91}$$

where

$$D = \tfrac{1}{3}\int_0^\infty \mathrm{Re}\,\overline{\mathbf{v}(0)\cdot\mathbf{v}(\tau)}\mathrm{d}\tau, \tag{7.92}$$

is the macroscopic self-diffusion constant. The imaginary counterpart to (7.92) cancels exactly the first term in (7.89). Rahman (1963) and De Bar (1963) have derived a modified form for $w(\tau)$ which more clearly reveals its relation to the mean square displacement,

$$w(\tau) = \tfrac{1}{6}\left[1 - i\tanh\left(\tfrac{1}{2}\beta\hbar\frac{\mathrm{d}}{\mathrm{d}\tau}\right)\right]\overline{(\mathbf{r}(\tau)-\mathbf{r}(0))^2}. \tag{7.93}$$

The quantum corrections to $w(\tau)$ originate from two sources, firstly the quantum mechanical evaluation of the mean square displacement and secondly the term $i\tanh\left(\tfrac{1}{2}\beta\hbar\dfrac{\mathrm{d}}{\mathrm{d}\tau}\right)$ which is connected to recoil effects and should not be ignored in classical liquids.

For completeness we also write the intermediate scattering function in the Gaussian approximation,

$$I_s(\mathbf{Q},\tau) = \exp\left[-Q^2 w(\tau)\right]. \tag{7.94}$$

A formal derivation of equations (7.94) and (7.89) was given by Rahman $et\ al.$ (1962). Generally the exponential in (7.94) contains also terms

---

* See the discussion in "Inelastic Scattering of Neutrons in Solids and Liquids", Vol I, p. 226. IAEA, Vienna, 1963.

proportional to Q^4, Q^6, etc., as for anharmonic solids. The coefficients contain irreducible correlation functions of four or more velocities and thus the Gaussian approximation implies neglect of these higher order correlations. A similar proof and approximation has been given by Kubo (1962) for application to magnetic relaxation effects.

7.10 Introduction of the Velocity Frequency Function

The most convenient way of introducing the atomic motions into the cross-section for incoherent scattering seems to be through a generalized frequency spectrum. This was suggested by Egelstaff (1961), and these ideas have later been worked out in detail also by others (Egelstaff and Schofield, 1962; Rahman et al., 1962; Schofield, 1962). Egelstaff found that one can define a frequency distribution $z(f)$ for a liquid, being a natural generalization of the phonon distribution function for a harmonic solid. In this formulation it is very easy to take into account both the moment relations and the fluctuation-dissipation theorem, which form the basic foundations of the scattering problem. Besides this $z(f)$ reveals very clearly the various aspects of the single particle motion and this makes a great simplification when trying to make specific assumptions on the form of $z(f)$, which at present has to be based mainly on intuition.

It turns out to be convenient to define the distribution function as (essentially) the Fourier transform of the imaginary part of the velocity auto-correlation function as follows (see Rahman et al., 1962; Schofield, 1962):

$$\text{Im } \overline{\mathbf{v}(0) \cdot \mathbf{v}(\tau)} = \frac{3\hbar}{2M} \int_0^\infty f z(f) \sin (f\tau) \, df. \qquad (7.95)$$

Introducing of a spectral function as above is indeed a conventional procedure when calculating auto-correlation functions in stochastic processes. The fluctuation-dissipation theorem, which relates the real and imaginary parts of the auto-correlation function, implies

$$\text{Re } \overline{\mathbf{v}(0) \cdot \mathbf{v}(\tau)} = \frac{3\hbar}{2M} \int_0^\infty f \coth \left(\tfrac{1}{2} \beta \hbar f \right) z(f) \cos (f\tau) \, df. \qquad (7.96)$$

By integrating both sides of (7.95) and using the commutation rules for position and velocity one finds that

$$\int_0^\infty z(f) df = 1 \qquad (7.97)$$

and one can furthermore show that $z(f)$ is non-negative.

Using the above formulation we get for the width function

$$w(\tau) = \int_0^\infty [g(f,0)-g(f,\tau)]z(f)df \qquad (7.98)$$

with

$$g(f,\tau) = \frac{\hbar}{2Mf}\left\{\frac{1}{e^{\beta\hbar f}-1}e^{-if\tau}+\left(\frac{1}{e^{\beta\hbar f}-1}+1\right)e^{if\tau}\right\}, \qquad (7.99)$$

which is exactly the same form as found earlier for a harmonic solid (equations (7.33 and 7.35)). The difference lies in the properties of the frequency distribution $z(f)$.

Integration of equation (7.96) gives the following expression for the self-diffusion constant:

$$D = \frac{\pi}{2M\beta}z(0), \qquad (7.100)$$

and is thus determined by the value of $z(f)$ for zero frequency. For a harmonic solid $z(f)\sim f^2$ for small frequencies and hence diffusion is absent.

From the data presented in Section 7.7 one may conclude that a liquid should behave very much like a solid for high frequency motions whereas for low frequency motions diffusion should play an essential role. The $z(f)$ obtained from Langevin's equation is *

$$z(f) = \frac{2}{\pi\zeta}\frac{1}{1+f^2/\zeta^2}, \qquad (7.101)$$

where $\zeta = 1/MD\beta$. It has its maximum for $f = 0$ and decreases monotonically. One might expect the proper frequency function for a liquid to go approximately as in (7.101) for low frequencies and approximately as for a Debye solid for larger frequencies (see Fig. 7.4).

Particularly if there is a strong dip in $z(f)$ as indicated in the figure we should be able to separate the motion into two distinct parts, one diffusive part and one vibratory part. The area under the two peaks gives roughly the relative number of degrees of freedom which go into diffusive motion and vibratory motion, respectively. For instance, all motions are diffusive if the spectrum in equation (7.101) is used throughout and correspondingly vibratory if a Debye spectrum is used. A combination of these two spectra (cf. equation 7.130).

$$z(f) = a\frac{2}{\pi\zeta}\frac{1}{1+f^2/\zeta^2}+(1-a)\frac{3f^2}{f_D^3}, \quad f<f_D$$

$$= a\frac{2}{\pi\zeta}\frac{1}{1+f^2/\zeta^2} \qquad\qquad , \quad f>f_D, \qquad (7.102)$$

* Note that $\overline{\mathbf{v}(0)\cdot\mathbf{v}(\tau)}$ in (7.57) is real and should be replaced, therefore, by $\mathrm{Re}\,\overline{\mathbf{v}(0)\cdot\mathbf{v}(\tau)}$, where the imaginary part follows using the fluctuation-dissipation theorem.

12*

where a gives the relative weight of the two types of motions, leads to a modified relation between ζ and the diffusion constant D, namely

$$\zeta = a/MD\beta. \tag{7.103}$$

The relaxation time for the velocity correlation function (see (7.57)) increases as a decreases. The experiments indicate indeed an increase by a factor of 10–100, giving a relaxation time of the order 10^{-11}–10^{-12} sec.

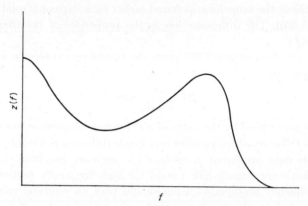

FIG. 7.4. An illustration of a probable frequency function for a liquid.

We may also describe this in terms of an effective mass for diffusion,

$$M^* = M/a \tag{7.104}$$

with

$$\zeta = 1/M^*D\beta. \tag{7.105}$$

A single atom may be imagined to diffuse in co-operation with its immediate surroundings which should increase the apparent mass of the diffusing atom. We shall in the next section briefly describe a model by Egelstaff based on these latter ideas.

In water, for instance, hydrogen is the essential scatterer and is bound in molecules to an oxygen atom. We have in this case diffusive and translational motions, where the hydrogen atom moves together with its molecule, and also rotatory and vibratory motions, where the hydrogen atom rotates and vibrates relative to the oxygen atom. The first two kinds of motions give a $z(f)$ roughly as in Fig. 7.4 and the other two kinds of motions give rise to a broad peak in $z(f)$ around 0·06 eV (hindered rotations) and sharp peaks at much higher frequencies (internal vibrations of the molecule). If considering the first two types of motions only we may introduce the molecular mass as the effective mass of the hydrogen atom and treat the motion as that for the rigid molecule.

Recently, Rahman (1964) has reported some interesting numerical results on liquid argon. He has carefully solved the classical equations of motion for a set of 864 particles (using a computer) and from the data has determined the velocity autocorrelation function, the corresponding spectral function $z(f)$, and also the time-dependent pair-correlation functions $G(\mathbf{r},\tau) - G_s(\mathbf{r},\tau)$. His results are in qualitative agreement with what has been said above. The velocity auto-correlation function deviates significantly from a pure exponential function, which is obtained from Langevin's equation, and becomes in fact, negative for times larger than 4×10^{-13} sec. The spectral function has a distinct maximum for $f = 0 \cdot 25 \; kT/\hbar$ as in Fig. 7.4. However, the curve does not show any dip between a diffusive and a vibrational part. Furthermore, $G_s(\mathbf{r},\tau)$ deviates somewhat from a Gaussian shape. The ratio of the fourth and second moments, $\overline{r^4}/(\overline{r^2})^2$, is about 10 % larger than expected on a Gaussian model for times of the order 2–5×10^{-12} sec. For smaller and larger times this deviation tends to zero as it should. The time evolution of the pair-correlation function shows a very significant deviation from that obtained in the convolution approximation (equation (7.72)). This led Rahman to suggest another approximate relation between $G(\mathbf{r},\tau)$ and $G_s(\mathbf{r},\tau)$.

Some few comments should be added about these results. The calculations have been carried out for quite a high temperature, $94 \cdot 4°$K, whereas the melting point is $84 \cdot 4°$K at 1 atm. We may expect the solid like behaviour to be more pronounced at lower temperatures. The inert liquids are characterized by an interaction potential which has a very steep repulsive part and a shallow attractive part. This makes them differ considerably from liquid metals, for instance, and one should expect the latter to show more of a solid-like behaviour. Inelastic neutron scattering data indicate, indeed, that this is the case (see Chapter 8).

7.11 Discussion of Various Explicit Dynamical Models

No calculations of the Van Hove correlation functions have been carried out so far which can be claimed to be firmly based on the dynamical equations of motion for a liquid. Various models have been constructed which should manifest some of the most essential features of the atomic motions. In this way it has been possible to understand most of the experimental results, which at first might have been somewhat surprising. In addition the ideas of simultaneous diffusive and vibratory motions of the atoms have been clarified. We shall describe briefly some of the models proposed in connection with neutron scattering and stress the conclusions one may draw from their success or failure. It should be emphasized that the models are all crude and can only be expected to give the trend. This should be kept in mind particularly when comparing the various models.

Model I

Before any detailed experiments were carried out Vineyard (1958) proposed using the macroscopic diffusion equation for $G_s(\mathbf{r},\tau)$;

$$\frac{\partial}{\partial \tau} G_s(\mathbf{r},\tau) = D\nabla^2 G_s(\mathbf{r},\tau), \qquad (7.106)$$

with the initial condition $G_s(\mathbf{r},0) = \delta(\mathbf{r})$. Then he followed the classical interpretation of the self correlation function. D is the macroscopic self-diffusion constant. The solution is easily found to be

$$G_s(\mathbf{r},\tau) = (4\pi D|\tau|)^{-3/2} \exp\left[-r^2/4D|\tau|\right], \qquad (7.107)$$

and for the scattering law we get

$$S^{\mathrm{inc}}(\mathbf{Q},\omega) = \frac{1}{\pi}\frac{DQ^2}{\omega^2+(DQ^2)^2}. \qquad (7.108)$$

This distribution becomes (for fixed Q) Lorentzian and the full energy width is given by the expression

$$\Delta E = 2\hbar DQ^2, \qquad (7.109)$$

and furthermore the area under the peak is unity.

The width function $w(\tau) = D|\tau|$ does not have the proper behaviour for small times; it should go as τ^2 for $\tau \to 0$. This was corrected by basing the calculations on Langevin's equation instead (see equations (7.89) and (7.57)) which leads to a width function

$$w(\tau) = D[|\tau|-(1-e^{-\zeta|\tau|})/\zeta], \qquad (7.110)$$

where $\zeta = 1/M\beta D$. We then have $w(\tau) = D|\tau|$ for $t \gg 1/\zeta$ and $w(\tau) = \tau^2/2M\beta$ for $\tau \to 0$. As mentioned before, $1/\zeta$ comes out very small and this makes the deviation from (7.108) to be significant only for large frequencies. The full width of the peak remains essentially unchanged.

We have still the defect in $w(\tau)$ that it is real and hence violates the fluctuation-dissipation theorem. This was corrected by Schofield (1961, 1962) and Egelstaff (1961) and they introduced a time $y = (\tau^2 - i\beta\hbar\tau)^{\frac{1}{2}}$ (see the comments to equations (7.73)) and proposed for convenience an expression *

$$w(\tau) = D[(y^2+1/\zeta^2)^{\frac{1}{2}}-1/\zeta] \qquad (7.111)$$

for the width function. This leads to the right limits

$$\begin{aligned} w(\tau)&\to D|\tau|, && \tau\to\pm\infty \\ &\to -i\hbar\tau/2M+\tau^2/2M\beta, && \tau\to 0. \end{aligned} \qquad (7.112)$$

This expression gives essentially the same numerical results as above. The

---

* Later on we shall describe a model where these authors use this form with a redefined ζ in order to explain the quasi-elastic scattering.

difference becomes significant only for large frequencies where the intensity is small anyway.

The experimental results showed clear deviations from the predictions obtained above (Brockhouse, 1958; Hughes *et al.*, 1960; Larssen *et al.*, 1961). The most significant discrepancies concerned the width of the quasi-elastic peak which was definitely less than obtained from (7.109). In the results of Hughes *et al.* (1960) it was less by an order of magnitude. Furthermore the wings corresponding to larger energy transfers were found to decrease less rapidly than predicted. Comparison with scattering from polycrystalline samples showed a striking similarity and this made a closer comparison between the atomic motion in solids and liquids highly appropriate.

Model II

Due to the failure to explain the experimental results for water on a simple diffusion model as above, Brockhouse (1958) made some calculations assuming jump diffusion. These ideas were later taken up by Singwi and Sjölander (1960a) and generalized in several respects. Essentially the same ideas, but somewhat less general, were considered independently by Chudley and Elliot (1961); Oskotskii (1963) has more recently further generalized the model proposed by Singwi and Sjölander.

They consider the atoms to be trapped part of the time by the surrounding atoms and making oscillatory motions as in a solid, and part of the time performing a diffusive type of motion. Two characteristic times enter in the model, the average time τ_0 the atom stays vibrating before it goes into diffusive motion and the average duration time τ_1 for the diffusive motion before the atom gets trapped again. If $\tau_1 \ll \tau_0$ the diffusion mechanism becomes essentially that of a jump diffusion.

The assumptions made by Chudley and Elliot (1961) are more restricted than in the other cases and the results are probably also least satisfactory. In this case, as for Singwi and Sjölander (1960a), the vibrations are assumed to occur around fixed positions, interrupted by diffusive motions. Even though the latter authors are not restricted to jump diffusion the most significant results are given for that case as a contrast to Vineyard's model. Oskotskii modifies the model of Singwi and Sjölander by allowing the centre of vibration to diffuse continuously and introduces in that way a combination of continuous diffusion and jumps.

The following form for the scattering law applicable to the quasi-elastic scattering is obtained:

$$S_{\text{q.e.}}^{\text{inc}}(\mathbf{Q},\omega) = \frac{e^{-2W}}{\pi} \cdot \frac{p(Q)}{\omega^2 + [p(Q)]^2}. \tag{7.113}$$

The full width is given by

$$\Delta E = 2\hbar p(Q). \tag{7.114}$$

e^{-2W} is the Debye-Waller factor for the oscillatory motion and

$$2W = \tfrac{1}{6}Q^2\overline{u^2}, \tag{7.115}$$

where $\overline{u^2}$ is the mean square displacement for the oscillations. The various authors find for $p(Q)$ the following expressions

$$p(Q) = \frac{1}{\tau_0}\left(1 - \frac{\sin Ql}{Ql}\right) \quad \text{(Chudley-Elliot)} \tag{7.116a}$$

$$= \frac{1}{\tau_0}\left(1 - \frac{e^{-2W}}{1 + DQ^2\tau_0}\right) \quad \text{(Singwi-Sjölander)} \tag{7.116b}$$

$$= \frac{1}{\tau_0}\left(1 + D_0Q^2\tau_0 - \frac{e^{-2W}}{1 + DQ^2\tau_0}\right) \quad \text{(Oskotskii)} \tag{7.116c}$$

l is the jump distance in the model of Chudley and Elliot and the diffusion constant is then given by $D = l^2/6\tau_0$. D_0 is the diffusion constant for the motion of the centre of vibration in the model of Oskotskii.* These expressions should reduce to DQ^2 for $Q \to 0$. Equation (7.116b) has this limit when $\overline{u^2} \ll 6D\tau_0$, or when the size of the thermal cloud is very much less than the jump length and this the physical basis for the model.

We notice that for large Q the width is governed by τ_0 in (7.116a,b) and is independent of Q. In equation (7.116c) it is given by D_0 which is much less than D and hence gives a much slower Q-dependence than the simple diffusion model (7.109). The integrated intensity is determined by the Debye-Waller factor e^{-2W} and is less than unity. These conclusions were drawn also by Brockhouse from more simple arguments. The inelastic scattering was assumed to be essentially that of a solid.

One finds experimentally a characteristic Debye-Waller factor corresponding in water to a Debye temperature around $130°K$ (Brockhouse, 1958; Larssen et al., 1961) and one gets a Q-dependence of the width which can be understood on the basis of (7.116). A detailed discussion of these results is given in Chapter 8.

Even though the main conclusions drawn from the model are supported by experiments it certainly has a limited validity. The time τ_0 should decrease for increasing temperature, and as pointed out by Egelstaff (1962) this should give closer agreement between (7.116b) and the simple diffusion result for higher temperatures, which does not seem to be generally valid for liquids. Equation (7.116c) suffers from the same defect and the oscillations in (7.116a) as a function of Q are certainly not confirmed by any experiment. In recent experiments on glycerol Larsson et al. (1963) do find a temperature variation

---

* In equations (7.116b,c) the correct limit DQ^2 for $Q \to 0$ is reached only approximately.

as predicted above and this may, according to Egelstaff, show that in this case we have mainly jump diffusion. In the opposite case he argues that the diffusion is mainly of a continuous nature (these points are discussed in Chapter 8 also).

The inelastic scattering is certainly treated too crudely. The harmonic vibrations should be strongly damped and the theoretical predictions show too much structure in the inelastic part. It was erroneously concluded by Singwi and Sjölander (1960a) that agreement with results of Hughes et al. (1960) was obtained.*

Model III

A more detailed discussion of the diffusive motion on a microscopic time scale has been given by Egelstaff (1962b) and Schofield (1962). Egelstaff (1962b) bases his arguments on a picture of self-diffusion as a co-operative pheno-menon. Neighbouring atoms are assumed to be strongly correlated in their motion and in order to eliminate all arbitrary parameters in the model he simply assumes a certain number of atoms to move together rigidly in a Brownian motion. Langevin's equation should, according to Egelstaff, rather describe the erratic motion of these more or less rigid "globules" and hence the mass entering should be the mass of the globule. We may call this the effective mass M^* for the diffusing atom (see the comments following (7.104)). The relaxation time obtained from Langevin's equation is then increased by the factor M^*/M, which gives the ratio between the globule mass and the mass of a single atom. As already stated earlier Langevin's equation gives improper short time behaviour and also violates the fluctuation-dissipation theorem. Egelstaff and Schofield, therefore, introduced the variable $y = (\tau^2 - i\beta\hbar\tau)^{\frac{1}{2}}$ and assumed the following width function for the diffusive motion:

$$w_D(\tau) = D[(y^2 + 1/\zeta^2)^{\frac{1}{2}} - 1/\zeta], \qquad (7.117a)$$

where D is the macroscopic self-diffusion constant and $\zeta = 1/M^*\beta D$. The total width function contains also contributions from hindered translations and other kinds of motions, which give rise to inelastic scattering, and can be included in a width function $w_B(\tau)$. Hence we have

$$w(\tau) = w_D(\tau) + w_B(\tau). \qquad (7.117b)$$

At the present stage the detailed shape of the quasi-elastic peak is insignifi-cant and probably only the width of the peak is essential and this is controlled by the single parameter ζ. For increasing ζ the quasi-elastic peak becomes narrower. The particular form given in (7.117a) was chosen in order to make

* A mistake in the normalization was made.

it possible to get a closed expression for the corresponding Fourier transform (Egelstaff and Schofield, 1962):

$$\tilde{S}_D^{\text{inc}}(\mathbf{Q},\omega) = \int_{-\infty}^{\infty} e^{-i\omega\tau} \exp[-Q^2 w_D(\tau)]d\tau =$$

$$\exp[Q^2D/\zeta - \hbar\beta\omega/2]\frac{1}{\pi}\frac{Q^2D/\zeta'}{[\omega^2+(DQ^2)^2]^{\frac{1}{2}}} \cdot K_1\{[\omega^2+(DQ^2)^2]^{\frac{1}{2}}/\zeta'\}, \quad (7.118)$$

where $1/\zeta' = (1/\zeta^2 + \hbar^2\beta^2/4)^{\frac{1}{2}}$ and $K_1(z)$ is the modified Bessel function of the second kind. This gives a quasi-elastic peak whose width becomes for $Q^2D/\zeta \ll 1$ the same as for simple diffusion,

$$\Delta E = 2\hbar DQ^2, \quad (7.119)$$

and for $Q^2 D/\zeta \gg 1$

$$\Delta E = 2\hbar(2\ln 2)^{\frac{1}{2}}(DQ^2\zeta')^{\frac{1}{2}}. \quad (7.120)$$

The scattering law can conveniently be written in the following form

$$S^{\text{inc}}(\mathbf{Q},\omega) = \int_{-\infty}^{\infty} S_D^{\text{inc}}(\mathbf{Q},\omega-\omega')S_B^{\text{inc}}(\mathbf{Q},\omega')d\omega', \quad (7.121)$$

where $S_D^{\text{inc}}(\mathbf{Q},\omega)$ corresponds to $w_D(\tau)$ and $S_B^{\text{inc}}(\mathbf{Q},\omega)$ to $w_B(\tau)$. $w_B(\tau)$ contains the internal motions of the globules and can be assumed to be solid-like and for the calculation of $S_B^{\text{inc}}(\mathbf{Q},\omega)$ a phonon-type expansion can be used.

Egelstaff connects the friction constant ζ to the coefficient of shear viscosity η through Eyring's formula

$$\eta = 1/2R_g\beta D, \quad (7.122)$$

where $2R_g$ is the diameter of the globule. We may now determine R_g from the mass of the globule, M^*, considering each atom to occupy a volume v_a. This leads to the relation

$$\frac{4\pi}{3}R_g^3 = v_a\frac{M^*}{M}, \quad (7.123)$$

where $M^*/M = 1/M\beta D\zeta$. By combining equations (7.122) and (7.123) we get for the constant ζ, which enters in (7.117a), the following relation:

$$\frac{1}{\zeta} = \frac{4\pi}{3}\frac{M\beta D}{v_a}\left(\frac{1}{2\eta\beta D}\right)^3. \quad (7.124)$$

The measured width of the quasi-elastic scattering gives information on the size of the globules or phrased more properly an average correlation distance. It is stated that in many cases the radius of the globule does not depend significantly on the temperature (over a limited temperature range) and then $1/\zeta$ varies essentially as $D\beta$, which increases with temperature. As a consequence the width of the quasi-elastic peak departs further from the simple diffusion result for higher temperatures, which is just the opposite to what was obtained from a jump diffusion model. Experimental data on various liquid metals have indeed given this trend and from this Egelstaff concludes that in these cases continuous diffusion dominates.

It is very illustrative to look at the numbers for $1/\zeta$ which Egelstaff (1962b) obtains from direct comparison with experiments (see Table 7.6 below):

TABLE 7.6

	Temp. (°C)	$1/\zeta$ $(10^{-12}$ sec$)$
Na	110	2·0
	155	2·5
	200	2·8
Pb	330	7·5
	396	7·7
	462	7·8
	350	~10
	600	~20
Sn	258	3·5
	306	4·5
	350	5·0
H_2O	24	1·1
	75	1·5
	22	2·6
	70–92	~3·5

TABLE 7·7

	Temp. (°C)	Diameter (Å)	$1/\zeta$ $(10^{-12}$ sec$)$
Na	98	16·5	1·8
	200	17·4	3·1
Pb	350	13·3	3·9
	600	11·0	4·8
Sn	300	12·2	3·2
	590	9·2	2·8
H_2O	0	21·6	1·3
	100	21·0	7·8

In Table 7.7 are quoted some values for the globule diameters, calculated from equation (7.122), and for $1/\zeta$ from equation (7.124).

The above model is in a sense the extreme opposite to jump diffusion where single atoms are assumed to make rapid position changes without dragging other particles. The crudeness in some of the assumptions made should not mask the basic merit of the model. One should certainly be able to put these ideas, perhaps with some modifications, on a firm basis. The co-operative motion of several atoms can be described by some correlation function which extends over a certain distance in space. The globule diameter above will then correspond to an average correlation length. However, such a general formal treatment will require an equation of motion for the correlation function, which it should be possible to solve. We have at present no such equation and, therefore, one is forced to make drastic simplifying assumptions.

Model IV

A model which in some respects is more advanced than those discussed above was suggested by Rahman et al. (1962) based on the ideas of Brownian motion of an atom. Some of these aspects were discussed in Section 7.7 and what was said there can be used as a basis for the model to be described here.

It was argued that when an atom is moving slowly there is no restoring force except a friction term, which is assumed proportional to the velocity of the atom. For fast atoms one should expect a damped oscillatory motion. The displacement of the atom shall be assumed to consist of a large number of statistically independent contributions, similar to the normal modes in solids;

$$\mathbf{R}(\tau) = \sum_s \xi_s(\tau). \tag{7.125}$$

A convenient consequence of this assumption is that $G_s(\mathbf{r},\tau)$ becomes Gaussian. For $\xi_s(\tau)$ they assumed the stochastic equation

$$\ddot{\xi}_s(\tau) + \zeta_s \dot{\xi}_s(\tau) + f_s^2 \xi_s(\tau) = \frac{1}{M} \mathbf{F}_s(t) \tag{7.126}$$

for f_s larger than a certain limit frequency f'. Each "mode" is characterized by a certain frequency f_s and friction constant ζ_s and $\mathbf{F}_s(t)$ is a stochastic force with a white spectrum.

The velocity auto-correlation function obtained from equation (7.126) was given earlier in (7.62). It does not lead to any diffusion. In order to bring in diffusion it was assumed that all "modes" corresponding to $f_s < f'$ have no restoring force and should, therefore, be governed by the equation

$$\ddot{\xi}_s(\tau) + \zeta_0 \dot{\xi}_s(\tau) = \frac{1}{M} \mathbf{F}_s(t), \tag{7.127}$$

which yields the velocity correlation function given in equation (7.57) and gives a finite diffusion constant.

The assumptions made here are certainly great oversimplifications of reality but should give the main features correctly. The stochastic equations should be understood as giving the average motion of an atom and the separation in "modes" should be considered as a kind of spectral decomposition of the motion. The vibrations are strongly anharmonic which is equivalent to large damping of the harmonically decomposed motions. In close analogy to the solid case it was assumed that $\zeta_s = 2\gamma f_s$, where γ is an adjustable parameter. The distribution of f_s was further assumed to be that of a Debye solid and a characteristic Debye frequency was introduced, f_D. These two parameters characterize the vibratory motion. One is not completely justified in assuming that all slow motions go into diffusion. Long wavelength longitudinal vibrations exist and some of the higher frequency transverse "modes" may go into diffusion also. Concerning the longitudinal sound waves they are so few compared to the high frequency "modes" that no essential difference is made by neglecting them. The details of the model are certainly not significant and probably only the relative number of diffusive "modes" to the number of vibratory "modes" is important and this is determined by the frequency f', which is the third adjustable parameter. The fourth parameter is the friction constant ξ_0.

By varying the parameters one can move from a harmonic Debye solid ($f' = 0$, $\gamma = 0$) to purely Langevin motion ($f' = f_D$). One finds for $w(\tau)$ the asymptotic form

$$w(\tau) \to D\tau + C, \tag{7.128}$$

where

$$D = \frac{1}{M\beta\zeta_0}\left(\frac{f'}{f_D}\right)^3, \qquad C = \frac{1}{M\beta}\left[\frac{3}{f_D^2}\left(1 - \frac{f'}{f_D}\right) - \frac{1}{\zeta_0^2}\left(\frac{f'}{f_D}\right)^3\right]. \tag{7.129}$$

The factor $(f'/f_D)^3$ means that ζ_0 is smaller than for the case of purely Langevin motion, giving a narrowing of the quasi-elastic peak. This was achieved in a somewhat different way in model II. However, the two parameters, f' in this model and τ_0 in the other model, are related to each other. An increase of the time τ_0 should correspond to a decrease of the number of diffusive "modes", i.e. a decrease of f'.

The fluctuation–dissipation theorem is automatically taken into account if the above classical model is used only for calculating the real part of the velocity correlation function or more conveniently the frequency spectrum obtained from (7.96). The moment relations will put some restrictions on the frequency-function. Some detailed calculations based on this model are given by Rahman *et al.* (1962). One gets for the frequency function the following expression:

$$z(f) = \left(\frac{f'}{f_D}\right)^3 \frac{2}{\pi\zeta_0} \frac{1}{1+f^2/\zeta_0^2} + \frac{3f^2}{f_D^3} \frac{2\gamma}{\pi} \int\limits_{f'^2}^{f_D^2} \frac{x\,dx}{(x-f^2)^2+4\gamma^2 f^2\,x}. \qquad (7.130)$$

The first term gives rise to quasi-elastic scattering whereas the second term is mainly responsible for the inelastic scattering. Figure 7.5 shows the spectrum which gave a good fit to the experimental results for liquid lead.

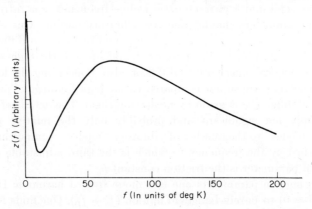

Fig. 7.5. Frequency function for liquid lead obtained from comparison with experiments (Rahman *et al.* (1962)).

Out of the four adjustable parameters one was fixed by the diffusion constant. The exact value for γ turned out not to be significant. In order to fit the inelastic scattering the damping of the harmonic oscillations had to be very large and then the shape of the curves were very insensitive to the exact value of γ.

A comparison of the two last models is most illuminating. In spite of the very different views taken in the two cases the two models seem to be identical. The numerical difference depends only on the particular choices made for the width functions and is probably completely insignificant when considering the crudeness of the models. In the last model one has concentrated attention on a single atom. Whatever the motion of the surrounding atoms may be, this single atom makes some erratic movements. If one should happen to know the actual positions of the surrounding atoms for various times one could, of course, determine the force acting on the single atom and from this its motion. One may then find that several atoms are moving together for some time. The parameters which enter in one model can fairly directly be converted into the parameters of the other model. For instance, a comparison between equations (7.117a) and (7.128) and (7.129) gives:

$$w_B(\infty) = \frac{1}{M\beta}\frac{3}{f_D^2}\left(1 - \frac{f'}{f_D}\right), \quad \zeta = \zeta_0, \quad M^*/M = (f_D/f')^3. \quad (7.131)$$

Due to the fact that the last model is a single particle model it is extremely difficult to connect the parameters to the coefficient of viscosity, etc. It should be possible to get the specific heat fairly directly and an actual calculation with proper choice of parameters will quite certainly give a value close to that of a solid. In the collective approach in model III one is able to find a more direct relation to the viscosity. Egelstaff has taken a result available in the literature.

7.12 Concluding Remarks

The ideas of oscillatory and diffusive motions in liquids are very old and are strongly stressed in the pioneering work of Frenkel (1946). Earlier, such ideas were essentially based on the thermodynamic properties of liquids which showed strong similarity to those of solids. However, the conclusions one could draw from such experiments were far from decisive. Ultrasonic experiments as well as experiments on nuclear magnetic resonance could only cover quite low frequency motions which are in no way characteristic of the high-frequency thermal motions of the atoms. The neutron scattering experiments have definitely shown that the old ideas of simultaneous diffusive and vibratory motions are right and they have also given strong evidence that the high-frequency motions are very similar to the motions in solids. One has so far not been able to reveal the complete details of the atomic motions and it is at present not clear whether neutron scattering will ever be able to do that. A detailed study of the coherent scattering in liquids is probably necessary to give more decisive information on short wavelength collective motions.

Most of the earlier theoretical work has been concentrated on long-wavelength motions as, for instance, calculation of the macroscopic transport coefficients. Very crude assumptions have been made about the thermal motions of the atoms, which have been shown by neutron scattering to be far from true. This may not be serious for the calculation of the macroscopic quantities but nevertheless that does not justify the assumptions. We may recall the success of the Debye theory for solids when calculating the thermal properties. The Debye frequency spectrum is, however, far from realistic and fails to give correct values for quantities which depend more sensitively on the atomic motions. The cell model of Lennard-Jones and Devonshire stresses the solid-like motion but it corresponds to the Einstein model of a solid and not to a collective model as the Debye model or Born-von Kármán model. Furthermore diffusion is neglected in that model. We know that in a solid the collective aspect is essential and there seems to be no reason why the collective aspect should be less important in liquids. Recent neutron scattering experiments indicate that this is indeed the case. The construction of simple models as reported in the last section have played an important role for the interpretation of the experimental results and have been necessary for drawing conclusions. However, they are all too crude and preliminary to be considered as dynamical theories for liquids. In recent years one has made remarkable progress in studying quantum many-body systems such as electron gas, nuclear matter, etc. In these cases it has proved convenient to introduce dynamical correlation functions to describe the average motion of the system. In this respect the procedure resembles the treatment of the motion of a single atom by Langevin's equation. An essential point in these treatments is that the apparent interaction between the particles in the medium is often found to be different from the actual interaction between free particles.

Acknowledgement

The author wishes to express his thanks and appreciation to Mr. Erik Svensson, who has collected the experimental data presented in Section 7.7.

References

Aamodt, R., Case, K. M., Rosenbaum, M. and Zweifel, P. F. (1962). *Phys. Rev.* **126**, 1165.

Alnatt, A. R. and Rice, S. A. (1961). *J. chem. Phys,* **34**, 2156.

Ambegaokar, V., Conway, J. M. and Baym, G. (1965). *In* "Lattice Dynamics", ed. by R. F. Wallis, p. 261. Pergamon Press, New York; (1965). *J. Phys. Chem. Solids* Suppl. 1.

Ambegaokar, V. and Maradudin, A. A. (1964). Westinghouse Research Laboratory 64-929-100 P2.

Andrade, E. N. da C. and Dobbs, E. R. (1952). *Proc. roy. Soc.* **A211**, 12.

De Bar, R. B. (1963). *Phys. Rev.* **130**, 827.

Barker, J. A. (1963). "Lattice Theories of the Liquid State". Pergamon Press, Oxford.

Barker, J. A. and Dobbs, E. R. (1955). *Phil. Mag.* **46**, 1069.

Baym, G. (1961). *Phys. Rev.* **121**, 741.

Beecroft, R. I. and Swenson, C. A. (1961). *J. Phys. Chem. Solids* **18**, 329.

Bernard, W. and Callen, H. B. (1959). *Rev. mod. Phys.* **31**, 1017.

Bett, K. E., Weak, K. E. and Newitt, D. M. (1954). *Brit. J. appl. Phys.* **5**, 243.

Born, M. and Green, H. S. (1946). *Proc. roy. Soc.* *A***188**, 10.

Boyle, A. J., Burnbury, D. St. P., Edwards, C. and Hall, H. E. (1961). *Proc. phys. Soc.* **77**, 129.

Brockhouse, B. N. (1958). Suppl. *Nuovo Cimento* **9**, 45.

Brockhouse, B. N. (1961). *In* "Inelastic Scattering of Neutrons in Solids and Liquids", p. 113. IAEA, Vienna.

Brockhouse, B. N. and Pope, N. K. (1959). *Phys. Rev. Letters*, **3**, 259.
Brockhouse, B. N., Bergsma, J., Dasannacharya, B. A. and Pope, N. K. (1963). *In* "Inelastic Scattering of Neutrons in Solids and Liquids", Vol. I, p. 189. IAEA, Vienna.
Callen, H. B. (1962). *In* "Fluctuation, Relaxation and Resonance in Magnetic Systems", ed. by D. Ter Haar, Oliver & Boyd, Edinburgh.
Callen, H. B. and Welton, T. A. (1951). *Phys. Rev.* **83**, 34.
Chudley, C. T. and Elliot, R. J. (1961). *Proc. phys. Soc.* **77**, 353.
Cini-Castagnoli, G. and Ricci, F. P. (1960). *Nuovo Cimento* **15**, 795.
Cocking, S. J. and Guner, Z. (1963). *In* "Inelastic Scattering of Neutrons in Solids and Liquids", Vol. I, p. 237. IAEA, Vienna.
Cole, G. H. A. (1956). *Rep. Progr. Phys.*, **XIX**, 1.
Cusack, N. E. (1963). *Rep. Progr. Phys.* **XXVI**, 361.
Dasannacharya, B. A. and Rao, K. R. (1965). *Phys. Rev.* **137**, A417.
Davis, H. T., Rice, S. A. and Sengers, J. V. (1961). *J. chem. Phys.* **35**, 2210.
Domb, C. (1958). Suppl. *Nuovo Cimento* **9**, 9.
Egelstaff, P. A. (1961). *In* "Inelastic Scattering of Neutrons in Solids and Liquids", p. 25. IAEA, Vienna.
Egelstaff, P. A. and Schofield, P. (1962). *Nucl. Sci. Engng* **12**, 260.
Egelstaff, P. A. (1962a). The scattering of cold neutrons by metals, AERE Report R–4101. H.M.S.O., London.
Egelstaff, P. A. (1962b). *Advanc. Phys.* **11**, 203.
Egelstaff, P. A. (1963). *In* "Inelastic Scattering of Neutrons in Solids and Liquids", Vol. I, p. 65. IAEA, Vienna.
Egelstaff, P. A. (1965). *Brit. J. appl. Phys.* (to be published).
Egelstaff, P. A. (1965). *In* "Lattice Dynamics", ed. by R. F. Wallis, p. 699. Pergamon Press, New York; (1965). *J. Phys. Chem. Solids*, Suppl. 1,
Elliot, R. J. and Stern, H. (1961) *In* "Inelastic Scattering of Neutrons in Solids and Liquids", p. 61. IAEA, Vienna.
Fabelinskii, I. L. (1956). *Soviet Phys. Dokl.* **1**, 115.
Fisher, I. Z. (1962). *Soviet Phys. Uspekhi* **5**, 239.
Fraunfelder, H. (1962). "The Mössbauer Effect". Benjamin, New York.
Frenkel, J. (1946). "Kinetic Theory of Liquids". Oxford University Press, Oxford.
Furukawa, K. (1962). *Rep. Progr. Phys.* **XXV**, 395.
Gebhardt, E. and Wörwag, G. (1951). *Z. Metallk.* **42**, 358.
Gebhardt, E., Becker M. and Schäfer, S. (1952). *Z. Metallk.* **43**, 292.
Gebhardt, E. and Detering, K. (1959). *Z. Metallk.* **50**, 379.
De Gennes, P. G. (1959). *Physica* **25**, 825.
De Gennes, P. G. (1961). *In* "Inelastic Scattering of Neutrons in Solids and Liquids", p. 239. IAEA, Vienna.
Gingrich, N. S. (1943). *Rev. mod. Phys.* **15**, 90.
Ginzburg, V. L. (1958). *Soviet Phys. J.E.T.P.* **7**, 170.
Glauber, R. J. (1952). *Phys. Rev.* **87**, 189; (1955), **98**, 1692.
Green, H. S. (1952). "The Molecular Theory of Fluids." North-Holland Publ. Co., Amsterdam.
Green, H. S. (1960). *Handb. Phys.* **X**, 1.
Green, M. S. (1952). *J. chem. Phys.* **20**, 1281.
Hahn, H. (1963). *In* "Inelastic Scattering of Neutrons in Solids and Liquids", Vol. I, p. 37. IAEA, Vienna.
Hahn, H. (1961). *Z. Phys.* **165**, 569.

Herzfeld, K. F. and Litovitz, T. A. (1959). "Absorption and Dispersion of Ultrasonic Waves". Academic Press, New York.

Hoffman, R. E. (1952). *J. chem. Phys.* **20**, 1567.

Hughes, D. J., Palevsky, H., Kley, W. and Tunkelo, E. (1960). *Phys. Rev.* **119**, 872.

Van Itterbeck, A., Grevendonk, W., Van Dahl, N. and Forrez, G. (1959). *Physica* **25**, 1255.

Kadanoff, L. and Martin, P. C. (1963). *Ann. Phys.* **24**, 419.

Kahn, A. A. (1964). *Phys. Rev.* **134**, A367.

Kashchev, V. N. and Krivoglaz, M. A. (1961). *Soviet Phys. Solid State* **3**, 1107.

Kirkwood, J. G. (1946). *J. chem. Phys.* **14**, 180.

Kirkwood, J. G. and Boggs, E. M. (1942). *J. chem. Phys.* **10**, 394.

Kirkwood, J. G., Maun, E. K. and Alder, B. J. (1950). *J. chem. Phys.* **18**, 1040.

Kirkwood, J. G., Lewinson, V. A. and Alder, B. J. (1952). *J. chem. Phys.* **20**, 929.

Kleppa, O. J. (1950). *J. chem. Phys.* **18**, 1331.

Kokkedee, J. J. J. (1962). *Physica* **28**, 374.

Kokkedee, J. J. J. (1963). *In* "Inelastic Scattering of Neutrons in Solids and Liquids", Vol. I, p. 15. IAEA, Vienna.

Kosaly, G. and Turner, R. E. (1962). *Phys. Letters* **2**, 266.

Kothari, L. S. and Singwi, K. S. (1959). "Solid State Physics", Vol. 8 p. 110.

Krivoglaz, M. A. (1962). *Soviet Phys. Solid State* **3**, 2015.

Kubo, R. (1957). *J. phys. Soc. Japan* **12**, 570.

Kubo, R. (1962). *In* "Fluctuation, Relaxation and Resonance in Magnetic Systems", p. 23, ed. by D. Ter Haar. Oliver & Boyd, Edinburgh.

Kubo, R. (1963). *J. Math. Phys.* **4**, 174.

Landau, L. D. and Placzek, G. (1934). *Phys. Z. Soviet,* **5**, 172.

Landolt-Börnstein. (1961). Zahlenwerte und Funktionen aus . . ., 6. aufl. Springer-Verlag, Berlin.

Lange, N., Pippel, N. and Bendel F. (1959). *Z. phys. Chem.* **212**, 238.

Larsson, K. E., Holmryd, S. and Otnes, K. (1961). *In* "Inelastic Scattering of Neutrons in Solids and Liquids", p. 329. IAEA, Vienna.

Larsson, K. E. and Dahlborg, U. (1963). *In* "Inelastic Scattering of Neutrons in Solids and Liquids", p. 317. IAEA, Vienna.

Larsson, K. E., Dahlborg, U. and Jovic, D. (1965). *In* "Inelastic Scattering of Neutrons", Vol. II, p. 117. IAEA, Vienna.

Lax, M. (1964). *J. Phys. Chem. Solids* **25**, 487.

Liquid Metals Handbook (1965). U.S. Government Printing Office, Washington.

Maradudin, A. A. and Fein, A. E. (1962). *Phys. Rev.* **128**, 2589.

Martin, P. and Schwinger, J. (1959). *Phys. Rev.* **115**, 1342.

Meyer, R. E. and Nachtrieb, N. H. (1955). *J. chem. Phys.* **23**, 1851.

Mori, H. (1958). *Phys. Rev.* **112**, 1829.

Naghizadeh, J. and Rice, S. A. (1962). *J. chem. Phys.* **36**, 2710.

Nelkin, M. S. (1960). *Phys. Rev.* **119**, 741.

Nelkin, M. S. (1961). *In* "Inelastic Scattering of Neutrons in Solids and Liquids", p. 3. IAEA, Vienna.

Nelkin, M. and Ghatak, A. (1964). *Phys. Rev.* **135**, A4.

Oskotskii, V. S. (1963). *Soviet Phys. Solid State* **5**, 789.

Percus, J. K. and Yevick, G. J. (1958). *Phys. Rev.* **110**, 1.

Placzek, G. (1952). *Phys. Rev.* **86**, 377.

Pochapsky, T. E. (1951). *Phys. Rev.* **84**, 553.

Prigogine, I. (1957). "The Molecular Theory of Solution". North Holland Publ. Co., Amsterdam.

Rahman, A. (1963). *Phys. Rev.* **130**, 1334.

Rahman, A. (1964). *Phys. Rev.* **136**, A405.

Rahman, A., Singwi, K. S. and Sjölander, A. (1962). *Phys. Rev.* **126**, 986, 997.

Randolph, P. D. (1964). *Phys. Rev.* **134**, A1238.

Rice, S. A. and Alnatt, A. R. (1961). *J. chem. Phys.* **34**, 2144.

Rosenbaum, M. and Zweifel, P. F. (1965). *Phys. Rev.* **137**, B271.

Rothman, S. J. and Hall, L. D. (1956). *Trans. Amer. Inst. Mining Met. Petrol Engrs* **206**, 199.

Rowlinson, J. S. (1959). "Liquids and Liquid Mixtures." Butterworths, London.

Rubin, R. (1960). *J. math. Phys.* **1**, 309.

Rubin, R. (1961). *J. math. Phys.* **2**, 373.

Ruijgrok, Th. W. (1963). *Physica* **29**, 617.

Rytov, S. M. (1958). *Soviet Phys. J.E.T.P.* **6**, 130, 401, 513.

Schofield, P. (1960). *Phys. Rev. Letters* **4**, 239.

Schofield, P. (1961). *In* "Inelastic Scattering of Neutrons in Solids and Liquids", p. 39. IAEA, Vienna.

Schofield, P. (1962). *In* "Fluctuation, Relaxation and Resonance in Magnetic Systems," p. 207. ed. by D. Ter Haar, Oliver & Boyd, Edinburgh.

Singwi, K. S. and Sjölander, A. (1960a). *Phys. Rev.* **119**, 863.

Singwi, K. S. and Sjölander, A. (1960b). *Phys. Rev.* **120**, 1093.

Singwi, K. S. and Sjölander, A. (1964). *Physics Letters* **9**, 120.

Singwi, K. S. (1964). *Phys. Rev.* **136**, A969.

Singwi, K. S. and Feldman, G. (1965). *In* "Inelastic Neutron Scattering in Solids and Liquids", Vol. II, p. 85. IAEA, Vienna.

Sjölander, A. (1958). *Ark. Fys.* **14**, 315.

Sjölander, A. (1964). "Phonons and Phonon Interactions", Aarhus Summer School Lectures 1963, ed. by T. A. Bak, p. 76. Benjamin, New York.

Stewart, J. W. (1959). *J. Phys. Chem. Solids* **12**, 122.

Summerfield, G. C. and Zweifel, P. F. (1963). *Phys. Rev.* **131**, 1149.

Thomson, B. V. (1963). *Phys. Rev.* **131**, 1420.

Turchin, V. F. (1963). "Slow Neutrons". Госатомиздат, Москва, (in Russian).

Turner, R. E. (1961). *Physica* **27**, 260.

Van Hove, L. (1954). *Phys. Rev.* **95**, 249.

Van Hove, L. (1958). *Physica* **24**, 404.

Van Hove, L., Hugenholtz, N. M. and Howland, L. P. (1961). "Quantum Theory of Many-Particle Systems". Benjamin, New York.

Van Leeuwen, J. M. J., Groenveld, J. and De Boer, J. (1959). *Physica* **25**, 792.

Vineyard, G. H. (1958). *Phys. Rev.* **110**, 999.

Wainwright, T., and Alder, B. J. (1958). Suppl. *Nuovo Cimento* **9**, 116.

Yang, L., Kado, S. and Derge, G. (1958). *Trans Amer. Inst. Min. Met. Petrol Engrs* **212**, 628.

Yip, S. and Nelkin, M. S. (1964). *Phys. Rev.* **135**, A1241.

Zhdanova, N. F. (1957). *Soviet Phys. J.E.T.P.* **4**, 749.

CHAPTER 8

Experimental Results on Liquids

K. E. Larsson

Royal Institute of Technology, Stockholm, Sweden

8.1 Introduction.. 347
8.2 Neutron Scattering Experiments on Water............................ 350
8.3 Liquid Hydrogen.. 367
8.4 Various Hydrogenous Liquids.. 373
8.5 Glycerol... 378
8.6 Coherent Scattering from Liquid Metals............................. 387
8.7 Liquid Sodium.. 398
8.8 Liquid Argon... 402
8.9 Liquid Bromine... 407
References.. 409

List of Symbols

B	Volume per nucleus in a crystal	R_M	Radius of molecule
c	Characteristic time for onset of diffusion	$\sqrt{\overline{u^2}}$	r.m.s. Displacement of an atom
F_τ	Structure factor for plane τ in crystal	x^2	m.s. Displacement deduced from Debye-Waller factor
f_1	Jump frequency	Z	Structure factor for a polycrystal
f'	Maximum frequency for diffusive modes	ΔQ_ω	Width of neutron peak at constant ω
f_D	Effective Debye frequency (h.f. cut-off)	ΔQ_0	Width at constant ω for elastic process
J	Quantum number for rotation	ϵ_0	Activation energy for diffusion
R_0	Correlation range	τ_0	Correlation time (sometimes time between jumps)
R_G	Radius of globule		

8.1 Introduction

Thermal neutrons are almost perfect probe particles to be sent into a many-body system like a liquid for reasons discussed by van Hove (1954). The fluctuation phenomena in a liquid (or a solid) may be characterized by a correlation range, R_0, of the order of 10^{-8} cm and a correlation time, τ_0, of the order of 10^{-13} sec. The time variation of the fluctuation affects the energy and angular distribution of scattered particles only if the probe particle spends at least a time, τ_1, comparable to τ_0 over the correlation range R_0. For a slow neutron having a velocity comparable to the atomic velocity, $\tau_1 \sim \tau_0$, and thus it spends a sufficiently long time in an interaction region to "see" the changes occurring. It is obvious that under most conditions a fast neutron will not see the changes occurring in detail, whereas a slow one will see considerable detail. van Hove's treatment shows that the important variables are the momentum and energy transferred rather than the incident energy and angle of scatter. Thus a high energy neutron may be used to obtain the same information as given by a slower neutron, but high resolution and small scattering angles are necessary. It is then possible, even in this case, to see the small energy changes occurring round the ingoing energy which reflect the various modes of motion in which the scattering centre was occupied during the interaction with the neutron. If, however, the momentum transfer is too high (say) corresponding to a 0·5 Å wavelength neutron scattered at 90°, then the only fluctuation observed would be that equivalent to a perfect gas. A suitably chosen neutron experiment may see both diffusive and vibratory motions performed by the scattering nuclei. On the other hand for very low momentum transfers nothing but the diffusive motions would be observed. The neutron undergoes a momentum change $\Delta p = \hbar|\mathbf{Q}|$ in the scattering process, where $|\mathbf{Q}| = |\mathbf{k} - \mathbf{k}_0|$, and k, k_0 are the scattered and ingoing neutron wave vectors. From the uncertainty relation it follows that the neutron's observation range is

$$\Delta x \sim \frac{\hbar}{\Delta p} = \frac{1}{|\mathbf{Q}|} \tag{8.1}$$

If k_0 is suitably chosen Q may be varied in the experiment so that an adjustment round the value of about $\Delta x \sim 10^{-8}$ cm may be performed.

These general conclusions are clearly reflected in most neutron scattering experiments on liquids. The great majority of such experiments have been performed with neutrons of wavelength 4–6 Å. This is true for practically all those experiments concerned with the study of diffusive motions and those motions of vibratory character corresponding to energies less than 100 meV. The beryllium filter technique can be used to produce the ingoing spectrum, or a monochromatizing chopper is used together with the filter, or in other cases a rotating crystal is used to select the ingoing long wavelength neutrons (see Chapter 2).

Two different types of incident neutron spectrum have been employed for the work described in this chapter. One of them, called the "full cold neutron spectrum", consists of the entire spectrum passed by a filter—usually a Be filter (see Chapter 3). This spectrum has a sharp rising edge at the filter cutoff (3·95 Å for Be) and at longer wavelengths, or lower energies, the intensity falls off as $E dE$. For diffusion studies the broadening of the sharp rising edge is frequently observed. The second type of spectrum is the "line spectrum" where one of the velocity or wavelength selection techniques described in Chapter 2 and 3 has been employed to isolate a narrow band of neutron velocities, whose width is usually about 2–8 %. The broadening of this "line" can then be used to study diffusion processes.

Because of the low ingoing neutron energy most of the inelastically scattered neutron spectrum corresponds to energy gain processes. For large energy gains the scattered intensity is cut down by a population factor $\exp(-\hbar\omega/kT)$, and therefore there is an upper limit to the possible range of energy gains that may be studied. For a sample temperature corresponding to $kT \sim 0.025$ eV this makes the observation of an energy gain greater than 0.1–0.15 eV virtually impossible. In this case the energy loss method is the only solution, and such experiments have been performed with the aid of triple axis crystal spectrometers, phased rotor spectrometers and the beryllium filter detector technique in conjunction with a crystal monochromator (see Chapter 3).

The wavelength resolution attained in the majority of the cases of liquid diffusion studies is of the order of 1–3 % for the scattered neutrons, although it has in some cases been as poor as 10 % or as good as 0.5 %. This means that the resolution width of the ingoing neutron spectrum is, for instance, 0.08 Å at 4 Å. If a 4 Å neutron is used, its energy is 5.2 meV and an energy change of about 0.1 meV is the limit of resolution. All methods used involve a decrease in the resolution with increasing neutron energy such that at an energy gain of 100 meV the corresponding resolution width would be about 10 meV in the example given above.

Ideally the initial scattering experiment to perform on liquids would be to investigate a completely incoherent scatterer, because only in this case are all the motions simply related to the cross-section (see Section 1.5). Also most theoretical efforts (Chapter 7) have gone into the prediction of the doubly differential scattering cross-section for an incoherent scatterer. For simplicity the scatterer should be a monatomic liquid. Liquid vanadium would be such a scatterer but as the containment of this highly corrosive liquid presents a formidable problem, no such experiments have so far been made. An approximation to the ideal case is presented by some hydrogenous liquids like water or liquid hydrogen. Water was studied very extensively because of the ease of obtaining good scattering samples and because it is a reactor moderator. A number of other hydrogenous liquids have been studied such as alcohols, glycerol, oleic acid, methane, pentane, diphenyl, diphenyloxide. In all these liquids, the hydrogen nucleus is the main scatterer and also it scatters incoherently. The diffusive and vibrational motions in hydrogenous liquids will be discussed in detail in Sections 8.2 to 8.5.

If a deuteron is substituted for the proton in H_2O the question arises whether there is a strong coherent effect in the scattering picture. Experiments indicate that some effect occurs although the magnitude is not well known. The question of whether the coherent momentum conservation rule $\mathbf{k} - \mathbf{k}_0 = \mathbf{q} + 2\pi\boldsymbol{\tau}$ well known in crystal scattering (Chapter 5) has any meaning in a liquid is more clearly studied in some experiments on liquid metals. Inelastic scattering experiments, performed on liquid lead, tin, sodium and aluminium, seem to indicate that the analogy between a liquid and a solid may be carried very far and they will be discussed in Sections 8.6 and 8.7.

Of interest also are experiments performed on liquid argon, a monatomic non-metallic liquid with weak binding between atoms, and on liquid bromine, which is a relatively simple molecular liquid. Unfortunately liquid argon is both a coherent and an incoherent scatterer, which somewhat complicates the interpretation of the scattered neutron spectrum.

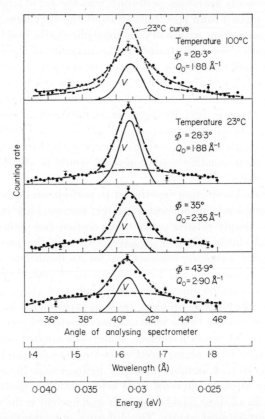

FIG. 8.1. Measured energy distributions of 1·62 Å neutrons scattered by water specimens at 23°C and 100°C and at various scattering angles ϕ and with the momentum transfers centred round the values Q_0. The curves marked V indicate the instrumental resolution.

8.2 Neutron Scattering Experiments on Water

The liquid investigated most thoroughly is water, and a review of the main lines in the history of neutron scattering on water will show essential steps in the development of the field.

In some preliminary experiments on room temperature water, Brockhouse (1958) used the crystal spectrometer technique and ingoing neutrons of wavelengths of 1·2 and 1·6 Å. An example of his data is shown in Fig. 8.1, and it may be seen how the data divide intuitively into a "quasi-elastic" peak and an inelastic background. The "elastically" scattered neutron intensity varies very strongly with angle and Brockhouse found that this angular distribution could be described by a Debye-Waller factor $\exp(-x^2Q^2)$. He estimated the constant x^2 to be 0·12–0·16 corresponding to a root-mean-square displacement $\sqrt{u^2}$ of the hydrogen nucleus of $\sim$1 Å. As however a high ingoing neutron energy was used, the resolution was too poor to reveal details of the inelastic component. It was speculated that the inelastic component could be described by the mass 18 gas model cross-section formula. Other experiments using the beryllium filter-chopper method revealed a peak in the inelastic spectrum at about 0·07 eV, which was attributed to a hindered rotation of a water molecule. A transition at a similar energy had already been discovered in Raman spectroscopy and assigned to the hindered rotation of the molecule.

After having subtracted the inelastic intensity with the aid of the mass 18 gas formula, Brockhouse compared his quasi-elastic intensity with the predictions of two models. As the intensity of the quasi-elastic peak varied with angle as $\exp(-x^2Q^2)$ it is probable that a thermal cloud is set up by the proton bound to the water molecule similar to the well known phenomenon in solids. In contrast to the case for solids this cloud must expand with time and in the limit of long times the cloud must develop as $D\tau$, as predicted by the simple diffusion theory. Here D is the coefficient of self diffusion. This theory gives a cross-section of the type (see Section 7.11)

$$\frac{d^2\sigma}{d\Omega d\omega} = \text{const.} \ \frac{e^{-x^2Q^2}DQ^2}{(DQ^2)^2 + \omega^2} \tag{8.2a}$$

The angular variation is determined mainly by the Debye-Waller factor as for a solid but the width, ΔE, of the line is given by

$$\Delta E = 2\hbar DQ^2 \tag{8.2b}$$

as discussed at equations (7.109) and (7.114). Using tracer measured values for the diffusion coefficient Brockhouse compared his experimental quasi-elastic lines with those calculated from equation (8.2a). The experimental line widths were considerably narrower than the calculated ones (Fig. 8.2). Simple, continuous diffusion thus cannot be the true reason for the line broadening and the diffusive behaviour in water.

Brockhouse considered another extreme model by assuming that diffusion occurs in large jumps corresponding to an activation process as in a solid. In between the jumps, which occur with a frequency f_1, there is ample time to allow for thermal cloud formation. This model gives a cross-section

$$\frac{\mathrm{d}^2\sigma}{\mathrm{d}\Omega\mathrm{d}\omega} = \mathrm{const.}\ \frac{f_1\,e^{-x^2Q^2}}{f_1^2+\omega^2} \qquad (8.3)$$

Again there is a Debye-Waller factor governing the intensity variation with angle but the width $\varDelta E$ of the line is now given by $2\hbar f_1$. From dielectric relaxation time measurements on water at 25°C a value of $8\cdot3\times10^{-12}$ sec was taken for $1/f_1$, which is the average time between jumps. It was clear,

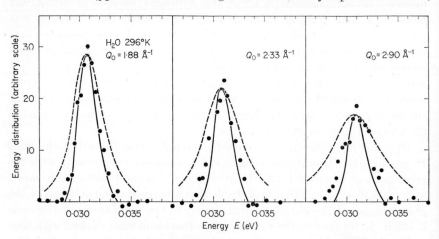

Fig. 8.2. The "elastic" components of the spectra of Fig. 8.1 plotted as a function of energy. The resolutions measured with vanadium are shown as heavy lines. The dashed lines are calculated from the simple diffusion theory.

however, that the quasi-elastic lines calculated in this way were too narrow. From these results it was concluded that the true diffusive process in water is a mixture of both the processes mentioned above.

Using the rotating crystal technique Brockhouse (1959) repeated the study of the quasi-elastic intensity with 4·15 Å incident neutrons and a much higher resolution corresponding to a full width at half maximum of 0·18 Å at 4 Å. The study was extended to cover ice as well as liquid water at temperatures from +4·5°C to +70°C. Also a study was made of heavy water. A broadening of the quasielastic line as a function of temperature was observed and after having subtracted an inelastic background using the mass 18 gas model, a Lorentzian function of the simple diffusion type (equation (8.2a)) was used to fit the data. From this fit effective values of D were derived, which came out about half the D values obtained by tracer methods. This was taken as confirmation that simple diffusion cannot describe the diffusive process in water but rather that a variety of diffusive motions must occur.

A study of cold neutron scattering from water was made by Hughes *et al.* (1960). Using "the full cold neutron spectrum" they analysed the energy of the scattered neutrons at an angle of 90° with the aid of chopper and time-of-flight technique (Chapter 2). The resolution in this measurement was 3 %

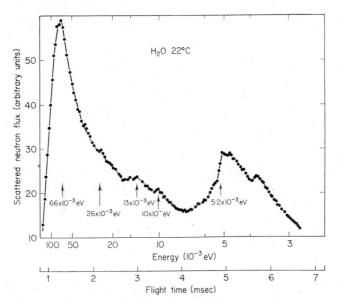

FIG. 8.3. The time-of-flight spectrum of cold neutrons scattered at 90° by a light water sample at 22°C. The arrow at $5 \cdot 2 \times 10^{-2}$ eV marks the edge of the "elastic" peak and the ingoing neutron spectrum, the others show various inelastic peaks for large energy gains. These data have not been corrected for the chopper "cut-off" function—Fig. 2.5—which affects the relative magnitude of the elastic and inelastic regions.

at 4 Å, or a ΔE of 0·32 meV at 5·2 meV. This study gave surprising results (Fig. 8.3) as follows:

1. Instead of a diffusion broadened quasi-elastically scattered peak they observed a reproduction of the ingoing beryllium filtered spectrum including the sharp break at 3·952 Å. Within their statistical accuracy they were not able to see any line broadening at all in the sense expected from the formulae (8·2a) or (8·2b).

2. They observed small energy transfers at 0·5–0·7 meV on both sides of the sharp beryllium edge.

3. A broad inelastic scattered spectrum rich in detail was observed. Distinct energy transfers of 61, 21, 8 and 5 meV were observed and compared to Raman spectra.

The absence of a diffusion broadening of the quasi-elastic peak seemed in contradiction to the observations of Brockhouse. Also another study of the quasi-elastically scattered peak at 45°C resulted in a failure to observe any diffusion broadening. In fact it was concluded by Hughes *et al.* that the width of their peak was less than 10 % of the value predicted by the formula $\Delta E = 2\hbar D Q^2$. These authors drew the conclusion that the effective mass of the scatterer must be much larger than that of a single molecule, implying strong binding of the scattering proton in liquid water.

To test the possible gas-like behaviour of the water molecules a scattering experiment was performed on water vapour at 105°C and 20 atm pressure. The data could not be explained by the mass 18 gas formula (Fig. 8.4). A

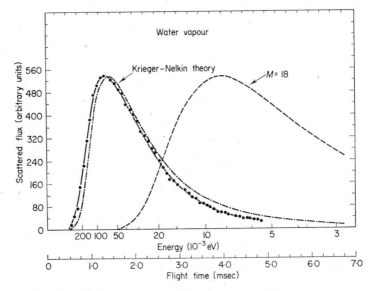

FIG. 8.4. The time-of-flight spectrum of cold neutrons scattered at 90° by water vapour at 20 atmospheres pressure. The dashed curve showing the reasonable fit with the experiment is a calculated distribution based on the Krieger-Nelkin theory. The distribution predicted by the gas model, with a scattering centre mass of 18, is also given.

better fit to the experimental data on water vapour was obtained by the Krieger-Nelkin cross-section formula in which some account is taken of the vibrational, rotational and translational effects (Chapter 9). The further discussion of molecular data given in Fig. 10.9, for example, shows that the momentum transfer was too great to see the mass 18 peak in this case.

The origin of the small energy transfers at ± 0.5–0.7 meV, however, could not be explained. Transitions in the rotational spectrum of the free water molecule of the same magnitude had been computed but such transitions would have been smeared out by the recoil effect—the Doppler broadening. A hindrance of the rotations on the other hand immediately increases the energy. The peak at an energy transfer of 61 meV corresponds to the hindered rotation peak discussed earlier.

About this time, several neutron scattering experiments on water were performed. Using the "full cold neutron spectrum" and the filter chopper technique Larsson et al. (1960) performed a series of measurements on light and heavy water. In a first series of experiments the resolution was 0·12 Å at 4 Å but was later improved to 0·08 Å. The neutron spectrometer allowed scattering angles between 30° and 90° to be investigated. Again the same type of scattered spectrum rich in detail was observed at room temperature.

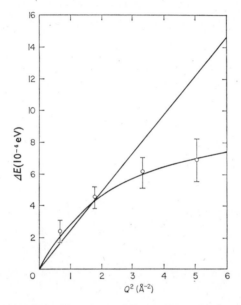

FIG. 8.5. Observed line width values as a function of the square of the momentum transferred in a quasi-elastic scattering process in water at 20°C. The straight line corresponds to the prediction of the continuous diffusion model, the curved line to the quasi-crystalline model, equation (8.4).

Analysis of the quasi-elastic intensity showed that its angular variation could be described by $\exp-0{\cdot}142Q^2$, i.e. by a Debye-Waller factor as in a solid. From the number 0·142 a Debye temperature of 130°K was derived assuming that the mass of the scatterer was 18. It was also shown that a diffusive line broadening was occurring. It was found that the line broadening was about half of that which could be expected on the simple diffusion assumption at 90° angle ($Q^2 \simeq 5$ Å^{-2}, Fig. 8.5.) The observations of Larsson et al. thus showed a line width broader than that of Hughes et al. and more of the same order as that of Brockhouse.

The shape of the line width curve was such that it could be analysed using a model formulated by Singwi and Sjölander (1960) which extended the ideas behind equation (8.3). In this model the molecules perform vibrations in a position for a certain time before they jump to another position, a picture proposed for liquids much earlier by Frenkel (1946). The line width formula used is (see equation (7.116))

$$\Delta E = \frac{2\hbar}{\tau_0}\left(1 - \frac{e^{-x^2Q^2}}{1+Q^2D\tau_0}\right) \tag{8.4}$$

It is seen by series expansion of (8.4) that when $Q \to 0$ and $\overline{u^2} \ll 6D\tau_0$, ΔE reduces to the simple diffusion case (8.2), and if $Q^2 \to \infty$ the line width

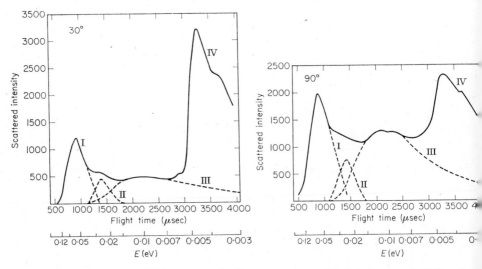

FIG. 8.6. The time-of-flight spectra of cold neutrons scattered from light water at 20°C and at scattering angles 30° and 90°. The dashed lines represent separation of the spectra into various inelastically (curves I, II and III) and elastically (curve IV) scattered parts.

reduces to $2\hbar/\tau_0$ in agreement with Brockhouse's formula (8.3). Singwi and Sjölander (1960) used this model to interpret the data of Hughes et al. (1960) and concluded that τ_0 must be greater than 4×10^{-12} sec, a time very long compared to the periods of vibration in a lattice. This period is given by the Debye temperature and is of the order of 10^{-13} sec. In the case of the data of Larsson et al. (1960) shown in Fig. 8.5, the value of τ_0 is 1.5×10^{-12} sec. These values will be discussed again at the end of this section.

With these results in mind, Larsson et al. studied the variation of inelastic intensity with scattering angle to discover if the formula used for incoherent scattering from a solid was applicable. The energy transfers in the inelastic spectrum were divided into several parts shown in Fig. (8.6). The lowest, marked by III in this figure, should correspond to acoustic and optical vibrations with the molecule as a dynamic unit, and its area corresponds to the integrated doubly differential cross-section

$$\int \frac{d^2\sigma}{d\Omega dE}\, dE \to \frac{d\sigma}{d\Omega}$$

The ratio of the areas under these curves at angles of 90° and 30° was evaluated, giving an experimental value 2·70. If on the other hand the inelastic cross-section in the Debye approximation with $\Theta_D = 130°$K was calculated for $\Phi = 30°$ and $\Phi = 90°$ including multiphonon terms, the same ratio was 2·60. The angular variation of the intensity of the low energy part, 0–25 meV, of the inelastic spectrum could thus be described by a Debye model with $\Theta_D = 130°$K, in good agreement with the Debye temperature determined from the intensity of the quasi-elastic component.

Another approach was developed by Egelstaff (1961) and has been described (in part) in Section 7.10. In addition to relating the frequency function $z(\omega)$ to the velocity correlation function he showed how it was related to the cross-section or scattering law. The required relation is obtained by expanding the cross-section in powers of Q^2 and is (see equation (1·43)):

$$z(\omega) = \frac{M}{kT}\left[\frac{\omega^2}{Q^2}\tilde{S}_s(Q,\omega)\right]_{Q\to 0} \tag{8.5}$$

To obtain $z(\omega)$ it is necessary to measure $S(Q,\omega)$ over a wide range of momentum and energy transfers and extrapolate the results to $Q = 0$. Frequency spectra for H_2O at 20°C and 150°C were obtained by Egelstaff et al. (1961, 1963) using this method and their room temperature result is given in Fig. 8.7. This spectrum shows the hindered rotation peak discussed earlier and a low energy peak due to intramolecular vibrations. At 150°C the hindered rotational peak was still clearly visible and its energy was approximately the same as at room temperature.

In order to perform the extrapolation Egelstaff et al. assumed that G_s was Gaussian in r (see discussion in Section 7.9). From this assumption and the measured frequency spectrum they calculated $S(Q,\omega)$ by the method described by Egelstaff and Schofield (1962). Also given in Fig. 8.7 is the fit of these calculations to their data; the accuracy of the fit tends to confirm the validity of the Gaussian approximation and to justify the extrapolations. They also took care that their calculations and derived spectra satisfied the theoretical moments given at equation (7.15). The departure of the data from the calculations at the lowest values of Q was ascribed by these authors to multiple scattering in the sample and to non-Gaussian terms in $G_s(r,\tau)$.

In a new series of measurements on light and heavy water Larsson and

Dahlborg (1962) covered temperatures in light water and ice from $-3°C$ to $+92°C$ and in heavy water and ice from $-2°C$ to $+300°C$. With cold neutrons it is impossible to cover a large range of Q values, and therefore the extrapolation method of Egelstaff cannot be used. This is particularly true for large energy transfers. Therefore Larsson *et al.* used the principle that cross-sections measured at as small an angle of observation as possible must

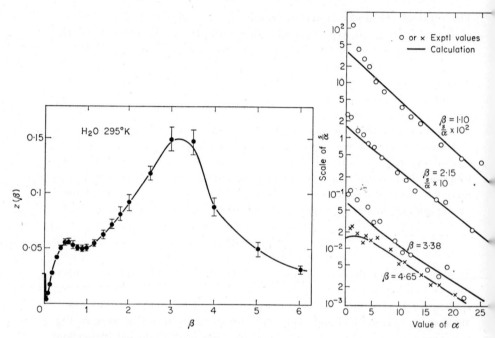

Fig. 8.7. The left part of the figure shows the frequency spectrum $z(\beta)$ for H_2O at $22°C$ derived by the extrapolation technique of Egelstaff ($\beta = \hbar\omega/kT$). The right part of the figure shows the technique of extrapolation of the observed data to $Q = 0$ for a constant β to obtain a point on the $z(\omega)$ distribution. Actually Q is not used as a variable but rather the dimensionless $\alpha = \hbar^2 Q^2/2MkT$. The solid lines are calculated using the theory of Egelstaff and Schofield (1962).

contain a minimum contribution from Q^4 and higher terms. This is particularly true if the Debye-temperature is not too small, that is if the binding of the dynamical unit that scatters the neutron is rather strong. Thus an angle of observation of 30° was used for the measurement of the scattered spectrum and the one-phonon term in the phonon expansion formula was used to calculate $z(\omega)$ from the observations. Tests were made that the frequency spectra derived from the data at 30° and 90° angle of observation, which should of course give the same $z(\omega)$, did not give too different results.

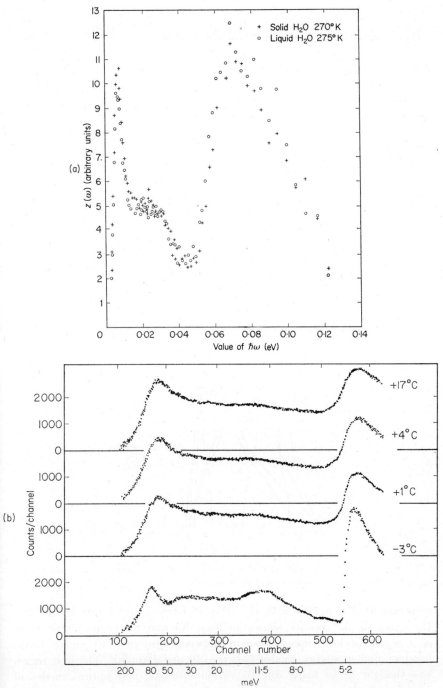

Fig. 8.8. Spectra for H_2O derived from measurements on the solid and liquid phases: (a) $z(\omega)$ function derived by Larsson and Dahlborg (1962); (b) raw data of Golikov *et al.* (1965), the quasi-elastic peak is at 5·2 meV.

The most striking results are those obtained from ice and low temperature water. Larsson and Dahlborg found that the frequency spectra derived from ice at −3°C and water at +2°C are coincident (Fig. 8.8a). Golikov *et al.* (1965) found a difference between water and ice (Fig. 8.8(b)); their ice spectrum agreeing with the spectra of Fig. 8.8(a) while their water

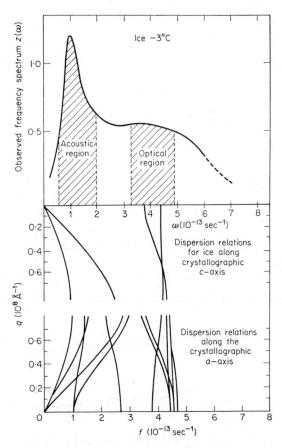

FIG. 8.9. The low energy part of the observed frequency spectra for H_2O at −3°C compared with dispersion relations calculated for ice.

spectrum at 1°C agrees with the data of Larsson and Dahlborg at 22°C. However, all the results shown in Figs. 8.7 and 8.8 suggest that there is a region of low energy motions between zero and 40 and a broad band of higher energy modes between 40 and 120 meV. The first region was thought of as being due to various acoustic and optical modes of motion with the molecule as a dynamical unit and the second as a region of hindered rotations of the molecule as previously discussed. The first assumption received support from a calculation by Forslind (1954) of the dispersion relations in ice. The low energy region of high intensity in the frequency spectrum corresponds nicely to the regions where the calculated dispersion relations occur most densely (Fig. 8.9). The second assumption was checked experimentally by performing the same scattering experiment on heavy water. It turned out that the high energy peak was shifted down in energy in about the ratio of $\sqrt{2}$ as it should be if the dynamical unit was in the second case mass 2 and in the first case mass 1. Also the low energy part of the spectrum did not move along the energy scale when deuterons were substituted for protons, which agrees with the assumption that the mass of the dynamical unit in light water was 18 and in heavy water 20. A change proportional to $\sqrt{(20/18)} = 1.05$ could not be distinguished in the experiment and may perhaps have occurred.

In the case of heavy water interference effects may be expected. Insufficient work has been done so far to elucidate these phenomena (see Chapter 7). The frequency spectra for light and heavy water are alike (disregarding the shift in the hindered rotation peak discussed above). It seems probable therefore that the distortion of the derived frequency spectra caused by coherent scattering effects could be small at least at the higher frequencies.*

Larsson and Dahlborg (1963) derived a frequency spectrum for several temperatures up to 300°C for heavy water. The similarity of the spectra at all temperatures probably means that there exists a rather long delay time before diffusion sets in, even at the highest temperatures. Also it was found that the prominent hindered rotation peak in the frequency spectrum of D_2O moves from 56 meV at 278°K to about 40 meV at 573°K. Over the temperature range 295–425°K, Egelstaff et al. (1963) report that the energy of the hindered rotation peak of H_2O does not shift significantly. This means that there is still a strong hindrance of the rotational motions of the molecules even at high temperature because for free rotation the peak energy should decrease (Chapter 9).

The main difference between the frequency spectra of Egelstaff et al., Larsson et al. (Figs. 8.7 and 8.8) and Golikov et al. is the magnitude of the low energy peak at 10 meV. This difference requires further and detailed study.

Several other experiments have been performed on water. In particular the existence or non-existence of the sharp peaks at energy changes of ± 0.5 meV announced by Hughes et al. stimulated much further research. Using a mechanical monochromator giving a spectrum of a full width of 0.6 Å at 4 Å, Cribier and Jacrot (1961) studied the quasi-elastic peak of neutrons scattered

---

* See, however, the calculations of Butler (1963), and comments of Egelstaff et al. (1963).

13*

at 90° from light water at temperatures of 30° and 43°C. At both temperatures they observed a considerable line broadening but no sign of the small peaks reported by Hughes *et al.* In fact they found that their results could be described by simple diffusion theory (Fig. 8.10). This analysis differs from the others described here in that no allowance was made for inelastic background on the long wavelength side (compare Fig. 8.1 and 8.10). By fitting the neutron cross-section formula (8.1) to their result, they found values for

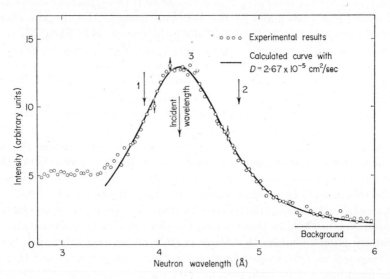

Fig. 8.10. The wavelength spectrum of neutrons of energy 5 meV scattered from light water at 27°C. The solid line represents the distribution calculated on the basis of simple diffusion theory. The arrow marked 2 shows the position of the small energy transfers reported by Hughes *et al.*, the arrow 1 shows the frame overlap limit (Chapter 2) and 3 shows the position of a Bragg reflection from the container (Cribier and Jacrot, 1961).

D in good agreement with both magnetic resonance and tracer measured diffusion constants, but the measured widths were about 70 % higher than those of Brockhouse and Larsson *et al.* This is to be expected from the method of analysis.

Another neutron study of room temperature light water was performed by Stiller and Danner (1961). Using the beryllium detector technique (Chapter 3) they investigated the inelastic as well as the quasi-elastic scattering region. Their resolution at the beryllium edge energy, 5·2 meV, was given as 0·15 meV. They observed a broad inelastic spectrum, rich in detail and a quasi-elastic peak, which they considered to be only very little broadened. The width of the quasi-elastic line over the angular range of observation from 30° to 90° varied linearly between 0·17 and 0·23 meV.

These values are much smaller than those of Brockhouse *et al.* and Larsson *et al.* but may be comparable to or slightly larger than those of Hughes *et al.* Also small peaks were observed near the quasi-elastic line. One at about 0·7 meV was attributed to water but they also observed other small peaks which they considered as due to instrumental effects.

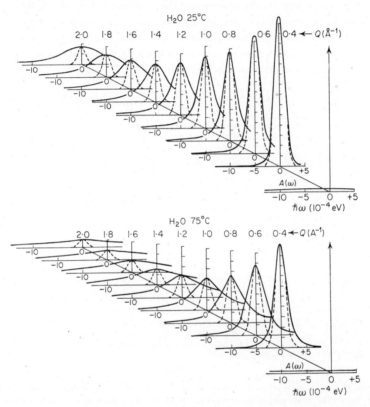

FIG. 8.11. The energy distributions of 4·059 Å neutrons scattered from H_2O at 25°C and 75°C for momentum transfers in the range $0·4 < Q < 2Å^{-1}$. The energy resolution of the spectrometer is shown as dashed curves.

In another series of experiments using the rotating crystal technique but now with a higher resolution, 0·2 meV at 4 Å, Sakamoto *et al.* (1962) repeated the systematic study of the quasi-elastic scattering from water made earlier by Brockhouse. The intensity at small energy transfers was used to obtain the scattering function $S(Q,\omega)$ (equation (7.11)) over its most intense region and for a large range of Q values. Sample temperatures of 25° and 75°C were employed, and the results are summarized in Fig. 8.11. These experimenters did not see any sign of the small energy transfers observed by Hughes *et al.*, by Larsson *et al.* and by Stiller and Danner. On the other hand a considerable line broadening was observed at a Q value corresponding to 90° angle of observation somewhat smaller than that observed by Larsson *et al.*, much larger than that of Stiller and Danner and smaller than that given by Cribier and Jacrot. Due to theoretical work by several authors (Sections 7.10 and 7.11) it was now universally understood that the line width curves, ΔE against Q^2, have to approach the simple diffusion line as Q tends to zero. Such a behaviour was observed, and the slope of the line width curves as $Q \rightarrow 0$, which should be $2\hbar D$, was in agreement with D values obtained by tracer and other long time observation methods.

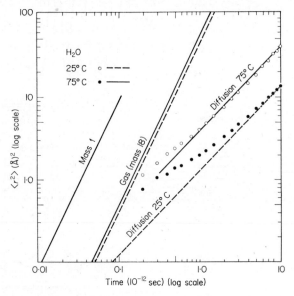

FIG. 8.12. The measured mean square displacement $\langle r^2 \rangle$ of a proton in water at times $2 \times 10^{-13} < \tau < 10^{-11}$ sec and at two temperatures 25° and 75°C compared to various theoretical calculations.

van Hove's cross-section formulation (equation (7.8)) shows that the space and time fourier transform of $S(Q,\omega)$ is the self correlation function $G_s(r,\tau)$. Also the slope of the intermediate scattering function at $Q = 0$ (equation (7.10)) is equal to the mean square deviation $\overline{u^2}$ of a molecule from the origin as a function of time. The latter quantity is related to G_s by

$$\overline{u^2} = \int_0^\infty r^2 4\pi r^2 G_s(r,t)\mathrm{d}r \qquad (8.6)$$

Sakamoto *et al.* transformed their data to obtain $I(Q,t)$ and hence $\overline{u^2}$.

The values of $\overline{u^2}$ for the two temperatures 25° and 75°C are plotted in Fig. 8.12. Given in the figure are the predicted variations of $\overline{u^2}$ for the simple diffusion case and for two examples of the gas model (mass 18 and mass 1). It is seen how the experimental points for long times coincide nicely with the prediction of the diffusion theory. At 25°C a deviation occurs at a time of about 3×10^{-12} sec. This time should be compared to the residence time of 1.5×10^{-12} sec derived from an application of the Singwi-Sjölander model to the data of Larsson et al. as described above, and the time of 2×10^{-12} sec obtained by Egelstaff and described in Section 7.9 (see Table 7.6). There is a very gratifying agreement between the three results, and they indicate that a simple diffusion does not set in until a time of the order of 2×10^{-12} sec has elapsed. Also, at 75°C the corresponding time appears to be in the range of 10^{-12} sec. It is clear that the gas model predictions are not in agreement with the observations in this time range.

A high resolution study of the quasi-elastic scattering from water at 25°C was performed by Bajorik et al. (1963) using a pulsed fast reactor as a source and a beryllium filter to produce the sharp edge at 4 Å (Chapter 2 and 3). The resolution at 4 Å was as high as 0·03 meV. A broadening was observed at the angle of 75° of 0·6 meV in good agreement with the data of Larsson et al. (Fig. 8.5), about half the value predicted by simple diffusion, somewhat higher than the data of Sakamoto et al., three times higher than the data of Stiller and Danner and much higher than the data of Hughes et al. Also Bajorik et al. saw a wavy structure on both sides of the quasi-elastic line with the possibility of a peak at 0·6 meV. Due to the size of the statistical errors the authors were, however, unable to state with certainty whether there are low energy peaks or not.

Kottwitz et al. (1963) measured the Debye-Waller factor (via the quasi-elastic intensity as a function of Q) for various values of the incident neutron energy, and showed that the results were dependent upon the energy used. They used momentum transfers in the range $Q = 0.4\text{--}7$ A^{-1}. This result illustrates the difficulty of extracting the quasi-elastic peak from data where the inelastic contributions (and perhaps the anharmonic terms also) are large.

As stated in Chapter 7, there are no fundamental theories for liquids which may be compared to the experimental results, and only a few models have been worked out. An important quantity in these models is the width $w(\tau)$ (equation 7.27) describing the spreading out in time of the density probability function for the particle, which is related to the velocity correlation function of equation (7.95) to (7.98). In Brockhouse's (1958) treatment two basically different assumptions for $\omega(\tau)$ were made. A semi-crystalline model for water proposed by Singwi and Sjölander (1960) has already been referred to above. Another model which attempts to describe both diffusive and hindered translation motions (acoustic vibrations) is the stochastic model developed by Rahman *et al.* (1962) (see Section 7.11). A model of similar content was earlier given by Schofield (1961). The model of Rahman *et al.* resulted in $w(\tau)$ containing both a diffusive part and a vibratory part, in agreement with the intuitive division of the experimental data of Fig. 8.1 into two parts. The differential cross-section of this model was compared to the room temperature water data of Larsson and Dahlborg with moderate success. One of the most important variables in this model is the ratio $(f'/f_D)^3$ which is a measure of the number of degrees of freedom $3\Delta N$ that goes into diffusion out of the total number of degrees of freedom $3N$. The best fit corresponds to $\Delta N/N = 0\cdot0014$, a very small number. In Egelstaff's (1962) analysis, also described in Section 7.11, this number is given by the ratio of the small peak at the origin of the frequency spectrum of Fig. 8.7 to the total area of the spectrum. A number $\sim 10^{-3}$ is obtained. It should be stressed that these models describe only the basic motion, and refer to simple monatomic liquids. No model has been worked out which is intended to give a detailed picture of the motions of a complicated substance like water.

Although a general picture of the dynamics of water has emerged from the data discussed above, there are many discrepancies between the various measurements. Some of these are due to experimental inaccuracies while others are due to differences in the corrections applied and methods of analysis. This is illustrated by the fact that the original data are sometimes in better agreement than the derived quantities.

Two general ways of interpreting the data have been employed, one based on the spectral density of the velocity correlation function and the other based on the space time correlation function $G_s(r,\tau)$. The latter gives a physical picture of the atomic and molecular motions which can be easily understood, but which obscures specific modes of vibration or rotation. However, the former presentation shows up such modes and their relative importance but lacks the pictorial advantage of G_s. Certain situations favour one or the other method, and the difficulties of numerical analysis met with in deriving these functions will vary from case to case. Consequently, there can be no universal choice of which method to use. However, for water at temperatures near to room temperature the spectral density method seems particularly useful.

To sum up, the experiments performed on water showed that:

1. the motion of the scattering centres cannot be described by a gas model or by a simple diffusion model;

2. the diffusion process is probably delayed by a time τ_0, of about 10^{-12} sec;

3. this delay time permits the development of vibratory motions in a relatively fixed or slowly moving position. All vibrations with frequencies $>1/\tau_0$ are developed and contribute to the frequency spectrum;

4. the structure of the frequency spectrum reveals several details about the molecular and protonic motions. In some cases the molecule is the dynamical unit, in other cases the proton only;

5. possibly there exists in water small energy transfers of the order of 0·7–0·5 meV. The origin of these transfers, if they exist, is unknown.

8.3 Liquid Hydrogen

Liquid hydrogen has been of considerable interest since the early stages of development of the experimental techniques and theories of inelastic scattering. Experimentally there is the possibility of increasing the flux of cold neutrons that can be extracted from a reactor or from a moderator surrounding an accelerator target. An obvious solution to this problem is to cool down the whole moderator or to let the neutrons coming from a bigger moderator pass through a smaller, very cold moderator from which the cold neutron flux could be extracted. The use of liquid hydrogen for this purpose was discussed in Chapter 4. A theoretical discussion of scattering by the hydrogen molecule is given in Section 9.7.

From the theoretical point of view hydrogen is interesting as it is known to exist in two forms, para- and ortho-hydrogen. In para-hydrogen the nuclear spins of the two hydrogen nuclei of the molecule are oriented anti-parallel and in the ortho-form the spins are parallel. This alignment in the molecule causes a considerably larger coherence effect in liquid hydrogen than in other hydrogenous substances where the spins are thought of as being randomly oriented resulting in almost completely incoherent scattering. Also because of the relatively strong binding between the atoms in the molecule compared with a much weaker inter-molecular binding, the molecule is supposed to be relatively free to move, almost as in a gas.

Quantum mechanically, the rotational states of the free hydrogen molecule are given by

$$\epsilon = \frac{h^2}{Ma^2} J(J+1) = 0.015 \frac{J(J+1)}{2} \text{ eV} \tag{8.7}$$

where M is the proton mass and a is the distance between the protons which is 0·75 Å. Even values of the quantum number J correspond to the para state and odd numbers to the ortho state. In addition there is a continuum of energy levels corresponding to the motion of the molecule within the shallow potential well determined by the neighbouring molecules. The allowed rotational states are given in Table 8.1.

Some years ago there was considerable interest in the study of the assumed spin dependence of the n–p interaction. Schwinger and Teller (1937) derived theoretical expressions for the total cross-section as a function of neutron energy for the case of hydrogen gas and four different possible interactions. The neutron energy was assumed to be less than 50 meV, so that only $J = 1$ excitations are possible. The possible interactions are then

$0 \rightarrow 0$ para–para (elastic scattering)
$0 \rightarrow 1$ para–ortho (inelastic scattering)
$1 \rightarrow 1$ ortho–ortho (elastic scattering)
$1 \rightarrow 0$ ortho–para (inelastic scattering)

Of the calculated cross-sections (Fig. 8.13 upper part) the $0 \rightarrow 1$ transition shows an interesting threshold behaviour. The excitation of the level at 15 mV does not occur until the neutron energy is about 23 mV. The reason

TABLE 8.1

Energy levels of liquid hydrogen

J		ϵ(eV)
Para	Ortho	
0		0
	1	0·015
2		0·045
	3	0·090
4		0·150

for this is the conservation of momentum in the collision of a mass 1 neutron and a mass 2 molecule requires that at threshold 1/3 of the energy remains in translational motion of the neutron and recoil molecule. The threshold is thus to be found at 23 meV.

Total cross-section measurements on liquid para-hydrogen (99·75 %) and on a mixture of 75 % ortho and 25 % para hydrogen were performed by McReynolds and Whittemore (1963) using low energy neutrons from an electron linear accelerator. The hydrogen sample was held at its boiling point of 20·4°K at atmospheric pressure. The cross-section studies were performed in the range 0·5 meV to about 0·25 eV (Fig. 8.13 lower part). The cross-section of the paraform shows a behaviour in general agreement with the Schwinger-Teller theory. Actually the solid lines in the low energy region are based on the Schwinger-Teller theory for hydrogen gas and adjusted so as to fit data on hydrogen gas. They are given for the experimetally unobtainable pure para and ortho forms whereas the experimental data apply to the mixtures mentioned above.

The fact that the para-hydrogen results agree rather closely with the gas suggests the para molecule is practically free to recoil as in a gas and is almost unaffected by binding forces. A closer inspection of the experimental results (see the insert of Fig. 8.13b) showed, however, that the rise in the para-hydrogen cross section corresponding to the $0 \to 1$ transition occurs not as

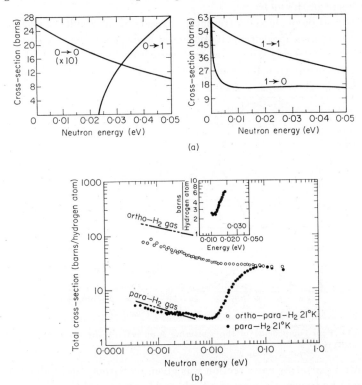

(a)

(b)

FIG. 8.13. (a) Theoretical elastic $(0 \to 0)$ and inelastic $(0 \to 1)$ scattering cross-sections of para-hydrogen molecules calculated by Schwinger and Teller (1937). Theoretical elastic $(1 \to 1)$ and inelastic $(1 \to 0)$ scattering cross-sections of ortho-hydrogen molecules. (b) Total neutron cross-sections of liquid para-hydrogen and mixed para–ortho-hydrogen as measured by the transmission method (McReynolds and Whittemore, 1963).

23 meV but closer to 15 meV. This would indicate that the molecule is bound rather strongly in the sense that its centre of mass is fixed with respect to the surrounding molecules. The momentum seems to be taken up not by a single molecule but rather by a large group of molecules and all the kinetic energy of the neutron goes into raising the molecule from the $J = 0$ para to the $J = 1$ ortho state. This conclusion seems to be in contradiction with the result that the gas type total cross section describes the observed data approximately in the low energy region. Also the edge

in the para cross-section at 15–20 meV should be broadened by the inter-molecular binding forces: the experiments, however, indicate a sharpness of the step in the cross-section which qualitatively indicates free rotation. There is thus a group of features which are in agreement with the gas like free rotation behaviour and another group which indicates a stronger binding or confinement of the molecule.

A clarification of these contradictory aspects of the results of slow neutron total cross-section measurements on liquid hydrogen is expected to be given by inelastic scattering studies, as each transition like 0→0 or 0→1 is separated on the energy transfer scale. A theoretical treatment of the slow neutron

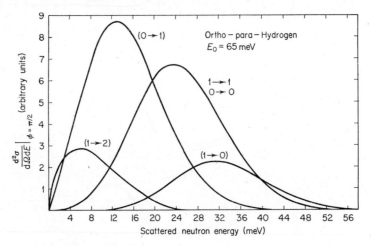

Fig. 8.14. Four components of the scattering from ortho-hydrogen at 90° for neutrons with $E_0 = 65$ meV.

differential scattering cross-section was given by Sarma (1961) who described the liquid hydrogen as a gas of simple rigid rotators. When the intermolecular forces are neglected the differential incoherent cross-section is

$$\frac{d^2\sigma}{d\Omega d\omega} = 4\left(\frac{M}{\pi kT}\right)^{\frac{1}{2}} \frac{k}{k_0} \frac{P_{J\to J'}}{Q} \exp -M \frac{\left[\hbar\omega - (\epsilon_{J'} - \epsilon_J) - \frac{\hbar^2 Q^2}{4M}\right]^2}{kT\hbar^2 Q^2} \quad (8.8)$$

where as usual $\mathbf{Q} = \mathbf{k} - \mathbf{k}_0$ and $\mathbf{k}$ and $\mathbf{k}_0$ are the neutron wave vectors before and after scattering. The formula is identical with the normal gas formula for the differential cross-section with the exception of the term $P_{J\to J'}$, which is the transition probability for the rotational state J going to the state J' and the term $\epsilon_{J'} - \epsilon_J$ in the exponential which describes the energy transfer between the two rotational levels. The contribution of the first few transitions $J \to J'$ to the differential cross-section of ortho–para hydrogen as calculated by Sarma's formula for an ingoing neutron energy of 65 mV and for a scattering angle of 90° shows the importance of the various transitions (Fig. 8.14).

A differential cross-section measurement on liquid hydrogen at 20·4°K for almost pure para and for an ortho–para mixture of ratio 2 : 1 was performed by Whittemore and Danner (1963). They used the electron linear accelerator time-of-flight spectrometer described in Section 2.14. The resolution was relatively poor and the ingoing energies were 65 and 40 meV which are high, and these factors prevented the structure of the transitions

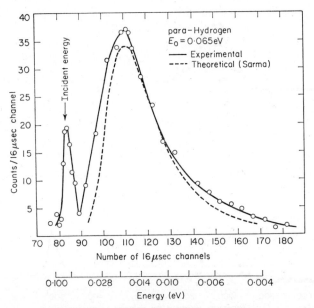

FIG. 8.15. Time-of-flight spectrum of 65 meV neutrons scattered by a 1-mm layer of para-hydrogen. Theoretical predictions based on the perfect gas model are shown as a dashed curve.

being observed. The results obtained showed general agreement with the assumed gas-like behaviour of the hydrogen molecules (Fig. 8.15). The peak of the observed distribution of neutrons and the peak of the calculated distribution using Sarma's formula coincide rather well. As the peak position is very sensitive to the mass of the recoiling unit this is taken as an indication that the recoiling mass is 2 and not larger. As, however, the energy transfer at the peak position is about 50 meV, several rotational states are excited. Therefore, the mass is expected to be the mass of the molecule. The observed neutron distribution is about 20 % broader than the calculated one. Basically this is due to the fact that the average kinetic energy of the molecule is greater than for a free gas. However, in detail, several reasons for the observed additional broadening may exist: collisions between nearest-neighbour

molecules will cause a broadening of all scattering components. In the
liquid state the lifetime of the excited states may be reduced which
would cause an additional broadening in all the scattered distributions.
Nuclear magnetic resonance measurements have shown that there is
a dependence of the nuclear relaxation time on different concentrations
of ortho-hydrogen which means that there is an interaction between ortho-
and para-hydrogen molecules. Thus when a para-ortho transition occurs in
para-hydrogen the molecule in the final state interacts with its surroundings,

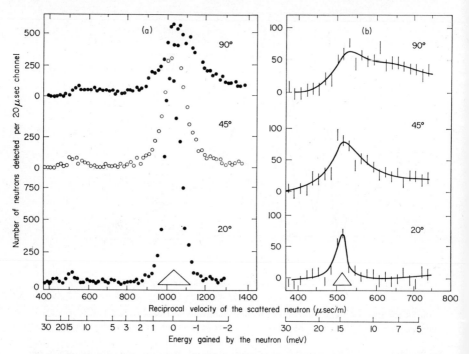

FIG. 8.16. Scattered spectra from liquid ortho-hydrogen at 15°K, using a line spectrum at
1030 μsec/m.

which might cause a broadening. Besides, the ortho–ortho quadrupole interaction is known to exist and to be rather strong. This interaction could cause
neighbouring molecules to react and would hence cause an extra broadening
in the energy distribution of neutrons scattered from ortho-hydrogen.

Egelstaff *et al.* (1964) used the cold neutron scattering technique (Chapter
2) to measure the scattered neutron spectra from solid hydrogen at 12°K
and liquid hydrogen at 15°, 18° and 21°K. The specimen of hydrogen was
contained in a series of parallel stainless steel tubes, 1 mm diameter with wall
thickness 0·05 mm, in a cryostat and the ratio of ortho- to para-hydrogen

was a few percent less than the room temperature value of 3 : 1. An example of their results is shown in Fig. 8.16, which gives distributions in reciprocal velocity of initially 4 Å neutrons scattered from liquid hydrogen at 15°K at various angles. The ortho–para conversion line at 510 μsec/m and the quasi-elastic peak at 1030 μsec/m were clearly resolved. The ortho–para conversion line is shown at the right of the figure on an enlarged scale, and it is clear that the time-of-flight corresponding to maximum intensity varied with angle. However, it was shown that this effect disappears when the data are corrected for the detailed balance factor and time-of-flight is converted to a constant energy interval scale. The data at all temperatures were consistent with an ortho–para conversion energy of 15·2 $\pm$ 0·5 meV, which may be compared to the value of the transition in the gas of 14·7 meV deduced from the $J = 3$ to 1 ortho transition measured in infra-red experiments (Herzberg, 1960).

As can be seen from Fig. 8.16 the width of the quasi-elastic and ortho–para conversion lines is a function of angle of scatter in agreement with the remarks made above. The widths are made up of three components: first due to the instrumental resolution which is almost independent of angle, second due to the diffusive and acoustic wave motions of the molecules, third due to the splitting of the triplet ortho state. The instrumental resolution is indicated on the figure, and the diffusive motions of the atoms can be calculated from the measured diffusion coefficient (the values of Hass *et al.* (1960) were used). At 18°K the observed widths of the lines are greater than calculated by about a factor 2. The contribution due to acoustic modes was estimated empirically from the variation with angle and, after allowing for this, the residual width due to the splitting of the triplet state was about $\pm$0·5 meV.

In summary the experiments indicate that in both ortho and para liquids the interaction between rotational states and other states is small. The translational motion is restricted as expected from the known value of the diffusion coefficient.

8.4 Various Hydrogenous Liquids

The experiments performed on water clearly show the possibilities of the neutron scattering technique in the study of the dynamics of protons in a hydrogenous liquid. Of particular interest is the fact that the diffusion process is delayed for a considerable length of time, so that time is allowed for a vibratory motion to develop. Of course this vibratory motion has to be thought of as strongly damped.

The experiments on water may have one drawback: the variation of the viscosity η of water between 0° and 100°C is limited, being between 1·79 and 0·28 centipoise. This fact manifests itself in a relatively small variation of the self diffusion coefficient D within the same temperature range; nuclear magnetic resonance studies show a variation of D from 0.97 to 8.65×10^{-5} cm^2/sec. Obviously it would be of interest to study other associated liquids such that wider ranges of the self diffusion coefficient could be covered. Various degrees of association should correspond to different ranges of viscosity and therefore to a marked variation in the diffusion properties as seen in the neutron scattering, i.e. a strong variation in quasi-elastic line width and intensity and also in the intensity and details of the inelastically scattered spectrum.

Series of measurements have been performed by Saunderson and Rainey (1963) on the lower alcohols, methyl (CH_3OH), ethyl (C_2H_5OH), and n-amyl alcohols ($C_5H_{11}OH$), at room temperature. The viscosities at 20°C of these liquids are 0.60, 1.20 and 3.75 centipoises respectively. Measurements have also been performed on glycerol (C_3H_5OH), oleic acid ($C_{17}H_{33}COOH$) and pentane (C_5H_{12}) by Larsson and Dahlborg (1963). Of particular interest is glycerol, which was studied in the liquid phase from -7 to $+180$°C, and over this temperature range its viscosity varies from 230 poises to 2.1 centipoises. This work will be discussed in detail in the next section. Oleic acid was studied in the liquid phase between $+20$°C and 170°C corresponding to a viscosity range between 40 and 1.4 centipoises. Pentane was studied from -35°C to $+20$°C corresponding to a viscosity range between 0.43 and 0.23 centipoise. Liquid methane CH_4 at -171°C has been investigated by several groups. Studies on liquids like Dowterm "A", which is a mixture of diphenyl and diphenyl oxide, and benzene, have also been reported by Gläser (1963), Gläser et al., (1965). There is thus a great deal of experimental material on hydrogenous liquids.

For their systematic series of experiments on the alcohols Saunderson and Rainey (1963) used two complementary techniques. The cold neutron method involving a monochromatizing chopper (Chapter 2) to produce a line spectrum was used to obtain the quasi-elastically scattered peak and the inelastic energy gain spectrum up to about 100 meV. At this point the population factor has cut the intensity down to values so low that the data become uncertain. Therefore an energy loss experiment is necessary to study the high energy region. Using an aluminium single crystal and the reflecting planes (111), (220) amd (331) a high ingoing neutron energy was selected and the neutrons scattered from the sample were detected using a beryllium filtered detector (described in Chapter 3). In this way energy transfers up to 230 meV were studied. Examples of the results obtained on the three alcohols at two angles of observation are given in Fig. 8.17. Similarly an example of the results obtained on methyl alcohol by the beryllium detector technique (marked ELB) and the cold neutron technique (marked CN) in the region of high energy transfers are given in Fig. 8.18.

The shape of the ingoing cold neutron spectrum is given approximately by the quasi-elastic peak obtained for amyl alcohol at an angle of 20°. The neutron intensity distributions of Fig. 8.17 are typical of most of the hydrogenous liquids. There is a strong variation of the inelastic intensity with angle of observation and the intensity of the quasi-elastic peak drops

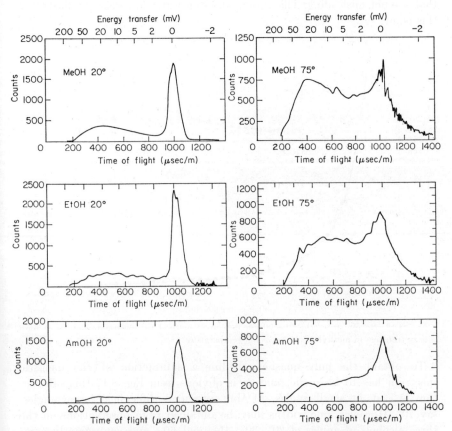

FIG. 8.17. Time-of-flight spectra of cold neutrons scattered from methyl, ethyl and n-amyl alcohols at scattering angles of 20° and 75° and room temperature. The figures are chart records of the raw data; much of the fine structure is due to the counting statistics.

sharply with increasing angle. Also the width of the quasi-elastic peak increases with angle. The inelastic and quasi-elastic intensity thus varies with angle much in the same way as in a solid.

Two physical processes are assumed to lie behind the quasi-elastic intensity, the first has to do with diffusive long time motions corresponding to a continuum of very small energy transfers. These motions are supposed to build up the main part of the quasi-elastic peak. The second (giving the inelastic background) is assumed to correspond to somewhat shorter time motions of the nature of strongly damped oscillations of the scattering unit. It should be emphasized that the interpretation of the line broadening is no simple matter and requires a very careful treatment in order to give results that are not misleading. The various data on water have clearly illustrated this point.

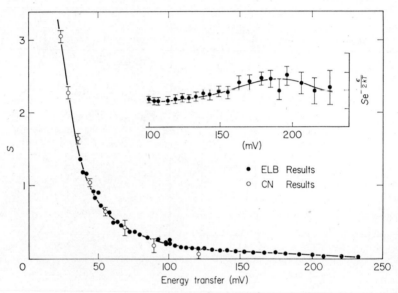

FIG. 8.18. Results from the "beryllium detector" method to investigate details of high energy transfers in methyl alcohol at room temperature.

To obtain the pure quasi-elastic line a subtraction of the inelastic spectrum has to be made, and as is obvious from Fig. 8.17 this subtraction is easy at small angles, 20°, but extremely difficult at larger angles, say 70°. However, line widths may be obtained from observations on the three alcohols at angles of 20°, 30°, 45°, and 60°, and conveniently compared to the predictions of the simple diffusion model, equation (8.2), by plotting them as a function of Q^2. An approximate agreement between this model and the methyl alcohol data was obtained within the Q-region investigated. For ethyl alcohol on the other hand the experimental values correspond to a D value about twice that obtained by tracer methods of measurement. For amyl alcohol the D value derived from the neutron data is about 1×10^{-5} cm²/sec, while the value expected from a macroscopic measurement is less than 0.5×10^{-5} cm²/sec. These results suggest that low energy modes of motion of the protons (or of the whole molecule) are being excited in the experiments and lead to the observed widths. The origin of these modes is not clear, although they may arise from a mechanism similar to the splitting of the ortho-hydrogen levels discussed in the last section. Similar effects have been observed in glycerol, oleic acid and pentane.

The inelastic spectra all show the same appearance as the spectra obtained from water. By comparing the spectra to those that should have been obtained from a perfect gas of mass 1 and 3, it was clearly shown that the assumption of a point mass model was inadequate. The gas model spectrum changes shape very radically with angle which is not in agreement with observation. Optical investigations on the motions of the hydroxyl (OH) group had shown that probably this group is involved in polymer bonding which would impede rotation of the molecule in the liquid. Also a free rotation of the methyl (CH_3) group seemed rather improbable at room temperature as barriers of 60–160 meV towards free rotation exist. Thus it is supposed that a large part of the inelastic spectrum corresponds to hindered rotational motions of the methyl group. As there is a marked change between the three alcohols with an increasing number of methylene groups (CH_2), it was concluded that the motions of these groups also contribute to the inelastic spectrum in the energy transfer range 0–100 meV. The rise in the intensity of the higher energy part of the spectrum at about 180 mV (Fig. 8.18) is taken as an indication that O—H bending modes as well as CH_3 stretching vibrations are excited.

The measurements reported by Hautecler and Stiller (1963) on methane, CH_4, at $-171°C$ were carried out by the use of the beryllium detector technique (Chapter 3). A great uncertainty in these measurements was caused by the use of a beryllium filter of only 7 cm thickness. There was thus a considerable transmission of neutrons of energy greater than 5·2 meV. After appropriate corrections a scattered spectrum rich in detail was obtained. The various energy transfers observed were compared to transitions between rotational levels assuming that the molecule is free to rotate and most of the levels observed were identified as being due to transitions between free rotator levels. This is supposed to be due to the fact that the CH_4 molecule has an almost perfect spherical symmetry. As a consequence of the free rotational motion it was suggested that the simple diffusion model, equation (8.2), should describe the small translational motions observed in the quasi-elastic peak. A D value of $3·8 \times 10^{-5}$ cm²/sec was derived which may be compared to the measured value of $2·7 \times 10^{-5}$ cm²/sec. The agreement between the two observed D values is satisfactory.

Dasannacharya et al. (1965) studied the inelastic scattering of 4 Å neutrons from liquid methane using the rotating crystal technique (Chapter 2). They observed a distinct region in the spectrum which corresponded to rotational states, and compared their data to spectra calculated via the treatment of Griffing (discussed in Chapter 9). By this means they showed that the rotational states were greatly broadened; a result in conflict with the data of Hautecler and Stiller (1963). However, it should be noted that the rotating crystal technique is more reliable over this energy range than is the beryllium detector technique. The widths of the quasi-elastic peaks measured by Dasannacharya *et al.* were consistent with the measured D value of $2\cdot 7 \times 10^{-5}$ cm^2/sec.

Harker and Brugger (1965) have studied liquid methane using the phased chopper technique (Chapter 2) and incident neutron energies of 25, 70 and 100 meV. Again they compared their data with calculated curves based on Griffing's treatment. Some differences were observed at low values of Q, which they attributed to a vibrational state at 17 meV. However, these data seem to differ from the calculated results in the same way as that of Dasannacharya *et al.*, so that the former explanation is a possibility here also.

Summarizing the results of the scattering studies from the alcohols and liquid methane, it is notable that for methyl alcohol with a viscosity of 0·60 centipoise and for methane with a viscosity of 0·14 centipoise, there is agreement between the simple diffusion prediction for the translational modes of motion and the observed data. The molecules in question have a relatively simple and symmetric structure in both cases. Also it has to be borne in mind that the experimental errors are large, as the separation between the inelastic and the quasi-elastic components is a difficult operation. But it seems beyond all doubt that, for the higher alcohols with less symmetric molecules, there is a definite discrepancy between the simple diffusion theory and the observations such that the observed widths are larger than predicted. This means either that the neutron finds the proton considerably more mobile than the parent molecule or that low energy modes of motion exist with periods of $\sim 10^{-12}$ sec.

8.5 Glycerol

Larsson and Dahlborg (1964) used the full cold neutron spectrum and a chopper time-of-flight apparatus (Chapter 2, Fig. 2.7) to study glycerol. In this experiment, as well as in most other experiments described in this chapter, the transmission of the samples varied between 80 and 92 %, in order to reduce the probability for multiple scattering to a minimum. A special method of isolating the quasi-elastic peak from the inelastic background was employed, based on the assumption that the top of the quasi-elastically scattered cold neutron spectrum is well defined and that the bottom of the sharp beryllium edge is broadened in the same way as the top. If one had a true step function spectrum and a simple Lorentzian or Gaussian broadening function this would be correct. In practice the incident spectrum is folded with a broadening function (for example, a Lorentzian for the natural width plus a Gaussian resolution function, or, alternatively, two Gaussian functions), and the calculated spectrum compared to the observed. The method of comparison involves drawing the tangent to the broadened beryllium edge as shown at Fig. 8.19; the broadening A to B is then compared to the calculated values to find the natural line width ΔE. This analysis of the broadening

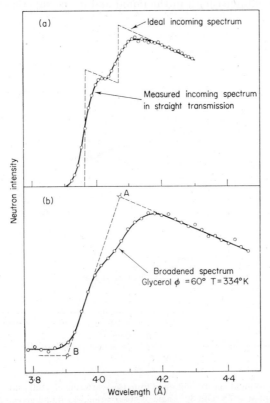

FIG. 8.19. The principle of analysis of the broadening of the sharp edge of the beryllium filtered neutron spectrum. (a) The shape of the edge region observed in straight transmission. The dashed curve is the spectrum expected for infinitely good resolution. (b) The shape of the edge region as observed in quasi-elastic scattering from glycerol at $+96°C$ and $60°$ angle of scattering. The definition of the observed width value is given from the difference between A and B.

is restricted to a minimum of 0·03 meV and a maximum of 0·8 meV when the resolution is 0·2 meV. The lower limit is determined by the resolution and the upper limit by the difficulty of making the separation when the line broadening is too large, the errors being largest at these two limits.

Employing this method of analysis the quasi-elastic scattering from glycerol was studied at temperatures from $-7°C$ to $180°C$ and within an angular range of 20° and 90°. Examples of some extreme cases of neutron spectra are given in Fig. 8.20. The type of spectra already observed for water and the alcohols were obtained in the present case.

The results of the line width analysis are interesting (Fig. 8.21) since some of the observations were made on the solid state. Thus spectra from glycerol at −7°C were obtained both in the liquid and in the superheated solid state

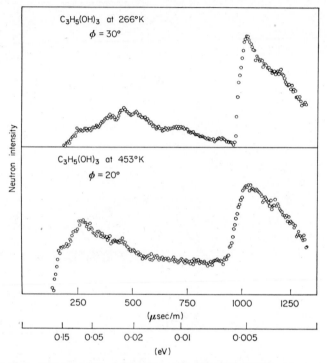

Fɪɢ. 8.20. Time-of-flight spectra obtained from the scattering of a full cold neutron spectrum in (1) solid glycerol at −7°C and 30° angle of observation, (2) liquid glycerol at +180°C and 20° angle. Data corrected for instrumental effects.

(glycerol has a melting point of −89°C but may exist in a superheated solid state up to +17°C), and the same line broadening was observed in both states at the same temperature. This fact is very significant showing a low frequency mode of motion which gives a faster rate of movement on the timescale 10^{-12} sec than simple diffusion. The line width curves show the flattening off typical of jump diffusion (see formulae (8.3) and (8.4) and the discussion in connection with them). This is particularly true for the high viscosity region of the glycerol data, −7°C and 20°C. It is, however, of particular importance that at the highest temperature studied, which was 180°C, the line width curve flattens off.

From these line width data it is possible to derive values for an effective self-diffusion coefficient for the scattering centre, just by drawing the tangent to the line width curves at the origin. The slope of these lines is $2\hbar D$ according to equation (8.4). If the data at the lower temperatures are affected by low frequency modes of vibration or rotation then these values of D will be larger than the long time diffusion coefficients.

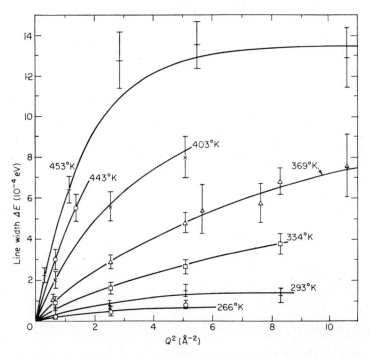

FIG. 8.21. Experimentally determined line widths as a function of the square of the momentum transfers for glycerol at temperatures from $-7°C$ to $+180°C$.

Now assume that it is possible to describe this diffusion coefficient by the aid of an activation energy, ϵ_0, as in a solid (see equation (7.55)):

$$D = Ce^{\frac{-\epsilon_0}{kT}} \tag{8.9}$$

The validity of this assumption may be tested by plotting the logarithm of the experimental values for D against $1/T$, and the result is given at Fig. 8.22.

Values of the diffusion constant for water obtained earlier gave, when plotted in this way, a straight line with a slope corresponding to an average value of ϵ_0 of 3 kcal/mole. The D values obtained from glycerol form a straight line in the low temperature region between $-7°C$ and about $100°C$, also with a slope corresponding to an activation energy of 3 kcal/mole. Diffusion constants for glycerol are not known but, for comparison, a value may be calculated on the basis of known values of the viscosity coefficient using the Eyring formula

$$D = \frac{kT}{2R_m\eta} \tag{8.10}$$

where R_m is the radius of the molecule. In this way D values are obtained which are 10^{-3} of the neutron values at $-7°C$ and 10^{-2} at $20°C$. From about $100°C$ and up there is agreement between the observed and the

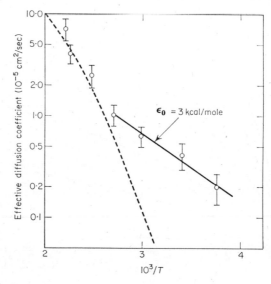

Fig. 8.22. Experimentally determined values of the diffusion coefficient on a logarithmic scale against inverse temperature for glycerol. The dotted line is the diffusion coefficient calculated by use of equation (8.10).

calculated values and an average value of ϵ_0 in this region is 7·5 kcal/mole. This demonstrates the high mobility of the proton in a temperature region where the viscosity is larger than about 10 centipoise. It was suggested by Larsson and Singwi (1962) that the neutron observes the breakage of single hydrogen bonds in the low temperature region. The energy of 3 kcal/mole is of the correct order and in rather good agreement with other measurements. When a hydrogen bond is broken a molecular group such as CH_2OH or a CHOH group might perform a partial rotation perhaps through a bond angle. The lifetime of such a hydrogen bond would thus be much shorter than the delay time before diffusion sets in, and so simple diffusion is not the rate determining process for the motion of the protons. On the other hand with increase of temperature there comes a point where the three hydrogen bonds between the molecule under observation and three neighbouring molecules are all broken simultaneously. The molecule which contains the scattering proton is then relatively freely diffusing and there is agreement between the measured and calculated D values. The diffusion is now the rate determining process. In this way the value 3 kcal/mole both for water and for glycerol is given a natural explanation.

The value of the line width in the limit of large Q values should be $\Delta E = 2\hbar/\tau_0$ according to equation (8.4), where it is assumed that the scattering centre is vibrating for a time τ_0 before it diffuses away. The constant x^2 in

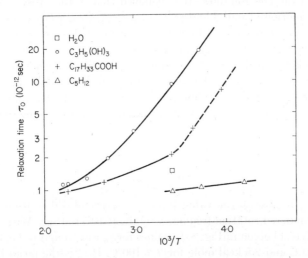

FIG. 8.23. Values of the relaxation time τ_0 for water, glycerol, oleic acid and pentane from the observed line width curves. The broken part of the curve for oleic acid was obtained from measurements in the solid state.

the Debye-Waller factor $(x^2 Q^2)$ was determined directly in separate studies of the angular variation of the quasi-elastic intensity. The values of τ_0 obtained by fitting to (8.4) showed several surprising features (Fig. 8.23). For glycerol the relaxation time τ_0 drops from 2×10^{-11} sec at $-7°C$ to a relatively constant value round 1×10^{-12} sec in the temperature region where agreement between the predictions of D by the Eyring formula and the neutron values of D was found.

For all the liquids studied so far there seems to be a limiting value of τ_0. It is striking that for both pentane and water which are low viscosity liquids the time τ_0 is about 10^{-12} sec at all the temperatures. It seems that when the molecules begin to move freely without strong coupling to neighbours, the relaxation time τ_0 reaches the limiting value 10^{-12} sec. This idea is supported by observations of dielectric and ultrasonic relaxation times in glycerol. The dielectric relaxation times observed in glycerol at lower temperatures are two or three orders of magnitude longer than the neutron observed times τ_0. It is believed that the dielectric relaxation times are connected with formation and destruction of polymeric clusters. If the observed dielectric relaxation time curve is extrapolated to higher temperatures it intersects the neutron curve in the region of 400–450°K. There should thus be a complete de-polymerization of big clusters in glycerol at temperatures round 450°K. The ultrasonic measurements on the other hand give in the lower temperature region values for the relaxation times which are only one order of magnitude larger than the neutron data. It is believed that in the ultrasonic measurements the motion of individual molecules against each other is observed. If this curve is extrapolated to higher temperature it also intersects the neutron curve in the temperature region round 450°K.

If the relaxation time τ_0 is considered as a mean life time for an H-bond or the average time during which a proton in an H-bond would perform the out-of-plane hindered rotations before the bond is broken and the whole CH_2OH group performs a partial rotation (rotational isomerism) then it would be logical to assume that τ_0 could be calculated from

$$\tau_0 = \frac{2\pi}{\omega_{hr}} \, e^{\frac{\epsilon_0}{kT}} \tag{8.11}$$

where $\hbar \, \omega_{hr}$ is close to the value 70 meV in glycerol (taken from Fig. 8.20). ω_{hr} is the hindered rotation frequency of about 10^{14} rad/sec. With the values of τ_0 for glycerol given in Fig. 8.23 values for ϵ_0 were found to be 3 kcal/mole for $T < 100°C$ and 2·5 kcal/mole for $T > 100°C$. If τ_0 is the mean life-time of one H-bond, it would follow as a consequence that for $T > 100°C$ the total activation energy to break *three* H-bonds would be 7·5 kcal/mole, which is in agreement with the direct determination of ϵ_0 for $T > 100°C$ both from these neutron data and from a direct study of the activation energy from the co-efficient of viscosity. If this interpretation of the data was correct, it would follow that

$$\eta = \eta_0 \, e^{\frac{3\epsilon_0}{kT}} = c \cdot \tau_0^3 \tag{8.12}$$

As η is measured in the classical way and τ_0 is derived from the present neutron studies an agreement between the predicted form (equation (8.12)) and observations would speak very strongly in favour of the hypothesis and data treatment given above. When the measured pairs of η and τ_0 are plotted one finds (Fig. 8.24) an almost perfect agreement with the predicted curve

$\eta = c \cdot \tau_0^3$. It thus seems verified that the neutron observes the partial rotations of the molecular groups CH_2OH and of the ethylene groups in the case of pentane and oleic acid. The broadening of the quasi-elastic peak is caused by the uncertainty in position of the scattering protons. In the cases investigated (including the alcohols) the quasi-elastic peak is thus of rotational origin.

Another way of plotting the line width data was proposed by Egelstaff (1962) in his work on various models for the diffusive motions in liquids. He suggested that ΔE should be plotted against DQ^2, so that simple

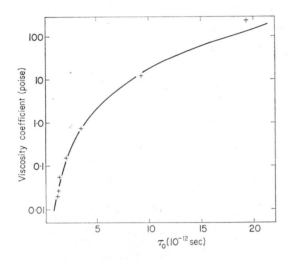

FIG. 8.24. Observed viscosity as a function of observed relaxation time. Full curve corresponds to the relation $\eta = 1.74 \times 10^{34} \tau_0^3$.

diffusion theory is represented by a straight line with the slope $2\hbar$. In the case of the glycerol data it was found that for temperatures below 400°K the curves lay one above the other and with increasing temperatures tended toward the simple diffusion line. These cases correspond to the region of D values where there was no agreement between the neutron determined values and the calculated ones. In contrast at the higher temperatures all the measurements give coincident results. Oleic acid, pentane and water when plotted in this way give curves indistinguishable from the high temperature glycerol curve.

In order to interpret such line width plot, the combination DQ^2 used as an abscissa may be given a physical meaning. According to equation (8.1) the observation range Δx for the neutron is $\sim 1/Q$. On the other hand it is well known that the displacement δx of a molecule in the time interval t_{obs}

14

is given, according to the Einstein stochastic formula, by $\overline{\delta x^2} = 6Dt_{\text{obs}}$. Identifying δx and Δx one obtains

$$t_{\text{obs}} = \frac{1}{6DQ^2} \tag{8.13}$$

The variable DQ^2 thus corresponds to the time that would be necessary for the neutron to see the particle diffuse over the distance δx. Thus if the neutron interaction occurs with a large Q value the observation time is so short that only the first part of the development of the thermal cloud is seen corresponding mainly to the solid-like vibratory behaviour. As, however, the Q value decreases the observation time increases, and the neutron now sees both the asymptotic diffusive behaviour and the solid-like

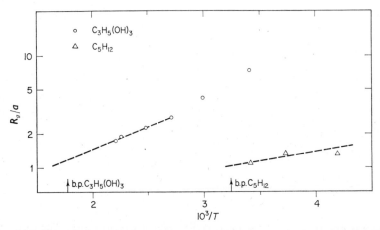

Fig. 8.25. The ratio between the radius R_g of a cluster of molecules and the value a (the cube root of the volume of one molecule) for observations on glycerol and pentane. The dotted line is an extrapolation of data to show that R_g/a tends to 1 at the boiling point.

vibratory behaviour. Using the analogy of a microscope, one might say that when Q is large, the aperture of the microscope is so small that only one period of vibration is observed. When Q is small it is possible that within the field of view in the microscope a thermal cloud develops about one position followed by a jump to another position. Then the observer has seen one elementary period of the diffusive process. The universal width curve thus shows that the period for a diffusive step is $\sim 10^{-12}$ sec for several liquids at such temperatures that η is low.

It is worthwhile deriving the number of degrees of freedom for diffusion using the methods described in Chapter 7. At a temperature of 293°K it is found that $\Delta N/N = 0.001$. This indicates that the relative number of degrees of freedom going into diffusive modes of motion is very small at this temperature as expected from the analysis already presented. At 369°K one obtains $\Delta N/N = 0.011$. This number is still very small but about ten times larger than the corresponding number at 293°K.

The small number of degrees of freedom may be interpreted using Egelstaff and Schofield's model (Section 7.11). Remembering that $M/M^* = \Delta N/N$, equation (7.124) can be used to obtain the ratio (R_g/a) of the radius of a "globule" to the radius of the volume occupied by a molecule. Such a calculation was made by Larsson and Dahlborg (1964) for glycerol and pentane, using the neutron-measured D values. It turned out (Fig. 8.25) that the ratio R_g/a decreased sharply with temperature and tended to 1 when extrapolated to the boiling points of the liquids investigated. This result thus seems to verify the idea that there is a considerable cluster formation in the associated hydrogenous liquids and that the cluster size tends toward the size of one single molecule at the boiling point.

The inelastically scattered spectra obtained from glycerol were used to derive frequency spectra $z(\omega)$, using the method described in the preceding section on water. The principle approximations were to neglect the Debye Waller factor and to neglect the correction for multiphonon terms. This procedure of course might cause some distortion in the spectral shape, as discussed for water. The frequency spectrum for glycerol showed a broad peak at the same position as the hindered rotation peak of water, namely near 70 meV. Several peaks were identified with corresponding intensity maxima observed in Raman spectra and probably some are of rotational origin. As already pointed out in connection with water very few theoretical models exist to which the data may be compared. In particular no theory can at present give a full account to the complete spectrum observed in the neutron measurements.

8.6 Coherent Scattering from Liquid Metals

Although the measurements performed on the incoherently scattering hydrogenous liquids have been of great value in increasing our understanding of liquid dynamics, the main drawback is that in all cases the scattering hydrogen atom is bound in a complicated way to a molecule which in turn is weakly bound to its neighbours. The situation should be different for a liquid metal in which each atom is surrounded by similar atoms.

Experimental accessibility has determined the majority of cases investigated, and it has turned out that most of the metals studied in the liquid phase are coherent scatterers. Thus measurements have been performed on liquid lead, Egelstaff (1954), Brockhouse (1955), Brockhouse and Pope (1959), Turberfield (1962) Cotter (1962), Cocking and Egelstaff (1965), and on liquid tin, Palevsky (1961), Brockhouse et al. (1963), Cocking and

Guner (1963). Experimentally these are easy as the melting points of the solids are 600·5°K for lead and 505°K for tin, while both nuclei have almost 100 % coherent scattering cross-sections. Liquid sodium has been studied too by Cocking (1963) and Randolph (1964). Sodium has a melting point of 370·6°K and a scattering cross-section which is half and half coherent and incoherent: σ_{coh} is 1·55 barn while σ_{incoh} is 1·85 barns. This case will be discussed in Section 8.7. Finally liquid aluminium with a melting point of 932·8°K has been investigated by Larsson et al. (1960; 1965) and by Cocking (1965). Aluminium is also a coherent scatterer and shares with lead the advantage that careful studies of the neutron scattering from the solid state have been performed (Chapter 5).

Lead at room temperature has a Debye temperature of 90°K which may decrease to about 80°K at the melting point. Egelstaff (1954) measured the mean energy transfer occurring when 8 Å neutrons are scattered by the liquid at temperatures between 600°K and 800°K. From these data he estimated the Debye temperature in the liquid state to be ~60°K. This corresponds to an energy of 6 meV. If therefore a neutron scattering experiment is performed with the intention of seeing the inelastic spectra in detail, the ingoing neutron energy has to be low, preferably in the cold neutron region below 5 meV. If neutrons having energies in the range 25–50 meV are used there is little hope of seeing detail in scattered neutron spectrum because the energy resolution dE/E would have to be considerably better than 5 %. Also if a higher ingoing energy is used the line broadening can be so large at larger angles of observation that small inelastic peaks are hidden in the broad quasi-elastic peak. This is so because the Q values increase with angle and the line broadening is always found to increase with Q.

There are several ways of looking at the results obtained in a scattering experiment. One way is to use the data to try to derive the correlation function $G(\mathbf{r},\tau)$ which in the classical limit is the average number density at a point $\mathbf{r}$ at the time τ when it is known that there was an atom at the origin at time zero. This function may be obtained as (see equation (7.8) and following)

$$G(r,\tau) = \frac{1}{2\pi^2} \int_0^\infty I(Q,\tau) \frac{\sin Qr}{Qr} Q^2 dQ \qquad (8.14)$$

where $I(Q,\tau) = \int_{-\infty}^{+\infty} S(Q,\omega)\, e^{i\omega\tau}\, d\omega$. The difficulties in such a use of the data are that the resolution function has to be unfolded from the observed intensity distribution before the $S(Q,\omega)$ is obtained (or divided out of the transformed functions), and also that observations have to be made which cover a large region in Q,ω-space—the most important part of it—as an integration is made over this space. This means that either various ingoing energies should be used to cover a large region in Q,ω-space or a rather high ingoing energy and a large angular interval of scattering should be used.

A study of liquid lead at 620°K along these lines was made by Brockhouse and Pope (1959). Three sets of results were taken with ingoing wavelengths of 1·36, 2·22 and 4·13 Å respectively and a Q-range from 1 Å^{-1} to 7 Å^{-1} was covered. The triple axis crystal spectrometer technique was used to obtain the two shorter wavelengths 1·36 and 2·22 Å, while the rotating crystal technique was used to obtain the 4·13 Å data. The transmission of the lead sample in this work was 78 % which resulted in an estimated multiple scattering contribution of 29 % at large Q values. Also various simplifying assumptions were made to obtain $S(Q,\omega)$ from the observed intensity, the most important of which was that Q is approximately constant at each angle of scatter. The energy resolution was assumed to be constant in a series of measurements and no correction was applied for the resolution in Q-space. The experimental results show no signs of maxima resulting from a frequency spectrum and each result essentially consisted of a broad peak centred round the ingoing energy.

The analysis of these scattering patterns along the lines just given gives a rather interesting result. Figure 8.26 shows the time dependence (in units of 10^{-13} sec) of both the intermediate scattering function $I(Q,\tau)$ and $G(r,\tau)$. At $\tau = 0$ both $I(Q,0)$ and $G(r,0)$ show the behaviour known from the analysis of X-ray patterns obtained from liquids (Gingrich, 1943); that is $G(r,0) = g(r) + \delta(r)$, where $g(r)$ is the instantaneous pair correlation function and $\delta(r)$ is the self correlation function at time zero. As the time proceeds $I(Q,\tau)$ decreases and $G(r,\tau)$ becomes correspondingly smeared out. The structure of the pair correlation function $G_d(r,\tau)$ becomes smeared out due to the diffusion of the atoms in the first neighbour spheres, and the second neighbour spheres, etc. Simultaneously the self-correlation function $G_s(r,\tau)$ becomes broader and lower corresponding to the diffusion of the atom at the origin. From the patterns of $G_s(r,\tau)$ and $G_d(r,\tau)$ it is possible to derive the root-mean-square deviation of an atom from its position at time zero. The width of the self-correlation function gives $\sqrt{u_s^2}$ and the width of the pair correlation function gives correspondingly $\sqrt{u_d^2}$. The width of $G_d(r,\tau)$ was determined only for the ring of first neighbours from the difference between the line at $r = 3\cdot5$ Å and the position at half maximum on the inward edge of the peak.

These results are plotted at Fig. 8.27 and it is interesting to note that apart from a different starting point at $\tau = 0$, the two values of $\sqrt{u^2}$, tend to follow the same curve. This curve has several interesting features. The width of the self-correlation function starts out from the origin as it would do for a perfect gas for which the width increases with time as $v\tau$, where v is a component of the particle velocity $\sqrt{kT/M}$. In an intermediate region between times of 2 and 8×10^{-13} sec a complicated motion occurs.

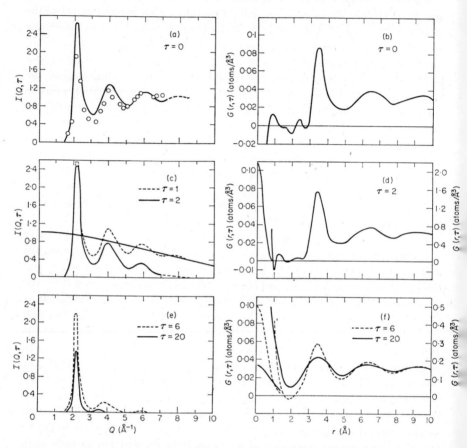

FIG. 8.26. Intermediate scattering function $I(Q,\tau)$ and correlation function $G(r,\tau)$ for lead at various values of τ. The time is measured in units of 10^{-13} sec, and the right hand scale of $G(r,\tau)$ applies to the peak near the origin (G_s) while the left hand scale refers to the remainder of G (i.e. to G_d).

It is in this time region that any vibratory motions should first develop. The Debye temperature of about 80°K corresponds to a Debye time ($t_D = \hbar/k\theta_D$) of 6×10^{-13} sec. The frequency spectrum of the vibratory motions, if there is one, would thus fall in the range from about 6×10^{-13} sec towards longer times. Probably the resolution of the experiment was too low to reveal details of this kind.

When a time of about 10^{-12} sec is reached the atoms are found in a state of slow and probably hindered translation. The slope of the width curve in this time region is smaller than that calculated from the self diffusion coefficient measured by tracer techniques. In the time range observed in this experiment, i.e. up to a time of 2.5×10^{-12} sec, the atoms seem to diffuse at much slower rate than is found in a long time study of the diffusion

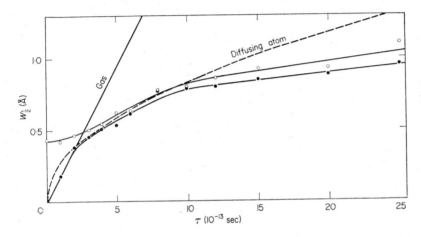

FIG. 8.27. The radius (Å) at half maximum of the self-correlation function (closed circles) and the half width at half maximum of the correlation function for first neighbours (open circles) as a function of the time, deduced from the data of Fig. 8.26.

process. Ultimately the width curve has to reach the slope given by the tracer measurement of D. The result on lead thus indicates a considerable delay time before the simple diffusion behaviour is reached, which is in analogy with the results obtained on hydrogenous liquids. The delay time also seems to be of the same magnitude.

It is rather instructive to compare these results for liquid lead with those obtained by Turberfield (1962) and Cotter (1962). In both cases a spectrum was measured for 5 meV neutrons scattered at 90° and the data was compared to the predictions of various models. Cotter's work will be described in detail. His data for liquid lead at 603°K show some structure in the inelastic region (Fig. 8.28). An intense peak is observed at the quasi-elastic position, and the line broadening extends out into the inelastic scattering region to such a degree that a separation of the spectra into parts is impossible. The interpretation of the observed spectrum is thus rather difficult.

Cotter made a study of the neutron scattering from a single crystal of lead at various temperatures up to 573°C with such an orientation of the crystal that only one or two single-phonon peaks were observed at a rather low energy. In this way the multi-phonon spectrum could be studied, and it was shown that it was well explained by the phonon expansion in the "incoherent" approximation (Chapter 1, Section 1.14)*. Cotter used the same formula in the liquid phase and after the subtraction of the calculated multi-phonon spectrum, he found a spectrum with a broad peak at 13–14 meV (i.e. an energy transfer of about 8 meV) which he interpreted as a very broadened single phonon peak. He used the width of this "single phonon peak" to derive a mean lifetime of 2×10^{-12} sec.

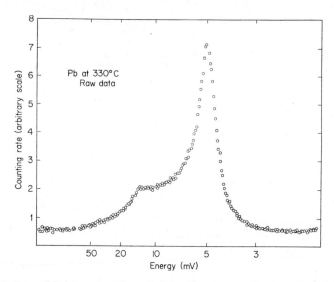

Fig. 8.28. Time-of-flight spectrum from the full cold neutron spectrum scattered in liquid lead at 603°K and 90° angle of scattering.

This method of interpretation is, however, approximate for several reasons. After subtraction of the multi-phonon contribution which in itself is an uncertain operation the resulting spectrum ranges from 16 meV to zero. When the crystal melts there is little reason to believe that single crystal ordered structure can exist, but it might be expected that a structure similar to the polycrystalline structure exists for short times. That is, round each atom in the liquid a certain local order should exist within some range which should be a few atomic distances. For short periods of time ($\sim 10^{-12}$ sec), this correlation region round each atom might be thought of as a crystallite in a polycrystal. These "crystallites" may be thought of as oriented at random so that neutrons are scattered from them as from a polycrystalline sample.

* A similar conclusion had been reached earlier by Larsson et al. (1960) for an aluminium single crystal using this technique.

In a polycrystalline sample the inelastically scattered spectrum is an integration over all orientations of the single crystal one-phonon peaks (Weinstock, 1944), and the scattered spectrum should therefore more nearly reflect the frequency distribution than does a single phonon. It has been shown by Egelstaff (1953) that (in the Debye approximation) the coherent doubly differential cross-section for the solid, polycrystalline case may be expressed as a product of the corresponding incoherent cross-section and a factor Z (which results from a summation of scattered neutron intensity over various orientations of the crystallite), i.e.

$$\left(\frac{d^2\sigma}{d\Omega d\omega}\right)_{coh} = \frac{b_{coh}^2}{b_{incoh}^2}\left(\frac{d^2\sigma}{d\Omega d\omega}\right)_{incoh} Z \qquad (8.15)$$

where

$$Z = \sum_{\tau}\frac{\pi F_{\tau}}{2B\tau Qq}.$$

Here F_{τ} is the structure factor for the plane including the multiplicity, B is the volume per nucleus in the crystal, τ is a reciprocal lattice vector and q is the phonon wave vector. τ has to fall in a region determined by $Q-q\leqslant 2\pi\tau\leqslant Q+q$. To arrive at this simple formulation it is assumed that the velocity of propagation of the waves in the crystal is independent of their plane of polarization and their wavelength.

Egelstaff (1962a) suggested a generalization of this treatment, in order to explain his data on liquid lead mentioned above. The summation in Z is replaced by an integration as the discrete lattice plane distribution is now replaced by a continuous atomic distribution round a central atom. Integration is performed between the limits $Q-q = Q_{min}$ and $Q+q = Q_{max}$. The structure factor F_{τ} in the integrand is replaced by the intensity defining liquid structure factor often referred to as $1+\gamma(Q)$. The liquid Z factor will then be

$$Z = \frac{1}{2qQ}\int\limits_{Q_{min}}^{Q_{max}} \mathscr{H}(1+\gamma(\mathscr{H}))d\mathscr{H} \qquad (8.16)$$

Also he improved this formula considering the fact that in the original crystal formula there enters a product $\hat{Q}\cdot V(q))^2$, where $V(q)$ is the polarization vector of the phonon and $\hat{Q}$ is a unit vector along $\mathbf{Q}$. If it is assumed that all waves are either pure longitudinal or pure transverse the product reduces to

$$\cos^2\Theta = \frac{Q^2+q^2-(2\pi\tau)^2}{2qQ} \text{ for the longitudinal component}$$

and

$$\sin^2\Theta = 1 - \frac{Q^2+q^2-(2\pi\tau)^2}{2qQ} \text{ for the transverse component}$$

14*

Θ is the angle between **q** and **Q**. The integrand in the liquid case and the summation in the solid case should be divided up in two contributions, a longitudinal and a transverse. The latter contribution has to be multiplied by 2 as there are in general two transverse branches and one longitudinal in the solid case. In the case of the transverse modes an exponential damping factor was included.

In applying this theory to the liquid phase it is assumed that "pseudophonons" exist. It has been shown that phonons exist in a solid close to the

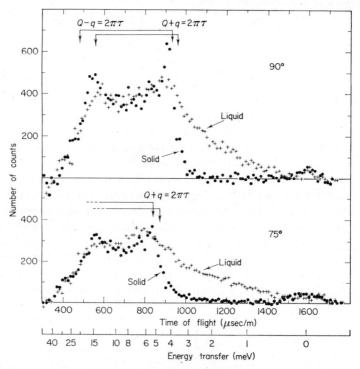

FIG. 8.29. Time-of-flight spectra of 2·1 meV (6·25 Å) neutrons scattered from solid tin at 210°C and from liquid tin at 240°C (Cocking and Guner, 1963).

melting point both for aluminium and for lead, so that the harmonic approximation for atomic motions applies there. Certainly strong deviations from the harmonic approximation must occur in the liquid phase where perhaps the oscillations should be damped out in a few periods.

Attempts have been made to use the simplified theory outlined above to explain experimental results. Experiments by Cocking and Guner (1963) on solid and liquid tin were performed using a line spectrum of incident neutrons of 4 or 6·25 Å wavelength corresponding to ingoing energies of 5 or 2·1 meV. On the basis of the known lattice constants and the liquid structure factor for tin it may be estimated that if 6·25 Å neutrons are used, there should be practically no quasi-elastic scattering at any scattering angle between 20° and 90°, whereas at the higher angles for 4 Å neutrons a considerable quasi-elastic scattering should appear. This was indeed verified experimentally. It is also seen that the spectra observed from solid tin at 210°C and liquid tin at 240°C are rather similar except for an increased scattered intensity at small energy transfers in the liquid phase (Fig. 8.29). Particularly at the angles of 75° and 90° it is visible how in the solid poly-crystalline phase there is a rather sharp low energy cut-off of the spectrum

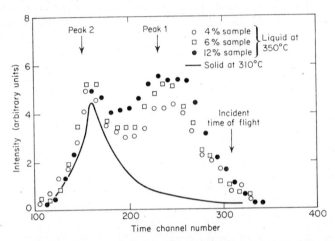

Fig. 8.30. Time-of-flight spectrum for 6·25 Å neutrons scattered by liquid lead at 350°C; data for several sample thicknesses are shown to demonstrate the effects of multiple scattering.

for $2\pi\tau = Q+q$ as expected from the theory. The observed intensity distribution may be understood for the polycrystalline case even on the simple assumption that the frequency spectrum is of the Debye form. The distribution of neutrons obtained from the liquid phase was, however, not successfully explained on the basis of the simple structure factor theory. The main reason for the failure stems from the intensity observed at small energy transfers. Egelstaff (1963) attempted to explain this by a calculation of the "$\tau = 0$ cross-section". As stated in the discussion of Chapter 7 following equation (7.83) this point does not contribute to the cross-section of a Debye solid for low energy neutrons; but due to the damping of the phonons in the liquid state some contribution might be possible there.

In a further series of experiments on liquid lead, Cocking and Egelstaff (1965) examined this question in detail. Measurements were made with various sample thicknesses as shown in Fig. 8.30. These results show that two peaks occur in the low energy part of the inelastic spectrum, one due to quasi-phonons with $\tau = 0$ which in the crystalline solid case corresponds to phonons in the first Brillouin zone. Such an observation of two peaks is possible only if a dispersion relation exists for which the energy and momentum conditions may be fulfilled twice for a given scattering angle. Calculations based on the hydrodynamic model (see Section 7.8) were employed to describe the first peak, while the model discussed at equation (8.15) can be used to describe the second peak. This peak comes at an energy transfer of 7 meV which is close to the energy of the peak discussed by Cotter.

The similarity between the polycrystalline scattering picture and the corresponding liquid scattering picture as well as the importance of multiple scattering was clearly demonstrated by measurements of Larsson and

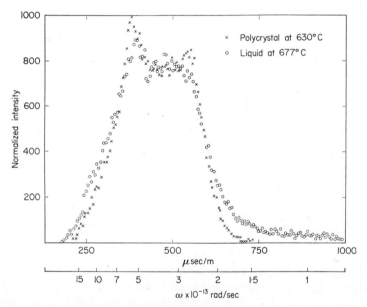

FIG. 8.31. Coherently scattered neutron spectra scattered from an aluminium polycrystal at 630°C, and a liquid sample at 677°C. The angle of observation in both cases was 60°, while the ingoing spectrum was the full cold neutron spectrum.

Dahlborg (1964) on aluminium. The temperature dependence of single phonon lines and the multiphonon spectrum obtained from a single crystal of aluminium was examined. It was reconfirmed that the phonon-expansion formula describes the observed multiphonon spectrum obtained from the coherently scattering aluminium crystal. The crystal was oriented in such a way that one single phonon line of low energy was observed, the temperature was raised and the crystal melted. It was found that in the liquid phase just above the melting point at 677°C the single phonon line disappeared and instead a broad spectrum ranging from a low energy transfer up to the same high energy limit as for the polycrystalline solid was observed.

If the same energy and momentum conditions are operating in the liquid and solid phases, one would expect both phases to show the low energy cut-off predicted by equation (8.16). The cut-off in solid aluminium was demonstrated by measurements at at temperature of 630°C (Fig. 8.31). A cut-off was observed in the liquid phase too as shown in the figure. Detailed calculations (Fig. 8.32) show that in the solid state the peak at $\omega = 2\cdot5 \times 10^{13}$ rad/sec

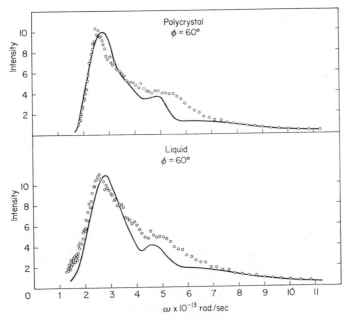

FIG. 8.32. Observed and calculated neutron spectra scattered from polycrystalline and liquid aluminium at 60° angle of observation. The results are given on an absolute energy scale such that for $\omega = 1 \times 10^{13}$ rad/sec the energy is $\hbar\omega = 6\cdot6$ meV. The ingoing cold neutron spectrum has its sharp edge at 5·2 meV or at $\omega = 0\cdot796 \times 10^{13}$ rad/sec.

is due to transverse modes. Also the neutron spectra scattered at 60° angle of observation from liquid aluminium at ~670°C in the form of a thick and a thin sample were compared. It was clearly shown that when the sample was thick (cylinder with diameter 6 cm and length 12 cm compared to the normal sample which was a plate 1·2 cm thick) there appears a multiply scattered neutron distribution superimposed on the singly scattered inelastic spectrum. After allowing for multiple scattering the $\tau = 0$ region for aluminium seems to be less intense than for lead or tin.

Physically, the experiments on solid and liquid metals clearly demonstrate that similar momentum conservation laws must operate in both cases. This point may be demonstrated quantitatively. The formula (8.15) for the one-phonon cross-section together with the (incoherent) phonon expansion formula including up to five phonon interactions, was used to calculate the polycrystalline differential cross-section of aluminium at 630°C and the same formulae with the structure factor modified according to (8.16) were used to calculate the liquid differential cross-section. A frequency spectrum of the shape actually measured for the solid was used and for details the reader is referred to the original paper (Larsson et al., 1965). The calculated cross-sections are compared to experiment in Fig. 8.32. They agree quite well with the main features of the observed neutron intensity distribution for the solid case. The agreement between theory and experiment is not good in detail for the liquid case although the main features are reproduced by this simple theoretical approximation. In contrast the incoherent one-phonon cross-section gives a much poorer comparison with the observed spectra.

The results indicate that there exists a frequency distribution in the liquid metals rather similar to the one obtained for the solid phase. Vibrations of short mean free path probably exist, but may be confined to small regions within which local order exists for a short time in the liquid phase. It is worth noticing that the pseudo-phonons discussed above have periods of about $(1-3) \times 10^{-13}$ sec, and that the two curves for lead given at Fig. 8.27 differ from each other in a time region from 0 up to about 3×10^{-13} sec. So within this short time period it should be meaningful to speak about distinct spherical shells of neighbouring atoms around a particular atom, and of the collective recoil of a group of atoms after interaction with a neutron, rather than the recoil of a single atom.

8.7 Liquid Sodium

An ideal case for investigation would be a completely incoherently scattering metal, which had a Debye temperature close to the melting temperature. This would ensure that the multi-phonon interactions would be suppressed to a minimum level in the solid phase close to melting. As one might expect that the solid-like properties would extend into the liquid phase, it would be easier to analyse and understand the liquid scattering picture too. A metal which is an almost completely incoherent scatterer is vanadium, but unfortunately it has the inconveniently high melting point of 1983°K. Furthermore liquid vanadium is chemically very active so its containment presents a formidable experimental problem especially since windows of the sample holder have to be thin, otherwise the neutron scattering from the sample would be blurred by the scattering from the container.

A case which nearly meets these requirements is sodium but unfortunately it is a mixed coherent and incoherent scatterer. Consequently the interpretation of data on sodium requires models for both processes. At small scattering angles the coherent quasi-elastic scattering ought to be very small. Consequently some model for the incoherent quasi-elastic scattering may be tried for an explanation of the observed spectrum. This was done by Cocking (1963) who used the model of Egelstaff and Schofield (see Section 7.11) to calculate the delay time before diffusion sets in. To

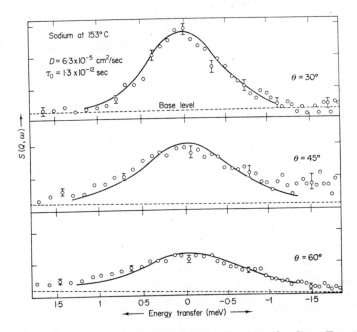

FIG. 8.33. Observed and calculated quasi-elastic peaks of liquid sodium. Experimental data of Cocking (1963) compared with the Egelstaff and Schofield model (Chapter 7).

perform this a value of the self diffusion coefficient taken from other studies was used. His results are shown in Fig. 8.33. The values for the delay time that corresponded to reasonable fits of the calculated cross-sections to the experimental intensity distributions were found to fall in the range $(1-2) \times 10^{-12}$ sec for temperatures of the liquid sodium of 108–198°C when the self diffusion coefficient is in the region of 6×10^{-5} cm²/sec. This value is of the same order as was derived from studies on hydrogenous liquids. Thus again we see that the delay of the diffusion process seems to be universal in all liquids. Cocking also made a comparison between the inelastic regions of the spectra (4 to 30 meV) for solid and liquid sodium and showed that they were very similar. This is additional evidence that a solid type frequency spectrum is applicable to the liquid state.

The scattering law (equation (1.34)) for liquid sodium between 100° and 200°C was measured by Randolph (1964). He employed the time-of-flight

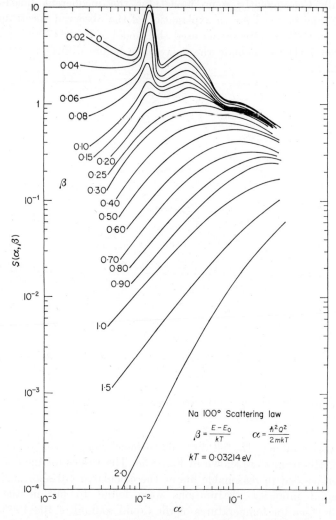

Fig. 8.34. Summary curves showing the scattering law, $\widetilde{S}(Q,\omega)$, for liquid sodium at 100°C. Note how the coherent fluctuations are damped as the energy transfer increases.

apparatus described in Section 2.10, and obtained energy distributions from zero to about 0·06 eV and momenta in the range $1 < Q < 10$ A⁻¹. This range of momentum transfer is greater than the range covered by Cocking in experiments described above. A summary of his data at 100°C is given in Fig. 8.34. It is easy to see from this figure that the convolution approximation (equation (7.71)) is not valid, because it predicts the same degree of interference at all energy transfers. In contrast the family of curves in Fig. 8.34, one for each value of ω, shows that the interference fluctuations which are clearly visible at $\omega = 0$ become rapidly damped as ω increases.

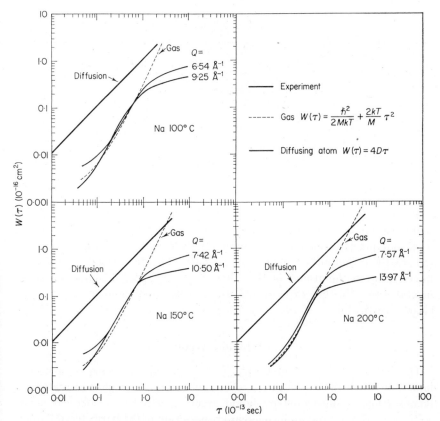

FIG. 8.35. Time dependent width functions for sodium, obtained by Fourier transformation of the scattering law assuming a Gaussian form for the self-correlation function.

In order to test the Gaussian approximation (Section 7.9), Randolph fourier transformed the data at a given Q value according to equation (7.94). In this way he obtained values of $w(\tau)_Q$, which should be independent of Q if the Gaussian approximation were valid. In Fig. 8.35 summaries of his results are given. It can be seen that $w(\tau)_Q$ is only weakly dependent upon Q confirming that a Gaussian self correlation function is a good first approximation.

However, some differences exist between the results obtained at low and high values of Q, indicating that higher order velocity correlations are significant.

In addition Randolph used his data to test the first moment theorem (equations (1.35) and (7.15)) with the results shown in the Table 8.2 (each figure is an average over the different momenta covered in this experiment).

TABLE 8.2

Measured zero and first energy moments for sodium compared to theoretical values

	Temperature (°C)	100	150	200
Zero moment $\dfrac{\text{Experiment}}{\text{Theory}}$		1·06	1·14	1·11
First moment $\dfrac{\text{Experiment}}{\text{Theory}}$		2·30	1·82	1·42

The "theoretical zero moment" is in fact the result of diffraction studies of liquid sodium by other workers and serves to check the absolute scale used by Randolph. He concludes that probably the experimental first moment is too great and that either this indicates a basic effect (e.g. velocity dependent forces between the atoms) or that there is an unexpected source of experimental error. Further experimental tests of the first moment theorem are clearly worthwhile.

8.8 Liquid Argon

The difficulties of interpretation of the neutron scattering data from a liquid, of which the nuclei give a mixed coherent and incoherent scattering cross-section, is illustrated by liquid argon. Argon has a coherent cross-section of 0·5 barn and an incoherent cross-section of 0·4 barn. Liquid argon is attractive as a subject for investigation for many reasons: (i) unlike the liquid metals the argon atom has closed electron shells and it would seem reasonable to perform calculations of the interactions between the atoms of liquid argon using a Lennard Jones potential or the Buckingham-Rice potential, the parameters of which are known or may be calculated; (ii) the liquid structure factor or pair density function $1 + \gamma(Q)$ is well known; (iii) unlike the lightest noble gas liquids, such as liquid helium, the quantum effects are negligible so that the liquid may be treated classically. The

Debye temperature of solid argon is low—only 80–90°K—so that any inelastically scattered neutrons revealing the existence of a frequency spectrum will appear close to the ingoing neutron line. A low ingoing neutron
energy is necessary and the resolution both of the ingoing spectrum as well
as the analysing system must be good in order to see these small effects.

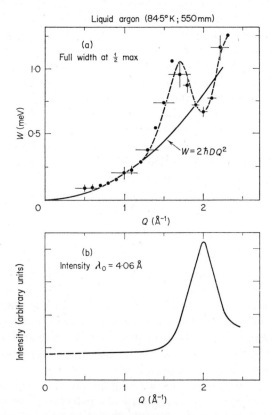

Fig. 8.36. (a) The observed width of the scattered neutron spectra for liquid argon compared to the prediction of the simple diffusion theory. (b) Integrated intensity under the
scattered neutron spectra for liquid argon, i.e. $S(Q)$.

A neutron scattering experiment on liquid argon at 84·5°K was performed
by Dasannacharya and Rao (1965). A rotating crystal spectrometer was used
to select neutrons of a wavelength of 4·06 Å and the resolution at the incoming energy was 2 % in wavelength or 2×10^{-4} eV. It was found
that with increasing value of the scattering angle in the range of Q values
from 0·4 to 1·6 Å^{-1}, the width of the quasi-elastic line increases whereafter
a *decrease* is observed giving a minimum at $Q = 2$ Å^{-1}. Then the width

increases again. There was no indication of the presence of frequency spectrum of the type observed in, for instance, liquid sodium.

This behaviour of the quasi-elastic line obtained from liquid argon might appear startling. From the point of view of the convolution approximation (Section 7.8) for coherent scattering in liquids the effect is inexplicable. This narrowing effect was, however, discussed by de Gennes, who calculated the moments of the scattered neutron distribution (see Section 7·3 for a discussion of the moments). By comparing the second and fourth moments he showed that the width should vary as $[1/S(Q)]^{\frac{1}{2}}$. The results shown in Fig. 8.36 confirm this prediction. In Fig. 8.36 it is seen how the measured line width values follow the simple diffusion approximation only for Q values up to about $1\cdot2$ Å^{-1}. For larger Q values the coherent contribution is important as expected because the neutrons observation time is now shorter and it consequently feels the coupling between the motions of an atom and its nearest neighbours. The integrated intensity under the observed quasi-elastic peaks (shown in the lower part of the figure) has a constant value for Q values up to about $1\cdot2$ Å^{-1}. In this region the intensity is mainly due to incoherent scattering. For higher Q values the integrated intensity shows the variation typical of coherent scattering.

Dasannacharya and Rao converted their data to the correlation function $G(r,\tau)$ in the way described earlier for water and lead, and found a similar qualitative behaviour. However, the width of the self-correlation function was found to follow the simple diffusion model more closely than the other cases.* This is shown in Fig. 8.37, where the simple diffusion model with a diffusion constant of $1\cdot8\times10^{-5}$ cm^2/sec seems to fit the data. It was concluded that this result is due to the loose binding in liquid argon. Qualitatively the calculations of Rahman discussed in Chapter 7 seem to be in agreement with these data, but a quantitative comparison is required before firm conclusions can be drawn.

Another study of the neutron scattering from liquid argon was performed by Kroo et al. (1964). Studies were made of a polycrystalline sample at 80°K as well as of a liquid sample at 88°K. The observations on polycrystalline argon showed the sharp breaks in the inelastically scattered neutron spectrum already discussed for the case of liquid metals (Sections 7.8 and 8.6). In the liquid case no sharp breaks were observed. In spite of this an average dispersion relation was derived following the method suggested by Egelstaff (1963). Several spectra were measured for such angles of observation such that the Q values in the inelastic scattering region fall near the first peak of the

---

* In a note added in proof Dasannacharya and Rao stated that a fit of the type $w(\tau)=a\tau^2+b$ gives a value of $1\cdot58\times10^{-5}$ cm^2/sec for D, which is consistent with the line width data in Fig. 8.36a. The value obtained for b corresponds to a delay time of 1×10^{-12} sec for diffusion to set in.

liquid structure factor $1+\gamma(Q)$. Then a plot is made of the intensity observed at constant energy transfers, $\hbar\omega$, as a function of Q. If there is coherent scattering it is expected to occur for τ values within the limits $Q-q<2\pi\tau<Q+q$ (compare equation (8.16) above and the discussion in connection with it). The width of the observed distribution as a function of Q would then be just $2q$, where q is an average "pseudo-phonon" wave number. As, however, the observations are performed for Q values round the first peak

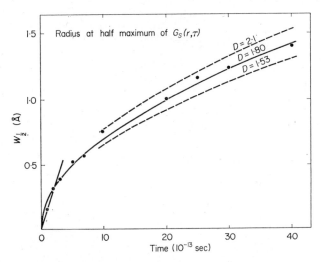

Fig. 8.37. The width of the self-correlation function for liquid argon as a function of time, compared to calculations based on the simple diffusion model with the values of D shown.

of the structure factor the neutron intensity distribution is approximately given by folding the first peak of $1+\gamma(Q)$ and the distribution of intensity within the allowed coherent zone. If both the distributions are assumed Gaussian the width $2q$ of the pseudo-phonon distribution is given by

$$2q = [(\varDelta Q_\omega)^2-(\varDelta Q_0)^2]^{\frac{1}{2}} \qquad (8.21)$$

where $\varDelta Q_\omega$ is the observed width of the plot of the neutron intensity at constant ω and $\varDelta Q_0$ is the width of the first peak of the structure factor $1+\gamma(Q)$. As the energy ω of the pseudo-phonon as well as its wave number q is known, a point $\omega(q)$ on an average dispersion relation is found. In this way a dispersion relation for liquid argon was experimentally obtained (Fig. 8.38). The value for the sound velocity in liquid argon thus obtained was 9.1×10^4 cm/sec whereas the corresponding observed figure for the poly-crystalline case was 1.13×10^5 cm/sec. The ratio of these figures is 0.8 ± 0.2 whereas the ratio of the Debye temperatures of liquid and solid argon is 0.6. The agreement is reasonable considering the simple model used. From studies of the quasi-elastic peak Kroo *et al.* found a line width variation in exact agreement with the observations of Dasannacharya and Rao (Fig. 8.36).

The implication of the results obtained on liquid argon is that collective modes of motion of the argon atoms exists analogous to those discussed

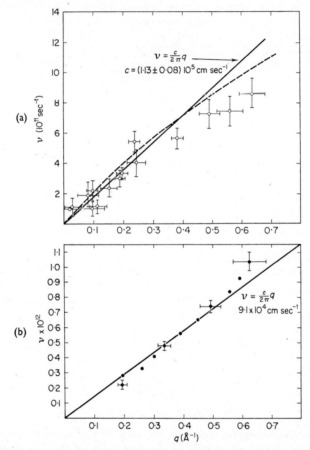

FIG. 8.38. Experimentally determined average dispersion relations for polycrystalline and liquid argon. (a) Polycrystal. The dashed curve is the calculated average dispersion relation. The straight line is a least squares fit to the lowest eleven points. The slope of this line gives the velocity of the modes. (b) Liquid. The straight line is a least squares fit giving the mode velocity.

for liquid metals. However, the data of Fig. 8.37 compared to Fig. 8·27 show that the interatomic forces in argon are weaker than those in lead. The following argument might be given to suggest that vibratory modes of motion exist in most liquids. According to simple diffusion theory the distance that an atom moves on the average during a time t is $\sqrt{6Dt}$, where D is the self-diffusion coefficient. If there exists a dispersion relation $\nu(q)$ a period $\tau = 1/\nu$ is associated to each wave number value $q = 2\pi/\lambda$. In liquids like liquid argon, liquid aluminium, liquid lead, etc., the τ value associated with a q value of about 0.5 Å^{-1} is larger than about 10^{-12} sec. As the D value is about 10^{-5} cm^2/sec in all cases this means that the distance (d) an atom moves in 10^{-12} sec is about 0.8 Å, according to simple diffusion theory. The wavelength λ of the pseudo-phonon corresponding to $q = 0.5$ Å^{-1} is of the order 10 Å. One thus finds $d \ll \lambda$. This must mean that the diffusive damping of the vibratory modes is modest. Thus several oscillations round an approximately stationary position should be possible for an atom and this would explain why frequency spectra may be derived which are similar to those obtained for solids. The hindrance of the free atomic motion is strong enough to allow damped periodic motions to occur.

8.9 Liquid Bromine

Several experiments have been reported on liquid bromine which is a diatomic molecular liquid. Cagliotti et al. (1963) compared the angular distribution for elastic and total scattering. In contrast to neutron measurements the angular distribution of scattered X-rays is directly related to the instantaneous correlation function $G(r,0) = g(r)$. However, if neutrons are used it is no longer self-evident that a study of $d\sigma/d\Omega$ gives $G(r,0)$, because the observation time is not short compared to the various relaxation times of the system of nuclei being observed. This means that a given angle does not correspond to a unique value of the momentum transfer, and corrections are necessary as described by Placzek (1952). On the other hand if an analyser is placed after the sample it may be set so as to select a narrow band of energies, say ΔE_A, at the ingoing neutron energy. The width of the ingoing neutron spectrum is denoted by ΔE_M, and when folded together ΔE_M and ΔE_A give the experimental width. This will correspond to an observation time which is fairly long. If, as in this example $\Delta E_M = 1.4 \times 10^{-3}$ eV and $\Delta E_A = 2.3 \times 10^{-3}$ eV the measurements give effectively a time average of $G(r,\tau)$ over a period $\Delta\tau$ of about 1.3×10^{-12} sec, which may be contrasted with the instantaneous distribution $g(r)$.

The angular distribution study performed by Caglioti et al. (1963) was carried out using a triple axis crystal spectrometer set to give a wavelength of 1.4 Å with the resolution widths of the monochromator and the analyser as above. The quasi-elastic angular distribution (Fig. 8.39) when compared with the corresponding conventional distribution of total scattering showed that the inelastic component in the analysed neutron picture was high at high Q values. An attempt to calculate this distribution was made utilizing the convolution approximation. The molecules of the liquid were assumed to move in two ways: one part of them, weight 23 %, was assumed to move like gas molecules and the other part, weight 77 %, to move like atoms in a solid. This ratio was deduced from the free volume theory of liquids. The solid-like Gaussian self correlation function having a width, $\overline{2u^2}$, independent of time was assumed for the solid part. The interference effects due to instantaneous space correlations among the nuclei in the liquid were supposed to be expressed by the distribution of total scattering. As seen in Fig. 8.39

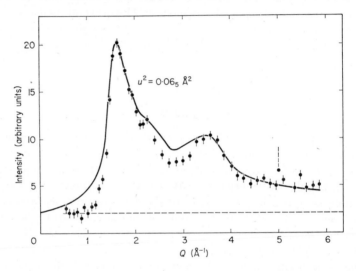

FIG. 8.39. Angular distribution of 1·4 Å neutrons scattered quasi-elastically from liquid bromine at room temperature. The bars represent the experimental data; the dashed horizontal line is the estimated level of multiple and incoherent scattering.

where the calculated distribution is given as a solid line, and arbitrarily normalized at $Q = 5$ Å^{-1}, there is surprisingly good agreement between the calculated curve and the measured values. The observed data are sharper than the calculated curve and this is due to the inelastic component of $1 + \gamma(Q)$ which is not allowed for in this treatment.

Coote and Haywood (1963) studied the inelastic scattering from liquid bromine at room temperature. They used their data to derive a frequency spectrum via the extrapolation technique discussed earlier (Section 8.2). The principal result is an energy level at ~ 8 meV which is well below the vibrational mode of the bromine molecule (40 meV) and may be due to hindered rotational motion. Coote and Haywood also used their data to check the moment theorem equation (1.35) and found that the experimental value could be as much as twice the theoretical value (compare the discussion on sodium at 8.7). However, they conclude that further work is needed to establish a reliable result. The vibrational mode at 40 meV was observed, however, by Antonini *et al.* (1964).

References

Antonini, M., Ascarelli, P. and Caglioti, G. (1964). *Phys. Rev.* **136**, 1280.

Bajorik, A., Golikov, V. V., Zhukovskaya, I., Shapiro, F. L., Shkatula, A. and Janik, E. A. (1963). *In* "Inelastic scattering of Neutrons in Solids and Liquids", Vol. I, p. 383. IAEA, Vienna.

Brockhouse, B. N. (1955). *Phys. Rev.* **98**, 1171.

Brockhouse, B. N. (1958). *Nuovo Cimento* **9** (Suppl.), 45.

Brockhouse, B. N. (1959). *Phys. Rev. Letters* **2**, 287.

Brockhouse, B. N., Bergsma, J., Dasannacharya, B. A. and Pope, N. K. (1963). *In* "Inelastic Scattering of Neutrons in Solids and Liquids", Vol. I, p. 189. IAEA, Vienna.

Brockhouse, B. N. and Pope, N. K. (1959). *Phys. Rev. Letters* **3**, 259.

Butler, D. (1963). *Proc. phys. Soc.* **81**, 294.

Caglioti, G. and Ascarelli, P. (1963). *In* "Inelastic Scattering of Neutrons in Solids and Liquids", Vol. I, p. 259. IAEA, Vienna.

Cocking, S. J. (1963). *In* "Inelastic Scattering of Neutrons in Solids and Liquids", Vol. I, p. 227. IAEA, Vienna.

Cocking, S. J. and Guner, Z. (1963). *In* "Inelastic Scattering of Neutrons in Solids and Liquids", Vol. I, p. 237. IAEA, Vienna.

Cocking, S. J. and Egelstaff, P. A. (1965). *Phys. Letters* **16**, 130.

Cocking (1965). To be published.

Coote, G. E. and Haywood, B. C. (1963). *In* "Inelastic Scattering of Neutrons in Solids and Liquids", p. 249. IAEA, Vienna.

Cotter, M. J. (1962). "Inelastic scattering of cold neutrons by solid and liquid lead". Dissertation, Fordham University, New York.

Cribier, D. and Jacrot, B. (1961). *In* "Inelastic Scattering of Neutrons in Solids and Liquids", p. 347. IAEA, Vienna.

Dasannacharya, B. A., Venkataraman, G. and Uscha Deniz, K. (1965). *In* "Inelastic Scattering of Neutrons", Vol. II, p. 157. IAEA, Vienna.

Dasannacharya, B. A. and Rao, K. R. (1965). *Phys. Rev.* **137**, A417.

Egelstaff, P. A. (1953). The inelastic scattering of cold neutrons by crystals, Part I, Theory. AERE Report N/R.1164. H.M.S.O., London.

Egelstaff, P. A. (1954). *Acta cryst.* **7**, 674 (a table of these results may be found in *Brit. J. Appl. Phys.* **10**, 1, 1959).

Egelstaff, P. A. (1961). *In* "Inelastic Scattering of Neutrons in Solids and Liquids", p. 25. IAEA, Vienna.

Egelstaff, P. A. (1962). *Advanc. Phys.* **11**, 203.

Egelstaff, P. A. (1962). The scattering of cold neutrons by metals. AERE Report R.4101, H.M.S.O., London.

Egelstaff, P. A. (1963). *In* "Inelastic Scattering of Neutrons in Solids and Liquids", Vol. I, p. 65. IAEA, Vienna.

Egelstaff, P. A., Cocking, S. J., Royston, R. and Thorson, I. M. (1961). *In* "Inelastic Scattering of Neutrons in Solids and Liquids", p. 309. IAEA, Vienna.

Egelstaff, P. A. and Schofield, P. (1962). *Nucl. Sci. Engng.* **12**, 260.

Egelstaff, P. A., Haywood, B. C. and Thorson, I. M. (1963). *In* "Inelastic Scattering of Neutrons in Solids and Liquids", Vol. I, p. 343. IAEA, Vienna.

Egelstaff, P. A., Haywood, B. C., Webb, F. J. and Baston A. H. (1964). *Phys. Letters* **12**, 2/3.

Frenkel, J. (1946). "Kinetic Theory of Liquids." Oxford University Press.

Forslind, E. (1954). Rep. No. 21. Swedish Cement and Concrete Research Institute at Royal Institute of Technology, Stockholm.

Gingrich, N. S. (1943). *Rev. mod. Phys.* **15**, 90.

Gläser, W. (1963). *In* "Inelastic Scattering of Neutrons in Solids and Liquids", Vol. I, p. 307. IAEA, Vienna.

Gläser, W., Ehret, G. and Merkel, A. (1965). *In* "Inelastic Scattering of Neutrons", Vol. II, p. 167. IAEA, Vienna.

Golikov, U. U. *et al.* (1965). *In* "Inelastic Scattering of Neutrons", Vol. II, p. 201. IAEA, Vienna.

Griffing, G. W. (1961). *Phys. Rev.* **124**, 1489.

Harker, Y. D. and Brugger, R. M. (1965). *J. chem. Phys.* **42**, 275.

Hautecler, S. and Stiller, H. (1963). *In* "Inelastic Scattering of Neutrons in Solids and Liquids", p. 423. IAEA, Vienna.

Hass, W. P. S. *et al.* (1960). *Physica* **26**, 834.

Herzberg, G. (1960). "Spectra of Diatomic Molecules", 2nd Ed. Van Nostrand, New York.

van Hove, L. (1954). *Phys. Rev.* **95**, p. 249.

Hughes, D. J., Palevsky, H., Kley, W. and Tunkelo, E. (1960). *Phys. Rev.* **119**, 872.

Kottwitz, D. A., Leonard, B. R. and Smith, R. B. (1963). *In* "Inelastic Scattering of Neutrons in Solids and Liquids", Vol. I, p. 382. IAEA, Vienna.

Kroo, N., Borgonovi, G., Sköld, K. and Larsson, K. E. (1964). *Phys. Rev. Letters*, **12**, 721.

Larsson, K. E., Dahlborg, U. and Holmryd, S. (1960). *Ark. Fys.* **17**, 369.

Larsson, K. E. and Dahlborg, U. (1962). *Reactor Sci. Tech.* **16**, 81.

Larsson, K. E. and Singwi, K. S. (1962). *Phys. Letters* **3**, 145.

Larsson, K. E. and Dahlborg, U. (1963). *In* "Inelastic Scattering of Neutrons in Solids and Liquids", Vol. I, p. 317. IAEA, Vienna.

Larsson, K. E. and Dahlborg, U. (1964). *Physica* **30**, 1561.

Larsson, K. E., Dahlborg, U. and Jovic, D. (1965). *In* "Inelastic Scattering of Neutrons", Vol. II, p. 117. IAEA, Vienna.

McReynolds, A. W. and Whittemore, W. L. (1963). *In* "Inelastic Scattering of Neutrons in Solids and Liquids", Vol. I, p. 263. IAEA, Vienna.

Palevsky, H. (1961). *In* "Inelastic Scattering of Neutrons in Solids and Liquids", p. 265. IAEA, Vienna.

Placzek, G. (1952). *Phys. Rev.* **86**, 377.

Rahman, A., Singwi, K. S. and Sjölander, A. (1962). *Phys. Rev.* **126**, 986 and 997.

Randolph, P. D. (1964). *Phys. Rev.* **134**, 1483.

Sakamoto, M., Brockhouse, B. N., Johnson, R. H. and Pope, N. K. (1962). *J. phys. Soc. Japan* **17**, Suppl. B-11, 370.

Sarma, G. (1961). *In* "Inelastic Scattering of Neutrons in Solids and Liquids", p. 397. IAEA, Vienna.

Saunderson, D. H. and Rainey, V. S. (1963). *In* "Inelastic Scattering of Neutrons in Solids and Liquids", Vol. I, p. 413. IAEA, Vienna.

Schofield, P. (1961). *In* "Inelastic Scattering of Neutrons in Solids and Liquids", p. 39. IAEA, Vienna.

Schwinger, J. and Teller, E. (1937). *Phys. Rev.* **52**, 286.

Singwi, K. S. and Sjölander, A. (1960). *Phys. Rev.* **119**, 863.

Stiller, H. and Danner, H. R. (1961). *In* "Inelastic Scattering of Neutrons in Solids and Liquids", p. 363. IAEA, Vienna.
Turberfield, K. C. (1962). *Proc. Phys. Soc.* **80**, 395.
Weinstock, R. (1944). *Phys. Rev.* **65**, 1.
Whittemore, W. L. and Danner, H. R. (1963). *In* "Inelastic Scattering of Neutrons in Solids and Liquids", Vol. I, p. 273. IAEA, Vienna.

CHAPTER 9

The Theory of Neutron Scattering by Molecules

J. A. Janik and A. Kowalska

Physical Institute of the Jagiellonian University, Krakow, Poland

9.1 Introduction.. 414
9.2 The Isotropic Harmonic Oscillator................................ 416
9.3 Sachs and Teller Mass Tensor Concept............................ 418
9.4 The Zemach and Glauber Formalism.............................. 422
9.5 Examples of Zemach and Glauber Cross-sections................... 428
9.6 An Approximate Theory for the Thermal Energy Region........... 432
9.7 Diatomic Molecules (particularly H_2)........................... 437
9.8 Scattering by Rotators.. 442
9.9 Time-dependent Correlation Function for an Atom in a Molecule.... 447
References.. 450

List of Symbols

a_ν	Scattering length of νth nucleus (free)	M_ν	Mass of νth nucleus
A	Rotational constant	$M_\nu^{(0)}$	Modified mass giving translation and rotation as pure translation
b_ν	Scattering length of νth nucleus (bound)		
B_ν	Spin weighted scattering length of νth nucleus (coherent bound)	$\mathcal{M}^{-1}$	Inverse mass tensor
		$\mathbf{n}$	$m\mathcal{M}^{-1}$
		$\mathbf{P}$	Momentum of molecule
B_ν'	Spin weighted scattering length of νth nucleus (incoherent bound)	$\mathbf{p}_\nu$	Momentum of νth nucleus
		$\tilde{Q}_x$	$-Q_x \Big/ \sqrt{\dfrac{2mf_x}{\hbar}}$
$\mathbf{C}_\nu^\lambda$	Normal amplitude vectors in mode λ	q_λ	Normal coordinate for mode λ
$\mathbf{d}_\nu$	Equilibrium position of the νth nucleus with respect to centre of mass of molecule	$\mathbf{R}$	Position of centre of mass of molecule
		$\mathbf{r}_\nu$	Position of νth nucleus
		$\mathbf{S}_\nu$	Spin of νth nucleus
E_J	Energy of rotator of angular momentum J	$\mathbf{s}$	Spin of neutron
		$\mathbf{V}_c$	Velocity of centre of mass of molecule
H'	Effective Hamiltonian obtained by replacing $\mathbf{p}$ by $(\mathbf{p} - \hbar\mathbf{Q})$	V_{ig}	Matrix element for transition between initial state i and final state g
$\mathscr{I}$	Moment of inertia tensor of molecule		
J, K, M	Angular momentum quantum numbers	z	Density of states
$\mathscr{K}_{\nu\nu}$	Effective inverse mass tensor of Krieger and Nelkin (equation (9.34c))	$\gamma_{\nu\nu'}$	Mean square displacement factor (analogous to Debye Waller factor)
		ζ	m/M
l	Orbital angular momentum quantum number (Sect. 9.4—9.7)	$\Theta_{\nu\nu}$	Angle between $\mathbf{r}_\nu$ and $\mathbf{r}_{\nu'}$
		θ	Scattering angle

μ	Reduced mass tensor		by the scattering lengths of
μ	Reduced mass of neutron–nucleus system		ν and ν' nuclei
μ'	Reduced mass of neutron–molecule system	$\psi_{P\nu}$	Wavefunction for proton
		$\psi_{N\nu}$	Wavefunction for neutron
Π_ν^+, Π_ν^-	Projection operators	Ω	Used after averaging bracket to denote averaging over molecular orientations
$X_{\nu\nu'}$	Component of intermediate scattering function weighted		

9.1 Introductory Remarks

Much of the experimental data concerning the scattering of neutrons by molecules consists of measurements of total cross-sections for scattering in the thermal energy region. However, some measurements have been carried out in which subthermal neutrons are used and also measurements of the angular and energy distribution of scattered neutrons.

It should also be noted that almost all experimental results concern the scattering of neutrons by molecules containing hydrogen. This is a consequence of the fact that the mass of the proton is practically equal to the mass of the neutron, which causes a great sensitivity of the total cross-section to chemical binding. Also the incoherence of the scattering by hydrogen gives rise to a monotonic dependence on the scattering angle. Therefore one does not obtain much more information from the differential cross-section $d\sigma_H/d\Omega$ (i.e. $\sigma_H(\theta)$) than from the total cross-section for scattering σ_H. However, in general the determination of the energy distribution of scattered neutrons (which leads to the cross-section $d\sigma/dE$ or $d^2\sigma/d\Omega dE$) gives more information about the scattering system than that obtainable from total cross-section measurements.

In the present chapter a description of the most important theories which are concerned with the problem of the scattering of neutrons by molecules is presented. These theories must in general take the influence of all molecular degrees of freedom into consideration. A molecule containing n atoms has $3n$ degrees of freedom. Of these, three correspond to the motion of the centre of mass of the molecule—translational motion—three to rotational degrees of freedom (except for linear molecules with only two), and the remaining $(3n-6)$ (or $(3n-5)$ in linear molecules) to internal degrees of freedom. In the gaseous state these three types of motion may, to a good approximation, be regarded as independent and uncoupled. In the liquid state, this may not be so. In particular, for non-spherical molecules there is the possibility of strong coupling between the rotational states of neighbouring molecules. One of the most fruitful applications of slow neutron scattering by molecules is to the investigation of this "hindered rotation"—both between molecules, and of groups of atoms within a single molecule.

Rotational and vibrational energy levels of molecules have been extensively studied using infra-red absorption and scattering techniques (Herzberg, 1945), and a great deal has been learnt about the positions of the levels and the coupling between the different types of motion. In neutron experiments many of the finer details of the vibrational spectra are lost due to a Doppler broadening effect caused by the translational and rotational motions of the molecules. Knowledge of the infra-red results is therefore very important in providing data about force constants and moments of inertia for theoretical calculations of neutron scattering cross-sections for molecules.

Only in the cases of diatomic molecules (such as hydrogen) and spherical molecules (methane) is it at all feasible to make a complete calculation from basic principles, of the neutron scattering. In these highly symmetrical molecules the wave-functions for the molecule can be expressed as products of rotator and harmonic oscillator wave-functions. Calculations for diatomic molecules are discussed in Section 9.7. However, depending on the neutron energy, only certain features of the motions of the atoms in the molecule are important in determining the neutron scattering cross-section, and it is then possible to treat approximately the unimportant motions.

If the neutrons possess an energy much higher than the chemical binding energy, the scattering nucleus may be treated as free, and the cross-section obtained is that of a free nucleus (σ^{free}). For neutrons in the neighbourhood of 30 meV (i.e. thermal neutrons), vibrations must be taken into account as well as the translations and rotations. However, if the temperature of the assembly of molecules is much greater than the energy level separation of the rotational states (e.g. for a diatomic molecule this condition is $\hbar^2/2I \ll kT$, where I is the moment of inertia of the molecule) then it is possible to treat the rotations semiclassically. If the neutron energy is also greater than the energy level separation this leads to the "mass-tensor" concept. This was introduced by Sachs and Teller (1941) on a purely classical basis. They calculated classically, the "hard-sphere" scattering between a neutron and an atom rigidly bound in a freely rotating molecule. The mass-tensor theory was shown by Krieger and Nelkin (1957), using the methods of Zemach and Glauber (1956), to result from a "short-collision time" approximation applied to the quantum mechanical theory.

For neutron energies which are not large compared to the difference in rotational levels, the classical treatment is not valid. The scattering must then be treated either by explicit consideration of possible rotational transitions, or in the time-dependent formalism by considering longer times in the interaction. The former is necessary if, in the scattering, individual transitions are observable, that is, not smoothed out by the Doppler effect of the translational motion. This will be the case if $\hbar^2/2I \lessgtr kT$. The latter approach is satisfactory if the Doppler effect is large.

This chapter starts from a description of the Fermi (1936) theory in which the degrees of freedom of the scattering system are approximated by a single harmonic vibration only. Then follows the Sachs and Teller (1941) treatment which takes only classical translations and rotations into account. These methods, although they cannot be used for an adequate description of the scattering by molecules, contain the concepts which were later adopted by others. In the subsequent sections the general formalism of Zemach and Glauber (1956) is given, together with its applications to the thermal, sub-thermal and intermediate energy regions. A separate discussion is made for the case of neutron scattering by diatomic molecules. Finally the time dependent formalism is briefly described.

These theories illustrate the complexity of our problem, namely a complete discussion of molecular motions and the relationships between these motions and the neutron scattering cross-sections; conversely, they illustrate the difficulty of interpreting the neutron scattering results unless detailed and accurate measurements are taken. The comparison of these theories with experiment and the conclusions on molecular behaviour are deferred until Chapter 10.

9.2 The Isotropic Harmonic Oscillator

Fermi (1936) gave the earliest theory of the scattering of slow neutrons by bound nuclei. He proved that the interaction between the neutron and the bound nucleus may be described by a pseudo-potential of the form

$$V = \frac{2\pi\hbar^2}{\mu} a_\nu \delta(\mathbf{r}_n - \mathbf{r}_\nu) \tag{9.1}$$

where $\mathbf{r}_n$, $\mathbf{r}_\nu$ are the position vectors for the neutron and the nucleus,

$$\mu = (mM_\nu)/(m + M_\nu)$$

is the reduced mass of the system neutron–nucleus, m being the mass of the neutron, M_ν the mass of the nucleus, and a_ν the so-called "free scattering length" of the nucleus. The pseudo-potential (9.1) may also be written in the form

$$V = \frac{2\pi\hbar^2}{m} b_\nu \delta(\mathbf{r}_n - \mathbf{r}_\nu) \tag{9.2}$$

where $b_\nu = a_\nu (1 + m/M_\nu)$ is the so-called "bound scattering length" of the nucleus (see equations (1.11)–(1.13)). Fermi considered the case where the given nucleus (in particular he considered a proton) could undergo an isotropic vibration only. This case is not realized in molecules and only approximately in some crystals as, for instance, in metal hydrides.

A neutron of the initial momentum $\hbar k_0$ is scattered by a proton which may be represented by the wave function $\psi_i(\mathbf{r}_p)$. After scattering we denote the neutron momentum by $\hbar k$, and the wave function of the proton by $\psi_g(\mathbf{r}_p)$.

The neutron scattering cross-section may be obtained by the method described in Section 1.6 (v_0 is the initial neutron velocity):

$$d\sigma = \frac{1}{\pi}\frac{v}{v_0}\sigma_{\mathrm{H}}^{\mathrm{free}}\left|\int e^{i(\mathbf{k_0}-\mathbf{k})\cdot\mathbf{r}_p}\,\psi_i(\mathbf{r}_p)\psi_g^*(\mathbf{r}_p)d\mathbf{r}_p\right|^2 d\Omega \tag{9.3}$$

where $\sigma_{\mathrm{H}}^{\mathrm{free}} = 4\pi a_{\mathrm{H}}^2$ is the scattering cross-section of free protons, v is the final neutron velocity.

For very low neutron energies (at which only elastic scattering is possible) $\psi_g = \psi_i$, $v = v_0 \sim 0$ and

$$d\sigma = \frac{1}{\pi}\sigma_{\mathrm{H}}^{\mathrm{free}}d\Omega; \quad \sigma = 4\sigma_{\mathrm{H}}^{\mathrm{free}} \tag{9.4}$$

We shall now consider the proton bound in a system by the potential of the harmonic oscillator type. Then

$$\psi(\mathbf{r}_p) = \psi_{n_x}(\xi)\psi_{n_y}(\eta)\psi_{n_z}(\zeta); \quad \mathbf{r}_p = (x,y,z)$$

where

$$\psi_s(\xi) = \frac{1}{\sqrt[4]{2\pi}\sqrt{s!}}\,e^{-\xi^2/4}\,\mathcal{H}_s(\xi); \, \xi = x\sqrt{\frac{2mf_x}{\hbar}}, \text{ etc.}$$

$\mathcal{H}_s(\xi)$ is the Hermite function, $s = n_x$, n_y, n_z are the vibration quantum numbers of the harmonic oscillator, and f_x, f_y, f_z are the frequencies of vibration along the x-, y-, z-axes.

If we assume for the initial state that of the lowest energy

$$(n_x = n_y = n_z = 0),$$

we may present the matrix element as the product of three integrals of the type:

$$\frac{1}{\sqrt{2\pi}}\frac{1}{\sqrt{s!}}\left[\frac{d^s}{da^s}\int_{-\infty}^{+\infty}e^{-(\xi-a)^2/2+i\tilde{Q}_x\xi}\,d\xi\right]_{a=0} = \frac{(i\tilde{Q}_x)^s}{\sqrt{s!}}\,e^{-\tilde{Q}_x^2/2}$$

where

$$\tilde{Q}_x = -Q_x\bigg/\sqrt{\frac{2mf_x}{\hbar}} = (k_0-k_x)\bigg/\sqrt{\frac{2mf_x}{\hbar}} \text{ etc.}$$

We obtain

$$d\sigma = \frac{1}{\pi}\frac{v}{v_0}\sigma_{\mathrm{H}}^{\mathrm{free}}\frac{\tilde{Q}_x^{2n_x}\tilde{Q}_y^{2n_y}\tilde{Q}_z^{2n_z}}{n_x!n_y!n_z!}\,e^{-\tilde{Q}^2}\,d\Omega$$

where $\tilde{Q}^2 = \tilde{Q}_x^2 + \tilde{Q}_y^2 + \tilde{Q}_z^2$.

15

Assuming that the oscillator is isotropic ($f_x = f_y = f_z = f$) we may write

$$\tilde{Q}^2 = \frac{E + E_0 - 2\sqrt{EE_0}\,\cos\theta}{\hbar f}$$

where E_0 and E are the initial and final neutron energies, and θ is the angle between k_0 and k.

Denoting by n the sum $n_x + n_y + n_z$ we may present the energy of the oscillator in the form $(n + \frac{3}{2})f\hbar$. Using this notation and performing the summation over all possible final states belonging to the given final energy of the proton (this procedure corresponds to the summation over all possible systems of n_x, n_y, n_z so that $n = n_x + n_y + n_z$) we obtain

$$d\sigma_n = \frac{2\sigma_H^{free}}{n!}\sqrt{\frac{E}{E_0}}\,\tilde{Q}^{2n}\,e^{-\tilde{Q}^2}\sin\theta\,d\theta = \frac{\sigma_H^{free}}{E_0}\hbar f\frac{\tilde{Q}^{2n}}{n!}\,e^{-\tilde{Q}^2}\,d\tilde{Q}^2$$

We may obtain the total cross-section for the excitation of the nth quantum state of the proton by integration over $\tilde{Q}$ within the limits

$$\tilde{Q}_{min} = \sqrt{\frac{E_0}{\hbar f}} - \sqrt{\frac{E}{\hbar f}}, \quad \tilde{Q}_{max} = \sqrt{\frac{E_0}{\hbar f}} + \sqrt{\frac{E}{\hbar f}}$$

Performing this integration, and taking additionally into account the formula

$$-\frac{1}{n!}\int x^n\,e^{-x}\,dx = e^{-x}\left[1 + \frac{x}{1!} + \ldots + \frac{x^n}{n!}\right] = F_n(x)$$

we obtain

$$\sigma_n = \frac{\sigma_H^{free}\hbar f}{E_0}[F_n(\tilde{Q}_{min}^2) - F_n(\tilde{Q}_{max}^2)] \tag{9.5}$$

For the special case of the elastic scattering we may write

$$\sigma_{n=0} = \frac{\sigma_H^{free}\hbar f}{E_0}\left(1 - e^{-\frac{4E_0}{\hbar f}}\right)$$

It should be noted that $\sigma_{n=0} \to 4\sigma_H^{free}$ if $E_0/\hbar f \to 0$.

By summation of the contributions of all possible σ_n, we obtain the cross-section

$$\sigma = \sum_n \sigma_n$$

which is presented in Fig. 10.18. The experimental verification of equation (9.5) is described in detail in Section 10.5.

9.3 Sachs and Teller Mass Tensor Concept

At neutron energies much higher than the rotational and vibrational quanta of the molecule scattering by bound nuclei may be treated in the same way as scattering by free ones. On the other hand if the neutron energy is much less than these values, the collision with the νth nucleus of mass M_ν influences only the transitional movement of the molecule as a whole, so that the cross-section may be written as

$$\sigma_\nu = \left[\frac{M_{\text{mol}}}{m+M_{\text{mol}}}\right]^2 \sigma_\nu^{\text{bound}} = \left[\frac{M_{\text{mol}}}{m+M_{\text{mol}}}\right]^2 \cdot \left[\frac{m+M_\nu}{M_\nu}\right]^2 \sigma_\nu^{\text{free}} \qquad (9.6)$$

where $\sigma_\nu^{\text{bound}}$ corresponds to the νth nucleus bound with an infinitely heavy molecule, and σ_ν^{free} corresponds to the free nucleus. For protons $\sigma_\nu^{\text{bound}} = 4\sigma_\nu^{\text{free}}$. M_{mol} is the mass of the molecule, m the mass of the neutron. This formula results directly from the Fermi pseudo-potential approximation (Chapter 1, Section 1.2). The intermediate case where the neutron energy is much higher than the rotational quantum and much lower than the quantum of vibrations in the molecule is more complicated. It is possible to consider classically the translational–rotational movement of the molecule, with, however, the assumption of various effective masses of the nuclei. For example, a neutron in collision with an H_2 molecule parallel to the H—H axis will observe an effective mass equal to $2m$ but when the collision occurs perpendicularly to H—H the effective mass equals m only.

Sachs and Teller (1941) assumed that there exists a linear dependence between the change of the velocity of the nucleus at the collision, and the change of neutron momentum by introducing the concept of a "mass tensor" in the following way.

A rigid molecule possesses 6 (or 5 if it is a linear molecule) degrees of freedom. The infinitesimal displacements of the molecule may be divided into two groups, i.e. a group of three (or two in the case of a linear molecule) displacements in which the relative position of the nucleus remains unchanged, and another group for which the angular momentum with respect to the nucleus is equal to zero. In slow neutron collisions the only significant contributions to the cross-section arise from neutrons possessing zero angular momentum with respect to the nucleus. Therefore only the displacements of the second group are contained in the changes of motion of the molecule. These displacements will be described by the movement of a so-called "mass point" coincident with the nucleus and possessing the nuclear velocity, the mass being a tensor.

In order to write down the two groups of displacements mentioned above we shall start from a description of the molecular motion by means of the angular velocity $\mathbf{f}$ around the centre of mass of the molecule, and of the velocity of the centre of mass $\mathbf{V}_c$. We then write $\mathbf{f}$ and $\mathbf{V}_c$ in the form:

$$\mathbf{f} = \mathbf{f}'+\mathbf{f}''; \quad \mathbf{V}_c = \mathbf{V}_c'+\mathbf{V}_c''$$

The displacements belonging to the first group are described by the velocities $\mathbf{f}'$, $\mathbf{V}_c'$ and therefore fulfil the condition:

$$(\mathbf{f}'\times\mathbf{r})+\mathbf{V}_c' = 0 \qquad (9.7a)$$

and those belonging to the second group are described by the velocities $\mathbf{f}''$, $\mathbf{V}_c''$ and fulfil the condition:

$$\mathscr{I}\mathbf{f}'' - M_{\mathrm{mol}}(\mathbf{r} \times \mathbf{V}_c'') = 0 \qquad (9.7\mathrm{b})$$

where $\mathbf{r}$ is the radius vector of the nucleus taken from the centre of mass of the molecule, and $\mathscr{I}$ its tensor of inertia.

The kinetic energy of the molecule is the sum of the kinetic energies of the two motions

$$2E_{\mathrm{mol}} = \mathbf{f}.\mathscr{I}\mathbf{f} + M_{\mathrm{mol}}V_c^2 =$$
$$= [\mathbf{f}'\mathscr{I}\mathbf{f}' + M_{\mathrm{mol}}V_c'^2] + [\mathbf{f}''\mathscr{I}\mathbf{f}'' + M_{\mathrm{mol}}V_c''^2]$$

The mixed terms vanish in view of (9.7a) and (9.7b). A collision of a neutron with the nucleus causes changes in vectors $\mathbf{f}$ and $\mathbf{V}_c$. These changes, however, as was pointed out above, are represented in the second type of vectors only, i.e. in $\mathbf{f}''$ and $\mathbf{V}_c''$. The motion of the first type (i.e. described by vectors $\mathbf{f}'$ and $\mathbf{V}_c'$) remains unchanged in the collision.

The "mass point" is not able to describe the complete motion of the molecule, as it possesses three degrees of freedom only. It is introduced in order to describe the motion of the second type ($\mathbf{f}''$, $\mathbf{V}_c''$). Let us assume that the momentum of the "mass point" is equal to the momentum of the molecule and the velocity is equal to the velocity of the nucleus. This assumption guarantees the momentum conservation of the system neutron–molecule if the momentum of the system neutron–"mass point" is conserved. Also the assumed motion of ($\mathbf{f}''$, $\mathbf{V}_c''$) automatically guarantees the conservation of the angular momentum with respect to the nucleus.

The linear dependence between the velocity $\mathbf{V}$ and the momentum $\mathbf{P}$ of the "mass point" will be defined as follows:

$$\mathbf{V} = \mathscr{M}^{-1}\mathbf{P} \qquad (9.8)$$

where $\mathbf{V}$ the velocity of the nucleus as well as of the "mass point" is equal to:

$$(\mathbf{f}'' \times \mathbf{r}) + \mathbf{V}_c'' \qquad (9.9)$$

$\mathbf{P}$, the momentum of the molecule as well as of the "mass point", is equal to $M_{\mathrm{mol}}\mathbf{V}_c''$, and $\mathscr{M}^{-1}$ is the inverse mass tensor.

Calculating $\mathbf{f}''$ from (9.7b) and substituting in the expression for $\mathbf{V}$ (9.9) we have

$$\mathbf{V} = [\mathscr{I}^{-1}(\mathbf{r} \times \mathbf{P})] \times \mathbf{r} + M_{\mathrm{mol}}^{-1}\mathbf{P}$$

In the coordinate system of principal axes of inertia, the above formula has the form

$$V_i = \left[\frac{r_j^2}{I_k} + \frac{r_k^2}{I_j} + \frac{1}{M_{\mathrm{mol}}}\right]P_i - \frac{r_i r_j}{I_k}P_j - \frac{r_i r_k}{I_j}P_k$$

where $\{r_i, r_j, r_k\}$ are coordinates of the nucleus in this system.

Now we may easily obtain the components of the inverse mass tensor

$$\{\mathcal{M}^{-1}\}_{ii} = \frac{r_j^2}{I_k} + \frac{r_k^2}{I_j} + \frac{1}{M_{\text{mol}}} ; \qquad \{\mathcal{M}^{-1}\}_{ij} = -\frac{r_i r_j}{I_k} \ (i \neq j) \qquad (9.10)$$

It is easy to see that the tensor $\mathcal{M}^{-1}$(and also $\mathcal{M}$) is symmetric. It is convenient to introduce a dimensionless tensor

$$\boldsymbol{n} = m\mathcal{M}^{-1} \qquad (9.11a)$$

and the reduced mass tensor

$$\boldsymbol{\mu} = \{\mathbf{1} + \boldsymbol{n}\}^{-1} \qquad (\mathbf{1} \text{ is the unit tensor}) \qquad (9.11b)$$

As an example, let us calculate the inverse mass tensor components for a proton bound in the H_2 molecule. Here we cannot use directly the formula (9.10) because the tensor of inertia has now the form

$$\mathscr{I} = \begin{pmatrix} 2r^2 m & 0 & 0 \\ 0 & 0 & 0 \\ 0 & 0 & 2r^2 m \end{pmatrix}$$

so that $I_2 = 0$, and therefore we have $\omega_2'' = 0$. We must start from (9.9), (9.7b), to obtain:

$$V_1 = \frac{r^2}{I_3} P_1 + \frac{1}{M_{\text{mol}}} P_1, \qquad V_2 = \frac{1}{M_{\text{mol}}} P_2, \qquad V_3 = \frac{r^2}{I_1} P_3 + \frac{1}{M_{\text{mol}}} P_3$$

From this we deduce that

$$\mathcal{M}^{-1} = \begin{pmatrix} \frac{r^2}{I_3} + \frac{1}{M_{\text{mol}}} & 0 & 0 \\ 0 & \frac{1}{M_{\text{mol}}} & 0 \\ 0 & 0 & \frac{r^2}{I_1} + \frac{1}{M_{\text{mol}}} \end{pmatrix} = \begin{pmatrix} \frac{1}{m} & 0 & 0 \\ 0 & \frac{1}{2m} & 0 \\ 0 & 0 & \frac{1}{m} \end{pmatrix}$$

(Compare the remarks at the beginning of this section concerning the effective mass of the proton in collision with the neutron.)

The density of final states of the neutron (and hence the cross-section for scattering) depends on the motion of the "mass point" in view of the fact that in the collision only the second type of molecular motion (described by the vectors $\mathbf{f}''$, $\mathbf{V}_c''$) changes. At this stage we shall not go on to the cross-section calculation, which will be deferred until Section 9.6. The next section will be devoted to a quantum mechanical calculation of molecular cross-sections.

9.4 The Zemach and Glauber Formalism

The first general quantum mechanical treatment of the scattering of neutrons by molecules which took into account the translational, vibrational, and rotational molecular degrees of freedom and also spin effects was given by Zemach and Glauber (1956). This theory is based on an interesting method in which the explicit summation over the contributions of all final states is avoided. The great importance of this step lies in the difficulty of exact summation due to the variety of possible transitions.

Zemach and Glauber assumed for the interaction potential between the neutron and the nucleus in the molecule the Fermi pseudo-potential (see (9.1), (9.2)):

$$V = \frac{2\pi\hbar^2}{m} b_\nu \delta(\mathbf{r}_n - \mathbf{r}_\nu)$$

where $\mathbf{r}_\nu$ is the position vector of the νth nucleus of the molecule. The perturbation potential for the interaction neutron–molecule is then equal to:

$$U = \frac{2\pi\hbar^2}{m} \sum_\nu b_\nu \delta(\mathbf{r}_n - \mathbf{r}_\nu) \tag{9.12}$$

We denote the initial and final neutron momentum by $\hbar\mathbf{k}_0$ and $\hbar\mathbf{k}$ respectively, the initial and final energy of the molecule by E_i and E_g, and the wave functions of the initial and final states of the molecule by ψ_i and ψ_g. The cross-section for scattering through an angle θ for the process in which such a transition from the initial to the final state of the system takes place has the form (generalization of (9.3)):

$$\sigma_{gi}(\theta) = \left[\frac{m}{2\pi\hbar^2}\right]^2 \frac{k}{k_0} \left| \langle \psi_g | \int e^{-i(\mathbf{k}-\mathbf{k}_0)\cdot\mathbf{r}_n} U d\mathbf{r}_n | \psi_i \rangle \right|^2$$

$$= \sum_{\nu\nu'} \frac{k}{k_0} \langle \psi_i | b_\nu \, e^{i(\mathbf{k}-\mathbf{k}_0)\cdot\mathbf{r}_\nu} | \psi_g \rangle \langle \psi_g | b_{\nu'} \, e^{-i(\mathbf{k}-\mathbf{k}_0)\mathbf{r}_{\nu'}} | \psi_i \rangle \tag{9.13a}$$

This formula is written in the laboratory system. In the centre of mass system for the neutron and the molecule, m in the above formula for $\sigma_{gi}(\theta)$ must be replaced by the factor μ' where

$$\mu' = \frac{mM_{\text{mol}}}{m + M_{\text{mol}}} \tag{9.13b}$$

Further we denote by $\hbar\mathbf{Q}$ the change of the neutron momentum in the scattering ($\mathbf{Q} = \mathbf{k} - \mathbf{k}_0$) and by $\hbar\omega$ the change of its energy. From the energy conservation law we have $\hbar\omega = E_i - E_g$. The lower limit is established by noting that the neutron cannot transfer more energy than it has, i.e. $\hbar\omega \geqslant -E_0$. For scattering at an angle θ, $\mathbf{k}$ and $\mathbf{Q}$ are functions of ω.

The scattering cross-section $\sigma_i(\theta)$ is obtained from $\sigma_{gi}(\theta)$ by summation over all final states. It is then necessary to average $\sigma_i(\theta)$ over the distribution of the molecular states which correspond to the temperature T. We may write $\sigma_i(\theta)$ in the following form:

$$\sigma_i(\theta) = \hbar \sum_g \int_{-E_0/\hbar}^{\infty} d\omega \delta(E_i - E_g - \hbar\omega)\sigma_{gi}(\theta) = \frac{1}{2\pi}\sum_g \int_{-E_0/\hbar}^{+\infty} d\omega \int_{-\infty}^{+\infty} d\tau \, e^{-i\omega\tau} e^{i(E_i - E_g)\tau/\hbar} \, \sigma_{gi}(\theta)$$

(9.14a)

where $\sum_g$ denotes the summation over the final states. Now we introduce the Hamiltonian H of the molecule. Since $e^{-iE_g\tau/\hbar}\psi_g = e^{-iH\tau/\hbar}\psi_g$ (and similarily for ψ_i) we obtain

$$\sigma_i(\theta) = \frac{1}{2\pi}\sum_g \sum_{\nu\nu'} \int_{-E_0/\hbar}^{+\infty} \int_{-\infty}^{+\infty} \frac{k}{k_0} e^{-i\omega\tau} \langle\psi_i|b_\nu\, e^{iH\tau/\hbar}\, e^{iQ\cdot r_\nu}\, e^{-iH\tau/\hbar}|\psi_g\rangle \times$$

$$\langle\psi_g|b_{\nu'}\, e^{-iQ\cdot r_{\nu'}}|\psi_i\rangle d\omega d\tau$$

Due to the closure relation of the complete system of functions ψ_g, i.e. due to the property (a discussion of this point is given by Kosaly, 1964):—

$$\sum_g |\psi_g\rangle\langle\psi_g| = 1$$

we may write

$$\sigma_i(\theta) = \frac{1}{2\pi}\sum_{\nu\nu'} \int_{-E_0/\hbar}^{+\infty} \int_{-\infty}^{+\infty} \frac{k}{k_0} e^{-i\omega\tau} \langle\psi_i|b_\nu b_{\nu'}\, e^{iH\tau/\hbar}\, e^{iQ\cdot r_\nu}\, e^{-iH\tau/\hbar}\, e^{-iQ\cdot r_{\nu'}}|\psi_i\rangle d\omega d\tau$$

The double differential cross-section for a molecule in the state i is found from the weighted scattering law $S_i(Q,\omega)$ (equation 1.34) for that state. (Each term in the scattering law is weighted by the scattering amplitudes for the nuclei ν, ν'.) In turn this is related to $\sigma_i(\theta)$ by:

$$\sigma_i(\theta) = \hbar \int_{-E_0/\hbar}^{+\infty} \sum_{\nu\nu'} b_\nu b_{\nu'} \frac{k}{k_0} S_{i\nu\nu'}(Q,\omega)d\omega$$

and hence:

$$\sum_{\nu\nu'} b_\nu b_{\nu'} S_{i\nu\nu'}(Q,\omega) = \frac{1}{2\pi}\sum_{\nu\nu'} \int_{-\infty}^{+\infty} e^{-i\omega\tau} \langle\psi_i|b_\nu b_{\nu'}\, e^{iH\tau/\hbar}\, e^{iQ\cdot r_\nu}\, e^{-iH\tau/\hbar}\, e^{-iQ\cdot r_{\nu'}}|\psi_i\rangle d\tau$$

(9.14b)

This is the basic equation used to evaluate the cross-section. The term $\nu = \nu'$ describes the scattering by the νth nucleus only (the self term of Van

Hove (1.26)), and is sometimes called "direct scattering". Terms with $\nu \neq \nu'$ describe interference effects (the distinct term of Van Hove (1.27)). We shall often in the following denote the expectation value appearing under the integral (9.14b) by $\chi_{\nu\nu'}$ (this is one term in the weighted intermediate scattering function).

It is convenient to write expression (9.14b) in terms of time dependent operators $A(\tau)$, which satisfy the Heisenberg equation of motion

$$i\hbar\frac{\mathrm{d}}{\mathrm{d}\tau}A(\tau) = A(\tau)H - HA(\tau)$$

The time dependent operators are related to the time independent ones by

$$A(\tau) = \mathrm{e}^{iH\tau/\hbar}\,A\,\mathrm{e}^{-iH\tau/\hbar}$$

The expectation value which appears in (9.14b) may now be written:

$$\chi_{i,\nu\nu'} = \langle\psi_i|b_\nu b_{\nu'}\,\mathrm{e}^{iQ\cdot r_\nu(\tau)}\,\mathrm{e}^{-iQ\cdot r_{\nu'}(0)}\,|\psi_i\rangle \qquad (9.15)$$

Alternatively, we may use another convenient modification which we obtain by applying the relation valid for an arbitrary function ψ:

$$(\mathrm{e}^{iQ\cdot r_\nu}\,\mathbf{p}_\nu\,\mathrm{e}^{-iQ\cdot r_\nu})\psi = (\mathrm{e}^{iQ\cdot r_\nu}\,(-i\hbar\nabla)\,\mathrm{e}^{-iQ\cdot r_\nu})\psi = (\mathbf{p}_\nu - \hbar Q)\psi$$

from which we obtain

$$\mathrm{e}^{iQ\cdot r_\nu}\,\mathbf{p}_\nu\,\mathrm{e}^{-iQ\cdot r_\nu} = \mathbf{p}_\nu - \hbar Q$$

Applying this relation to the Hamiltonian H of the molecule we may write

$$\mathrm{e}^{iQ\cdot r_\nu}\,\mathrm{H}(\ldots\mathbf{p}_\nu, r_\nu, \ldots)\,\mathrm{e}^{-iQ\cdot r_\nu} = \mathrm{H}(\ldots\mathbf{p}_\nu - \hbar Q, r_\nu, \ldots) = \mathrm{H}'_{(\nu)} \qquad (9.16a)$$

and therefore for the direct scattering or self term:

$$\chi_{\nu\nu} = \langle\psi_i|b_\nu^2\,\mathrm{e}^{iH\tau/\hbar}\,\mathrm{e}^{-iH'_{(\nu)}\tau/\hbar}\,|\psi_i\rangle \qquad (9.16b)$$

The Hamiltonian of the molecule may be written in the form (for uncoupled motions):

$$\mathrm{H} = \mathrm{H}_{tr} + \mathrm{H}_{rot} + \mathrm{H}_{vib} \qquad (9.17a)$$

(tr = translation, rot = rotation, vib = vibration). The corresponding wave function may be written as a product:

$$\psi = \phi\psi_{spin}; \quad \phi = \psi_{tr}\psi_{rot}\psi_{vib} \qquad (9.17b)$$

The position vector of the νth nucleus may be written in the form

$$\mathbf{r}_\nu = \mathbf{R} + \mathbf{d}_\nu + \mathbf{u}_\nu \qquad (9.17c)$$

where $\mathbf{R}$ is the position of the centre of mass of the molecule, $\mathbf{d}_\nu$ the equilibrium position of the νth nucleus in the c.m. system, and $\mathbf{u}_\nu$ the deviation from the equilibrium position caused by vibrations.

Now we shall discuss the spin part of the expectation value. Let us denote by $\mathbf{s}$ the neutron spin and by $\mathbf{S}_\nu$ the spin of the νth nucleus. The total spin of the system neutron–νth nucleus may take the values $S_\nu+\frac{1}{2}$ and $S_\nu-\frac{1}{2}$ only. The corresponding scattering lengths will be denoted by $b_\nu^{(+)}$ and $b_\nu^{(-)}$. We introduce the projection operators $\Pi_\nu^{(+)}$ and $\Pi_\nu^{(-)}$ defined by

$$\Pi_\nu^{(+)}\psi^{(+)} = \psi^{(+)} \qquad \Pi_\nu^{(-)}\psi^{(+)} = 0$$
$$\Pi_\nu^{(+)}\psi^{(-)} = 0 \qquad \Pi_\nu^{(-)}\psi^{(-)} = \psi^{(-)}$$

where $\psi^{(+)}$ and $\psi^{(-)}$ are the wave functions corresponding to the states of the neutron–νth nucleus system with the total spin $S_\nu+\frac{1}{2}$ and $S_\nu-\frac{1}{2}$. Applying the formula $2\mathbf{s}\cdot\mathbf{S}_\nu = S^2 - S_\nu^2 - s^2$ (where $\mathbf{S}$ is the total spin of the system neutron–νth nucleus) it is easy to show that the operators $\Pi_\nu^{(+)}$, $\Pi_\nu^{(-)}$ may be written as

$$\Pi_\nu^{(+)} = \frac{1+S_\nu+2\mathbf{s}\cdot\mathbf{S}_\nu}{2S_\nu+1} \qquad \Pi_\nu^{(-)} = \frac{S_\nu-2\mathbf{s}\cdot\mathbf{S}_\nu}{2S_\nu+1}$$

The scattering amplitudes, being spin-dependent operators now, may be written in the form

$$b_\nu = b_\nu^{(+)}\Pi_\nu^{(+)}+b_\nu^{(-)}\Pi_\nu^{(-)} \tag{9.18}$$

Applying the normal definition of the coherent scattering amplitude B_ν (as an average over all spin states) we obtain

$$B_\nu = \frac{\{2(S_\nu+\frac{1}{2})+1\}b_\nu^{(+)}+\{2(S_\nu-\frac{1}{2})+1\}b_\nu^{(-)}}{\{2(S_\nu+\frac{1}{2})+1\}+\{2(S_\nu-\frac{1}{2})+1\}}$$
$$= \frac{S_\nu+1}{2S_\nu+1}b_\nu^{(+)}+\frac{S_\nu}{2S_\nu+1}b_\nu^{(-)} \tag{9.19a}$$

Similarly, introducing the incoherent scattering amplitude B_ν',

$$B_\nu' = \frac{\{S_\nu(S_\nu+1)\}^{\frac{1}{2}}}{2S_\nu+1}(b_\nu^{(+)}-b_\nu^{(-)}) \tag{9.19b}$$

and taking the formula (9.18) into account we may write

$$b_\nu = B_\nu+2B_\nu'\frac{(\mathbf{S}_\nu\cdot\mathbf{s})}{\{S_\nu(S_\nu+1)\}^{\frac{1}{2}}} \tag{9.20}$$

In the case of an unpolarized neutron beam it is necessary to average over the neutron spin states. This averaging leads to zero for expressions containing the first power in $\mathbf{s}$ and to the value $\frac{1}{4}\mathbf{S}_\nu\cdot\mathbf{S}_{\nu'}$ for the average $\frac{1}{2}\sum_s(\mathbf{s}\cdot\mathbf{S}_\nu)(\mathbf{s}\cdot\mathbf{S}_{\nu'})$. Therefore the expectation value which is involved in the formula (9.14b) can be transformed into

$$\left\langle\psi_i\left|\frac{B_\nu B_{\nu'}+B_\nu'B_{\nu'}'(\mathbf{S}_\nu\cdot\mathbf{S}_{\nu'})}{\sqrt{S_\nu(S_\nu+1)S_{\nu'}(S_{\nu'}+1)}}\,e^{i\mathbf{Q}\cdot\mathbf{r}_\nu(t)}\,e^{-i\mathbf{Q}\cdot\mathbf{r}_{\nu'}(0)}\right|\psi_i\right\rangle \tag{9.21}$$

The assumption (9.17b) that the wave function of the molecule may be written as a product of the spatial and spin parts $\psi = \phi\psi_{\text{spin}}$, simplifies

15*

significantly the calculations as we have to average separately over the spin and spatial states. We obtain

$$\langle \psi_{\text{spin}} | \mathbf{S}_\nu \cdot \mathbf{S}_{\nu'} | \psi_{\text{spin}} \rangle = S_\nu(S_\nu+1)\delta_{\nu\nu'} \qquad (9.22)$$

and then the expectation value (9.21) may be written as

$$\chi_{\nu\nu'} = B_\nu B_{\nu'} \langle \phi_i | e^{i\mathbf{Q} \cdot \mathbf{r}_\nu(\tau)} e^{-i\mathbf{Q} \cdot \mathbf{r}_{\nu'}(0)} | \phi_i \rangle \qquad \nu \neq \nu'$$

and   (9.23)

$$\chi_{\nu\nu} = [B_\nu^2 + B_\nu'^2] \langle \phi_i | e^{i\mathbf{Q} \cdot \mathbf{r}_\nu(\tau)} e^{-i\mathbf{Q} \cdot \mathbf{r}_\nu(0)} | \phi_i \rangle \qquad \nu = \nu'$$

There is, however, a qualifying situation. If the molecule contains identical nuclei, the symmetry condition which the wave function must fulfil gives some restrictions of the total spin. For $\nu \neq \nu'$ we obtain an additional term in the cross-section due to the fact that now the expression analogous to (9.22) is different from zero for $\nu \neq \nu'$. This additional term in the expectation value has the form

$$B_\nu'^2 \langle \psi_i | \frac{\mathbf{S}_\nu \cdot \mathbf{S}_{\nu'}}{S_\nu(S_\nu+1)} e^{i\mathbf{Q}.\mathbf{r}_\nu(\tau)} e^{-i\mathbf{Q}.\mathbf{r}_\nu(0)} | \psi_i \rangle \qquad (9.24)$$

It should be noted that the "spin correlation" effect expressed by the term (9.24) plays a negligible role in almost all molecules provided that the temperatures are not too low compared to the rotational energy level separation. An exceptional case is that of the hydrogen molecule discussed below (Section 9.7).

Now we have to discuss the contribution to the translational part of the expectation value; since we are discussing an isolated molecule consider the monatomic gas. Neglecting the interatomic interactions the Hamiltonian of an atom of mass M and momentum $\mathbf{p}$ may be written as

$$\mathrm{H} = \frac{\mathbf{p}^2}{2M}$$

The "effective" Hamiltonian H' has the form

$$\mathrm{H}' = \frac{(\mathbf{p}-\mathbf{Q}\hbar)^2}{2M}$$

from which we obtain (using the formula (9.16b))

$$\langle \psi_i | e^{i\mathrm{H}\tau/\hbar} e^{-i\mathrm{H}'\tau/\hbar} | \psi_i \rangle = e^{i\tau(2\mathbf{p} \cdot \mathbf{Q}\hbar - Q^2\hbar^2)/2M\hbar} \qquad (9.25a)$$

(in (9.25a) $\mathbf{p}$ denotes a momentum eigenvalue) if the ψ_i function is an eigenfunction of the momentum and energy of the atom. Taking into account the distribution function for the momenta in thermal equilibrium, i.e.

$$D(T,\mathbf{p}) = \frac{1}{(2\pi MkT)^{3/2}} e^{-\mathbf{p}^2/2MkT},$$

we obtain the following expression for the thermal average of the expectation value (9.25a)

$$\int e^{i\tau(2\mathbf{p}\cdot\mathbf{Q}-Q^2\hbar)/2M} \, D(T,\mathbf{p})\mathrm{d}\mathbf{p} = e^{-(i\tau\hbar+kT\tau^2)Q^2/2M} \qquad (9.25b)$$

Then the expectation value from equation (9.14b) (the thermal average of which we* shall denote $\langle X_{\nu\nu'}\rangle_T$) is

$$\langle X_{\nu\nu'}\rangle_T = \{B_\nu B_{\nu'} + B'_\nu B'_{\nu'}\delta_{\nu\nu'}\} \, e^{-(i\tau\hbar+kT\tau^2)Q^2/2M_{\mathrm{mol}}} \times$$
$$\langle\psi_{\mathrm{rot}}| \, e^{i\mathbf{Q}\cdot\mathbf{d}_\nu(\tau)} \, V_{\nu\nu'} \, e^{-i\mathbf{Q}\cdot\mathbf{d}_{\nu'}(0)} \, |\psi_{\mathrm{rot}}\rangle_T \qquad (9.26a)$$

where $V_{\nu\nu'}$ corresponds to the vibrational movement of the molecule (9.26b). By introducing the normal coordinates q_λ and the amplitude vectors $\mathbf{C}_\nu^{(\lambda)}$ it is possible to express the displacement of the νth nucleus from the equilibrium position in the form

$$\mathbf{u}_\nu = \sum_\lambda \mathbf{C}_\nu^{(\lambda)} q_\lambda$$

Vectors $\mathbf{C}_\nu^{(\lambda)}(\tau)$ (as well as vectors $\mathbf{d}_\nu(\tau)$) are constant in the molecular system and perform a rotation with the molecule. Therefore when treated as operators and calculated at different times they do not commute. For this reason a complete separation of rotation from vibration is not possible. One may say that this is caused by the rotation of the vibrational axis during the collision time. It should be noted that the operators $\mathbf{C}_\nu^{(\lambda)}(\tau)$ and $\mathbf{C}_{\nu'}^{(\lambda)}(0)$ commute if calculated at equal times. Owing to these restrictions it is necessary to avoid any transposition of vectors $\mathbf{C}_\nu^{(\lambda)}(\tau)$ and $\mathbf{C}_{\nu'}^{(\lambda)}(0)$ in the calculation of $V_{\nu\nu'}$, which has the form

$$V_{\nu\nu'} = \langle\psi_{\mathrm{vib}}| \, e^{i\mathbf{Q}\cdot\sum_\lambda \mathbf{C}_\nu^{(\lambda)}(\tau)q_\lambda(\tau)} \, e^{-i\mathbf{Q}\cdot\sum_\lambda \mathbf{C}_{\nu'}^{(\lambda)}(0)q_\lambda(0)} \, |\psi_{\mathrm{vib}}\rangle_T \qquad (9.26b)$$

Introducing this into the formula (9.14b) we obtain the differential cross-section:

$$\langle\sigma_i(\theta)\rangle_T = \frac{1}{2\pi} \sum_{\nu\nu'} \int_{-E/\hbar}^{+\infty} \int_{-\infty}^{+\infty} \frac{k}{k_0} \, e^{-i\omega\tau} \, \langle X_{\nu\nu'}\rangle_T \, \mathrm{d}\omega\mathrm{d}\tau$$

and the double differential cross-section is obtained by omitting the integration over ω. Usually, however, in the computations the rotation and vibration effects are completely separated. The agreement with the experiment which is discussed in Chapter 10 leads to the conclusion that this assumption is not too drastic.

It should be noted here that the effect of interference scattering from different molecules which should be added to the above expression for the scattering cross-section is quite negligible for gases but increases, however, with increasing density of the scattering medium.

---

* This is the average denoted by $\bar{\chi}$ in Chapter 1.

9.5 Examples of Zemach and Glauber Cross-sections

Now let us calculate the cross-section taking into account separately the molecular degrees of freedom. We shall start from the differential cross-section of a monatomic gas neglecting spin dependence. $S(Q,\omega)$ may be obtained by introducing the expectation value (9.25b) into the formula (9.14b).

$$S(Q,\omega) = \frac{1}{\hbar}\sqrt{\frac{M}{2\pi kTQ^2}}\, e^{-\frac{M}{2kTQ^2\hbar^2}\left(\hbar\omega + \frac{Q\hbar^2}{2M}\right)^2} \qquad (9.27a)$$

where again M is the mass of the atom.

It appears that the differential cross-section can be presented as depending on the two parameters ζ and α defined by

$$\zeta = \frac{m}{M}; \quad \alpha^2 = \zeta\frac{kT}{E_0} = \frac{2}{3}\left(\frac{v_m}{v_0}\right)^2$$

where v_m is the mean thermal velocity of the gas molecules, v_0 is the velocity of the incident neutron, and E_0 its energy. If v_m/v_0 is small, we may expand $\langle\sigma(\theta)\rangle_T$ into a series in α, obtaining,

$$\langle\sigma(\theta)\rangle_T \cong b^2\left\{\frac{1}{(1+\zeta)^2}\left[\frac{(\zeta\cos\theta + \sqrt{1-\zeta^2\sin^2\theta})^2}{\sqrt{1-\zeta^2\sin^2\theta}}\right] + \frac{\alpha^2}{2}\left[\frac{1-\zeta(3-2\zeta)\sin^2\theta}{(1-\zeta^2\sin^2\theta)^{5/2}}\right]\right\}$$

Performing the integration over θ we obtain for low temperatures or high neutron energies:

$$\langle\sigma\rangle_T \cong 4\pi b^2\left\{\frac{1}{(1+\zeta)^2} + \frac{T}{2E_0}\frac{\zeta}{(1+\zeta)^2}\right\} \qquad (9.27b)$$

and in the limit of large α (i.e. high temperatures or low neutron energies)

$$\langle\sigma\rangle_T = 4\pi b^2\frac{1}{(1+\zeta)^2}\frac{2\alpha}{\sqrt{\pi}}$$

The total cross-section tends to infinity when the neutron energy tends to zero because of the thermal motion of the atoms.

Now let us discuss the cross-section due to the rotational degrees of freedom only, in the special cases of the linear molecule and the spherical top. In these cases we consider the scattering object as a point which may move on the surface of a sphere of the radius $d = |\mathbf{d}|$. We denote the mass of this point by M and its scattering amplitude by b. The Hamiltonian of the scatterer has the form

$$\mathrm{H} = \frac{\mathbf{L}^2}{2Md^2} = \frac{(\mathbf{d}\times\mathbf{p})^2}{2Md^2}$$

where $\mathbf{L}$ is its angular momentum. The two molecular forms considered now possess $\mathrm{H}_{\mathrm{rot}}$ equal to $\mathbf{L}^2/2I$ (where I is the moment of inertia of the molecule). Therefore the direct scattering by a nucleus in such a molecule (which is at the distance d from the molecular mass centre) may be considered by the model described above, introducing an effective mass $M_{eff} = I/d^2$ instead of M. In order to obtain the expectation value we apply the formula (9.16a), and introduce the expression H' defined by:

$$H' = \frac{[\mathbf{d} \times (\mathbf{p} - \mathbf{Q}\hbar)]^2}{2M_{eff}d^2}$$

Remembering that $\mathbf{d}$ does not commute with $\mathbf{L}$, but does commute with the neutron momentum change $\mathbf{Q}\hbar$ we obtain:

$$H' = \{\mathbf{L}^2 + \mathbf{Q}\hbar \cdot [(\mathbf{d} \times \mathbf{L}) - (\mathbf{L} \times \mathbf{d})] + (\mathbf{d} \times \mathbf{Q}\hbar)^2\}/2M_{eff}d^2$$

The scattering rotator may be characterized by the angular momentum quantum number l. It is convenient to denote by $\langle \chi \rangle_l$ the expectation value averaged over all possible directions of the rotational axis:

$$\langle \chi \rangle_l = \frac{b^2}{2l+1} \sum_{\mu=-l}^{l} \langle \psi_{l\mu} | e^{iH\tau/\hbar} e^{-iH'\tau/\hbar} |\psi_{l\mu} \rangle$$

In order to obtain the cross-section Zemach and Glauber use a power series expansion in the ratio m/M_{eff}. Such a series is obtained when the expectation value is written as a cumulant expansion:

$$\langle \chi \rangle_l = b^2 \sum_{n=0}^{\infty} \frac{c_n}{\hbar^n} \left(\frac{i\tau}{M_{eff}} \right)^n$$

Now we can formally present $S_l(Q,\omega)$ by means of the derivatives of the δ function:

$$S_l(Q,\omega) = \sum_{n=0}^{\infty} \left(-\frac{1}{\hbar M_{eff}} \right)^n c_n \delta^{(n)}(\omega)$$

Remembering that

$$\int f(x)\delta^{(n)}(x)dx = (-1)^{(n)} f^{(n)}(0)$$

and that $\omega = \hbar(k^2 - k_0^2)/2m$, we may write the differential cross-section as:

$$\left(\frac{d\sigma}{d\Omega} \right)_l = \frac{b^2}{k_0} \sum_{n=0}^{\infty} \left(\frac{1}{\hbar M_{eff}} \right)^n \left[\left(\frac{d}{d\omega} \right)^n kc_n \right]_{\omega=0}$$

$$= \frac{b^2}{k_0} \sum_{n=0}^{\infty} \left(\frac{m}{M_{eff}} \right)^n \left[\left(\frac{1}{\hbar^2 k} \frac{d}{dk} \right)^n kc_n \right]_{k=k_0} \qquad (9.28)$$

The zero-order term of such an expansion in powers of τ gives the so-called static approximation for the cross-section, which, according to Placzek (1952), may be defined as the average of the cross-section of the system consisting of nuclei fixed in definite positions, over the configurations of the initial state of the real system. The static approximation gives in our case of a single scatterer, the constant cross-section equal b^2. The succeeding terms are inelastic corrections; the expansion in powers of τ is simultaneously an expansion in powers of the molecular excitation energies $E_f - E_i$ as may be seen from (9.14a). The time τ on which the expectation value depends may be interpreted as the "collision time" according to Wick (1954). Large neutron energy suggests a short collision time and justifies the expansion in powers of τ (see below, the expansion (9.29) valid for large values of $k_0 d$). For the simple model now under discussion we obtain:

$$\langle \chi \rangle_l = b^2 \left\{ 1 - \frac{i\tau}{M_{\text{eff}}} \frac{\hbar Q^2}{3} + \left(\frac{i\tau}{M_{\text{eff}}} \right)^2 \hbar^2 \left[\frac{Q^4}{15} + \frac{Q^2(l^2+l+1)}{6d^2} \right] + \cdots \right\}$$

and for the cross-section:

$$\left(\frac{d\sigma}{d\Omega} \right)_l = b^2 \left\{ 1 + \frac{m}{M_{\text{eff}}} \tfrac{4}{3}(1 - \cos\theta) + \left(\frac{m}{M_{\text{eff}}} \right)^2 \left[(1 - \cos\theta)(\tfrac{4}{3} - \tfrac{4}{5}\cos\theta) + \right. \right.$$
$$\left. \left. \tfrac{1}{3}\frac{(l^2+l+1)}{(k_0 d)^2} \right] + \cdots \right\} \qquad (9.29)$$

In the limit $k_0 d \to \infty$ we obtain a result identical to that for a classical rotator, i.e. effectively neglecting the contributions of the operator $\mathbf{L}$ in H and H'. It should be noted that it is still necessary to perform a thermal averaging over l. It is interesting to compare this expansion of $\langle \chi \rangle_l$ with the general expansion given at equation (7.76a), in order to see the effect of the rotational states when $\tau \to 0$.

The interference effects caused by the existence of more than one scattering nucleus in the molecule may be treated in a similar way to the direct scattering. It is not, however, possible to make any classical approximation; the effect is of quantum origin. We shall consider this effect for two nuclei in a rigid molecule which is either of linear form or a spherical top. The molecule performs a rotation with the angular momentum $\mathbf{L}$. Its Hamiltonian is then $H = \mathbf{L}^2 / 2I$. Let us denote by $\mathbf{d}_1$ and $\mathbf{d}_2$ the position vectors of the nuclei. The expectation value for the interference term averaged over all orientations of the angular momentum at a given value l has the form:

$$\langle \chi_{12} \rangle_l = b_1 b_2 \langle \psi_l | \, e^{iH\tau/\hbar} \, e^{i\mathbf{Q}\cdot\mathbf{d}_1} \, e^{-iH\tau/\hbar} \, e^{-i\mathbf{Q}\cdot\mathbf{d}_2} \, |\psi_l\rangle_{\text{av}}$$
$$= b_1 b_2 \langle \psi_l | \, e^{iH\tau/\hbar} \, e^{i\mathbf{Q}\cdot(\mathbf{d}_1-\mathbf{d}_2)} \, e^{i\mathbf{Q}\cdot\mathbf{d}_2} \, e^{-iH\tau/\hbar} \, e^{-i\mathbf{Q}\cdot\mathbf{d}_2} \, |\psi_l\rangle_{\text{av}}$$

With the definitions:

$$\mathbf{d}_{12} = \mathbf{d}_1 - \mathbf{d}_2$$
$$H'_{(2)} = e^{i\mathbf{Q}\cdot\mathbf{d}_2} \, H \, e^{-i\mathbf{Q}\cdot\mathbf{d}_2}$$

and using the identity $H\psi_l = E_l\psi_l$, we may write

$$\langle \chi_{12} \rangle_l = b_1 b_2 \langle \psi_l | \, e^{i\mathbf{Q}\cdot\mathbf{d}_{12}} \, e^{-i\tau(H'_{(2)}-E_l)/\hbar} \, |\psi_l\rangle_{\text{av}}$$

Now we expand $\langle X_{12}\rangle_l$ into series in τ. In the zero-order approximation for elastic scattering, we have:

$$\langle X_{12}\rangle_l \cong b_1 b_2 \langle \psi_l | \, e^{i\mathbf{Q}\cdot\mathbf{d}_{12}} \, |\psi_l\rangle_{av} = \frac{b_1 b_2}{4\pi}\int e^{i\mathbf{Q}\cdot\mathbf{d}_{12}}\,d\Omega = j_0(Q d_{12}) b_1 b_2$$

where j_0 is a spherical Bessel function and the averaging is carried out classically. A similar contribution to the cross-section will arise from $\langle X_{21}\rangle_l$. Therefore we obtain

$$\langle \sigma_{12}(\theta)\rangle_{av} \cong 2 b_1 b_2 j_0(Q d_{12}) \tag{9.30}$$

Now we shall discuss the cross-section due to vibrational degrees of freedom only, assuming thus $\mathbf{R}$, $\mathbf{d}_\nu$, and $\mathbf{C}_\nu^{(\lambda)}$ to be fixed. We shall write the expectation value averaged over the initial states (in the thermal equilibrium) according to formula (9.26b). Due to the dynamical independence of normal oscillations the coordinates commute and we may write

$$e^{i\mathbf{Q}\cdot\mathbf{u}_\nu(\tau)} = \prod_\lambda e^{i\mathbf{Q}\cdot\mathbf{C}_\nu^{(\lambda)}(\tau)\,q_\lambda(\tau)}$$

Also, due to the same property, the thermal distribution function for the molecule may be expressed as a product corresponding to a unique set of normal vibrations and then:

$$V_{\nu\nu'} = \prod_\lambda V_{\nu\nu'}^{(\lambda)} = \prod_\lambda \langle e^{i\mathbf{Q}\cdot\mathbf{C}_\nu^{(\lambda)}\,q_\lambda(\tau)}\, e^{-i\mathbf{Q}\cdot\mathbf{C}_\lambda^{(\lambda)}\,q(0)}\rangle_T$$

Applying the creation and annihilation operators $a^\dagger, a$ for the quantization of a harmonic oscillator, we may write for $q_\lambda(\tau)$:

$$q_\lambda(\tau) = i\sqrt{\frac{\hbar}{2f_\lambda}}(a\,e^{if_\lambda\tau} - a^\dagger\,e^{-if_\lambda\tau})$$

(where f_λ is the frequency of the λth normal vibration). Then, using the theorem

$$\langle e^{\tilde{Q}}\rangle_T = e^{\frac{1}{2}\langle \tilde{Q}^2\rangle_T}$$

where $\tilde{Q}$ is any one multiple of an oscillator coordinate or a linear combination of them, we obtain

$$V_{\nu\nu'}^{(\lambda)} = \exp\{-\tfrac{1}{2}[(\mathbf{Q}\cdot\mathbf{C}_\nu^{(\lambda)})^2 + (\mathbf{Q}\cdot\mathbf{C}_{\nu'}^{(\lambda)})^2]\langle q_\lambda^2(0)\rangle_T + (\mathbf{Q}\cdot\mathbf{C}_\nu^{(\lambda)})(\mathbf{Q}\cdot\mathbf{C}_{\nu'}^{(\lambda)})\langle q_\lambda(\tau)q_\lambda(0)\rangle_T\}$$

$$\tag{9.31}$$

$$\langle q_\lambda(\tau)q_\lambda(0)\rangle_T = \frac{\hbar}{2f_\lambda}\{\langle aa^\dagger\rangle_T\,e^{-if_\lambda\tau} + \langle a^\dagger a\rangle_T\,e^{if_\lambda\tau}\}$$

bearing in mind that $\langle a^\dagger a\rangle_T = 1/(e^{\frac{\hbar f_\lambda}{kT}}-1)$. Using the modified Bessel functions I_n we obtain for the expectation value:

$$V_{\nu\nu'}^{(\lambda)} = \exp\left\{-\frac{\hbar}{4f_\lambda}\left[(\mathbf{Q}\cdot\mathbf{C}_\nu^{(\lambda)})^2+(\mathbf{Q}\cdot\mathbf{C}_{\nu'}^{(\lambda)})^2\right]\coth\left(f_\lambda\hbar/2kT\right)\right\}\times$$

$$\sum_{n=-\infty}^{+\infty} e^{inf_\lambda\tau}\,e^{-(nf_\lambda\hbar)/2kT}\,I_n\left(\frac{\hbar(\mathbf{Q}\cdot\mathbf{C}_\nu^{(\lambda)})(\mathbf{Q}\cdot\mathbf{C}_{\nu'}^{(\lambda)})}{2f_\lambda\sinh\left(\hbar f_\lambda/2kT\right)}\right) \qquad (9.32)$$

and for the scattering law:

$$\sum_{\nu\nu'}b_\nu b_{\nu'}S_{\nu\nu'}(Q,\omega) = \frac{1}{2\pi}\sum_{\nu\nu'}b_\nu b_{\nu'}\int_{-\infty}^{+\infty}e^{-i\omega\tau}\,e^{i\mathbf{Q}\cdot(\mathbf{d}_\nu-\mathbf{d}_{\nu'})}\prod_\lambda V_{\nu\nu'}^{(\lambda)}d\tau$$

The various possible excitation processes are characterized by the energy transfer $\omega = \sum_\lambda n_\lambda f_\lambda$.

Considering the time-dependent $\mathbf{C}_\nu^{(\lambda)}$ discussed at equation (9.26b), a modified formula for $V_{\nu\nu'}^{(\lambda)}$ in place of (9.32) must be used which takes into account the noncommutativity of $\mathbf{C}_\nu^{(\lambda)}(\tau)$ and $\mathbf{C}_\nu^{(\lambda)}(0)$. In general, to evaluate the cross-section we must use the expansion of $\langle\chi_{\nu'\nu}\rangle$, given by (9.26a), in powers of Q^2.

9.6 An Approximate Theory for the Thermal Energy Region

Krieger and Nelkin (1957) take the method of Zemach and Glauber as their starting point and apply a specific approximation procedure in averaging over initial states of the molecule. This approximation limits the region of validity of the theory to energies much higher than the separation of rotational energy levels and at the same time lower than the threshold of the vibrational excitation. Their theory has been widely used, because of its generality, for molecules of an arbitrary structure. It gives convenient formulae for the total scattering cross-section as well as for the differential one.

The weighted scattering law is, according to (9.14b) and (9.23) given by

$$\sum_{\nu\nu'}b_\nu b_{\nu'}S_{\nu\nu'}(Q,\omega) = \sum_{\nu\nu'}(B_\nu B_{\nu'}+B'_\nu B'_{\nu'}\delta_{\nu\nu'})\frac{1}{2\pi}\int_{-\infty}^{+\infty}e^{-i\omega\tau}\langle\overline{\chi}_{\nu\nu'}\rangle_T d\tau \qquad (9.33)$$

where

$$\overline{\chi}_{\nu\nu'} = \langle\psi_i|\,e^{i\mathbf{Q}\cdot\mathbf{r}_\nu(\tau)}\,e^{-i\mathbf{Q}\cdot\mathbf{r}_{\nu'}(0)}\,|\psi_i\rangle$$

and the spin correlation has been neglected.

Now let the neutron energy E_0 be much higher than the rotational levels of the molecule, that is $E_0\gg\sqrt{kTA}$ where A is the rotational constant of the molecule, ($\sqrt{kTA}$ is equal to the level separation in the vicinity of the most probable level). This condition guarantees that the collision time is small compared with the period of rotation:

$$\text{collision time } t \sim \frac{\hbar}{E_0} \ll \frac{\hbar}{\sqrt{kTA}} \sim \frac{\hbar}{Al} \sim \frac{1}{\omega},$$

hence period of rotation $\gg t$. Here I is the moment of inertia of the molecule, $\omega/2\pi$ the frequency of rotation, $\hbar l$ the angular momentum of the molecule and Al is approximately equal to the separation of two neighbouring rotational levels. If, at the same time, we assume $kT \gg A$ (which means that a great number of rotational levels are excited because $Al \sim \sqrt{kTA}$, i.e. $l \gg 1$), we have the so-called quasi-classical approximation in which the wave functions of a rigid rotator may be replaced by the wave packets of well defined orientation of the molecule and its angular momentum. Also the interaction of rotational and vibrational degrees of freedom are neglected (see remarks in connection with formula (9.26a)). Hence

$$\langle \overline{X}_{\nu\nu'} \rangle_T = \langle \overline{X}_{\nu\nu'}^{\text{tr}} \rangle_T \langle \overline{X}_{\nu\nu'}^{\text{rot}} \rangle_T \langle \overline{X}_{\nu\nu'}^{\text{vib}} \rangle_T$$

The translational part may be written immediately by applying the Zemach and Glauber formula (9.25b) for a free gas molecule:

$$\langle \overline{X}_{\nu\nu'}^{\text{tr}} \rangle_T = e^{-\frac{Q^2}{2M_{\text{mol}}}(i\tau\hbar + kT\tau^2)}$$

It is easy to show that the rotational part is strongly connected with the Sachs and Teller mass tensor. In fact

$$\langle \overline{X}_{\nu\nu'}^{\text{rot}} \rangle_T = \langle \psi_{\text{rot}} | e^{i\mathbf{Q}\cdot\mathbf{d}_\nu(\tau)} e^{-i\mathbf{Q}\cdot\mathbf{d}_{\nu'}(0)} | \psi_{\text{rot}} \rangle_T$$
$$= \langle \psi_{\text{rot}} | e^{i\mathbf{H}\tau/\hbar} e^{-i\mathbf{H}'_{(\nu)}\tau/\hbar} e^{i\mathbf{Q}\cdot\mathbf{d}_\nu(0)} e^{-i\mathbf{Q}\cdot\mathbf{d}_{\nu'}(0)} | \psi_{\text{rot}} \rangle_T$$

where H denotes the Hamiltonian of a rigid rotating molecule and $\mathbf{H}'_{(\nu)}$ denotes the Hamiltonian H in which $\mathbf{p}_\nu$ is replaced by $\mathbf{p}_\nu - \mathbf{Q}\hbar$. Let us denote by $\mathscr{I}$ the inertia tensor of the molecule and by $\mathbf{L} = \sum_s \mathbf{d}_s \times \mathbf{p}_s$ its total angular momentum, where $\mathbf{d}_s = \mathbf{d}_s(0)$. Now $\mathbf{H} = \frac{1}{2}\mathbf{L}\mathscr{I}^{-1}\mathbf{L}$ and we introduce the tensors

$$\mathscr{K}_{(ss')} = \mathscr{D}^T_{(s)}\mathscr{I}^{-1}\mathscr{D}_{(s')} \tag{9.34a}$$

where

$$\mathscr{D} = -\mathscr{D}^T = \begin{pmatrix} 0 & -d_z & d_y \\ d_z & 0 & -d_x \\ -d_y & d_x & 0 \end{pmatrix} \tag{9.34b}$$

Applying this notation we may write

$$\mathbf{L} = \sum_s \mathscr{D}_{(s)}\mathbf{p}^s$$
$$\mathbf{H} = \frac{1}{2}\sum_{ss'}\mathbf{p}_s\mathscr{K}_{(ss')}\mathbf{p}_{s'}$$
$$\mathbf{H}'_{(\nu)} = \mathbf{H} - \frac{1}{2}\hbar\mathbf{Q}\mathscr{D}^T_{(\nu)}\mathscr{I}^{-1}\mathbf{L} - \frac{1}{2}\hbar\mathbf{L}\mathscr{I}^{-1}\mathscr{D}_{(\nu)}\mathbf{Q} + \frac{1}{2}\hbar^2\mathbf{Q}\mathscr{K}_{(\nu\nu)}\mathbf{Q} \tag{9.34c}$$

In the quasi-classical approximation we consider the operators as commuting: therefore, taking an average over the Boltzmann distribution for $\mathbf{L}$ values we obtain:

$$\langle \chi_{\nu\nu'}^{\text{rot}} \rangle_T = \langle e^{-i\tau[Q\mathscr{D}(\nu)\mathscr{I}^{-1}\mathbf{L}+\frac{1}{2}\hbar Q\mathscr{K}(\nu\nu)Q]} \rangle_T \, e^{i\mathbf{Q}\cdot(\mathbf{d}_\nu-\mathbf{d}_{\nu'})}$$

$$= e^{i\mathbf{Q}\cdot(\mathbf{d}_\nu-\mathbf{d}_{\nu'})} \, e^{-\frac{i\tau}{2}\hbar Q\mathscr{K}(\nu\nu)Q} \frac{\displaystyle\int e^{-i\tau Q\mathscr{D}(\nu)\mathscr{I}^{-1}\mathbf{L}} \, e^{-\frac{\mathbf{L}\mathscr{I}^{-1}\mathbf{L}}{2kT}} \, d\mathbf{L}}{\displaystyle\int e^{-\frac{\mathbf{L}\mathscr{I}^{-1}\mathbf{L}}{2kT}} \, d\mathbf{L}}$$

$$= e^{i\mathbf{Q}\cdot(\mathbf{d}_\nu-\mathbf{d}_{\nu'})} \, e^{-\frac{1}{2}Q\mathscr{K}(\nu\nu)Q(i\tau\hbar+kT\tau^2)} \tag{9.34d}$$

Combining the rotational and translational part together we have

$$\langle \chi_{\nu\nu'}^{\text{tr}} \rangle_T \langle \chi_{\nu\nu'}^{\text{rot}} \rangle_T = e^{i\mathbf{Q}\cdot(\mathbf{d}_\nu-\mathbf{d}_{\nu'})} \, e^{-\frac{1}{2}(Q\mathscr{M}_{(\nu)}^{-1}Q)(i\tau\hbar+kT\tau^2)}$$

where

$$\mathscr{M}_{(\nu)}^{-1} = \mathscr{K}_{(\nu\nu)} + \frac{1}{M_{\text{mol}}}\mathbf{1} \tag{9.34e}$$

($\mathbf{1}$ is the unit tensor).

Comparing the components of $\mathscr{M}_{(\nu)}^{-1}$ with the formula (9.10) we can see that $\mathscr{M}_{(\nu)}$ is identical with the Sachs and Teller mass tensor for the νth nucleus.

The vibrational part averaged over the Boltzmann distribution may be taken from Zemach and Glauber (9.32). If we assume that the molecules are initially in their vibrational ground states, and that the neutron has an energy lower than the vibrational threshold, we must obtain the expression (9.32) in a form independent of time. This corresponds to $T = 0$ for vibrations. Now

$$\langle \chi_{\nu\nu'}^{\text{vib}} \rangle_{T=0} = \prod_\lambda e^{-\frac{\hbar}{4f_\lambda}[(\mathbf{Q}\cdot\mathbf{C}_\nu^{(\lambda)})^2+(\mathbf{Q}\cdot\mathbf{C}_{\nu'}^{(\lambda)})^2]} \tag{9.35}$$

with the normalization condition: $\sum M_\nu(\mathbf{C}_\nu^{(\lambda)})^2 = 1$ for each value of λ (M_ν, mass of the νth nucleus). There remains a dependence on molecular orientations which is contained in the rotational and vibrational part of the expectation value. Let us denote an averaging over molecular orientations by $\langle \ \rangle_\Omega$. The total average over initial states has the form:

$$\langle \bar{\chi}_{\nu\nu'} \rangle_{T,\Omega} = \langle e^{i\mathbf{Q}\cdot(\mathbf{d}_\nu-\mathbf{d}_{\nu'})} \, e^{-\frac{1}{2}(Q\mathscr{M}_{(\nu)}^{-1}Q)(i\tau\hbar+kT\tau^2)} \langle \bar{\chi}_{\nu\nu'}^{\text{vib}} \rangle_{T=0} \rangle_\Omega$$

We use now an approximation, replacing this average by a product of averages, i.e.:

$$\langle \bar{\chi}_{\nu\nu'} \rangle_{T,\Omega} = \langle e^{i\mathbf{Q}\cdot(\mathbf{d}_\nu-\mathbf{d}_{\nu'})} \rangle_\Omega \, \langle e^{-\frac{1}{2}(Q\mathscr{M}_{(\nu)}^{-1}Q)(i\tau\hbar+kT\tau^2)} \rangle_\Omega \, \langle \bar{\chi}_{\nu\nu'}^{\text{vib}} \rangle_{T=0,\Omega}$$

It is easy to calculate the average of the first part

$$\langle e^{i\mathbf{Q}\cdot(\mathbf{d}_\nu-\mathbf{d}_{\nu'})} \rangle_\Omega = j_0(Qd_{\nu\nu'})$$

where j_0 is the spherical Bessel function of the zero-order and $d_{\nu\nu'} = |d_\nu - d_{\nu'}|$. This follows immediately from the expansion of $e^{i\mathbf{Q}\cdot(\mathbf{d}_\nu-\mathbf{d}_{\nu'})}$ into a series of

Legendre functions. In the second part we make a further approximation by replacing the average of the whole expression by an average in the exponent.

$$\left\langle e^{-\frac{1}{2}(\mathbf{Q}\mathcal{M}_{(\nu)}^{-1}\mathbf{Q})(i\tau\hbar + kT\tau)}\right\rangle_\Omega \cong e^{\left\langle -\frac{1}{2}(\mathbf{Q}\mathcal{M}_{(\nu)}^{-1}\mathbf{Q})(i\tau\hbar + kT\tau^2)\right\rangle_\Omega}$$

Taking into account that

$$\left\langle \mathbf{Q}\mathcal{M}_{(\nu)}^{-1}\mathbf{Q}\right\rangle_\Omega = \tfrac{1}{3}Q^2 \,\text{trace}\,(\mathcal{M}_{(\nu)}^{-1}) = Q^2/M_\nu^{(0)} \tag{9.36a}$$

we obtain

$$\left\langle e^{-\frac{1}{2}(\mathbf{Q}\mathcal{M}_{(\nu)}^{-1}\mathbf{Q})(i\tau\hbar + kT\tau^2)}\right\rangle_\Omega = e^{-\frac{Q^2}{2M^{(0)}}(i\tau\hbar + kT\tau^2)} \tag{9.36b}$$

This result may be interpreted as a replacement of the translational-rotational effects by translation with a modified mass $M_\nu^{(0)}$.

The discussion of the validity of the above approximation shows that some improvement may be achieved by replacing $M_\nu^{(0)}$ by another quantity $\overline{M}_\nu$, which, however, in most cases is very close to $M_\nu^{(0)}$.

There remains the vibrational part

$$\left\langle \overline{\chi}_{\nu\nu'}^{\text{vib}}\right\rangle_{T=0,\Omega} \cong \prod_\lambda \left\langle e^{-\frac{\hbar}{4f_\lambda}[(\mathbf{Q}\cdot\mathbf{C}_\nu^{(\lambda)})^2 + (\mathbf{Q}\cdot\mathbf{C}_{\nu'}^{(\lambda)})^2]}\right\rangle_\Omega$$

We apply a similar approximation as above averaging in the exponent

$$\left\langle \overline{\chi}_{\nu\nu'}^{\text{vib}}\right\rangle_{T=0,\Omega} \cong e^{\Sigma\left\langle -\frac{\hbar}{4f_\lambda}[(\mathbf{Q}\cdot\mathbf{C}_\nu^{(\lambda)})^2 + (\mathbf{Q}\cdot\mathbf{C}_{\nu'}^{(\lambda)})^2]\right\rangle_\Omega}$$

Using the same averaging procedure as in formula (9.36a) we obtain

$$\left\langle \overline{\chi}_{\nu\nu'}^{\text{vib}}\right\rangle_{T=0,\Omega} \cong e^{-Q^2\gamma_{\nu\nu'}}$$

where

$$\gamma_{\nu\nu'} = \sum_\lambda \frac{\hbar}{12f_\lambda}[(\mathbf{C}_\nu^{(\lambda)})^2 + (\mathbf{C}_{\nu'}^{(\lambda)})^2] \tag{9.37}$$

The accuracy of this approximation depends on the magnitude of the orientation-dependent term appearing in the argument of the exponential in (9.35).

The final expression for the expectation value is

$$\left\langle \overline{\chi}_{\nu\nu'}\right\rangle_{T,\Omega} \cong j_0(Qd_{\nu\nu'})\,e^{-Q^2\gamma_{\nu\nu'}}\,e^{-\frac{Q^2}{2\overline{M}_\nu}(i\tau\hbar + kT\tau^2)} \tag{9.38a}$$

Introducing this into formula (9.33), we obtain the expression for the scattering law

$$S_{\nu\nu'}(Q,\omega) \cong [B_\nu B_{\nu'} + B_\nu' B_{\nu'}'\delta_{\nu\nu'}]\frac{1}{2\pi}\int_{-\infty}^{+\infty} d\tau \left\{ e^{-i\omega\tau}\,j_0(Qd_{\nu\nu'})\,e^{-Q^2\gamma_{\nu\nu'}} \times \right.$$

$$\left. e^{-\frac{Q^2}{2\overline{M}_\nu}(i\tau\hbar + kT\tau^2)} \right\} \tag{9.38b}$$

and for the angular distribution of scattered neutrons:

$$\langle\sigma(\theta)\rangle_{T,\Omega} \cong \sum_{\nu\nu'}[B_\nu B_{\nu'}+B'_\nu B'_{\nu'}\delta_{\nu\nu'}]\sqrt{\frac{\overline{M_\nu}}{2\pi kT}}\frac{1}{k_0}\int\limits_{-E_0/\hbar}^{\infty}d\omega\Big\{\frac{k}{Q}j_0(Qd_{\nu\nu'})\,e^{-Q^2\gamma_{\nu\nu'}}\times$$

$$e^{-\frac{\overline{M_\nu}}{2kTQ^2}\left(\omega+\frac{Q^2\hbar}{2\overline{M_\nu}}\right)^2}\Big\} \qquad (9.38c)$$

The various physical effects can be seen by inspection of the terms inside the curly brackets of equation (9.38c). First the term j_0 includes interference effects coming from scattering by the atoms composing one molecule. Secondly the exponential term $\exp(-Q^2\gamma_{\nu\nu'})$ is a "Debye Waller factor" for the vibrational modes and gives the amplitude of the zero order term (elastic term). Thirdly the remaining term (which has been Fourier transformed between equations (b) and (c)) is a perfect gas term for particles of effective mass $\overline{M_\nu}$: this term includes the combined effects of rotation and translation. In the case of direct scattering we may obtain the total neutron scattering cross-section of νth nucleus in the form

$$\langle\sigma_{(\nu)}(E_0)\rangle_{T,\Omega} \cong \pi[B_\nu^2+B'^2_\nu]\frac{2\bar{f}\hbar^2}{E_0}\{\mathrm{erf}\,(\sqrt{C})-\sqrt{1-p}\;e^{-C_p}\,\mathrm{erf}\,(\sqrt{C(1-p)})\}$$

$$(9.38d)$$

where

$$\bar{f}=\frac{1}{4m\gamma_{\nu\nu}},\qquad \mathrm{erf}\,(\tau)=\frac{2}{\sqrt\pi}\int\limits_0^\tau e^{-t^2}\,dt,\qquad C=\frac{\overline{M_\nu}E_0}{mkT}$$

$$p=\frac{1}{1+\alpha_1^2/4\alpha_2},\qquad \alpha_1=\frac{m+\overline{M_\nu}}{mkT},\qquad \alpha_2=\frac{2\overline{M_\nu}\gamma_{\nu\nu}}{\hbar^2kT}$$

This last formula is especially important for molecules containing hydrogen in view of the fact that $B_H^2\ll B_H'^2$ which allows interference effects to be neglected. (B_H is the coherent and B'_H the incoherent scattering amplitude for hydrogen).

The scattering of slow neutrons by molecules, with similar assumptions, was investigated by Messiah (1951). The common feature of these two treatments lies in considering translational-rotational degrees of freedom by the Sachs and Teller mass tensor. As concerns vibrations, the Krieger and Nelkin (K.N.) treatment takes into consideration the ground state only. Messiah's calculation, however, considers also transitions to the first three excited vibrational states but without taking into account thermal agitation and interference effects. He considers only those molecules for which the scattering process possesses a cylindrical symmetry with respect to the axis joining the nucleus under consideration and the molecular centre of mass. This makes it possible to perform the averaging over orientations without applying those approximations which were discussed in connection with the K.N. theory. The molecules which possess the property of symmetry needed by Messiah are H_2, CH_4 and some others. For these two molecules Messiah carried through cross-section calculations, and Krieger and Nelkin found that their calculations for the same molecules in the thermal energy region were in agreement with Messiah's. The agreement between the two theories shows the adequacy of the approximations in averaging over molecular orientations used by Krieger and Nelkin.

9.7 Diatomic Molecules (particularly H_2)

The calculations presented so far, based on the Zemach and Glauber treatment, are valid only when the neutron energy is large compared to the rotational energy separation. For lower neutron energies it is necessary to consider the rotational states of the molecule in more detail. The simplest type of molecule to consider is the diatomic molecule, where rotational wave functions are known and the matrix elements for the scattering can be calculated.

A separate discussion of the hydrogen molecule is justified by the much stronger spin correlation effects than for other molecules and also because a well developed theory exists. The problem was treated theoretically by Schwinger and Teller (1937), Hammermesh and Schwinger (1946), Brimberg (1956), Anselm (1957) and Løvseth (1962). Some discussion of this case was given in Chapter 8 (Section 8.3) where the theory of Sarma (1961) was described briefly. It is obvious that the neutron scattering cross-section for H_2-molecules might be calculated by applying the methods discussed earlier, i.e. those of Sachs and Teller, Messiah, and Krieger and Nelkin (see Figs. 10.6 and 10.8). However, these treatments consider rotation classically and neglect the spin correlation and so are inadequate. We shall discuss now Brimberg's treatment, which he applied to the scattering by H_2-molecules, presenting it in a mathematical form which makes possible an application to other diatomic molecules (of two identical atoms). It should be pointed out here that Brimberg and Løvseth calculate the effect of vibrations on the cross-section which is not the case for the other treatments cited above.

Brimberg starts from the Hamiltonian of three particles

$$\left\{ -\frac{\hbar^2}{2} \sum_{\nu=1}^{3} \frac{1}{m_\nu} \nabla_\nu^2 + V_{gi}(\mathbf{r}_1-\mathbf{r}_2) + V_{gi}(\mathbf{r}_1-\mathbf{r}_3) + U(\mathbf{r}_2-\mathbf{r}_3) \right\} \psi = E\psi \qquad (9.39)$$

where $m_1 = m$ is the neutron mass, $m_2 = m_3$ that of each proton (or other but equal nuclei), $V_{gi}(\mathbf{r}_1-\mathbf{r}_2)$ and $V_{gi}(\mathbf{r}_1-\mathbf{r}_3)$ are the interaction potentials neutron–nucleus, the subscripts i and g denote that now we deal with the interaction matrices which correspond to the transitions from the spin state χ_i to χ_g, and $U(\mathbf{r}_2-\mathbf{r}_3)$ is the interaction potential between the atoms in the molecule.

The equation (9.39) may be separated by the introduction of the co-ordinates (see Fig. 9.1):

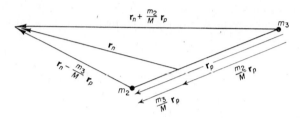

FIG. 9.1. Illustration of co-ordinates for diatomic molecule calculation (Brimberg, 1956).

$$\mathbf{r}_p = \mathbf{r}_2-\mathbf{r}_3 ; \qquad \mathbf{r}_n = (\mathbf{r}_1-\mathbf{r}_2)+\frac{m_3}{M}\mathbf{r}_p$$

$$\mathbf{r}_0 = \frac{m_1\mathbf{r}_1+m_2\mathbf{r}_2+m_3\mathbf{r}_3}{m_1+m_2+m_3}$$

(where $M = M_{\text{mol}} = m_2+m_3$, $\mathbf{r}_1$, $\mathbf{r}_2$, $\mathbf{r}_3$ are the position vectors referred to some fixed coordinate system) and by replacing the wave function of the whole system by the product:

$$\psi(\mathbf{r}_0,\mathbf{r}_n,\mathbf{r}_p) = \psi_0(\mathbf{r}_0)\psi'(\mathbf{r}_n,\mathbf{r}_p)$$

The motion of the centre of mass of the whole system may be described by the equation

$$-\frac{\hbar^2}{2M_0}\nabla^2\psi_0 = E'_0\psi_0 \qquad (M_0 = m_1+m_2+m_3)$$

and the function $\psi'(\mathbf{r}_n,\mathbf{r}_p)$ satisfies the equation

$$\left\{-\frac{\hbar^2}{2}\left(\frac{1}{M_1}\nabla_n^2+\frac{1}{M_2}\nabla_p^2\right)+V_{gi}\left(\mathbf{r}_n-\frac{m}{M}\mathbf{r}_p\right)+V_{gi}\left(\mathbf{r}_n+\frac{m_2}{M}\mathbf{r}_p\right)+U(\mathbf{r}_p)\right\}\psi' = E'\psi'$$

$$(9.40)$$

where $E'_0+E' = E$, $M_1 = \dfrac{mM}{m+M}$ is the reduced mass of the neutron–molecule system, and $M_2 = \dfrac{m_2m_3}{m_2+m_3}$ is the reduced mass of the molecule.

We wish now to solve the equation (9.40). We must find an auxiliary complete orthonormal system of functions which satisfy the equation:

$$\left\{-\frac{\hbar^2}{2M_2}\nabla_p^2+U(\mathbf{r}_p)\right\}\psi_{P\nu}(\mathbf{r}_p) = E_\nu\psi_{P\nu}(\mathbf{r}_p) \qquad (9.41)$$

$$\int \psi_{P\nu'}^*(\mathbf{r}_p)\psi_{P\nu}(\mathbf{r}_p)\mathrm{d}\mathbf{r}_p = \delta_{\nu'\nu}$$

The solution of the equation (9.40) may be written as a series expansion in these functions $\psi_{P\nu}(\mathbf{r}_p)$

$$\psi'(\mathbf{r}_n,\mathbf{r}_p) = \sum_\nu \psi_{N\nu}(\mathbf{r}_n)\psi_{P\nu}(\mathbf{r}_p)$$

This gives us the following equations for the functions $\psi_{N\nu}(\mathbf{r}_n)$

$$\left\{\frac{\hbar^2}{2M_1}\nabla_n^2+E'-E_\nu\right\}\psi_{N\nu}(\mathbf{r}_n) = \sum_{\nu'}\psi_{N\nu'}(\mathbf{r}_n)\int\left\{V_{gi}\left(\mathbf{r}_n-\frac{m_3}{M}\mathbf{r}_p\right)+V_{gi}\left(\mathbf{r}_n+\frac{m_2}{M}\mathbf{r}_p\right)\right\}\times$$
$$\psi_{P\nu'}^*(\mathbf{r}_p)\psi_{P\nu}(\mathbf{r}_p)\mathrm{d}\mathbf{r}_p \qquad (9.42)$$

We have now a system of coupled differential equations which may be replaced by a system of integral equations to which a method of successive approximations may be applied. The neutron wave function is represented as a plane wave:

$$\psi_{N\nu'}(\mathbf{r}_n) = \delta_{\nu'\nu_0}\,e^{i\mathbf{k}_{\nu_0}\cdot\mathbf{r}_n}$$

where $\hbar\mathbf{k}_{\nu_0}$ is the initial neutron momentum. Taking the usual pseudo-potential form of neutron interaction, and writing $\psi_{N\nu}(\mathbf{r}_n)$ asymptotically as an incident plane wave and an outgoing spherical wave, we calculate the cross-section in the normal way.

The interaction potential between the neutron and the nuclei is written as (see (9.20)):

$$V(\mathbf{r}_n-\mathbf{r}) = \frac{2\pi\hbar^2}{M_3}\left\{\frac{S+1}{2S+1}a_{s+\frac{1}{2}}+\frac{S}{2S+1}a_{s-\frac{1}{2}}+2(a_{s+\frac{1}{2}}-a_{s-\frac{1}{2}})\frac{\mathbf{s}.\mathbf{S}}{2S+1}\right\}\delta(\mathbf{r}_n-\mathbf{r})$$
$$(9.43)$$

where $a_{s\pm\frac{1}{2}}$ denotes free scattering length and $M_3 = m_1m_2/(m_1+m_2)$. Then the interaction which appears in the formula (9.40) may be written as (for $m_2 = m_3$):

$$V\left(\mathbf{r}_n-\frac{m_3}{M}\mathbf{r}_p\right)+V\left(\mathbf{r}_n+\frac{m_2}{M}\mathbf{r}_p\right) = \frac{2\pi\hbar^2}{M_3}\left\{\frac{S+1}{2S+1}a_{s+\frac{1}{2}}+\frac{S}{2S+1}a_{s-\frac{1}{2}}+\right.$$
$$+2(a_{s+\frac{1}{2}}-a_{s-\frac{1}{2}})\frac{\mathbf{s}.\mathbf{S}_1}{2S+1}\right\}\delta(\mathbf{r}_n-\tfrac{1}{2}\mathbf{r}_p)+\frac{2\pi\hbar^2}{M_3}\left\{\frac{S+1}{2S+1}a_{s+\frac{1}{2}}+\frac{S}{2S+1}a_{s-\frac{1}{2}}+\right.$$
$$\left.+2(a_{s+\frac{1}{2}}-a_{s-\frac{1}{2}})\frac{\mathbf{s}.\mathbf{S}_2}{2S+1}\right\}\delta(\mathbf{r}_n+\tfrac{1}{2}\mathbf{r}_p)$$

It is convenient to separate the symmetric and antisymmetric part with respect to the spins of the particles. In order to do this we shall introduce the notation:

$$\mathbf{S}_+ = \mathbf{S}_1 + \mathbf{S}_2 \quad \text{(the total spin of the molecule)}$$
$$\mathbf{S}_- = \mathbf{S}_1 - \mathbf{S}_2$$

where $\mathbf{S}_1$, $\mathbf{S}_2$ are the spin operators of the two identical scattering nuclei; $\mathbf{s}$ is the spin operator of the neutron. Now

$$V(\mathbf{r}_n - \tfrac{1}{2}\mathbf{r}_p) + V(\mathbf{r}_n + \tfrac{1}{2}\mathbf{r}_p) = \frac{2\pi\hbar^2}{M_3}\left[\frac{S+1}{2S+1}a_{s+\frac{1}{2}} + \frac{S}{2S+1}a_{s-\frac{1}{2}} + \right.$$
$$\left. + (a_{s+\frac{1}{2}} - a_{s-\frac{1}{2}})\frac{\mathbf{s}\cdot\mathbf{S}_+}{2S+1}\right][\delta(\mathbf{r}_n - \tfrac{1}{2}\mathbf{r}_p) + \delta(\mathbf{r}_n + \tfrac{1}{2}\mathbf{r}_p)] +$$
$$+ \frac{2\pi\hbar^2}{M_3}(a_{s+\frac{1}{2}} - a_{s-\frac{1}{2}})\frac{\mathbf{s}\cdot\mathbf{S}_-}{2S+1}[\delta(\mathbf{r}_n - \tfrac{1}{2}\mathbf{r}_p) - \delta(\mathbf{r}_n + \tfrac{1}{2}\mathbf{r}_p)]$$

The symmetric part is responsible for transitions at which the spin symmetry of the molecule does not change, i.e. for ortho→ortho and para→para transitions. The antisymmetric part induces the ortho→para and para→ortho transitions.

From the above expression we obtain the formula for the cross-section for scattering of an incident neutron from a state represented by $\mathbf{k}_{\nu_0}$ to another $\mathbf{k}_\nu$ with simultaneous transition of the molecule from a state represented by ν_0 to another ν, and the whole particle system from the spin state χ_i to another χ_g. The cross-section is written in the centre of mass system of all particles:

$$\sigma_{\nu\nu_0}(\theta,\phi) = \frac{v_{rc}}{v'_{rc}}\left(\frac{M_1}{M_3}\right)^2\left|\left[\left(\frac{S+1}{2S+1}a_{s+\frac{1}{2}} + \frac{S}{2S+1}a_{s-\frac{1}{2}}\right)\chi_g\chi_i + \right.\right.$$
$$+ (a_{s+\frac{1}{2}} - a_{s-\frac{1}{2}})\frac{\chi_g\mathbf{s}\cdot\mathbf{S}_+\chi_i}{2S+1}\left]\int e^{\frac{i}{2}(\mathbf{k}_{\nu_0} - \mathbf{k}_\nu)\cdot\mathbf{r}}\{\psi_{P_\nu}^*(\mathbf{r})\psi_{P_{\nu_0}}(\mathbf{r}) + \psi_{P_\nu}^*(-\mathbf{r})\psi_{P_{\nu_0}}(-\mathbf{r})\}d\mathbf{r} + \right.$$
$$\left. + (a_{s+\frac{1}{2}} - a_{s-\frac{1}{2}})\frac{\chi_g\mathbf{s}\cdot\mathbf{S}_-\chi_i}{2S+1}\int e^{\frac{i}{2}(\mathbf{k}_{\nu_0} - \mathbf{k}_\nu)\cdot\mathbf{r}}\{\psi_{P_\nu}^*(\mathbf{r})\psi_{P_{\nu_0}}(\mathbf{r}) - \psi_{P_\nu}^*(-\mathbf{r})\psi_{P_{\nu_0}}(-\mathbf{r})\}d\mathbf{r}\right|^2$$

$$(9.44)$$

where χ_i and χ_g are the products of spin functions of the neutron and the molecule in the initial and the final state, v_{rc} and v'_{rc} are neutron velocities relative to the molecular centre of mass in the initial and final state.

Now, applying the above computations to the H_2-molecule (with $s = \tfrac{1}{2}$) and performing the summation over the final spin states and the averaging over the initial ones we obtain the following four types of cross-section:

1. For ortho→ortho transitions $(S_+ = 1 \to 1)$

$$\sigma_{\nu\nu_0}(\theta,\phi) = \frac{v'_{rc}}{v_{rc}}\left(\frac{M_1}{M_3}\right)^2 \frac{1}{16}[(3a_1+a_0)^2+2(a_1-a_0)^2]|\beta_1|^2$$

2. For ortho→para transitions $(S_+ = 1 \to 0)$

$$\sigma_{\nu\nu_0}(\theta,\phi) = \frac{v'_{rc}}{v_{rc}}\left(\frac{M_1}{M_3}\right)^2 \frac{1}{16}(a_1-a_0)^2|\beta_2|^2$$

3. For para→ortho transitions $(S_+ = 0 \to 1)$

$$\sigma_{\nu\nu_0}(\theta,\phi) = \frac{v'_{rc}}{v_{rc}}\left(\frac{M_1}{M_3}\right)^2 \frac{3}{16}(a_1+a_0)^2|\beta_2|^2$$

4. For para→para transitions $(S_+ = 0 \to 0)$

$$\sigma_{\nu\nu_0}(\theta,\phi) = \frac{v'_{rc}}{v_{rc}}\left(\frac{M_1}{M_3}\right)^2 \frac{1}{16}(3a_1+a_0)^2|\beta_1|^2$$

where β_1 and β_2 denote the two integrals which are involved in the formula (9.44).

The equation (9.41) is an equation for the wave functions of the molecule. We solve it by the separation of variables. By introducing the quantum numbers of the angular momentum and of the projection of angular momentum (lm) we obtain

$$\psi_{P_\nu lm}(\mathbf{r}_p) = R_{\nu l}(\mathbf{r}_p)Y_{lm}(\theta,\phi)$$

where $Y_{lm}(\theta,\phi)$ are the spherical harmonics, and the $R_{\nu l}(\mathbf{r}_p)$ may be determined from the radial equation. In this equation the interaction potential between the two atoms in the molecule $U(\mathbf{r}_p)$ is not yet determined. If we take the molecule as a rigid rotator we may write

$$R_{\nu l}(r_p) = \frac{\sqrt{\delta(r_p-r_e)}}{r_e}$$

where r_e is the fixed distance between the nuclei in the molecule.

The problem was treated in this way in the papers of Schwinger and Teller (1937) and of Hammermesh and Schwinger (1946; 1947). Brimberg solves the radial equation for two further cases, i.e. interactions of the form of a harmonic isotropic potential and of the Morse potential. (The calculated results for a harmonic oscillator give the best fit to experimental points.) In order to find the function $R_{\nu l}(r_p)$ an approximate method was applied.

The integrals β_1 and β_2 may be written in a simpler form by taking into account that

$$\psi_{P_\nu lm}(-\mathbf{r}_p) = (-1)^l\,\psi_{P_\nu lm}(\mathbf{r}_p)$$

and denoting by $\mathbf{Q}\hbar$ the momentum transfer:

$$\beta_{1,2} = [1 \pm (-1)^{l+l_0}] \int e^{i\mathbf{Q}\cdot\mathbf{r}/2} \psi^*_{P_v lm}(\mathbf{r}) \psi_{P_{v_0} l_0 m_0}(\mathbf{r}) d\mathbf{r}$$

Substituting this into the cross-section formulas we may see that the ortho→ortho and para→para transition is connected with a change of l_0 (the initial angular momentum quantum number) by an even number. The ortho→para and para→ortho transition occurs when l_0 changes by an odd number. Also because of the Pauli exclusion principle the ortho state has the odd l_0 value and the para state possesses the even l_0 (the effect of spin correlation).

Finally it is necessary to average over the Maxwell distribution of the velocities of the molecules. For given l and l_0 we sum over the magnetic quantum number m and average over m_0. Then for every l_0 the cross-section is summed over all possible final rotational states l and afterwards a mean value of the resulting cross-section is formed taking into account the probability of the molecule being in a rotational state l_0 at a temperature T.

The a_1 and a_0 values may be obtained from the total scattering cross-section for free protons

$$\sigma_H^{\text{free}} = 4\pi[\tfrac{3}{4}a_1^2 + \tfrac{1}{4}a_0^2] = \frac{\pi}{4}[(3a_1 + a_0)^2 + 3(a_1 - a_0)^2] = 20\cdot366 \text{ barns,}$$

and from the experiments which give the coherent scattering amplitude $B_H = \tfrac{1}{2}(3a_1 + a_0) = -0\cdot378 \times 10^{-12}$ cm. Hence

$$a_1 = 0\cdot57 \times 10^{-12} \text{ cm}; \quad a_0 = -2\cdot38 \times 10^{-12} \text{ cm}$$

The Brimberg calculation gives a curve which fits the experimental total cross-section in the energy region $0\cdot003$–$0\cdot8$ eV (Fig. 10.1(d)). For higher energies the observed deviation may be easily explained by the inelastic contributions connected with the molecular vibration, which were not taken into account in Brimberg's computations.

Similar quantum mechanical calculations of the total neutron scattering cross-section were performed by Løvseth (1962) for H_2, D_2, N_2 and O_2 molecules. The calculations were carried up to the threshold for excitation of the second vibrational level. Vibrations were treated by the harmonic oscillator model (see also Section 10.2).

9.8 Theory of Neutron Scattering by Rotators

The contribution of the rotational degrees of freedom of a general molecule to the scattering cross-section of neutrons was discussed in detail by both Volkin (1959) and Rahman (1961). This problem was considered also by Zemach and Glauber, and Krieger and Nelkin. Zemach and Glauber, however, treated a model which could be applied only to a linear or spherical molecule, whereas Krieger and Nelkin, due to their classical treatment of rotation limited the region of validity of their results.

Volkin and Rahman consider the problem of general molecules and of various energy regions. Volkin's treatment is based on that of Zemach and Glauber and adopts formula (9.14b) for the scattering law.

We shall take into account only the rotational degrees of freedom, and will assume therefore that the molecule may be presented as a rigid rotator with a fixed centre of mass. The initial steps are the same as those given in Section 9.6 up to equation (9.34c) for the Hamiltonian.

$$H = \tfrac{1}{2}\mathbf{L}\mathscr{I}^{-1}\mathbf{L}$$

The complete commuting set of observables for our system is formed by: the square of the angular momentum L^2, the projection L_z of $\mathbf{L}$ on a space-fixed axis, and the projection $L_{z'}$ on an axis fixed in the molecule. Let us denote by J, M, K the corresponding quantum numbers. (In previous sections, J has been denoted by l). For a symmetric rotator (in which the axis fixed in the molecule is at the same time the axis of symmetry) the above observables commute with the Hamiltonian and hence the quantum numbers J, M, K may be used for the determination of the energy eigenfunctions which we shall denote by ψ_{JKM}. For a given J there exists a degeneracy in respect to M. For a symmetric rotator we have additionally a degeneracy for $\pm K$. The wave functions for the symmetric rotator satisfy:

$$\mathbf{L}^2\psi_{JKM} = J(J+1)\hbar^2\psi_{JKM}, \quad L_z\psi_{JKM} = \hbar M\psi_{JKM}, \quad L_{z'}\psi_{JKM} = \hbar K\psi_{JKM}$$

$$\int d\overline{\omega}\psi_{JKM}^*\psi_{J'K'M'} = \delta_{JJ'}\delta_{KK'}\delta_{MM'} \quad d\overline{\omega} = \sin\beta d\beta d\alpha d\gamma$$

where α, β and γ are the three Euler angles which define the position of the axes of the rotator with respect to axes fixed in the space. ψ_{JKM} may be expressed by matrix elements of the Jth irreducible unitary representation of the group of rotations:

$$\psi_{JKM} = \sqrt{\frac{8\pi^2}{2J+1}}\,D_{MK}^J(\alpha,\beta,\gamma) \qquad (9.45)$$

The energy eigenstates of the asymmetric rotator may be written as

$$|JM\rangle = \sum_{K=-J}^{J} \alpha_K |JKM\rangle$$

(where $|JKM\rangle$ denotes an energy eigenstate of the symmetric rotator specified above as $\psi_{JKM}(\alpha,\beta,\gamma)$. We shall consider the scattering by a rotator with the angular momentum J and the energy E_J.* The expectation value

---

* The energy eigenvalues of the asymmetric rotator are labelled by two quantum numbers, E_J is written above for brevity.

must be averaged over the orientations of the angular momentum, and we denote this average by $\langle X_{\nu'\nu}\rangle_J$. We may write:

$$\langle X_{\nu'\nu}\rangle_J = \frac{b_{\nu'}b_\nu}{2J+1} \sum_{M=-J}^{J} \langle JM| \, e^{i\mathbf{Q}\cdot\mathbf{d}_{\nu'\nu}} \, e^{-i\tau(H'_{(\nu)}-E_J)/\hbar} \, |JM\rangle$$

$$= b_{\nu'}b_\nu \sum_{K'K=-J}^{J} \alpha_{K'}^{*}\alpha_K \widetilde{\langle X_{\nu'\nu}\rangle}_{JK'K} \tag{9.46}$$

where

$$\widetilde{\langle X\rangle}_{JK'K} = \frac{1}{2J+1} \sum_{M=-J}^{J} \langle JK'M| \, e^{i\mathbf{Q}\cdot\mathbf{d}_{\nu'\nu}} \, e^{-i\tau(H'_{(\nu)}-E_J)/\hbar} \, |JKM\rangle$$

Now consider the classical case. In view of (9.46) we may neglect in H (and in $H'_{(\nu)}$) terms containing L for large values of $k_0 d_\nu$. If (as in the Krieger and Nelkin theory) we denote by $\mathcal{K}_{(\nu\nu)}$ the tensor $\mathcal{D}^T\mathcal{I}^{-1}\mathcal{D}$ where $\mathcal{D}$ is given by the formula (9.34b), we obtain for the direct scattering using the formula (9.45)

$$\langle \bar{X}_{\nu\nu}\rangle_{JK'K} = \frac{\delta_{K'K}}{8\pi^2} \int d\bar{\omega} \, e^{-i\tau\hbar(\mathbf{Q}\mathcal{K}_{(\nu\nu)}\mathbf{Q})/2}$$

and

$$S_{cl}(Q,\omega) = \frac{1}{8\pi^2}\frac{1}{\hbar} \int d\bar{\omega}\,\delta(\omega + \tfrac{1}{2}\hbar\mathbf{Q}\mathcal{K}_{(\nu\nu)}\mathbf{Q})$$

It should be noted that $S_{cl}(Q,\omega)$ does not depend on J or α_K and therefore it is not dependent on the initial state of the molecule. The effective integration leads to elliptic integrals. Volkin gives also a formula for the differential cross-section $\sigma_{cl}(\theta)$ as an expansion into a power series in $m\kappa$ where m is the neutron mass, and κ denotes one of the eigenvalues of the tensor $\mathcal{K}_{(\nu\nu)}$. This expansion is equivalent to an expansion into a series in the ratio of the neutron mass to the "effective mass" of the molecule.

Because of the complicated form of the above mentioned formula as well as of other formulas for cross-sections given by Volkin, we will discuss the method briefly without writing them in an explicit form. An expansion in the ratio of neutron mass to the "effective mass" of the molecule may be obtained from the formula (9.46) written in the form (for direct scattering):

$$\langle X_{\nu\nu}\rangle_J = \frac{b_\nu^2}{2J+1} \sum_{M=-J}^{J} \langle JM| \, e^{-i\tau(A+B+C)/\hbar} \, |JM\rangle$$

where

$$A = H-E_J, \quad B = \tfrac{1}{2}\hbar[\mathbf{L}\mathcal{I}^{-1}(\mathbf{Q}\times\mathbf{d}_\nu)+(\mathbf{Q}\times\mathbf{d}_\nu)\mathcal{I}^{-1}\mathbf{L}], \quad C = \frac{\hbar^2}{2}\mathbf{Q}\mathcal{K}_{(\nu\nu)}\mathbf{Q}$$

(the classical approximation corresponds to neglect of the terms A and B

leaving only C in the exponential). An expansion of the expectation value in the following form is then used.

$$\langle X_{\nu\nu'}\rangle_J = \sum_{n=0}^{\infty} c'_n (i\tau)^n$$

Substituting this expression into the formula for the double differential cross-section we may write in analogy with (9.28):

$$\langle\sigma(\theta)\rangle_J = \frac{b^2}{k_0}\sum_n \left[\left(\frac{m}{\hbar^2 k}\frac{\mathrm{d}}{\mathrm{d}k}\right)^n (kc'_n)\right]_{k=k_0}$$

This is an expansion into a power series in the ratio $m(d_\nu)_i^2/I_j$ and at the same time an expansion in $1/k_0 d_\nu$, as in the Zemach and Glauber theory. In particular we may obtain from the Volkin formula that of Zemach and Glauber for the case of a linear rotator.

The formula for the scattering cross-section may be obtained in a different way from that described above; that is without applying the general Zemach and Glauber formalism. In fact it is possible to perform directly a summation of the partial cross-sections for transitions from a given initial state to the subsequent final rotational states. We shall describe briefly this method of treating the problem used by Rahman (1961).

Let us consider the differential cross-section for the scattering of a neutron of an energy which is of the same order of magnitude as the separation of the rotational states in the molecule. In the system in which the centre of mass of the neutron and the molecule is fixed we may write (see equation (9.13a,b))

$$\sigma(\theta) = \left(\frac{M_{\mathrm{mol}}}{m+M_{\mathrm{mol}}}\right)^2 \frac{k}{k_0}\left|\langle\psi_i|\sum_\nu b_\nu\, e^{i\mathbf{Q}\cdot\mathbf{r}_\nu}|\psi_g\rangle\right|^2 \qquad (9.47)$$

where $\mathbf{r}_\nu$ is the position vector of the νth nucleus with respect to the molecular centre of mass. In order to take into account the rotational degrees of freedom only we shall assume that b_ν is independent of the nuclear spin and consider a matrix element of the form

$$\langle\psi_{\mathrm{rot},i}|\, e^{i\mathbf{Q}\cdot\mathbf{r}_\nu}|\psi_{\mathrm{rot},g}\rangle$$

Let us denote by $(\nu\nu')$ the following expression

$$(\nu\nu') = \langle\psi_{\mathrm{rot},i}|\, e^{i\mathbf{Q}\cdot\mathbf{r}_\nu}|\psi_{\mathrm{rot},g}\rangle[\langle\psi_{\mathrm{rot},i}|\, e^{i\mathbf{Q}\cdot\mathbf{r}_{\nu'}}|\psi_{\mathrm{rot},g}\rangle]^*$$

In order to calculate the matrix element we shall expand the wave function $(\tilde\psi)$ of a general asymmetric molecule as a series containing the wave functions of a symmetric top. For a state characterized by the quantum numbers L, J, M, this expansion is:

$$\tilde\psi_{LJM} = \sum_K \alpha_{LJK}\psi_{JKM}$$

In order to discuss the transition from the state LJM to $L'J'M'$ we substitute for $e^{i\mathbf{Q}\cdot\mathbf{r}_\nu}$ the following expansion (in which θ, ϕ denote the spherical coordinates of the scattering nucleus in the system fixed relative to the molecule, α, β, γ are the Euler angles which define the position of axes fixed in the molecule, in a system fixed in space)

$$e^{i\mathbf{Q}\cdot\mathbf{r}_\nu} = 4\pi\sum_{lm}(i)^l(-1)^m j_l(Qr_\nu)Y_{lm}(\beta,\gamma)Y_{lm}(\theta,\phi)$$

To obtain the cross-section we must calculate the expression $(\nu\nu')$, and to obtain, for instance, the interference terms containing ν and ν' it is necessary to sum the expression $(\nu\nu')+(\nu'\nu)$ over the final states (i.e., over the M' values) and to average over the initial states (i.e. over M). Let us denote the expression obtained in this way $\langle(\nu\nu')\rangle_{\mathrm{av}}$. From the general results obtained by Rahman the formula (9.30) of Zemach and Glauber may be derived as a special case in which the functions $\psi_{\mathrm{rot},i}$, $\psi_{\mathrm{rot},g}$ reduce to spherical harmonics ($K = K' = 0$). Then we obtain:

$$\langle(\nu\nu')\rangle_{\mathrm{av}} = 2\sum_l(2l+1)j_l(Qr_\nu)j_l(Qr_{\nu'})\sqrt{\frac{4\pi}{2l+1}}P_{l,0}(\Theta_{\nu\nu'})[C(JlJ';\,00)]^2$$

where $\Theta_{\nu\nu'}$ denotes the angle between r_ν and $r_{\nu'}$ and $C(\ldots)$ is a Clebsch–Gordan coefficient. In order to compare this expression with the Zemach and Glauber theory we must perform a summation over all final states J'. This gives

$$2\sum_l(2l+1)j_l(Qr_\nu)j_l(Qr_{\nu'})\sqrt{\frac{4\pi}{2l+1}}P_{l,0}(\Theta_{\nu\nu'})$$

which is simply an expansion of the function of $2j_0(Qr_{\nu\nu'})$ ($r_{\nu\nu'} = |\mathbf{r}_\nu-\mathbf{r}_{\nu'}|$) so that we have obtained the result of Zemach and Glauber in the lowest degree of approximation.

Cross-section calculations for the H_2O molecules of water vapour were performed by Goryunov (1957) and later by Khubchandani and Rahman (1960). Goryunov's results are limited to a neutron energy much smaller than the first vibrational level (0·19 eV) and to temperatures low enough to ensure that the molecules are in their ground vibrational state. Assuming this we may consider them as rigid asymmetric rotators. In his calculations Goryunov summed for $J\leqslant3$. Khubchandani and Rahman showed that it is not satisfactory to neglect the $J\geqslant4$ contributions. They applied the Goryunov method but took $J\leqslant8$ into consideration (for $T=300°K$ and a single neutron energy only, i.e. 0·6 meV). It appeared that the contributions of J from 4 to 8 give approximately as much cross-section as $J\leqslant3$. The total cross-section obtained by Khubchandani and Rahman for the scattering of 0·0006 eV neutrons by H_2O molecules was 290 barns.

Rahman's treatment for the case of the spherical molecule was used by Griffing (1961, 1963) to calculate the partial differential cross-section of the CH_4 molecule. The reason for these calculations was a discrepancy between the experimental results of Randolph et al. (1961) and the theory of Krieger and Nelkin (see Section 10.5). Griffing's treatment starts from the Zemach Glauber formula (9.14a) and considers separately the translational, vibrational, and rotational degrees of freedom, treating the first two in the same way as is done in the KN theory. The rotational part of the expectation value is evaluated by Rahman's method with the assumption that the initial rotational states have a Boltzmann thermal distribution function for a spherical top. This gives for the rotational part of the scattering law (proton direct scattering only)

$$S_{rot}(Q,\omega) = \frac{\sum_J (2J+1+2p)(2J+1) \exp\left(-\dfrac{J(J+1)\hbar^2}{2IkT}\right) \sum_{n=|p|}^{2J+p} j_n^2(Qd)}{\sum_J (2J+1)^2 \exp\left(-\dfrac{J(J+1)\hbar^2}{2IkT}\right)} \cdot \delta(\hbar\omega - \epsilon) \quad (9.48)$$

where J and $J+p$ are the quantum numbers of the initial and final rotational states and j_n is a spherical Bessel function. Thus the energy transfer is given by

$$\epsilon = \frac{\hbar^2 pJ}{I} + \frac{\hbar^2 p(p+1)}{2I}$$

which connects p and J in (9.48). The whole of the direct scattering is obtained through a convolution of this term with the term due to the translational and vibrational states. Several comparisons with experiment have been made using the expression (9.48) which will be discussed in Chapter 10 (see also Section 8.4). If the momentum transfer (Q) is small, the Doppler broadening of (9.48) by the translational motion is small and the peaks predicted by (9.48) should be observable unless there is coupling between the modes. At high values of Q (where many of the experiments have been done) the Doppler broadening is so large that the rotational peaks are smeared together. Equation (9.48) will be referred to as the Rahman-Griffing result.

9.9 Time-dependent Correlation Function for an Atom in a Molecule

The problem of slow neutron scattering may be very generally formulated by applying the Van Hove correlation function. As it has been already pointed out in Chapter 1, the scattering by molecules needs a special treatment, which has formed the subject of the present chapter. We shall not give here a detailed description of the space time correlation functions (Van Hove, 1954), but we wish to present a derivation of the frequency function $z(\omega)$ [equation (1.45)] for a molecule.

As in the KN theory we shall assume that nuclei may be treated as Boltzmann particles without any spin correlation. Then according to Van Hove we may write the following formula for the double differential cross-section:

$$\frac{d^2\sigma}{d\Omega dE} = \frac{d^2\sigma^{coh}}{d\Omega dE} + \frac{d^2\sigma^{inc}}{d\Omega dE}$$

We shall consider here the incoherent scattering only (see the remark after 9.38d). For this case we may write:

$$\frac{d^2\sigma^{inc}}{d\Omega dE} = \frac{k}{k_0} \sum_\nu B_\nu'^2 S_{inc}^{(\nu)}(\mathbf{Q},\omega) \tag{9.49}$$

The scattering law $S_{inc}^{(\nu)}$ which depends only on the dynamics of the scattering system, may be written in the following form (see equation (1.34))

$$S_{inc}^{(\nu)} = \frac{1}{2\pi\hbar} \int_{-\infty}^{\infty} I_s^{(\nu)}(\mathbf{Q},\tau)\, e^{-i\omega\tau}\, d\tau \tag{9.50a}$$

$$I_s^{(\nu)} = \int G_s^{(\nu)}(\mathbf{r},\tau)\, e^{i\mathbf{Q}\cdot\mathbf{r}}\, d\mathbf{r} \tag{9.50b}$$

The self-correlation function $G_s^{(\nu)}(\mathbf{r},\tau)$ is analogous to the classical self-correlation function $G_{so}^{(\nu)}(r, \tau)$, which determines the probability that a particle which at time $\tau = 0$ was at the position $\mathbf{r} = 0$, will at time τ occupy the position $\mathbf{r}$.

We now introduce the Gaussian approximation proposed by Vineyard (this approximation will be indicated by a subscript 0) in which $G_{so}^{(\nu)}(\mathbf{r},\tau)$ is assumed to have the form

$$G_{so}^{(\nu)}(\mathbf{r},\tau) = \{\pi[w_0^{(\nu)}(\tau)]^2\}^{-\frac{3}{2}} \exp\left(-\frac{r^2}{[w_0^{(\nu)}(\tau)]^2}\right) \tag{9.51}$$

(this is discussed in Section 7.9). $[w_0^{(\nu)}(\tau)]^2$ is two-thirds of the mean square distance that the atom ν moves in time τ.

Equation (9.51) is clearly not correct for a molecule whose centre of mass is fixed, since then the displacement of an atom from its initial position cannot exceed twice its distance from the centre of mass, but when this rotational motion is combined with translations and vibrations, (9.51) may nevertheless be a good approximation.

When the translational, rotational and vibrational degrees of freedom are treated independently, $[w_0^{(\nu)}(\tau)]^2$ can be expressed as a sum of terms for each

$$[w_0^{(\nu)}(\tau)]^2 = [w_{0\ tr}^\nu]^2 + [w_{0\ rot}^{(\nu)}]^2 + [w_{0\ vib}^{(\nu)}]^2 \tag{9.52}$$

For free molecules

$$[w_{0\ tr}^{(\nu)}]^2 = 2[v^{(0)}]^2\tau^2 \tag{9.53}$$

where $v^{(0)} = \left(\dfrac{2kT}{M_{\mathrm{mol}}}\right)^{\frac{1}{2}}$ is one-third the mean square velocity of the molecule.

For rotations $|w^{(v)}_{0\,\mathrm{rot}}|^2$ can be shown to be *at short times*

$$[w^{(v)}_{0\,\mathrm{rot}}]^2 = \langle 2kT\mathbf{u}_v \mathscr{K}_{vv'}\mathbf{u}_{v'}\rangle_\Omega \tau^2 \tag{9.54}$$

where $\langle \ldots \rangle_\Omega$ denotes arranging over molecular orientations. $\mathscr{K}_{vv'}$ is the tensor introduced by Krieger and Nelkin (equation (9.34a)), $\mathbf{u}_v$ is the unit vector in the direction of the momentum of the vth nucleus.

Equation (9.54) is clearly only valid for τ small compared to the inverse of the mean angular velocity of the atom $\tilde{t} \ll \left(\dfrac{I}{kT}\right)^{\frac{1}{2}}$. Schofield (1962) has given formulae valid at all times for an atom moving on a sphere. This is expressed in terms of the spectral function of the velocity correlation function for the atom (Chapter 7).

$$[w^{(v)}_{0\,\mathrm{rot}}]^2 = \frac{4kT}{M_v}\int \frac{z_0(\omega)}{\omega^2}(1-\cos\omega\tau)\mathrm{d}\omega. \tag{9.55}$$

For an atom moving on a sphere (i.e. the case of a diatomic molecule), Schofield gives

$$z_0(\omega) = \frac{2}{3}\cdot\frac{\frac{1}{2}I^2\omega^3}{(kT)^2}\cdot\mathrm{e}^{-\frac{I\omega^2}{2kT}} \tag{9.56}$$

The quantum mechanical equivalent of (9.55) is given at equation (7.96), and hence

$$[w^{(v)}_{\mathrm{rot}}]^2 = \frac{2kT}{M_v}\int \frac{z(\omega)}{\omega}\left(\coth\frac{\hbar\omega}{2kT}\cdot\cos\omega\tau - i\sin\omega\tau\right)\mathrm{d}\omega \tag{9.57}$$

where, in the case under consideration,

$$z(\omega) = \frac{2}{3}\frac{\displaystyle\sum_J J^2\,(\mathrm{e}^{-\hbar^2 J/IkT}-1)\,\mathrm{e}^{-\frac{\hbar^2}{2IkT}J(J+1)}\,\delta\left(\omega-\frac{\hbar J}{I}\right)}{\displaystyle\sum_J (2J+1)\,\mathrm{e}^{-\frac{\hbar^2}{2kIT}J(J+1)}} \tag{9.58}$$

It should be noted that the imaginary time shift discussed in Section 7.4, has not been applied to equation (9.57). Consequently the detailed balance factor is contained in equation (9.58). In the limit $\dfrac{\hbar^2}{IkT} \ll 1$, the sum over J in (9.58) can be replaced by an integral, and then $z(\omega)$ reduces to $z_0(\omega)$ defined by (9.56).

It is readily verified that (9.55) reduces to the averaged mass tensor expression in the limit $\tau \to 0$. For the vibration (in the ground state only) the

16

square of the most probable displacement may be taken as equal to the average over molecular orientation of the expression

$$[w_0^{(\nu)}{}_{\text{vib}}]^2 = \sum_\lambda (\tilde{C}_\nu^\lambda)^2 \frac{2\hbar}{f_\lambda} \qquad (9.59)$$

($\tilde{C}_\nu'$ and f_λ are introduced in Section 9.4).

Thus inserting (9.52) in (9.51) an expression for $G_{\text{so}}^{(\nu)}(\mathbf{r},\tau)$, in the Gaussian approximation is obtained, and hence $I_{\text{so}}^{(\nu)}(\mathbf{Q},\tau)$ can be calculated as

$$I_{\text{so}}^{(\nu)}(\mathbf{Q},\tau) = \exp\left(-\frac{\mathbf{Q}^2}{4}[w_0^{(\nu)}(\tau)]^2\right) \qquad (9.60)$$

Now apply a correction formula due to Schofield (1960) to obtain the quantum mechanical $I_{\text{so}}^{(\nu)}(\mathbf{Q},\tau)$,

$$I_{\text{s}}^{(\nu)}(\mathbf{Q},\tau) \simeq I_{\text{so}}^{(\nu)}\left(\mathbf{Q},\tau - \frac{i\hbar}{2kT}\right) \qquad (9.61)$$

which is correct to first order in $\hbar$. We find that in the short time approximation, formula (9.50) gives the same expression for the double differential cross-section as that obtained by Krieger and Nelkin for incoherent scattering.

References

Anselm, A. A. (1957). *Zh. eksper. teoret. Fiz.* **33**, 625.
Brimberg, S. (1956). Thesis, Stockholm.
Fermi, E. (1936). *Ric. Sci.* **7**, 13.
Goryunov, A. F. (1957). *J. nucl. Energy* **4**, 109.
Griffing, G. W. (1961). *Phys. Rev.* **124**, 1489.
Griffing, G. W. (1963). *In* "Inelastic Scattering of Neutrons in Solids and Liquids", Vol. I, p. 435. IAEA, Vienna.
Hammermesh, M. and Schwinger, J. (1946). *Phys. Rev.* **69**, 145.
Hammermesh, M. and Schwinger, J. (1947). *Phys. Rev.* **71**, 678.
Herzberg, G. (1945). "Infra-red and Raman Spectra". Van Nostrand, New York.
Khubchandani, P. G. and Rahman, A. (1960). *J. nucl. Energy* **A11**, 89.
Kosály, G. and Solt, G. (1964). "Scattering of Slow Neutrons by Molecules". The Central Research Institute for Physics, Budapest.
Krieger, T. J. and Nelkin, M. S. (1957). *Phys. Rev.* **106**, 290.
Løvseth, J. (1962). *Phys. Norvegica.* In press.
Messiah, A. M. L. (1951). *Phys. Rev.* **84**, 204.
Placzek, G. (1952). *Phys. Rev.* **86**, 377.
Rahman, A. (1961). *J. nucl. Energy* **A13**, 128.
Randolph, P. D., Brugger, R. M., Strong, K. A. and Schmunk, R. E. (1961). *Phys. Rev.* **124**, 460.
Sachs, R. G. and Teller, E. (1941). *Phys. Rev.* **60**, 18.
Sarma, G. (1961). *In* "Inelastic Scattering of Neutrons in Solids and Liquids", p. 397. IAEA, Vienna.

Schofield, P. (1960). *Phys. Rev. Letters* **4**, 239.

Schofield, P. (1962). Proceedings of Brookhaven Conference on Neutron Thermalization, p. RB–1. B.N.L. 719, Vol. I.

Schwinger, J. and Teller, E. (1937). *Phys. Rev.* **51**, 775; **52**, 286.

Van Hove, L. (1954). *Phys. Rev.* **95**, 249.

Volkin, H. C. (1959). *Phys. Rev.* **113**, 866; (1960) **117**, 1029.

Wick, G. C. (1954). *Phys. Rev.* **94**, 1228.

Zemach, A. C. and Glauber, R. J. (1956). *Phys. Rev.* **101**, 118, 129.

CHAPTER 10

Neutron Scattering Experiments on Molecules

J. A. JANIK and A. KOWALSKA

Physical Institute of the Jagiellonian University, Krakow, Poland

10.1	Introduction	453
10.2	Total Cross-section Data on Hydrogenous Gases	454
10.3	Angular and Energy Distribution Data on Hydrogenous Gases	460
10.4	Hydrogenous Liquids	467
10.5	Metal Hydrides	476
10.6	Ammonium Salts	481
10.7	Various Hydrogenous Solids	487
10.8	Experiments with Non-hydrogenous Molecules	489
10.9	Concluding Discussion	492
	References	493

Symbols as for Chapter 9

10.1 Introduction

In this chapter we discuss the results obtained from neutron scattering experiments with molecular systems—as solids, liquids or gases. Before intense neutron sources were available, experiments on the scattering of neutrons by molecules were performed using neutron sources which gave a Maxwellian-ike velocity distribution, such as the moderated (Ra+Be) or similar sourlces. Some experiments of this kind were carried out by Carrol (1941), Gilbert (1946) and Janik (1951), but they will not be discussed here. We limit ourselves to cross-section measurements made with monenergetic neutrons and various theories described in Chapter 9 will be used to try to understand the underlying physics.

The main part of this chapter will be concerned with cross-section measurements on gases, liquids and solids containing hydrogen. As pointed out in Section 9.1, the hydrogen cross-section is so large that, in such experiments, the neutron is sensitive mainly to the motions of the protons. For the liquids and solids, the results are considered only from the point of view of well defined molecular models. Our discussion on gases is divided into two parts—total cross-section work and angular or energy distributions. The model used most extensively will be that of Krieger and Nelkin (1957) and it will be shown that in many cases a good fit to the total cross-section is obtained. For the detailed energy distributions, however, rotational states can be seen and more detailed treatments (e.g. Griffing, 1961) are required.

One of the most frequently observed features in the neutron data is a contribution from first order rotational scattering, and many of the experiments have been concerned with the question of whether the molecular rotations are free in the liquid or solid state. A test of this is often stated to be given by a fit of the data to the K.N. formula, equation (9.38). This test is clearly insufficient as equations (9.56) and (9.48) which are also based on the idea of free rotation give different results. The former equation gives the classical and the latter equation the quantum formula for rotational cross-sections. A fit to either of these equations is a better test of free rotation (the area of $z(\omega)$ in equation (9.56) being fixed by the K.N. effective mass), but not convincing on its own because of a margin of doubt about the parameters to be used. Another technique which is sometimes employed is to compare cross-sections for gaseous molecules to the cross-section for the same molecule in the solid or liquid state. This technique is useful but some theory of the complete behaviour of the molecule in the solid or liquid state is required before even this method can be made convincing. Because of these uncertainties the conclusions of various authors differ although the initial data is usually in agreement.

Many experiments have been conducted on hydrogeneous solids, particularly metal hydrides and ammonium salts. Separate sections will be devoted to these subjects, which represent cases where the vibrational or rotational states are dominant respectively.

Finally, we give a short discussion of some non-hydrogenous molecular systems which have been studied recently.

10.2 Total Cross-section Data on Hydrogenous Gases

As was discussed in Chapter 9, the calculation of the scattering of neutrons by molecules involves various approximations according to the magnitude of the momentum transfer. The aim of these approximations is to characterize the translational, rotational and vibrational degrees of freedom of the molecule. For the analysis of total cross-section data it is convenient to separate the discussion into two parts corresponding to the thermal and sub-thermal energy regions. This separation is justified in view of the difference in the average momentum transfer for these regions which leads to different ways of considering vibration and rotation.

A treatment of the thermal region which may be applied easily to different types of molecule is that of Krieger and Nelkin (1957), later referred to as K.N. (see Section 9.6). These authors treat molecular vibrations quantum-mechanically but include only the elastic term; rotations, however, are treated on the basis of the Sachs and Teller (1941) mass tensor. It should be remembered here that the K.N. treatment is restricted to cases where the vibrational levels are well separated from the rotational ones. Better results can be obtained by numerical computations using the general formalism of Zemach and Glauber (1956) described in Section 9.4.

From a practical point of view it is important to know when the simple theory of Krieger and Nelkin is justified and when the more complicated and tedious calculations (of Zemach and Glauber for example) should be applied. An analysis of this problem has been made by Kosaly and Solt (1963) and gave the following results, in terms of the temperature (T), rotational constant (A), and the combination $Q^2/2M$. The Sachs and Teller mass tensor approximation may be used only where

$$\frac{\hbar^2 Q^2}{2M} \gg A \; ; \; kT \gg A \tag{10.1}$$

One may then say that the Sachs and Teller mass tensor approximation is typically a large recoil, high temperature one.

Kosaly and Solt (1964) have shown further that the Krieger and Nelkin approximation gives results close to the mass tensor approximation only for small Q values or for very high temperatures. The condition of small Q values conflicts with (10.1). Hence the K.N. approximation may only be applied for an "intermediate case".

$$A \ll \frac{\hbar^2 Q^2}{2M} \ll kT \tag{10.2}$$

In order to obtain cross-sections on the K.N. basis equation (9.38d) must be employed. It is therefore necessary to calculate the mass tensor of the nucleus under consideration in the molecule (to obtain the values $\overline{M}_\nu$), and the vibrational amplitudes and frequencies for all vibrational modes of the molecule (to obtain the values $\bar{f}$). Calculations have been made for the molecules H_2, CH_4, C_2H_4, NH_3, H_2O, H_2S and C_6H_6, and only hydrogen atoms in the molecule were taken into account. Due to the incoherence of the scattering by hydrogen the interference terms were not taken into consideration, and also it was assumed that the other nuclei gave a constant additional cross-section equal to their free atom cross-section. Values of the constants used are shown in Table 10.1.

Figure 10.1(a) shows the experimental points of Melkonian (1949) and the results of calculations for the CH_4 molecule. In the thermal region the experimental points are in agreement with calculation. It should be noted that the calculations of Messiah (1951) for CH_4 molecules also gave a good fit to the experimental results in the thermal energy region.

Figure 10.1(b) presents a comparison between the experimental points of Melkonian (1949) and of Janik et al. (1961a) together with the K.N. calculations for gaseous ethylene (C_2H_4). Good agreement with the K.N. theory below 0·1 eV is evident. Above this energy inelastic effects become important.

In Figure 10.1(c) the experimental points of Janik *et al.* (1960, 1961a) and of Rush *et al.* (1960) are compared to a calculation for gaseous ammonia. There is good agreement between the curve and the experimental points of Janik *et al.* which were obtained in the two different experiments. The points of Rush *et al.*, which cover all regions, seem to be systematically different from the results of Janik *et al.* and the model.

TABLE 10.1 K.N. Constants for several molecules

Molecule	$\overline{M}_H$ (proton masses)	$\bar{f}$(meV)	T(°K)
C_2H_4	5·81	105·5	300
CH_4	3·40	165·6	300
NH_3	2·85	193·5	300
H_2O	2·05	342·1	400
H_2S	2·29	250·7	300
CH_3SH $\begin{cases} \text{for SH} \\ \text{for } CH_3 \end{cases}$	7·06 6·95	44·4 $\Big\}$ 94·8	360

The experimental points of Heinloth (1961) for water vapour are compared to calculation in Fig. 10.1(d). In this case there is a clear disagreement. Because of the similarity between the molecules of H_2O and H_2S it is interesting to compare the data on these two gases. Figure 10.1(e) shows the comparison between the experimental points of Tubbs *et al.* (1962) and the K.N. model for gaseous H_2S. One sees some disagreement between them, which in view of the similar result for H_2O may suggest that the approximation of Krieger and Nelkin is not valid for these molecules. Schofield (1963) suggests that the K.N. method of calculating the effective mass may be in error for highly asymmetric molecules such as H_2O or H_2S. In both cases the agreement between calculated and experimental cross-sections would be greatly improved by a slight increase in M_ν.*

* It should be pointed out that T. Springer (Private communication) reports new results for water in much better agreement with the K.N. model than those of Heinloth.

FIGS. 10.1(a)–(e) Total neutron cross-section as a function of neutron energy for several molecules. (a) CH_4 molecules. ●, Experimental points of Melkonian (1949). Curve: K.N. model; (b) C_2H_4 molecules. ●, Experimental points of Melkonian (1949); ×, experimental points of Janik *et al.* (1961a). Curve: K.N. model; (c) NH_3 molecules. △, ○, Experimental points of Janik *et al.* (1960, 1961a). ×, experimental points of Rush *et al.* (1960). Curve: K.N. model; (d) H_2O molecules. ×, Experimental points of Heinloth (1961). Curve: K.N. model; (e) H_2S molecules. ●, Experimental points of Tubbs *et al.* (1962). Curve: K.N. model.

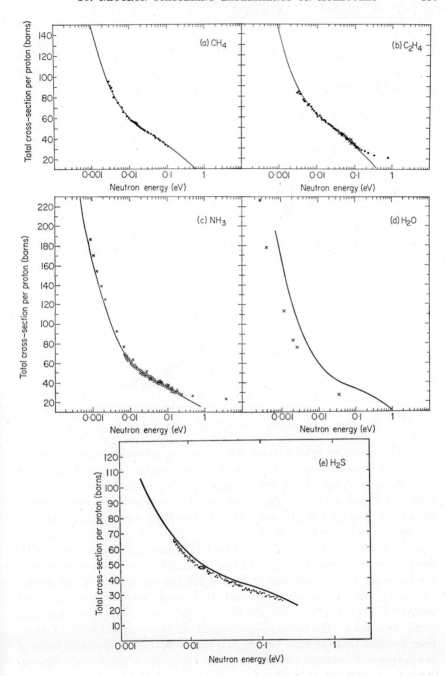

It seems useful to show in one figure (Fig. 10.2) the K.N. curves for various molecules. It is easy to see the inadequacy of the model at higher energies where the cross-sections do not approach the value $\sigma_H^{free} = 20 \cdot 36$ b. Further, the similarity of the curves is striking; this due to the correlation between $\overline{M}$ and $\overline{f}$ shown in Table 10.1.

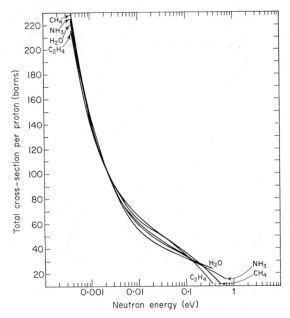

Fig. 10.2. A comparison of the K.N. curves for various molecules.

We shall consider briefly molecules performing internal hindered rotation (Fig. 10.3). Some early investigations of neutron scattering by such molecules were made by Janik (1953, 1954), Janik et al. (1961a), Budzanowski et al. (1957) and Kolos (1954). The experimental cross-section versus energy curves for gaseous CH_3SH and CH_3OH (Borowski and Rzany, 1962) lie systematically higher than the K.N. curves calculated under the assumption that the hindered rotation of the SH (or OH) group with respect to the CH_3 group may be formally treated as one of the $3N-6$ normal vibrations in the molecule. In the calculations for CH_3SH the coefficients of the secular equation given by Ryskina (1948) and the hindered rotation barrier heights given by Kilb (1955), Solimene and Dailey (1955) and Kojima and Nishikawa (1957) were used. (The parameters obtained are shown in Table 10.1.) Apart from the fact that (at least for CH_3SH) the evaluation of a proper value of the barrier still remains an open problem, the neutron results may be considered as evidence of inelastic contributions to the total cross-sections corresponding to transitions between the hindered rotation levels. These contributions must cause an increase of the cross-section as compared to the K.N. curve, which does not take into account such transitions.

There are not many experiments which have used sub-thermal neutrons (energy lower than~10 meV). Some of the results have been shown in Figs. 10.1 together with the results for the thermal energy region. Only for two molecules is it possible to compare calculation (see Sections 9.7 and 9.8) and experiment. These are the H_2 molecule, for which calculations considering rotation quantum-mechanically were made by Brimberg (1956) and Løvseth

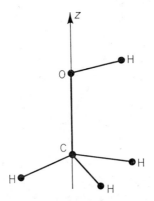

FIG. 10.3. CH_3OH molecule, which performs hindered internal rotation.

(1962) and the H_2O molecule for which similar calculations were made by Goryunov (1957) and then by Khubchandani and Rahman (1960). Volkin's (1959) result for the sub-thermal region has not yet been applied in useful calculations. It should be pointed out that the rotation of the H_2 molecule must be treated quantum-mechanically in the thermal energy region in view of the fact that the rotational quantum is large (0·015 eV) (see also Section 8.3). Figure 10.4 shows the experimental points of Melkonian (1949) for H_2 gas and the results of calculations made on the basis of the K.N. model, and by Brimberg (1956). Brimberg obtains a better fit to the experimental points. It should be mentioned that the calculations of Messiah (1951) coincide (for H_2 molecules) with those of Krieger and Nelkin in the thermal energy region.

In the case of the H_2O molecule the calculations of Khubchandani and Rahman (1960) in which rotation is treated quantum-mechanically were made for one energy only, i.e. for 0·6 meV (see Section 9.7). Their cross-section value for this energy (per proton in the H_2O molecule) and for the temperature 300°K is 290 barns, which is significantly higher than either the K.N. or the Sachs-Teller results. As discussed earlier the experimental points of Heinloth (1961) lie below the K.N. curve over the whole region. The

disagreement between those experimental values and the theoretical value of
Khubchandani and Rahman is therefore even larger. It is worthwhile
observing, that the experimental points of Rush *et al.* (1960) for gaseous
ammonia in the sub-thermal region are in only slight disagreement with
calculation (Fig. 10.1(c)) which is surprising, at so low an energy.

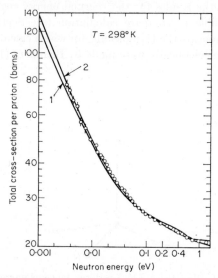

FIG. 10.4. Total neutron scattering cross-section of protons in H_2 molecules against neutron
energy. Experimental points Melkonian (1949). Curves: 1, K.N. model and 2, theory of
Brimberg and Løvseth.

The results discussed in this section show clearly that the total cross-
section, of a variety of molecules in gaseous form, can be described by the
K.N. model. This means that for those molecules we can compare calculated
and measured average parameters $\overline{M}_\nu$ and $\overline{f}$, and find reasonable agreement.
For more detailed information it is necessary to extend the energy range to
lower energies (for rotational information) or to higher energies (for vibrational information). Alternatively the analysis of angular and energy spectra
of scattered neutrons must be used and this will be discussed in the following
section.

10.3 Angular and Energy Distribution Data on Hydrogenous Gases

The total scattering cross-sections are calculated by double integration
(over angles and energies) of the differential cross-section $d^2\sigma/d\Omega dE$. Therefore from the theoretical point of view the determination of the cross-
section $d^2\sigma/d\Omega dE$ or even $d\sigma/dE$ or $d\sigma/d\Omega$ is more basic than the determination of σ_T. Experimental difficulties, however, result in the material on

differential cross-sections being limited, and the experiments in which $d^2\sigma/d\Omega dE$ for gases was obtained, include only CH_4, C_3H_8, NH_3, H_2S and H_2 molecules.

The angular distribution $(d\sigma/d\Omega)$ of scattered neutrons has been measured for the molecules CH_4, C_2H_4 and H_2. Measurements on CH_4 for the incident neutron energy 0·0732 eV were made by Alcock and Hurst (1951) and for

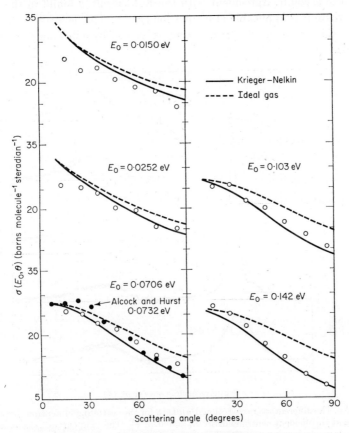

FIG. 10.5. The differential cross-section $d\sigma/d\Omega = \sigma(E_0,\theta)$ for the scattering of neutrons by methane molecules (Randolph *et al.*, 1961; Alcock and Hurst, 1951).

incident neutron energies of 0·0150 eV, 0·0252 eV, 0·0706 eV, 0·103 eV and 0·142 eV by Randolph *et al.* (1961). In the Alcock and Hurst experiments the scattered neutron intensity was measured for various angles, but the determination of the absolute cross-section value $d\sigma/d\Omega$ was, however, not attempted. In the paper of Randolph *et al.*, the $d\sigma/d\Omega$ values were obtained by using the measured $d^2\sigma/d\Omega dE$ data and performing an integration over energy. These results are presented in Fig. 10.5 together with the theoretical curves, which were calculated on the basis of the K.N. model by applying equation (9.38). The effective mass value $\overline{M}_H = 3\cdot2$ m was used instead of $3\cdot4$ m suggested by Krieger and Nelkin. Another theoretical calculation was made on the basis of the ideal gas approximation with the mass $3\cdot2$ m. These calculations take neither the interference effects nor the scattering by carbon nuclei into account. Agreement with the K.N. result is found in the energy region where it is applicable (see equation (10.1)). The decrease of the cross-section relative to the ideal gas result is caused by vibrations of the CH_4 molecule.

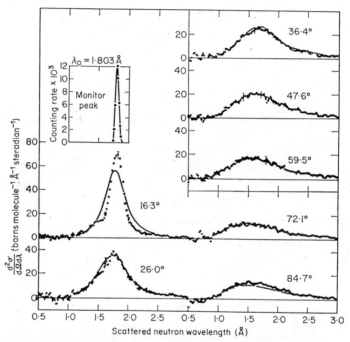

FIG. 10.6. The differential cross-section $d^2\sigma/d\Omega dE$ for the scattering of neutrons by methane molecules at the incident neutron energy $E_0 = 0\cdot0252$ eV. The solid curves were obtained on the basis of the E.A. treatment (Randolph *et al.*, 1961).

It is worth mentioning that (as was shown by Krieger and Nelkin) calculations based directly on the Zemach and Glauber treatment (1956) give results close to those given in Fig. 10.5. Good agreement between the K.N. model and the measured angular distributions of scattered neutrons was also obtained by Bally *et al.* (1963) for gaseous ethylene and hydrogen.

In the experiments of Randolph *et al.* (1961) measurements of the double differential cross-section were made for five values of the incident neutron energy (given above). Figure 10.6 shows the results for various scattering angles θ, and for a chosen value of the neutron energy, 0·0252 eV. The results were interpreted on the basis of the following three theoretical models.

1. The K.N. model. Calculations were made as above using $\overline{M}_H = 3\cdot2\,m$ instead of $3\cdot4\,m$ ($3\cdot2\,m$ is based on a calculation of $\overline{M}_H$ by Griffing and McMurry (unpublished)).

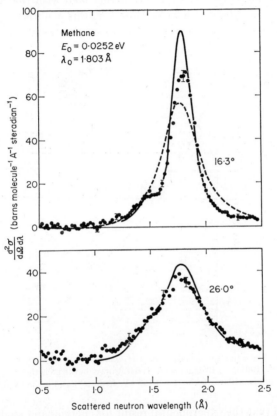

Fig. 10.7. A comparison of the Krieger and Nelkin model (- - -) and the Griffing model (—); with experiment.

2. The approximation of the ideal gas (I.G.) with the mass $3\cdot2\,m$. This approximation is obtained from the K.N. formula by setting the exponential factor due to the vibrations equal to unity.

3. The Zemach and Glauber treatment (1956) in which an "exact averaging" (E.A.) over directions was performed. The influence of carbon nuclei and the H–H and C–H interference effects were also taken into consideration.

The theoretical curves E.A. which are almost identical with the K.N. curves are presented as continuous lines in Fig. 10.6.

Both the E.A. and K.N. treatments give a good fit to the experimental points except for small incident energies (0·015 eV and 0·0252 eV) and small scattering angles (16·3° and 26·0°). The disagreement for $E_0 = 0·015$ eV and 0·0252 eV was unexpected in view of the fact that the experimental total cross-section curve for CH_4 agrees very well with the K.N. curve for energies as low as about 0·005 eV. However, this confirms that the double differential cross-section is more sensitive to the rotational spectrum than the

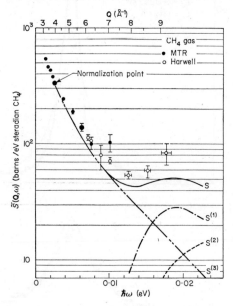

FIG. 10.8. $\widetilde{S}(Q,\omega)$ as a function of $(\mathbf{Q},\omega)$ for CH_4 gas near the molecular vibrational modes. ●, Randolph et al. (1961), ○, Brugger et al. (1964). Curve marked S is the sum of zero oscillator term (S^3), plus single oscillator terms for 0·163 eV mode (S^1) and 0·188 eV mode (S^2).

total one, and that the experimental result for energies and angles mentioned above should be calculated using a theory which treats rotation quantum-mechanically. Such a theoretical attempt was made by Griffing (1961, 1963) (see Section 9.7). A comparison between the K.N. and Griffing results and the experimental points of Randolph et al. for $E_0 = 0·0252$ eV and $\theta = 16·3°$ is presented in Fig. 10.7. One can see that Griffing obtains a much narrower quasi-elastic peak than K.N. and another small peak corresponding to neutron energy gain. It must be noted that this inelastic peak does not correspond to a single transition between the rotational levels but is the envelope of a curve corresponding to several transitions gathered around this energy. In any case, it is clear that the experimental points provide evidence of such an inelastic peak caused by the molecular rotation.

Measurements by Brugger *et al.* (1964) of the scattering law for large energy transfers have detected the lowest vibrational state of the methane molecule. Their results are shown at Fig. 10.8, compared to calculations based on the Griffing model with vibrational modes added via Zemach and Glauber's formula. The observed intensity is significantly greater than the calculated value suggesting that either an appreciable correction to the data has been overlooked or that the method of calculation is not accurate. Contributions from the stretching mode at 0·36 eV and multiple excitations of lower energy modes were examined and found to be negligible.

Results similar to those for CH_4 were obtained for C_3H_8 molecules (Strong *et al.*, 1962). A comparison was made with the K.N. model only, in a modified form which takes into account the single quantum changes of the three lowest vibrational modes. Again some deviations for small incident energies and small scattering angles were observed. One may believe that they are of the same origin as those observed for methane. Similar results were obtained by Strong *et al.* (1965) for NH_3 gas and for H_2S gas. The data on these molecules confirms the usefulness of the K.N. method in the region specified by equation (10.2). Over this region the comment made at the end of Section 10.2 is applicable.

Another experiment in which $d^2\sigma/d\Omega dE$ was measured for ammonia, methane, and hydrogen was reported by Webb (1963). The wavelength of the incident neutrons was a "line spectrum" at 4 Å. Figure 10.9 shows the cross-section as a function of the velocity of the scattered neutrons for gaseous ammonia and several angles of scattering. At 20° a quasi-elastic peak is observed, which decreases in intensity for higher scattering angles and completely disappears at 75° and 90°. Also, an energy gain peak at about 0·01 eV was obtained which increases in intensity with increasing angles. This peak is the envelope of the rotational levels of the NH_3 molecule, similar to those discussed in connection with methane. Webb (1963) shows that an ideal gas model with $M = 17$ gives the correct shape and behaviour for the quasi-elastic peak, which confirms that it is due to translational motion. The solid line in Fig. 10·9 is a calculation using the K.N. model. As expected this does not show the rotational peak properly, this being particularly noticeable at 20°. Czerlunczakiewicz and Kowalska (1964) carried out calculations using the Griffing model for NH_3 gas, 20° scattering angle and 4 Å neutrons. They found a rotational peak in the position given at Fig. 10.9, which confirms the assignment of that peak to rotational states. At large angles the agreement with K.N. becomes increasingly better and explains the good agreement found for the total cross-section for 4 Å neutrons. Similar results with the quasi-elastic and inelastic rotational parts were obtained by the same author for 4 Å neutrons scattered by CH_4. For hydrogen at all angles there is a single broad spectrum of scattered neutrons with no appearance of an elastic peak.

A quantitative comparison between the theory and experiment for these results could be based on the classical rotator equation (9.56) since the level

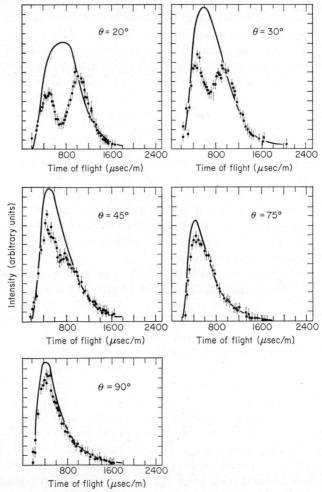

FIG. 10.9. The differential cross-section $d^2\sigma/d\Omega dE$ for the scattering of neutrons by ammonia molecules. The wavelength of the incident neutrons is 4 Å. Data of Webb (1963); the solid lines are K.N. calculations.

spacing is small compared to the energy transfers observed, but this has not yet been done. It seems evident, however, that an investigation of the rotational properties of molecules using cold neutrons is the most profitable of the techniques discussed here.

10.4 Hydrogenous Liquids*

It should be emphasized that the treatment given in this section differs from that of Chapter 8. We will consider here those phenomena, occurring in the scattering of neutrons by hydrogen-containing liquids which reflect the difference between the molecular situation in a liquid and a gas. It should be pointed out that in the case of large molecules (which possess a large effective mass $\overline{M}_H$) there is only a slight difference between the cross-sections in the liquid and gaseous states. As an example the results of Melkonian (1949) for gaseous and liquid n-butane are shown in Fig. 10.10.

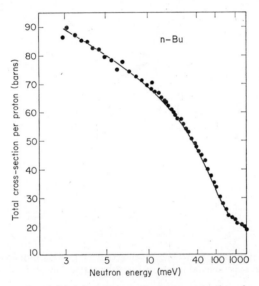

Fig. 10.10. The experimental total neutron scattering cross-section of protons in n-butane. Points correspond to the gas while the solid curve is that for liquid n-butane (Melkonian, 1949).

In the case of small molecules, such as H_2O, NH_3, H_2S, CH_4, one might expect a difference between the scattering cross-sections in the gaseous and liquid states. This difference is mainly caused by a difference in the behaviour of the molecular rotations. We can assume for all molecules that they rotate freely in the gaseous state, but for the same molecules in the liquid state various assumptions have been suggested.

At Fig. 10.11 the results obtained by Rogalska (1962) for liquid methane at a temperature of 117°K are shown. They lie almost exactly on the theoretical curve which was calculated for gas at the same temperature. The results

* Liquid hydrogen, a special case of a molecular liquid, has been covered in Section 8.3.

may be considered as a verification of the freedom of molecular rotations in liquid CH_4 (compare the discussion of Section 8.4). The experimental points for liquid H_2S (Rzany and Sciesinski, 1962) lie only slightly above those for gas showing a large degree of freedom of molecular rotations, explained by a lack of association.

In the case of water one may expect a hindrance of rotation owing to the existence of a strong hydrogen bond, and this hindrance may lead to the torsional vibration of H_2O molecules. A similar situation may arise in the case

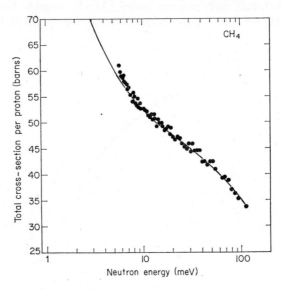

Fig. 10.11. Total neutron scattering cross-section of protons in liquid methane against neutron energy. ●, experimental points of Rogalska (1962). Curve: K. N. model.

of ammonia. There is a difficulty in forecasting the behaviour of liquid hydrogen sulphide. Physicochemical data suggest that hydrogen bonds do not occur in liquid H_2S, but the existence of a dipole moment of the H_2S molecule may lead to a hindrance of rotation in the liquid phase. In the case of liquid methane the existence of a free molecular rotation in the liquid state may be expected owing to the spherical symmetry of the molecular structure. However, in general the vapour–liquid transition should lead to a hindrance for molecular rotations.

In Fig. 10.12 a comparison is shown between the experimental results of Melkonian (1949) for liquid water, the K.N. model for water vapour at the same temperature and the Nelkin model discussed below. The experimental cross-section is much higher than the K.N. one. The liquid–vapour difference may be interpreted as being caused by the above-mentioned hindrance of rotation in the liquid state which leads to an increase of the effective mass $\overline{M}_H$. Also we must take into account the fact (known from molecular infra-red spectroscopy) that a vapour–liquid transition makes a small change in the internal vibrations of the molecule. A similar effect to that shown in Fig. 10.12 was obtained by Wanic (1959) and by Rzany and Sciesinski (1962) in the case of liquid ammonia. These results may be regarded as a verification of the hindrance of rotations in the case of NH_3 molecules.

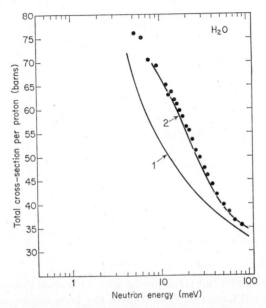

FIG. 10.12. Total neutron scattering cross-section of protons in liquid water against neutron energy. ●, Experimental points of Melkonian (1949). Curve 1: K.N. model for water vapour. Curve 2: Nelkin model for liquid water.

Further experiments in which the total cross-section technique was used are those of Heinloth (1961). In this paper the results for water, formic acid, and benzene as a function of temperature are presented. The temperature region in which the investigations were made covers the solid, liquid and gaseous states for the three substances. Figure 10.13 shows the temperature dependence of the total cross-sections of H_2O, C_6H_6 and $HCOOH$ for the energies 0·78 meV and 36 meV. It may be observed that there is an increase of the cross-section with the rise in temperature and steps at the solid–liquid transition (increase) and at the liquid–gas transition (decrease).

Heinloth gave the following interpretation of the results: in the solid state region, the scattering cross-section is a superposition of an elastic part and of two inelastic parts corresponding to a neutron energy gain and to a neutron energy loss. The analytical formula for these cross-sections contains temperature dependent factors and (as a constant parameter) the Debye temperature of the material. For the observed increase of the cross-section in the solid state region the inelastic scattering for neutron energy gain is responsible, and the step at the solid–liquid transition is interpreted as being the result of a decrease of the Debye temperature at this transition. It must be assumed in this interpretation that (at least in the vicinity of the melting point) a liquid

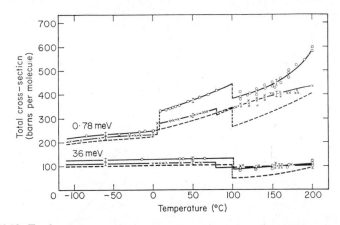

FIG. 10.13. Total neutron scattering cross-section of C_6H_6 ($\bigcirc$) and HCOOH ($\times$) molecules against the temperature of the sample (Heinloth, 1961). The curve for H_2O is shown as a broken line.

possesses a quasi-crystalline structure for which a certain Debye temperature may be accepted (Chapter 8). The step in the cross-section at the liquid–vapour transition may be interpreted (as was already done in the case of the results for H_2O and NH_3, described above) as being the result of a transition from hindrance to freedom of molecular rotations. An experimental comparison between the scattering by ice and water has been made also by Whittemore and McReynolds (1961). The results are consistent with the corresponding Heinloth data. Similar behaviour of D_2O is also reported by these authors.

The water cross-section was discussed in terms of a molecular model by Nelkin (1960). The experimental basis of his considerations was the observation (discussed in Section 8.2) of a well defined maximum at about 0·06 eV in the energy distribution of neutrons scattered by water. This maximum was interpreted as being caused by the hindered rotation of water molecules in the liquid state. Nelkin calculated the total neutron scattering cross-section for water in the energy interval 0·01–1 eV using an extension of the K.N. model and the following assumptions.

1. Translations in liquid water are free.

2. Three frequencies of internal vibration in the H_2O molecule are the same in the gaseous as in the liquid state.

3. Besides these frequencies there exists a torsional oscillation (hindered rotation) of frequency equivalent to 0·06 eV.

A comparison is shown in Fig. 10.12 between the experimental data of Melkonian (1949) and the results of Nelkin's calculations: there is good agreement between them.

It should be noted that the Nelkin model (3 internal vibrations plus hindered rotation of the whole molecule) explains the results of other experiments than total neutron scattering cross-section measurements, although it is too simple for an adequate description of the double differential cross-section (Goldman and Federighi, 1963; Egelstaff et al. 1963). Mikke (1961), for instance, measured the angular distribution of neutrons scattered by water and showed that it agreed with the Nelkin model calculations. Also in these experiments the average energy of scattered neutrons as a function of the angle of scattering was measured and this agreed with the Nelkin model for H_2O as well as for D_2O. In the case of D_2O a value of 0·04 eV was assumed for the hindered rotation frequency. The limitations of this model are emphasized at low values of Q, where the defects of assumption (1) become apparent.

A similar model for polythene was proposed by Goldman and Federighi (1963), which described the total cross-section reasonably well but again failed to explain the double differential cross-section. These results confirm that the total cross-section can be represented by certain integral and average properties of the material under investigation (represented in this case by the effective mass given to each vibration, and the vibrational energy, respectively).

In some cases one molecular mode can dominate the scattered neutron spectrum. An example of this kind is provided by the work of Boutin et al. (1963) on liquid HF shown in Fig. 10.14. They used an incident beam composed of the whole cold neutron spectrum (see Chapter 8) and measured the scattered neutron spectrum by the time-of-flight method. Figure 10.14 presents a comparison of the data for the solid and liquid phases which illustrates the strength of the mode at 69 meV. Boutin et al. conclude that this mode is an F–H–F bending frequency (ν_2) which, due to the strength of the hydrogen bond, persists into the liquid state. These data will be discussed again in Section 10.7.

Now consider total cross-section measurements for liquids composed of molecules having an internal rotation. In the thermal energy region measurements have been made for liquid CH_3SH and CH_3OH. The points obtained for liquid CH_3SH practically coincide with those for the gas (Borowski and Rzany, 1962) which is evidence that the barrier to hindered rotation does not change at the vapour–liquid transition in CH_3SH. The points obtained for liquid CH_3OH, on the other hand, lie higher than those for CH_3OH vapour. As the effect of association must be small (owing to the large effective mass of the CH_3OH molecule) one may interpret the difference obtained as being

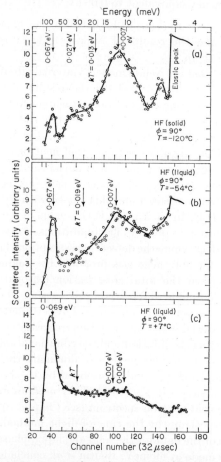

FIG. 10.14. Inelastic neutron spectra from the scattering of cold neutrons by HF (Boutin *et al.*, 1963). The lines through the experimental points are drawn by eye, and values of kT and energy levels are marked by arrows. Data on the solid is given at (a) while liquid data at two temperatures are given at (b) and (c).

caused by an increase of the hindered rotation frequency at the transition point. This is in agreement with the Raman spectroscopy experiments which suggest that the hindered rotation frequency changes from $\sim$300 cm^{-1} to $\sim$600 cm^{-1} at the vapour–liquid transition in CH_3OH.

More quantitative measurements concerning other liquids in which the CH_3 groups perform a hindered rotation were reported by Rush et al. (1962a). On the basis of the correlation between the slope of the curve of cross-section against neutron wavelength in the sub-thermal region, and the rotational barrier it was possible to evaluate the barrier height. The results for o-xylene (1 kcal/mole) and also for p-xylene, m-xylene, mesitylene, and toluene (0·1–0·4 kcal/mole) in general agree with thermodynamic measurements. More details about the method of Rush et al. (1962a) will be given in the Section 10.5 in connection with the problem of rotation of NH_4-ions in solids. The total cross-section for sub-thermal neutrons will yield more information about the hindered rotation problem than that for thermal neutrons, because the momentum transfer is much larger for thermal neutrons and consequently the averaging over a variety of motions is more complete.

There have been a number of double differential cross-section measurements on molecular liquids which have been discussed in Chapter 8, Sections 8.2–8.5. Of particular importance when considering molecular models are the frequency spectra for water (Figs. 8.7 and 8.8), alcohols (Fig. 8.17) and glycerol (Fig. 8.23). These spectra show clearly the hindered rotational motion in the liquid state, but unfortunately no detailed theoretical discussion of such results has yet been given. It should be pointed out that the shape of these frequency spectra suggests that the Krieger-Nelkin formalism cannot be applied to condensed systems, because the rotational energies are not small compared to the neutron energy and are not well separated from the vibrational levels. The discussion of liquid hydrogen (Section 8.3) is important to molecular theory because it is one case where theory and experiment may be compared closely. The general agreement reported in Section 8.3 is therefore gratifying. In this section we shall discuss the rotational spectrum of methane only.

Janik et al. (1964) performed experiments on the angular and energy distribution of neutrons scattered by liquid methane and liquid methyl iodide. In the experiments Be-filtered cold neutrons were used (the full cold neutron spectrum) and the energy analysis of scattered neutrons was carried out by the time of flight method. Figure 10.15 presents the scattered neutron intensity against neutron wavelength (for 90° scattering angle) for liquid methane together with the Krieger and Nelkin curve (compare the 90° data of Fig. 10.9). Although it is natural to assume that the CH_4 molecules rotate freely in the liquid, there is a significant disagreement between the theory and experiment. Similar disagreement was obtained for liquid methyl iodide. Also the angular dependence of $d^2\sigma/d\Omega dE$ for these two substances is in disagreement with the Krieger and Nelkin theory. Dasannacharya et al. (1965) obtained results similar to those of Janik et al. (1964). They compared their data with calculations based on the Rahman-Griffing model and concluded that the rotational states are broadened. Their calculated curve is included in Fig. 10.15. Also the comparison of the Griffing and K.N. curves demonstrates (as expected) that the K.N. model gives spectra which are broader than expected from a more realistic treatment of rotations. These facts apparently conflict with the results Rogalska (1962) obtained for liquid methane using the total cross-section technique. However the total cross-section, which is an integrated value, may obey the Krieger and Nelkin theory while the differential cross-section gives a significant difference.

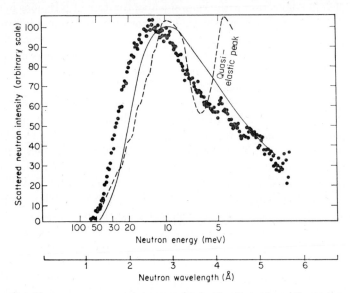

FIG. 10.15. Neutron spectrum after scattering by liquid methane. Scattering angle 90°. Temperature − 173°C. Solid curve: Krieger and Nelkin model (Janik *et al.*, 1964). Broken curve: Rahman-Griffing model (Dasannacharya *et al.*, 1965).

Otnes *et al.* (1965) have made a study of methane in gaseous, liquid and solid phases, using the same method as Janik *et al.* (1964). The results were compared with the Rahman-Griffing theory (equation (9.48)) for a gas and with a modified theory for liquid and solid methane. In the modified theory for liquid methane the translational part of the motion of the methane molecule was replaced by a continuous diffusion motion. The rotational and vibrational parts were unchanged. For solid methane the translational motion was neglected. The δ-function which represents each rotational level in this model was broadened by a Gaussian function representing the instrumental resolution. These results show that there are discrepancies between the Rahman-Griffing theory and the experiment for 35° scattering angle for gaseous methane, and between the modified theory and the results for 90°

and 35° scattering angles for liquid and solid methane. The observed inelastic
spectra are broader and more intense than the theoretical ones, in general
agreement with the earlier data. The possibility that proton-spin correlations
may contribute to the methane cross-section has been considered by Michael
(1965) and shown to be unimportant.

To conclude the discussion of this section we shall consider the neutron
scattering by polarized molecules of a "liquid crystal". In all existing
treatments of the scattering of neutrons by molecules, the final formulas are
obtained as a result of an averaging over molecular orientations. However,

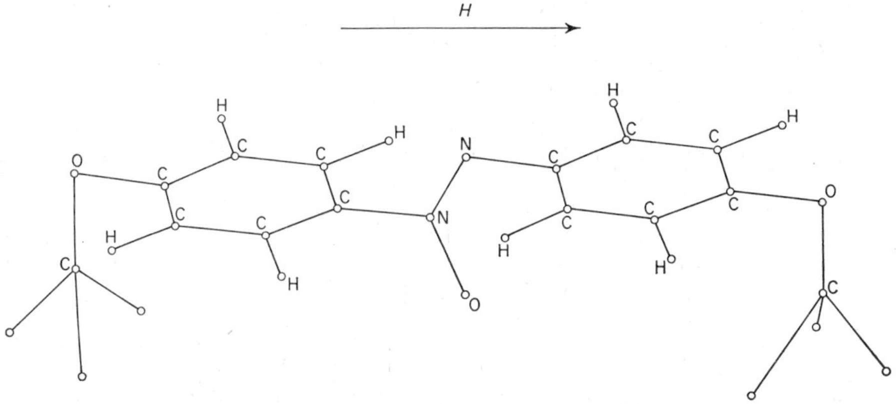

FIG. 10.16. Molecular structure of p-azoxyanisol.

in general, the molecular polarization affects the scattering cross-section.
It is difficult to find a substance in which the degree of ordering would be
large enough to show up this effect, but there is a group of suitable substances
known as liquid crystals. One of them is p-azoxyanisol; the molecular
structure of which is shown in Fig. 10.16. This material exists in a liquid-
crystalline phase in the temperature interval between the melting point
($\sim$119°C) and a temperature of $\sim$135°C. Above this temperature the substance exists in a normal-liquid phase. Due to a so-called diamagnetic anisotropy within the temperature limits of the liquid-crystal phase, the substance
is easily polarized in an external magnetic field and the degree of ordering
amounts to $\sim$70 %. When polarized the molecules of p-azoxyanisol have
their long axes parallel to the field.

Experiments on the scattering of neutrons by polarized and non-polarized
samples of p-azoxyanisol were made by Janik et $al.$ (1958, 1961b). Neutrons
were transmitted through a sample which was situated between the poles of
an electromagnet. The direction of the neutron beam was parallel to the
direction of the magnetic field (i.e. parallel to the direction of polarization in
the sample) and the neutrons passed through a slot in the poles. A difference

in neutron transmission was obtained when the sample was polarized ("field on" case) in comparison with the situation in the nonpolarized substance ("field off"). The effect was practically constant (for a given neutron energy) within the liquid-crystalline temperature interval, and disappeared above the transition point to the normal-liquid phase. This weak dependence of the effect on temperature corresponds to a similarly weak temperature dependence of the degree of ordering of molecules in p-azoxyanisol (Maier and Saupe, 1958, 1959).

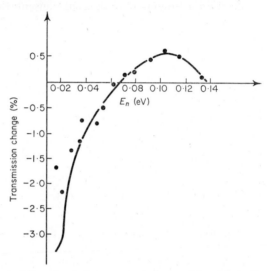

FIG. 10.17. Transmission change in p-azoxyanisol, caused by polarization, against neutron energy: a curve is drawn as the best fit to the experimental points. The difference between the curve and the points at the lowest energies represents an experimental correction.

On the other hand, the change of neutron transmission caused by polarization is a function of neutron energy. A temperature average (119–135°C) of the transmission change is shown in Fig. 10.17. The results may be semi-quantitatively explained by assuming that there exists a hindered rotation (torsional oscillation) of CH_3 groups around CO axes (which are nearly perpendicular to the long axes of the molecule) and a free rotation round the long axis of the molecule as a whole.

10.5 Metal Hydrides

In this and the following section we shall discuss only such effects as involve vibrations or rotations connected with the molecular structure of the solid body. One of the simplest examples is scattering by protons which may be considered as isotropic harmonic oscillators. As was discussed in Chapter 9

(Section 9.2), this is a problem studied by Fermi (1936). The theoretical total cross-section versus energy curve which he obtained is shown in Fig. 10.18 for an oscillator in its ground state. With increasing neutron energy the cross-section decreases monotonically from the value $4\sigma_H^{free}$ to σ_H^{free} at a neutron energy equal to the transition energy of the oscillator from its ground to the first excited state. This part of the curve corresponds to the elastic cross-section because, for a neutron energy smaller than hf, no energy exchange between the neutron and the scattering system is possible. At $E_0 = hf$ there is a local minimum of the cross-section; then follow successive minima for energies $E_0 = 2hf$, $3hf$, etc. The heights of the successive "Fermi hills" are

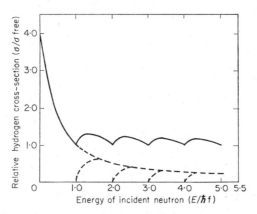

FIG. 10.18. Theoretically evaluated total neutron scattering cross-section of protons treated as isotropic harmonic oscillators (Fermi, 1936). The dotted line indicates individual contributions, while the solid line gives the total cross-section.

lower and lower so that for energies $E_0 \gg hf$ the cross-section for a free proton is obtained. In the energy region $E_0 > hf$ the cross-section is a superposition of an elastic and an inelastic part, where the inelastic part corresponds to the excitation of the higher energy states of the harmonic oscillator. This part becomes more and more important as the neutron energy increases.

The curve presented in Fig. 10.18 was obtained with the assumption that vibrating protons are bound to an infinite mass. This is equivalent to neglect of a Doppler effect caused by thermal motion of the environment of the proton. Calculations in which the Doppler effect is taken into account give two corrections as compared with the simple Fermi theory: (a) the cross-section value at $E_0 \to 0$ is not $4\sigma_H^{free}$ but increases to infinity, (b) "Fermi hills" are not separated by sharp minima at which the cross-section value is nearly σ_H^{free} but by more or less shallow minima of a shape which is dependent on the mass to which the oscillating proton is bound. This situation is shown in Fig. 10.19.

An experimental verification of the Fermi theory was not obtained until more than twenty years after its publication. This delay was caused by the lack of knowledge of the circumstances in which the proton may be treated as an isotropic harmonic oscillator. Experiments on the energy analysis of

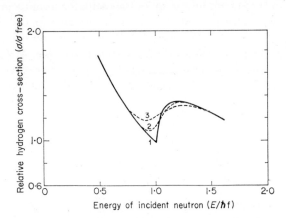

FIG. 10.19. The Fermi theory corrected for Doppler effect. Curve 1: the mass M to which the vibrating proton is bound is infinite. Curve 2: ZrH. Curve 3: MgH$_2$. (Whittemore and McReynolds, 1959.)

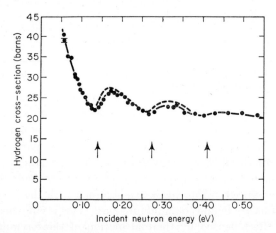

FIG. 10.20. Total neutron scattering cross-section of protons in a zirconium hydride sample. Experimental points of Whittemore and McReynolds (1959). The broken line denotes the places where a deviation from the Fermi theory occurs.

neutrons scattered from metal hydrides were carried out (Pelah *et al.*, 1957, Andresen *et al.*, 1957), and confirmed that the motion of the protons in many of these substances might be nearly that of isotropic harmonic oscillators (see Fig. 1.2(b)). This is equivalent to saying that, for a metal hydride crystal, there is an almost flat optic branch for which the protonic motion is dominant. Whittemore and McReynolds (1959) then performed total scattering cross-section measurements for protons in a zirconium hydride sample ($ZrH_{1.5}$). The results are shown in Fig. 10.20. Distinct "Fermi hills" are obtained which are in agreement with the Fermi theory corrected for the Doppler effect. Dotted lines denote those places in which there is a deviation from the theory. The deviations are probably caused by inaccuracy of the isotropic oscillator model (i.e. by deviations of the optic branch from a constant frequency); their smallness, however, suggests that this model is almost

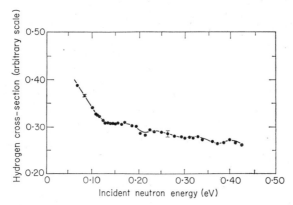

FIG. 10.21. Total neutron scattering cross-section of protons in magnesium hydride (Whittemore and McReynolds, 1959).

correct. From the energy value of the first minimum one may determine the energy hf of the oscillator. This is 0.130 ± 0.005 eV. Similar results were obtained for the case of yttrium hydride, where well defined "Fermi hills" were seen. Measurements for magnesium hydride (MgH_2) are presented in Fig. 10.21 and show that the Fermi model is, in this case, incorrect. This is expected because of the layer structure of magnesium hydride which causes anisotropy of the vibrations. As a result of the anisotropy there appear at least two frequencies of vibrations for protons in the crystal. Investigations of a similar kind were carried out by Bergsma and Goedkoop (1960, 1961) for palladium hydride and aluminium thorium hydride. The results for palladium hydride show an approximate applicability of the Fermi model, and the energy hf is in this case 0.06 eV; for $AlTh_2H_4$ the energy is 0.08 eV.

A measurement analogous to the total cross-section was made by Saunderson et al. (1962) who recorded the intensity at a 90° scattering angle as a function of the energy of the incident neutron beam. This result again shows a step (similar to Fig. 10.20) at the energy $E_0 = hf$, and is shown in Fig. 10.22. Parallel to the total cross-section measurements, an energy analysis of

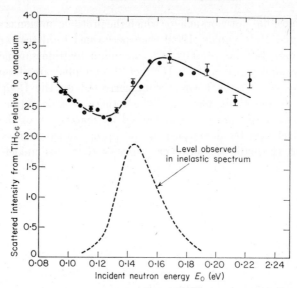

FIG. 10.22. Intensity scattered at 90° by $TiH_{0.6}$ as a function of neutron energy (Saunderson *et al.*, 1962). The lower part of the figure shows the spectrum found by Saunderson and Cocking (1963), and confirms that the increase in intensity occurs over the range of the optic mode.

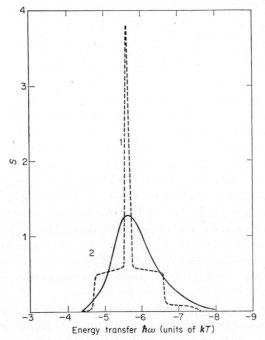

FIG. 10.23. Comparison of calculated spectrum (1) for a δ-function optic mode with the observed spectrum (2). (Saunderson and Cocking, 1963.)

scattered neutrons has been made for zirconium hydride, palladium hydride, aluminium thorium hydride, γ-titanium hydride and a few other hydrides. A single peak corresponding to $E = \hbar f$, or in some cases an additional peak corresponding to $E = 2\hbar f$, was observed (Pelah et al., 1957; Andresen et al., 1957; Woods et al., 1961; Bergsma and Goedkoop, 1961; Saunderson and Cocking, 1963). The zirconium hydride result was shown at Fig. 1.2(b). Some of the results show a broadening of the peak which cannot be attributed to the Doppler effect due to thermal motion of the lattice. This extra-broadening is due to a broad distribution of frequencies, and some remarks on this question have been made in Section 5.13. The calculations of Saunderson and Cocking (1963) for $TiH_{0.6}$ are shown in Fig. 10.23, and they confirm that the observed shape differs from the ideal single frequency model.

10.6 Ammonium Salts

Another example which may be discussed on the basis of a molecular model (in this case the hindered or free rotation of a certain molecular group), is provided by the experiments of Rush et al. (1960, 1961, 1962a and b) with crystals containing NH_4 ions. They measured cross-sections per proton in gaseous NH_3 and in polycrystalline NH_4I, NH_4Cl, NH_4Br, NH_4F, $(NH_4)_2CrO_4$, $(NH_4)_2Cr_2O_7$, NH_4CNS and NH_4ClO_4. The cross-section for gaseous ammonia has been discussed in Section 10.2 where the possibility of systematic errors was mentioned; however, because of the smallness of this possible error there is no uncertainty in the interpretation of the results of Rush et al. concerning the behaviour of NH_4 ions in crystals. The interpretation of these results is based on the fact that the total cross-section per proton as a function of neutron wavelength is, for very slow neutrons (5–12 Å), an almost straight line. A condition for obtaining this line is that the energy transfers are much greater than the incident neutron energy, and in terms of the scattering law (equation (1.34)) it is easy to show that its slope is given by

$$\text{slope (barns/Å)} = \frac{\sigma_b}{\pi\hbar}\sqrt{\frac{MkT}{2}} \int\limits_{-\infty}^{+\infty} \beta^{\frac{1}{2}} e^{-\beta/2} \tilde{S}(\alpha_1,\beta) \, d\beta \qquad (10.3)$$

$$\text{where } \alpha_1 = \frac{m\beta}{M}; \ \beta = \frac{\hbar\omega}{kT}.$$

The slope seems to be a simple function of the barrier for hindered rotation of the NH_4 ion in the crystal. Figure 10.24 shows a comparison of results obtained for some of these substances. From the similar values of the slope for NH_4I and NH_3 it may be concluded that the rotation of the NH_4 group in NH_4I is almost free. The entirely different shape of the curves for NH_4Cl,

17

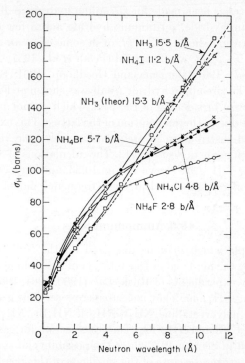

Fig. 10.24. Total neutron scattering cross-section of protons in NH$_3$ (gas), NH$_4$I, NH$_4$Cl, NH$_4$F, NH$_4$Br (Rush *et al.*, 1960). Figures show the slopes of corresponding curves.

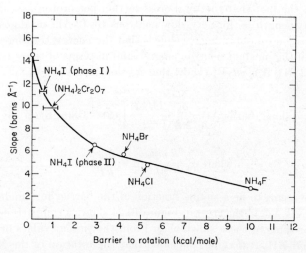

Fig. 10.25. Slope against barrier height calibration curve (Rush *et al.*, 1962a).

NH_4Br, and NH_4F suggests a hindrance of the rotation of the ammonium ion in these cases.

A comparison of these results with those obtained for other ammonium compounds gives similar slopes for NH_4Br, $(NH_4)_2CrO_4$ and NH_4CNS from which a similarity of hydrogen bond strengths, rotational barriers and torsional frequencies (~300 cm^{-1}) may be expected. The slope for NH_4ClO_4, on the other hand, is quite close to that for NH_3 gas giving evidence of almost free rotation of NH_4 ion in this crystal; the freedom of rotation appears even greater in NH_4ClO_4 than in NH_4I. Finally a comparison between the cross-section curves for $(NH_4)_2CrO_4$ and $(NH_4)Cr_2O_7$ indicated a much greater freedom of rotation for dichromate than for the chromate. The results are in good agreement with those obtained by the proton magnetic resonance method.

The correlation between the slopes and the barriers to rotation is shown in Fig. 10.25. Barrier heights shown in this figure were obtained from infra-red and nuclear magnetic resonance measurements, and the barrier for gaseous NH_3 was assumed to be zero. This curve may be treated as the calibration curve for other substances containing an ammonium group and, in view of the similarity of rotational masses of ammonium and methyl groups, perhaps also for substances in which the CH_3 group performs a hindered rotation. On the basis of this calibration curve one may derive a barrier of about 4 kcal/mole for both $(NH_4)_2CrO_4$ and NH_4CNS, and of only 0·1–0·2 kcal/mole for NH_4ClO_4. Barriers to rotation were estimated for $NH_4PF_6 \sim 0·2$ kcal/mole, for $(NH_4)_2S_2O_8 \sim 1$ kcal/mole and for $NH_4SO_3F \sim 1$ kcal/mole (Rush et al., 1962b). The same calibration curve applied to CH_3-groups led to the barrier values for some liquid methylobenzenes which were given in Section 10.4.

Measurements of the energy distributions of neutrons scattered by solid ammonium halides bring further information concerning the behaviour of the ammonium radical. The first results were obtained by Woods et al. (1961) applying the beryllium detector method (Chapter 3) and gave information on the energy loss of neutrons scattered by NH_4Cl. They observed peaks which may be interpreted as follows: one at 0·023 eV is probably connected with the optical vibration of the NH_4 radical against the Cl atom; one at 0·046 eV corresponds to the hindered rotation of the NH_4 ion; further peaks at 0·070 eV, 0·094 eV, 0·116 eV, 0·138 eV and 0·178 eV may be interpreted as combination bands of the 0·023 and 0·049 peaks and the bending mode of the NH_4 radical (0·178 eV). Most of the interest in the ammonium halides centres around the rotational motion of the ammonium radical, which in ammonium chloride has an energy of about 0·048 eV at 90°K. The width of the peak corresponding to this motion is very small at low temperatures but increases with increasing temperature. The peak intensity also changes with

17*

temperature and the curve showing this effect usually has a change in slope at the temperature of transition from hindered to free rotation.

An extensive study of ammonium halides using the beryllium detector method was made by Mikke and Kroh (1963) and by Venkataraman *et al.* (1963). In these experiments, the temperature dependence of the peaks was studied with special interest being paid to the λ transition region. In all samples (except in NH_4I at room temperature as seen in Fig. 10.26) well defined peaks corresponding to the hindered rotation of the NH_4 ion were obtained, and also other peaks similar to those reported for NH_4Cl by

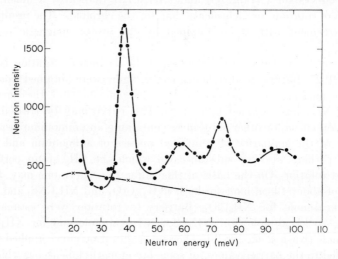

FIG. 10.26. Energy analysis for neutrons scattered by solid NH_4I (Mikke and Kroh, 1963). ●, Measurements at $-150°C$; ×, measurements at room temperature (beryllium detector method).

Woods *et al.* (1961). The hindered rotation peaks exist in β, γ and δ phases in agreement with the assumption that a transition from hindered to free rotation of the NH_4 ion is not responsible for λ points between these phases. In the case of NH_4I, however (which is the only substance existing in α phase at room temperature) the hindered rotation peak was not seen at $+20°C$, although this peak is quite distinct at $-20°C$ and at $-65°C$. This result may correspond to a transition from hindered to free rotation at the λ point between β- and α- phases for NH_4I. It remains an open question whether the NH_4 ion in ammonium iodide really rotates in the α-phase or whether the rotation (though not a torsional oscillation) is not completely free. Palevsky (1962) suggests that the rotation is not free on the basis of his cold neutron results: he compared the energy distribution of scattered neutrons with that calculated from the Krieger and Nelkin model applied to a freely rotating NH_4 ion and a significant disagreement was found. The results for NH_4Br (Palevsky, 1962) are, qualitatively, entirely different from those obtained for NH_4I and show a distict peak interpreted as arising from the torsional oscillation of the NH_4 group (Fig. 10.27).

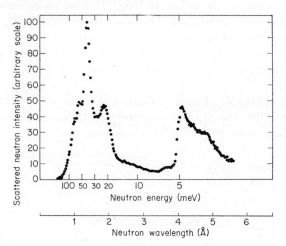

FIG. 10.27. Neutron spectrum after scattering by room temperature NH_4Br, scattering angle 90° (Palevsky, 1962). The full beryllium filtered cold neutron spectrum was used here, and it has roughly the shape of the right-hand portion of the curve.

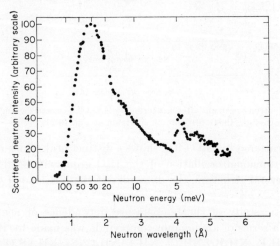

FIG. 10.28. Neutron spectrum after scattering by NH_4ClO_4, scattering angle 90°, room temperature (Janik et al., 1964). See note on spectrum at Fig. 10.27.

Broad distributions of scattered neutrons similar to that for NH_4I were obtained by Brajovic et al. (1963) and by Janik et al. (1964) for a number of

materials containing an NH_4 group. Figure 10.28 presents a typical example
of such a broad distribution obtained for NH_4ClO_4. Janik, J. M. *et al.* (1965)
measured the temperature dependence of neutron spectra for NH_4ClO_4 by
the Be-filter detector method and in this case they obtained a broad distribution even at temperatures as low as 78°K. This led to the conclusion that
the rotational freedom of NH_4 ion is especially large in NH_4ClO_4. It is worthwhile observing that broad distributions were obtained for those compounds
for which the total cross-sections measured by Rush, Taylor and Havens
(1960, 1961, 1962) had large slopes, which was interpreted as arising from
free rotation.

The result for NH_4ClO_4 (Fig. 10.28) should be compared with that obtained
by Janik *et al.* (1964) for $H_3O.ClO_4$ in view of the identity of crystal lattices
of the two compounds. Figure 10.29, which presents the energy distribution

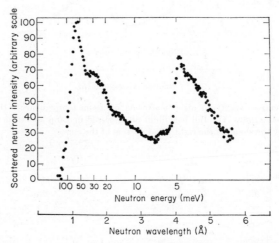

FIG. 10.29. Neutron spectrum after scattering by $H_3O.ClO_4$, scattering angle = 90°, room
temperature (Janik *et al.*, 1964). See note on spectrum at Fig. 10.27.

of neutrons scattered by $H_3O.ClO_4$, shows a distinct peak which may be attributed to the torsional oscillation of the H_3O group. Thus, in spite of the
identity of crystal structure, the dynamics of the NH_4 and H_3O groups are
different.

A systematic study of the temperature dependence of neutron spectra
obtained for a series of ammonium compounds was made by Bajorek *et al.*
(1965) for NH_4F, NH_4Br, NH_4Cl, NH_4I, NH_4CNS, $(NH_4)_2S_2O_8$, $(NH_4)_2SO_4$,
$(NH_4)_2CO_3$, and $(NH_4)_2(COO)_2$. They used a pulsed reactor source and a beryllium filter detector (Chapter 3). As a rule, they obtained for these substances
hindered rotation peaks at sufficiently low temperatures, whereas at sufficiently high temperatures neutron spectra had the form of a broad distribution

suggesting a free rotation of NH_4 groups. The position of peaks and the interpretation for ammonium halides is in agreement with the previous data described above.

Rush and Taylor (1965) studied three ferroelectric salts containing an ammonium ion: NH_4HSO_4, $(NH_4)_2SO_4$ and $(NH_4)_2BeF_4$. Their results indicated that the ferroelectric transitions cannot be explained by changes of rotational freedom.

When discussing ammonium compounds the anharmonicity of the torsional oscillation should be stressed. Data on this question was obtained by Venkataraman et al. (1964) for NH_4Cl. By applying the window filter method (Chapter 3) these authors (see Fig. 3.15) observed near the main torsional vibration peak (351 cm^{-1}), a second peak at 307 cm^{-1}. They interpret the main peak as being caused by the transition from the ground to the first excited torsional state whereas the satellite is believed to be caused by a transition from the first to the second level excited. The satellite peak does not appear at temperatures as low as 135°K, which supports this interpretation.

Measurements were made by Janik et al. (1964) for CH_3 groups in solid, liquid-crystalline and liquid p-azoxyanisol. A distinct torsional oscillation peak was obtained for the solid substance, whereas a broader distribution of scattered neutrons occurred for both liquid-crystalline and liquid substances. These distributions are, however, narrower than those obtained for NH_4I or NH_4ClO_4 so that it is possible that the rotation of CH_3-groups is hindered and even degenerates into a torsional oscillation for these phases.

10.7 Various Hydrogenous Solids

Solid methane was investigated by Stiller and Hautecler (1963) and also by Harker and Brugger (1965). These authors compared data on liquid and solid methane to theoretical calculations in order to decide whether the rotations were free. Stiller and Hautecler concluded that there was free rotation in the liquid but hindered in the solid, while Harker and Brugger concluded that free rotation occurred in both states. However, the latter workers found the data for both states differed from the Rahman-Griffing model calculations for free rotation and attributed the difference to a vibrational mode at 17 meV (see remarks on this subject in Sections 8.4 and 10.4).

Neutron scattering investigations were made for HF, HCl, HBr, KHF_2, KH_2F_3, and NaH_2F_3 by Boutin et al. (1963) and by Boutin and Safford (1965). In all these substances there is a similarity in the structure of F–H–F (or other halide) units which form long zigzag hydrogen bond chains. These authors observed strong peaks at certain frequencies in each case, which they interpreted as being a hydrogen frequency (e.g. Fig. 10.14). The frequency data on fluorides were plotted as function of F–F distance and compared to similar data on hydrogen bonded oxygen containing compounds. Their results are shown at Fig. 10.30 compared to the theory of Reid (1959). The agreement between the several results is striking.

K_2PO_4, K_2HPO_4 and KH_2PO_4 were studied by Pelah et al. (1959, 1964) and by Palevsky et al. (1963). The former authors compared results obtained by infra-red absorption, Raman scattering and neutron inelastic scattering. This is a worthwhile comparison because the selection rules are different for the different techniques and so by combining the results more insight can be gained into the problem. In the case of KH_2PO_4 they showed the existence of

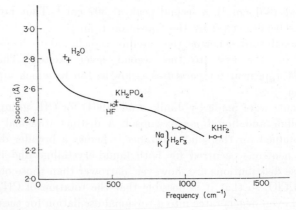

FIG. 10.30. Variation of the low frequency vibration of the hydrogen bond with O—H···O or F—H···F spacing. The theory of Reid (1959) for oxygen compounds is shown by the solid line, while experimental points for oxygen compounds are shown + and fluorine compounds ○ (Boutin et al., 1963).

very broad low energy hydrogen modes, which fact was used to support the idea that in the non-ferroelectric phase of this crystal there exists a slightly asymmetrical double minimum potential well where the protons tunnel quantum-mechanically. Below the ferroelectric transition point it is believed that the proton potential well becomes extremely asymmetric and the proton sticks to an oxygen in an orderly manner.

Low frequency motions of H_2O molecules in crystals (i.e. water of crystallization and absorbed molecules) were studied by Boutin et. al. (1964). The object of these measurements was to examine torsional and rotational motions of the H_2O molecule, the distribution of water molecules among various lattice sites and the effect of its environment on the translational modes of the H_2O molecule. Due to the somewhat restricted experimental data obtained, the conclusions were not definitive, but serve to indicate the direction for future experiments.

An interesting type of molecular compound, the so-called globular compound, has been studied by Becka (1963). He has carried out experiments on cyclohexane, 2,2-dimethylbutane, and 1,4-diazobicyclo-(2,2,2)-octane (DABCO). All of these materials undergo a transition from a low temperature ordered phase to a high temperature disordered phase. The neutron distributions scattered from cyclohexane and 2,2-dimethylbutane in the low temperature phase show broad, but reasonably well defined, inelastic peaks, which do not appear in the scattering from the high temperature phase. The experiments lead to the conclusion that these solids are dynamically disordered in the high temperature phase. In addition, changes in the elastic peaks have been attributed to the existence of "quasi-free rotation" of the constituent molecules. The scattering from DABCO shows no such behaviour, the patterns at 90°K and 360°K being nearly identical.

In addition to the substances discussed above experiments have also been performed on other hydrogeneous materials (e.g. hexamethylenetetramine, Becka, 1962; metaphosphoric acid, Egelstaff, 1965; crystalline polyethylene, Boutin et al., 1965)) in an effort to understand the role of the hydrogen vibrations in determining many properties, particularly where phase transitions are involved.

10.8 Experiments with Non-hydrogenous Molecules

The experimental material concerning neutron scattering by molecules which do not contain hydrogen is rather poor. The molecules investigated by the total cross-section method include N_2 and O_2 (Melkonian, 1949) and CF_4, CO_2 and N_2O (Fermi and Marshall, 1947). All these molecules show a large interference effect in the scattering, since O, N and C are monoisotopic elements composed of zero spin nuclei. Because of the interference the cross-section of the molecule is not simply the sum of the cross-sections of the constituent nuclei but it contains terms of the type $4\pi \sum_{\nu \neq \nu'} b_\nu b_{\nu'}$ where b_ν is the coherent scattering length of the νth nucleus. It is obvious that a correct theoretical interpretation of the experimental cross-sections must contain the effects of translation, rotation, vibration, interference, and, last but not least, the effects due to the correlation of spins of the nuclei in the molecule and possibly paramagnetic scattering of neutrons (for instance in the case of the O_2-molecule).

Theory and experiment have been compared for the total scattering cross-sections of O_2 and N_2. Theoretical calculations were made by Løvseth (1962) (see Section 9.5). For the O_2 molecule the contribution of paramagnetic scattering was calculated by Kleiner (1955). Experiments were made by Melkonian (1949) and by Palevsky and Eisberg (1955). Figures 10.31 and 10.32 show that there is good agreement between experiment and theory.

Angular distributions of neutrons scattered by non-hydrogeneous molecules were measured for gaseous, D_2 (Hurst and Alcock, 1951); O_2,CO_2 (Alcock and Hurst, 1949); N_2 and CF_4 (Alcock and Hurst, 1951). In all cases

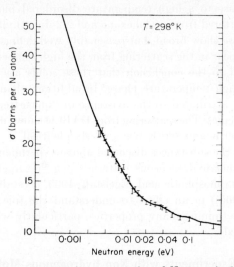

FIG. 10.31. Total neutron scattering cross-section of N atoms in N_2 molecules against neutron energy. Curve: calculation of Løvseth (1962). I—Experimental values of Melkonian (1949).

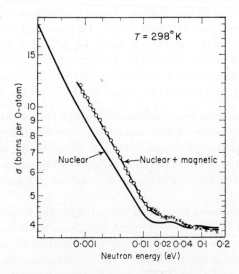

FIG. 10.32. Total neutron scattering cross-section of O atoms in O_2 molecules against neutron energy (Løvseth, 1962). $\bigcirc$, Palevsky and Eisberg (1955); $\times$, Melkonian (1949).

the incident neutron energy was 0·072 eV, and for a theoretical interpretation it is again necessary to take the interference into account. The classical treatment of rotation and the neglect of vibrational effects are reasonable

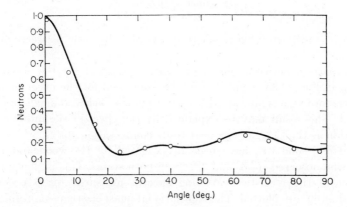

FIG. 10.33. The angular distribution of neutrons scattered by CF_4 molecules (Alcock and Hurst, 1951). The solid line corresponds to equation (10.4).

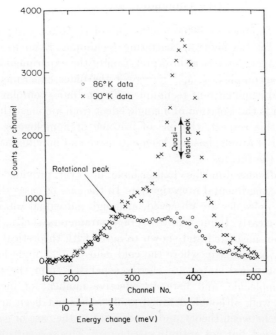

FIG. 10.34. Energy distribution of neutrons scattered by solid and liquid CF_4. The rotational peak is seen in both states (Haywood and Baston, 1965).

assumptions. On the basis of formula (9.38c), the following result is obtained for the intensity of the coherently scattered neutrons from a molecule:

$$\frac{d\sigma}{d\Omega} = \text{const.} \sum_{\nu'} b_\nu b_{\nu'} \frac{\sin x_{\nu\nu'}}{x_{\nu\nu'}} \qquad (10.4)$$

where $x_{\nu\nu'} = (2k_0 \sin \theta/2)d_{\nu\nu'}$, where $d_{\nu\nu'}$ is the distance between nuclei ν and ν'.

A comparison between the theory and experiment for the gaseous CF_4 is shown in Fig. 10.33. Similar results are obtained for the other molecules. However, for CO_2 a significant deviation from the theory at small angles was obtained. This result may be explained by the effect of the intermolecular interaction as the CO_2 gas was near to its condensation state.

Liquid and solid CF_4 have been investigated by Haywood and Baston (1965), who observed rotational effects in both states. This is shown in Fig. 10.34 where the inelastic scattering spectra measured for 6 Å neutrons scattered at 60° are plotted. The translational quasi-elastic peak in the liquid state is quite marked.

10.9 Concluding Discussion

The study of molecular behaviour is one of the most complex problems being tackled by the neutron scattering technique. Even for the simpler molecules a proper theoretical interpretation of the experimental results has not yet been accomplished, and moreover the older experiments could be much improved using current techniques. For the more complex molecules a major problem is the isolation of a single effect from amongst the competing processes. In this respect, the use of isotopic or homologous substitution (e.g. D or F for H atoms) has not been extensive and may find a much wider application in the future.

The results discussed in this chapter have, however, provided examples of most types of experimental investigation. In the case of gases the rotational states for the molecules are observed, although individual rotational states cannot be seen clearly. In most cases average parameters, such as the effective mass, have been measured and shown to agree with theoretical predictions. In some cases, particularly where the cold neutron technique has been employed, the rotational states are clearly separated from the translational modes of the molecule, and here an effective moment of inertia can be determined as well, although detailed analysis has not been accomplished. The agreement between theory and experiment in the case of gaseous molecules is fairly good, but not entirely satisfactory. This is surprising because it should be possible to calculate the neutron scattering cross-sections for a gas from first principles and without much uncertainty. Thus further work is needed to narrow down the discrepancies between the theory and experiment.

In the case of liquids the interaction between the different modes seems to have been observed. The simple models which are applicable to gaseous molecules do not explain the liquid results satisfactorily, partly because the rotational states are hindered and because of the coupling between rotational and vibrational states, but also because of the complicated translational motions which occur in a liquid. The studies on liquid crystals were of particular interest and indicated scope for further work.

In the case of solids the main fields of study so far have concerned metal hydrides and ammonium salts. In both areas there is a reasonable understanding of the experimental results, and a substantial amount of new information concerning these materials has been uncovered, although some of the experiments have been limited in scope due to technical difficulties. So far such work has uncovered only a part of a large field of physical chemistry which may be studied by neutron scattering methods. One area which was examined in a few experiments is the ferroelectric transition. This and other phase transitions warrant considerable further exploration, and here the work on molecules overlaps the dispersion law experiments which were discussed in Chapter 5.

The difficulties in interpreting coherent scattering for systems other than single crystals, were discussed in Chapter 8. These difficulties have inhibited experimental studies of non-hydrogenous molecular systems. The work reported in Section 10.8 indicates the status of this region, and one might expect more extensive programmes as the theory develops.

References

Alcock, N. F. and Hurst, D. G. (1949). *Phys. Rev.* **75**, 1609.

Alcock, N. F. and Hurst, D. G. (1951). *Phys. Rev.* **83**, 1100.

Andresen, A. F., McReynolds, A. W., Nelkin, M. S., Rosenbluth, M. N. and Whittemore, W. L. (1957). *Phys. Rev.* **108**, 1092.

Bajorik, A., Machekhina, T. A. and Parliński, K. (1965). *In* "Inelastic Scattering of Neutrons", Vol. II, p. 355. IAEA, Vienna.

Bally, D., Tarina, V. and Todireanu, S. (1963). *In* "Inelastic Scattering of Neutrons in Solids and Liquids", Vol. I, p. 451. IAEA, Vienna.

Becka, L. N. (1962). *J. chem. Phys.* **37**, 341.

Becka, L. N. (1963). *J. chem. Phys.* **38**, 1685.

Bergsma, J. and Goedkoop, J. A. (1960). *Physica* **26**, 744.

Bergsma, J. and Goedkoop, J. A. (1961). *In* "Inelastic Scattering of Neutrons in Solids and Liquids", p. 501. IAEA, Vienna.

Borowski, F. and Rzany, H. (1962). Private communication.

Boutin, H., Safford, G. J. and Brajovic, V. (1963). *J. chem. Phys.* **39**, 3135.

494   J. A. JANIK AND A. KOWALSKA

Boutin, H., Safford, G. J. and Danner, H. R. (1964). *J. chem. Phys.* **40**, 2670.
Boutin, H. and Safford, G. J. (1965). *In* "Inelastic Scattering of Neutrons", Vol II, p. 393. IAEA, Vienna.
Boutin, H., Prask, H., Trevino, S. F. and Danner, H. R. (1965). *In* "Inelastic Scattering of Neutrons", Vol. II, p. 407. IAEA, Vienna.
Brajovic, V., Boutin, H., Safford, G. J. and Palevsky, H. (1963). *J. Phys. Chem. Solids* **24**, 617.
Brimberg, S. (1956). Thesis, Stockholm.
Brugger, R. M., Rainey, V. and McMurray, H. (1964). *Phys. Rev.* **136**, A106.
Budzanowski, A., Grotowski, K., Janik, J. A., Kolos, W., Maniawski, F., Rzany, H., Shkatula, A. and Wanic, A. (1957). *Acta Phys. Polonica* **16**, 335.
Carrol, H. (1941). *Phys. Rev.* **60**, 702.
Czerlunczakiewicz, B. and Kowalska, A. (1964). *Acta. Phys. Polonica* **25**, 141.
Dasannacharya, B. A., Venkataraman, G. and Usha Deniz, K. (1965). *In* "Inelastic Scattering of Neutrons", Vol II, p. 157. IAEA, Vienna.
Egelstaff, P. A., Haywood, B. C. and Thorson, I. M. (1963). *In* "Inelastic Scattering of Neutrons in Solids and Liquids", Vol. I, p. 343. IAEA, Vienna.
Egelstaff, P. A. (1965). Physics of Non-Crystalline Solids, ed. by J. A. Prins, p. 127. North Holland Publ. Co., Amsterdam.
Fermi, E. (1936). *Ric. Scient.* **7**, 13.
Fermi, E. and Marshall, L. (1947). *Phys. Rev.* **71**, 666.
Gilbert, A. (1946). *Helv. phys. Acta* **19**, 285.
Goldman, D. T. and Federighi, F. D. (1963). *In* "Inelastic Scattering of Neutrons in Solids and Liquids", Vol. I, p. 389. IAEA, Vienna.
Goryunov, A. F. (1957). *J. nucl. Energy* **4**, 109.
Griffing, G. W. (1961). *Phys. Rev.* **124**, 1489.
Griffing, G. W. (1963). *In* "Inelastic Scattering of Neutrons in Solids and Liquids", Vol. I, p. 435. IAEA, Vienna.
Harker Y. D. and Brugger R. M. (1965). *J. Chem. Phys.* **42**, 275.
Haywood, B. C. and Baston, A. H. (1965). To be published.
Heinloth, K. (1961). *Z. Phys.* **163**, 218.
Hurst, D. G. and Alcock, N. F. (1951). *Canad. J. Phys.* **29**, 36.
Janik, J. A. (1951). *Acta Phys. Polonica* **11**, 146.
Janik, J. A. (1953). *Acta Phys. Polonica* **12**, 45.
Janik, J. A. (1954). *Acta Phys. Polonica* **13**, 167.
Janik, J. A., Krasnicki, S. and Murasik, A. (1958). *Acta Phys. Polonica* **17**, 483.
Janik, J. A., Janik, J., and Wanic, A. (1960). *Physica* **26**, 449.
Janik, J. A., Janik, J., Maniawski, F., Rzany, H., Shkatula, A., Sciesinski, J. and Wanic A. (1961a). *In* "Inelastic Scattering of Neutrons in Solids and Liquids", p. 297. IAEA, Vienna.
Janik, J. A., Krasnicki, S. and Murasik, A. (1961b). *In* "Inelastic Scattering of Neutrons in Solids and Liquids", p. 293. IAEA, Vienna.
Janik, J. A., Janik, J. M., Mellor, J. and Palevsky, H. (1964). *J. Phys. Chem. Solids* **25**, 1091.
Janik, J. M., Janik, J. A., Bajorik, A. and Parliński, K. (1965). *Phys. Stat. Solidi*, *9*, 905.
Khubchandani, P. G. and Rahman, A. (1960). *J. nucl. Energy* A**11**, 89.
Kilb, R. W. (1955). *J. chem. Phys.* **23**, 1736.
Kleiner, W. H. (1955). *Phys. Rev.* **97**, 411.
Kojima, T. and Nishikawa, T. (1957). *J. phys. Soc. Japan* **12**, 680.
Kolos, W. (1954). *Bull. Acad. Polon. Sci.* III **2**(59), 427.

Kosaly, G. and Solt, G. (1963). *Phys. Letters* **6**, 51.

Kosaly, G. and Solt, G. (1964). Private communication.

Krieger, T. J., and Nelkin, M. S. (1957). *Phys. Rev.* **106**, 290.

Løvseth, J. (1962). *Phys. Norveg.* **1**, 127.

Maier, W. and Saupe, A. (1958). *Z. Naturf.* **13a**, 564.

Maier, W. and Saupe, A. (1959). *Z. Naturf.* **14a**, 882.

Melkonian, E. (1949). *Phys. Rev.* **76**, 1750.

Messiah, A. M. L. (1951). *Phys. Rev.* **84**, 204.

Michael, P. (1965). *Phys. Rev.* **138A**, 692.

Mikke, K. (1961). *In* "Inelastic Scattering of Neutrons in Solids and Liquids", p. 351. IAEA, Vienna.

Mikke, K. and Kroh, A. (1963). *In* "Inelastic Scattering of Neutrons in Solids and Liquids", Vol. II, p. 237. IAEA, Vienna.

Nelkin, M. S. (1960). *Phys. Rev.* **119**, 741.

Otnes, K. *et al.* (1965). Private communication.

Palevsky, H. and Eisberg, R. M. (1955). *Phys. Rev.* **98**, 482.

Palevsky, H. (1962). *J. phys. Soc. Japan* **17**, Suppl. B-II, 367.

Palevsky, H., Otnes, K. and Wakuta, Y. (1963). *In* "Inelastic Scattering of Neutrons in Solids and Liquids", Vol. II, p. 273. IAEA, Vienna.

Pelah, I., Eisenhauer, C. M., Hughes, D. J. and Palevsky, H. (1957). *Phys. Rev.* **108**, 1091.

Pelah, I., Lefkovitz, I., Kley, W. and Tunkelo, E. (1959). *Phys. Rev. Letters* **2**, 94.

Pelah, I., Wiener, E. and Imry, J. (1964). *In* "Inelastic Scattering of Neutrons", Vol. II, p. 325. IAEA, Vienna.

Randolph, P. D., Brugger, R. M., Strong, K. A. and Schmunk, R. E. (1961). *Phys. Rev.* **124**, 460.

Reid, C. (1959). *J. chem. Phys.* **30**, 182.

Rogalska, Z. (1962). *Physica* **29**, 491.

Rush, J. J., Taylor, T. I. and Havens, W. W. (1960). *Phys. Rev. Letters* **5**, 507.

Rush, J. J., Taylor, T. I. and Havens, W. W. (1961). *J. chem. Phys.* **35**, 2265.

Rush, J. J., Taylor, T. I. and Havens, W. W. (1962a). *J. chem. Phys.* **37**, 234.

Rush, J. J., Safford, G. J., Taylor, T. I., and Havens, W. W. (1962b). *Nucl. Sci. Engng* **14**, 339.

Rush, J. J. and Taylor, T. I. (1965). *In* "Inelastic Scattering of Neutrons", Vol. II, p. 333. IAEA, Vienna.

Ryskina, S. J. (1948). *Zh. Fiz. Khim.* **22**, 25.

Rzany, H. and Sciesinski, J. (1963). *Physica* **29**, 488.

Sachs, R. G. and Teller, E. (1941). *Phys. Rev.* **60**, 18.

Saunderson, D. H. and Cocking, S. J. (1963). *In* "Inelastic Scattering of Neutrons in Solids and Liquids", Vol. II, p. 265. IAEA, Vienna.

Saunderson, D. H., Rainey, V. S., Booty, B. A. and Egelstaff, P. A. (1962). Unpublished.

Schofield, P. (1963). *In* "Inelastic Scattering of Neutrons in Solids and Liquids", Vol. I, p. 410. IAEA, Vienna.

Solimene, N. and Dailey, B. P. (1955). *J. chem. Phys.* **23**, 124.

Stiller, H. and Hautecler, S. (1963). *In* "Inelastic Scattering of Neutrons in Solids and Liquids", Vol. II, p. 281. IAEA, Vienna.

Strong, K. A., Marshall, G. D., Brugger, R. M. and Randolph, P. D. (1962). *Phys. Rev.* **125**, 933.

Strong, K. A., Harker, Y. D. and Brugger, R. M. (1965). *J. chem. Phys.* **42**, 1568.

Tubbs, N., Sagan, U., Rzany, H., Janik, J. and Janik, J. A. (1962). *Acta Phys. Polonica* **22**, 517.

Venkataraman, G., Usha Deniz, K., Iyengar, P. K., and Vijayaraghavan, P. R. (1963). *In* "Inelastic Scattering of Neutrons in Solids and Liquids", Vol. II, p. 253. IAEA, Vienna.

Venkataraman, G., Usha Deniz, K., Iyengar, P. K., Vijayaraghavan, P. R. and Roy, A. P. (1964). *Solid State Commun.* **2**, 17.

Volkin, H. C. (1959). *Phys. Rev.* **113**, 866.

Wanic, A. (1959). *Acta Phys. Polonica* **18**, 255.

Webb, F. J. (1963). *In* "Inelastic Scattering of Neutrons in Solids and Liquids", Vol. I, p. 457. IAEA, Vienna.

Whittemore, W. L. and McReynolds, A. W. (1959). *Phys. Rev.* **113**, 806.

Whittemore, W. L. and McReynolds, A. W. (1961). *In* "Inelastic Scattering of Neutrons in Solids and Liquids", p. 511. IAEA, Vienna.

Woods, A. D. B., Brockhouse, B. N., Sakamoto, M. and Sinclair, R. N. (1961). *In* "Inelastic Scattering of Neutrons in Solids and Liquids", p. 487. IAEA, Vienna.

Zemach, A. C. and Glauber, R. J. (1956). *Phys. Rev.* **101**, 118, 129.

Author Index

Numbers in italics are the pages on which the references are listed.

A

Abrahams, S. C., 119, *138*, *139*
Aamodt, R., 303, *342*
Abson, W., 176, *191*
Alcock, N. F., 461, 490, 491, *493*, *494*
Alder, B. J., 310, 318, *344*, *345*
Alexander, T. K., 70, 76, 92, *94*, 156, *191*
Allen, W. D., 175, *191*
Alnatt, A. R., 309, *342*, *345*
Ambegaokar, V., 239, *244*, 306, 308, *342*
Anderson, D. G., 185, *191*
Anderson, H. L., 127, *138*
Andrade, E. N. da C., 313, *342*
Andresen, A. F., 478, 481, *493*
Anselm, A. A., 437, *450*
Antal, J. J., 213, 214, *244*
Antonini, M., 214, 215, *244*, 409, *409*
Arase, T., 200, 203, 204, 205, 239, 242, *244*
Arnold, J. L., 117, *140*
Asami, T., 113, *139*
Ascarelli, P., 117, *138*, 407, 409, *409*
Avril, M., 92, *95*

B

Bacon, G. E., 21, *48*, 98, 99, 100, 101, 102, 112, 113, *138*, 257, *288*
Bajorik, A., 89, *94*, 137, *138*, 152, *191*, 365, *409*, 486, *493*, *494*
Bally, D., 462, *493*
Bardeen, J., 201, *244*
Barker, J. A., 309, 312, 316, *342*
Barrett, C. S., 106, *138*
Baston, A. H., 107, *139*, 160, *191*, 372, *410*, 491, 492, *494*
Baym, G., 239, *244*, 306, *342*
Becka, L. N., 217, 225, 238, *244*, 254, *289*, 489, *493*
Becker, M., 313, *343*
Bednarski, S., 105, *139*
Beecroft, R. I., 312, *342*
Bell, R. O., 235, *247*

Bendel, F., 314, *344*
Bendt, P. J., 117, *140*, 259, *288*
Bergere, R., 153, *191*
Bergsma, J., 238, *244*, 297, *343*, 387, *409*, 479, 481, *493*
Bernard, W., 302, *342*
Bett, K. E., 312, *342*
Birgeneau, R. J., 206, *244*
Blinowski, K., 122, *138*, 213, 214, *247*, 265, 266, 267, 271, 273, 283, 284, 286, *290*
Bloch, M., 272, 274, *288*, *290*
Blokhin, G. E., 151, 152, *191*
Blume, M., 34, 35, 37, *48*
Boggs, E. M., 310, *344*
Bollinger, L. M., 93, *96*, 185, 186, 189, 190, *191*
Bondarenko, I. L., 89, *94*, 152, 156, *191*
Booty, B., 479, 480, *495*
Borgonovi, G., 213, 214, 215, *244*, 404, *410*
Born, M., 195, 224, 226, 229, 240, *244*, 310, *342*
Borowski, F., 458, 471, *493*
Bouckaert, L. P., 196, *244*
Boutin, H., 471, 472, 487, 488, 489, *493*, *494*
Boyle, A. J., 306, *342*
Bowers, R., 208, 209, 242, *248*
Brajovic, V., 471, 472, 485, 487, 488, *493*, *494*
Breton, C., 112, *138*
Brimberg, S., 437, 438, *450*, 459, *494*
Brockhouse, B. N., 21, *48*, 56, 85, *94*, *96*, 98, 112, 114, 120, 121, 122, 123, 126, 127, 131, 132, 137, *138*, *139*, *140*, 200, 201, 203, 204, 205, 208, 209, 210, 211, 215, 216, 217, 219, 221, 223, 224, 225, 226, 227, 228, 236, 238, 239, 242, *244*, *245*, *247*, *248*, 254, 259, 260, 264, 266, 267, 268, 273, *289*, *290*, 297, 298, 333, 334, *342*, *343*, 351, 352, 363, 365, 387, 389, *409*, *410*, 481, 483, 484, *496*
Brooks, F. D., 182, *191*
Brout, R., 216, *244*, 272, *289*

Brugger, R. M., 56, 62, 70, 72, 74, 80, 83, 84, 88, 90, 93, *94, 96*, 207, 213, 214, 215, *244, 247*, 378, *410*, 447, *450*, 461, 462, 464, 465, 487, *494, 495, 496*

Brun, T., 283, 284, 286, *290*

Budzanowski, A., 458, *494*

Burnbury, D. St. P., 306, *342*

Butin, H., 485, *494*

Butler, D., 361, *409*

Butterworth, I., 149, 160, 163, 164, 167, *191*, 239, *244*

Bykov, V. N., 5, *48*

C

Cable, J. W., 280, *290*

Caglioti, G., 104, 109, 110, 111, 117, 125, *138*, 200, 203, 204, 205, 213, 214, 215, 239, 242, *244*, 407, 409, *409*

Caldwell, R. L., 178, *192*

Callen, H. B., 11, *48*, 302, *342, 343*

Carpenter, J. M., 72, *96*

Carrol, H., 453, *494*

Carter, R. S., 127, *138*, 201, 203, *244*

Carvalho, F., 210, *246*

Case, K. M., 303, *342*

Cassels, J. M., 18, 19, 20, *48, 94*

Ceulemans, H., 93, *94*

Chandrasekhar, S., 316

Chen, S. H., 211, *244, 248*

Chester, G. V., 195, *245*

Chrien, R. E., 144, *192*

Christ, J., 148, *191*

Chudley, C. T., 333, *343*

Cini-Castoagnoli, G., 314, *343*

Coceva, C., 187, *191*

Cochran, W., 209, 217, 218, 219, 221, 222, 225, 226, 227, 228, 233, 242, *245, 248*

Cocking, S. J., 69, 70, 72, 73, 76, *94, 95*, 156, 174, 181, 182, 183, 184, 185, 186, *191, 192*, 215, 237, 238, *245, 247*, 326, *343*, 357, 387, 388, 394, 395, 399, *409*, 480, 481, *496*

Cohen, E. R., 162, *191*

Cole, G. H. A., 309, *343*

Collins, M. F., 125, *138*, 213, *245*, 270, *289*

Connor, D. W., 65, *94*

Conway, J. M., 239, *244*, 306, *342*

Coote, G. E., 408, *409*

Cordes, J., 206, *244*

Corliss, L. M., 21, *48*

Cote, R. E., 93, *96*

Cotter, M. J., 387, 391, *409*

Cowley, R. A., 217, 221, 225, 226, 227, 228, 231, 232, 233, 235, 239, 242, 243, *245, 248*

Craggs, J. D., 175, *191*

Cribier, D., 203, 231, 232, *245*, 254, 255, 256, 261, 263, 273, 282, 283, 284, 285, 286, *289*, 361, 362, *409*

Curran, S. C., 175, *191*

Cusack, N. E., 316, *343*

Czerlunczakiewicz, B., 465, *494*

D

Dahlborg, U., 67, 69, *94, 95*, 201, 202, 203, 242, *246*, 326, 334, *344*, 355, 356, 358, 359, 361, 374, 378, 387, 388, 392, 396, 398, *410*

Dailey, B. P., 458, *496*

Danner, H. R., 89, *96*, 132, *139*, 156, 160, *192*, 362, 371, *411*, 488, 489, *494*

Dasannacharya, B. A., 122, *139*, 208, *246*, 260, *289*, 297, *343*, 377, 387, 403, *409*, 473, 474, *494*

Dash, J. G., 66, *94*

Davis, H. T., 309, *343*

De Bar, R. B., 327, *342*

De Boer, J., 310, *345*

de Gennes, P. G., 14, 42, 45, 48, *48*, 253, 258, 259, 260, 266, 278, 279, 280, 281, 287, *289*, 298, 299, 322, 327, *343*

Demidenko, Z. A., 217, 221, 228, *245*

Derge, G., 314, *345*

Deruytter, A., 93, *94*

Detering, K., 313, *343*

De Wames, R. E., 215, *245, 248*

Dick, B. G., 220, 226, *245*

Diefendorf, R. J., 235, *246*

Dixon, A. E., 209, *245*

Dobbs, E. R., 312, 313, *342*

Dolling, G., 69, *94*, 206, 209, 215, 217, 218, 221, 222, 229, 232, 236, *244, 245, 246, 248*

Domb, C., 311, *343*

Dracass, J., 185, *191*

Duffill, C., 69, *96*, 174, 181, 182, 183, 184, 185, 186, *192*

Duggal, V. P., 107, 132, *138*
Dunning, J. R., 55, 70, 85, *94*
Dyer, R. F., 65, 70, 72, *94*, 112, 132, *138*, 144, *191*
Dyson, F. P., 272, *289*

E

Edwards, C., 306, *342*
Egelstaff, P. A., 3, 14, 33, *48*, 55, 57, 64, ' 69, 70, 72, 75, 76, 78, *94*, *95*, *96*, 98, 127, 129, 130, *138*, 148, 149, 150, 156, 160, 163, 164, 167, 174, 179, 180, 181, 182, 183, 184, 185, 186, *191*, *192*, 210, 211, 215, 237, *245*, *248*, 293, 322, 323, 325, 326, 328, 332, 334, 335, 336, 337, *343*, 357, 358, 361, 366, 372, 385, 387, 388, 393, 395, 399, 404, *409*, *410*, 471, 479, 480, 489, *494*, *495*
Ehret, G., 210, *246*, 374, *410*
Eisberg, R. M., 489, 490, *495*
Eisenhauer, C. M., 5, *48*, 210, 211, 217, 238, *245*, *246*, *247*, 478, 481, *495*
Elliott, R. J., 44, 48, *48*, 216, *245*, 266, 278, 280, 281, 287, *289*, 306, 333, *343*
Englert, F., 272, *289*
Ericson, M., 261, 282, 289
Evans, J. E., 56, 62, 70, 72, 74, 80, 88, 93, *94*, *409*
Ewald, P. P., 201, 220, *245*

F

Fabelinskii, I. L., 315, *343*
Fankuchen, I., 106, *138*
Farnoux, B., 231, 232, *245*
Federighi, F. D., 471, *494*
Fein, A. E., 239, 240, 242, *247*, 306, *344*
Feldman, G., 326, *345*
Ferguson, G. A., 253, *289*
Fermi, E., 56, *95*, 127, *138*, 416, *450*, 477, 489, *494*
Fink, G. A., 55, 70, 85, *94*
Firk, F. W. K., 182, *191*
Fisher, I. Z., 309, *343*
Flanagan, T. P., 185, *191*
Foote, H. L., 104, *139*
Foreman, A. J. E., 199, *245*
Forrez, G., 312, *344*

Forslind, E., 361, *410*
Forte, M., 177, *191*
Fraunfelder, H., 298, *343*
Fray, S. J., 217, 218, 221, 233, *245*
Freeman, A.-J., 34, *48*
Frenkel, J., 309, 341, *343*, 356, *410*
Friedel, J., 201, *245*
Frikkee, E., 276, *289*
Frohlich, H., 231, *246*
Froman, P. O., 28, *49*
Fullwood, R. R., 153, *191*
Furukawa, K., 299, *343*

G

Gaerttner, E. R., 153, *191*
Gammel, J., 284, *289*
Ganesan, S., 232, *246*
Garg, J. D., 90, *95*
Gavin, W. R., 215, *247*
Gebhardt, E., 313, *343*
Ghatak, A., 325, *344*
Ghose, A., 217, *246*
Gilat, G., 209, 215, *245*, *246*
Gilbert, A., 453, *494*
Gingrich, N. S., 89, *96*, 299, *343*, 389, *410*
Ginther, R. J., 184, 185, 186, 189, *191*
Ginzburg, V. L., 315, *343*
Gläser, W., 86, 87, *95*, 210, *246*, 374, *410*
Glauber, R. J., 294, *343*, *345*, 415, 416, 422, *451*, 455, 462, 463, *496*
Gobert, G., 70, 85, *95*
Goedkoop, J. A., 238, *244*, 266, 269, 271, *290*, 479, 481, *493*
Goldman, D. T., 471, *494*
Golikov, V. V., 89, *95*, 127, *138*, 152, 184, *191*, 359, 360, 365, *409*, *410*
Golovkin, V. S., 5, *48*
Gordon, A., 284, *289*
Goryunov, A. F., 446, *450*, 459, *494*
Gouldings, F. S., 92, *94*
Green, H. S., 309, 310, 315, *342*, *343*
Green, M. S., 309, *343*
Grevendonk, W., 312, *344*
Griffing, G. W., *410*, 447, *450*, 453, 464, *494*
Groenveld, J., 310, *345*
Grotowski, K., 458, *494*
Guner, Z., 326, *343*, 388, 394, *409*

H

Haas, R., 69, *95*, 190, *191*, 210, 211, *246*
Hagihara, S., 117, *138*
Hahn, H., 239, 241, *246*, 306, *343*, *344*
Haken, K., 272, *289*
Hall, C. D., 314, *345*
Hall, H. E., 306, *342*
Halpern, O., 33, *48*
Hammermesh, M., 437, 441, *450*
Hardy, J. R., 217, 223, 227, 228, *246*, *247*
Harker, Y. D., 378, *410*, 465, 487, *494*, *496*
Harling, O. K., 86, *95*
Harris, D. H. C., 69, *95*, 174, 175, 179, 180, 181, 182, 183, 184, 185, 186, 189, *191*, *192*, 237, *245*
Hass, R., 132, *139*
Hass, W. P. S., 373, *410*
Hassitt, A., 33, *49*
Hastings, J. M., 21, *48*
Hatherly, M., 270, 273, 275, 283, *289*
Hautecler, S., 161, 168, *192*, 255, 256, *289*, 377, 378, *410*, 487, *496*
Havens, W. W., 90, *95*, 456, 460, 473, 481, 482, 486, *495*
Hay, H. J., 63, 64, 76, 78, *94*, *95*, 107, *138*
Haywood, B. C., 80, *95*, 160, *191*, 237, *246*, *343*, 357, 361, 372, 408, *409*, *410*, 471, 491, 492, *494*
Hazlewood, R., 63, 64, 93, *95*
Heap, B. R., 280, *289*
Heath, R. L., 190, *192*
Heaton, L., 106, 113, *138*, *139*
Heinloth, K., 456, 459, 469, 470, *494*
Herman, F., 217, 219, *246*
Herring, C., 267, *289*
Herzberg, G., 373, *410*, 415, *450*
Herzfeld, K. F., 314, 315, *344*
Hirakawa, K., 270, 273, 275, 283, *289*
Hoffman, R. E., 314, *344*
Holm, M. W., 103, *138*
Holmryd, S., 69, *94*, 201, 202, 203, 242, *246*, 333, 334, *344*, 355, 356, 388, 392, *410*
Holmyard, S., 67, 69, *95*
Holt, N., 67, 76, *94*, *95*, 109, *138*
Howell, W. D., 92, *94*
Howland, L. P., 306, *345*
Huang, K., 195, 224, 226, 229, 240, *244*
Hubert, P., 112, *138*

Hugenholtz, N. M., 306, *345*
Hughes, D. J., 5, 7, *48*, 62, 65, *95*, 127, 129, 132, *138*, 201, 203, 210, 211, 217, 238, *244*, *245*, *246*, *247*, 282, *290*, 333, 335, *344*, 353, 356, *410*, 478, 481, *495*
Hurst, D. G., 112, 113, 116, *138*, 461, 490, 491, *493*, *494*

I

Imry, J., 488, *495*
Iyengar, P. C., 109, 130, *139*
Iyengar, P. K., 100, 117, 119, 121, 122, 130, 132, 134, 135, 136, 137, *138*, *139*, *140*, 208, 213, 216, 219, 221, 224, 238, *244*, *246*, *248*, 260, *289*, 484, 487, *496*
Izuyama, T., 276, *289*
Izyumov, Yu, A., 253, *289*

J

Jacobsen, E. H., 203, *246*
Jacrot, B., 70, 85, *95*, 161, 166, 167, 169, *192*, 203, 231, 232, *245*, 254, 255, 256, 261, 263, 272, 273, 282, 283, 284, 285, 286, *289*, 361, 362, *409*
James, R. W., 99, *139*
Janik, E. A., 89, *95*, 365, *409*
Janik, J., 265, 266, 267, 271, 273, *290*, 455, 456, 458, 475, *494*, *496*
Janik, J. A., 127, *138*, 152, *191*, 453, 455, 456, 458, 473, 474, 475, 485, 486, 487, *494*, *495*, *496*
Janik, J. M., 473, 474, 485, 486, 487, *494*
Johanson, E. W., 113, *139*
Johnson, F. A., 217, 218, 221, 233, *245*
Johnson, M. H., 33, *48*
Johnson, R. H., 363, *410*
Jovic, D., 326, *344*, 388, 398, *410*

K

Kadanoff, L., 320, 324, *344*
Kado, S., 314, *345*
Kagan, Yu. M., 210, 211, *249*
Kahn, A. A., 310, *344*

Kanamori, J., 256, *289*
Kanzig, G. W., 233, *246*
Kaplan, H., 38, 40, 44, *48*, 217, *246*
Kaplan, T. A., 267, *289*
Karo, A. M., 227, *246*
Kaschev, V. N., 239, *246*, 306, *344*
Katzuki, A., 276, *290*
Kawasaki, K., 280, *281*, 290
Keffer, F., 38, 40, 44, *48*, 272, 274, *289*
Kellermann, E. W., 220, 226, *246*
Kerr, E. C., 117, *140*
Khubchandani, P. G., 446, *450*, 459, *494*
Kilb, R. W., 458, *494*
Kim, D. J., 276, *289*
Kirkwood, J. G., 309, 310, 316, *344*
Kirouac, G. J., 89, *95*
Kitano, Y., 238, *240*
Kittel, C., 233, *246*, 267, *289*
Kleb, R., 65, *94*
Klein, C. A., 235, *246*
Kleiner, W. H., 489, *494*
Kleppa, O. J., 312, *344*
Kley, W., 69, *95*, 132, *139*, 190, *191*, 210, 211, 216, *246*, *247*, 333, 335, *344*, 353, 356, *410*, 488, *495*
Knowles, J. W., 113, *139*
Kocinski, J., 281, *290*
Koehler, W. C., 280, *290*
Koenig, S. H., 201, 203, 212, *246*, *249*
Kohn, W., 199, 204, *246*, *248*
Kojima, T., 458, *495*
Kokkedee, J. J. J., 239, *246*, 306, *344*
Kolos, W., 458, *494*
Koltyy, V. V., 72, 73, *96*
Konstantinovic, J., 255, 256, 282, 283, 284, 285, 286, *289*
Koppel, J. U., 238, *249*
Kosaly, G., 303, *344*, 423, *450*, 455, *495*
Koster, G. F., 196, *246*
Kothari, L. S., 303, *344*
Kottwitz, D. A., 162, *192*, 365, *410*
Kouts, H., 142, 144, *192*
Kowalska, A., 465, *494*
Kozubowski, J., 203, 213, 214, *247*, *248*
Krasnicki, S., 287, *290*, 475, *494*
Krebbs, K. H., 69, *95*, 210, 211, *246*
Krebs, W., 190, *191*
Krieger, T. J., 415, 432, *450*, 453, 454, *495*
Krivoglaz, M. A., 239, *246*, 278, 281, *290*, 306, *344*

Kroh, A., 132, *139*, 238, *247*, 484, *495*
Kroo, N., 404, *410*
Kubo, R., 276, *289*, 302, 328, *344*
Kucher, T. I., 217, 221, 228, *245*

L

Lacaze, A., 167, *192*
Landau, L. D., 16, *48*, 279, *290*, 310, 315, 320, *344*
Landolt-Börnstein, 312, 313, *344*
Landon, H. H., 104, *139*
Lange, N., 314, *344*
Larsson, K. E., 62, 67, 69, *94*, *95*, 127, *139*, 179, *192*, 201, 202, 203, 242, *246*, 326, 333, 334, *344*, 355, 356, 357, 359, 361, 374, 378, 382, 387, 388, 392, 396, 398, 404, *410*
Lax, M., 306, *344*
Lee, T. C., 109, 130, *139*
Lefkovitz, I., 488, *495*
Lehman, G. W., 215, *245*, *248*
Leibfried, G., 195, 241, *246*
Leonard, B. R., 365, *410*
Leudik, V. A., 5, *48*
Lewinson, V. A., 310, *344*
Lewis, B., 170, *192*
Liforov, V. G., 89, *94*, 152, 156, *191*
Lifshitz, E. M., 16, *48*, 279, *290*, 310, 320
Lifshitz, I. M., 216, *246*
Litovitz, T. A., 314, 315, *344*
Lomer, W. M., 199, 212, *245*, *246*
London, H., 148, 149, 160, 163, 164, 167, *191*
Long, J., 92, *94*
Long-Price, D., 215, *246*
Loudon, R., 272, 274, *289*
Lovseth, J., 437, 442, *450*, 459, 489, 490, *495*
Low, G. G. E., 42, 45, *48*, 65, 70, 72, *94*, 132, *138*, 144, *191*, 208, *246*, 276, *290*
Lowde, R. D., 21, 44, *48*, 65, 71, 72, 76, 88, 89, 95, 99, 100, 101, *138*, 144, *191*, 253, 262, 264, 270, 273, 275, 276, 282, 283, *289*, *290*
Ludwig, W., 195, 241, *246*
Lyashtchenko, B. G., 207, *248*
Lyddane, R. H., 228, 232, *246*

M

McAlpin, W., 117, *139*
McClellan, L. W., 56, 88, *94*
MacFarlane, G. G., 223, *246*
Machekhina, T. A., 89, *94*, 137, *138*, 486, *493*
Mackintosh, A. R., 211, *247*
McLean, T. P., 223, *246*
McMurray, H., 464, 465, *494*
McReynolds, A. W., *96*, 106, *139*, 151, 153, 154, 155, 157, *192*, 238, *247*, 287, *290*, 368, 369, *410*, 470, 478, 479, 481, *493*, *496*
Maier, W., 476, *495*
Maier-Leibnitz, H., 147, 151, *192*
Maleev, S. V., 44, *48*, 253, *289*, *290*
Maliszewski, E., 213, 214, *247*
Mallett, J. F., 270, 273, 275, 283, *289*
Malmberg, P. R., 179, *192*
Maniawski, F., 455, 456, 458, 475, *494*
Maradudin, A. A., 216, 239, 240, 242, *245*, *247*, 306, 308, *342*, *344*
March, R. H., 208, 209, 242, *248*
Marsaguerra, A., 59, 73, *95*
Marshall, G. D., 465, *496*
Marshall, J., 56, *95*
Marshall, L., 56, *95*, 127, *138*, 489, *494*
Marshall, W., 31, 32, 48, *48*, 239, *244*, 266, 276, 278, 280, 281, 287, *289*, *290*
Marshall, W. C., 284, *289*
Marsongkohadi, Song, J., 109, 130, *139*
Martin, D. L., 209, *247*
Martin, P., 302, *344*
Martin, P. C., 320, 324, *344*
Mashkevitch, V. S., 217, 221, 226, *247*
Maun, E. K., 310, *344*
Maystryenko, A. N., 72, 73, *96*
Melkonian, E., 107, 108, 131, *139*, *140*, 455, 456, 459, 460, 467, 468, 469, 471, 489, 490, *495*
Mellor, J., 473, 474, 485, 486, 487, *494*
Menardi, S., 132, *139*
Meriel, P., 112, *138*
Merkel, A., 374, *410*
Merrett, D. J., 170, *192*
Messiah, A. M. L., 436, *450*, 455, 459, *495*
Meyer, R. E., 314, *344*
Michael, P., 475, *495*
Michaudon, A., 157, *192*

Mikke, K., 132, *139*, 238, *247*, 461, 484, *495*
Miller, H. G., 67, *96*
Mills, W. R., 178, *192*
Mitchell, D. P., 55, 70, 85, *94*
Mitchell, E. W. J., 223, *247*
Mitsui, T., 235, *247*
Modrzejewski, A., 105, *139*
Moffit, R., 149, 150, *191*
Møller, H. B., 131, *139*, 148, *192*, 211, *247*
Moore, W. E., 89, 92, *95*
Moreau, R., 92, *95*
Morgan, I. R., 178, *192*
Morgan, L., 284 *289*
Mori, H., 280, 281, *290*, 309, *344*
Mostovoi, V. I., 57, 62, *95*
Mozer, B., 207, 215, 216, *247*
Mueller, M. H., 106, 113, *138*, *139*
Murasik, A., 287, *290*, 475, *494*
Musgrave, M. J. P., 215, *247*
Myashita, K., 117, *138*
Myers, V. W., 216, *247*

N

Nachtrieb, N. H., 314, *344*
Naghizadeh, J., 314, *344*
Nakagawa, Y., 211, *247*
Nakamura, T., 272, 274, *290*
Nasuhoglu, R., 65, *95*
Natera, M. G., 109, 130, *139*
Navarro, O. D., 109, 130, *139*
Nelkin, M., 11, 12, *48*, 325, *344*, *345*
Nelkin, M. S., 238, *247*, 293, 299, *344*, 415, 432, *450*, 453, 454, 470, 478, 481, *493*, *495*
Neve d Mevergnies, M., 93, *94*
Newitt, D. M., 312, *342*
Nichikawa, T., 458, *495*
Nicholson, K. P., 177, 190, *192*
Nielsen, P., 283, 284, 286, *290*
Nikolayen, M. N., 89, *94*, 152, 156, *191*
Nilsson, G., 201, 242, *248*
Nimnanandon, T., 109, 130, *139*
Noe, E. N., 185, *191*

O

O'Connor, D. A., 86, *95*, 107, *139*
Oguchi, T., 38, *48*, 272, *290*

Ohno, Y., 113, *139*
Okamoto, K., 113, *139*
Okazaki, A., 45, *48*, 269, 270, 273, 275, 276, 288, *290*
Olsen, W. C., 144, *192*
Orlov, V. V., 89, *94*, 152, 156, *191*
Ornstein, L. S., 316
Oskotskii, V. S., 333, *344*
Ostrowski, D., 65, *94*
Otnes, K., 69, 70, *94*, *95*, 179, *192*, 207, 215, 216, *247*, 333, 334, *344*, 474, 488, *495*
Overhauser, A. W., 220, 226, *245*

P

Padlo, I., 213, 214, *247*
Pagès, A., 92, *95*
Palavsky, H., 70, *95*
Palensky, H., 473, 474, 485, 486, 487, *494*
Palevsky, H., 5, *48*, 62, 67, *95*, 127, *138*, *139*, 144, 179, *192*, 201, 203, 210, 211, 215, 217, 238, *244*, *245*, *246*, *247*, 282, *290*, 333, 335, *344*, 353, 356, 387, *410*, 478, 481, 484, 485, 488, 489, 490, *494*, *495*
Palinski, K., 89, *94*
Paoletti, A., 104, 109, 110, 125, *138*
Parette, G., 282, 283, 284, 285, 286, *289*
Parfenov, V. A., 89, *94*, 152, 156, *191*
Parlinski, K., 137, *138*, 486, *493*, *494*
Paskin, A., 204, *247*
Passell, L., 148, *192*, 283, 284, 286, *290*
Pattendon, N. J., 107, *139*
Pauli, G., 59, 73, *95*
Pauli, R., 179, *192*
Pearce, D. G., 161, 169, 170, *192*
Pease, R. S., 129, *138*
Pecjak, F. A., 179, *192*
Peckham, G., 125, *139*
Pegram, G. B., 55, 70, 85, *94*
Peierls, R. E., 195, *247*
Pelah, I., 5, *48*, 210, 211, 217, 238, *245*, *246*, *247*, 478, 481, 488, *495*
Percuss, J. K., 310, *344*
Peretti, J., 216, *247*
Peterson, J. S., 90, *95*
Petree, F., 91, *95*
Pevzner, M. I., 57, 62, *95*

Pickles, J. R., 64, 76, 93, *94*, *95*
Pineda, V. M., 109, 130, *139*
Pippel, N., 314, *344*
Placzek, G., 31, *48*, 193, 194, *247*, 299, 315, 323, *344*, 345, 407, *410*, 429, *450*
Pochapsky, T. E., 312, *345*
Poole, M. J., 155, *192*
Pope, N. K., 297, 298, *343*, 363, 387, 389, *409*, *410*
Prask, H., 489, *494*
Pressesky, A. J., 112, 113, 116, *138*
Prigogine, I., 309, *345*
Prince, E., 119, *139*
Pyrah, S., 176, *191*

Q

Quarrington, J. E., 217, 218, 221, 223, 233, *245*, *246*

R

Radkevich, I. A., 62, *96*
Raffle, J., 64, 76, 78, *94*, *95*
Rahman, A., 15, *48*, 299, 300, 318, 323, 327, 328, 331, 338, 340, *345*, 366, *410*, 442, 445, 446, *450*, 459, *494*
Rainey, V. S., 132, *139*, 374, *410*, 464, 465, 479, 480, *494*, *495*
Rainwater, J., 90, *95*
Randolph, P. D., 84, 90, *96*, 213, 214, 215, *247*, 326, *345*, 388, 400, *410*, 447, *450*, 461, 462, 464, 465, *495*, *496*
Rao, K. R., 107, 117, *138*, *139*, 200, 203, 204, 205, 213, 217, 225, *244*, *246*, 297, *343*, 403, *409*
Rao, L. R., 254, *289*
Reid, C., 488, *495*
Renninger, M., 107, *139*
Ribon, P., 157, *192*
Ricci, F. P., 104, 109, 110, 111, 125, *138*, 314, *343*
Rice, S. A., 309, 314, *342*, *344*, *345*
Ringo, G. R., 65, *95*
Riste, T., 253, 263, 265, 266, 267, 269, 271, 272, 273, 274, 276, 287, *289*, *290*
Roberts, V., 223, *246*
Rockwood, C. S., 92, *96*
Rogalska, Z., 467, 468, 474, *495*

Rosenbaum, M., 303, *342*, *345*
Rosenbluth, M. N., 238, *247*, 478, 481, *493*
Rosenstock, H. B., 200, 207, *247*
Rosolowski, J. H., 214, *247*
Rothman, S. J., 314, *345*
Rowe, J. M., 215, *247*
Rowlinson, J. S., 312, *345*
Roy, A. P., 109, 117, 130, 136, *139*, *140*, 213, 238, *246*, *248*, 487, *496*
Royston, R. J., 72, 73, 74, 75, *96*, 357, *409*
Rubin, R., *95*, 190, *191*, 210, 211, 216, *246*, *247*, 318, *345*
Ruijgrok, Th. W., 301, 325, *345*
Rupprecht, G., 235, *247*
Rush, J. J., 456, 460, 473, 481, 482, 486, 487, *495*
Rustad, R. M., 107, 108, 131, *139*, *140*
Ruta-Wala, K., *290*
Ryskina, S. J., 458, *495*
Rytov, S. M., 315, *345*
Rzany, H., 455, 456, 458, 468, 469, 471, 475, *493*, *494*, *495*, *496*

S

Sachs, R. G., 228, 232, *246*, 415, 416, 419, *450*, 454, *495*
Sáenz, A. W., 44, 45, *49*, 253, *289*, *290*
Safford, G. J., 92, *96*, 471, 472, 481, 485, 487, 488, *493*, *494*, *495*
Sagan, V., 456, *496*
Sailor, V. L., 104, 131, *139*
Saint-James, D., 203, *245*, 256, *290*
Sakamoto, M., 132, *138*, *140*, 238, 239, 242, *244*, *248*, 363, *410*, 481, 483, 484, *496*
Salmon, P. G., 176, *191*
Samulesen, E. J., 253, *290*
Sarma, G., 261, *289*, 370, *410*, 437, *450*
Satya Murthy, N. S., 122, *139*, 208, *246*, 260, *289*
Saunderson, D. H., 69, 96, 132, *139*, 149, 150, *191*, 223, 238, *247*, 374, *410*, 479, 480, 481, *495*, *496*
Saupe, A., 476, *495*
Schäffer, S., 313, *343*
Schenck, J., 190, *192*
Schiff, L. I., 7, *49*
Schmunk, R. E., 84, 90, *96*, 213, 214, 215, *247*, 447, *450*, 461, 462, 464, *495*

Schofield, P., 13, 14, 33, *48*, *49*, 162, *192*, 293, 299, 301, 323, 327, 328, 332, 335, 336, *343*, *345*, 357, 358, 366, 399, *409*, *410*, 449, 450, *450*, *451*, 456, *495*
Schwartz, R. B., 7, *48*
Schwinger, J., 302, *344*, 367, 369, *410*, 437, 441, *450*, *451*
Sciesinski, J., 455, 456, 458, 468, 469, 475, *494*, *495*
Seemann, K. W., 89, *95*
Segre, E., 55, 70, 85, *94*
Seitz, F., 225, *247*
Selove, W., 72, *96*
Semenov, V. A., 152, 156, *191*
Sengers, J. V., 309, *343*
Sham, L. J., 209, *248*
Shapiro, F. L., 89, *94*, *95*, 127, 137, *138*, 152, *191*, 365, *409*
Shimchak, G. F., 184, *191*
Shimizu, M., 276, *290*
Shkatula, A., 89, *95*, 127, *138*, 152, 184, *191*, 365, *409*, 455, 456, 458, 475, *494*
Shore, F. J., 131, *139*
Shrinivasan, R., 232, *246*
Shull, C. G., 89, *96*, 105, 108, 113, *139*, *140*, 282, *290*
Shulman, J. N., 184, *191*
Sinclair, R. N., 123, 132, *138*, *139*, *140*, 215, 238, 239, 242, *244*, *248*, 264, 266, 267, 268, *290*, 481, 483, 484, *496*
Singh, P. P., 144, *192*
Singh, V., 107, *138*
Singwi, K. S., 15, *48*, 299, 300, 301, 303, 322, 323, 326, 327, 328, 333, 335, 338, 340, *344*, *345*, 356, 365, 366, 382, *410*, 411
Sinha, S. K., 203, *248*
Sjölander, A., 15, 33, *48*, *49*, 293, 299, 300, 301, 303, 322, 323, 327, 328, 333, 335, 338, 340, *345*, 356, 365, 366, *410*, 411, Skold, K., 404, *410*
Sledziewska, D., 213, 214, *247*
Slovacek, R. E., 57, 58, *96*
Smirnov, V. I., 89, *94*, 152, 156, *191*
Smith, H. M. J., 217, *248*
Smith, J. C., 113, *138*
Smith, J. R., 67, *96*, 107, *139*
Smith, R. B., 365, *410*
Smith, S. D., 223, *246*
Smoluchowski, R., 196, *244*

Snelling, G. F., 190, *192*
Sokolvikii, W. W., 62, *96*
Solimene, N., 458, *496*
Solt, G., 423, *450*, 455, *495*
Sommer, H. S., 66, *94*
Soni, J. N., 109, 130, *139*
Sosnowski, A., 107, *139*
Sosnowski, J., 203, 213, 214, *247, 248*
Spaepen, J., 54, 89, *96*
Spencer, R. R., 107, *139*
Springer, T., 147, 148, *191, 192*, 456
Squires, G. L., 202, 203, *248*, 282, *290*
Stecher-Rasmussen, F., 148, *192*
Stedman, R., 62, *95*, 127, *139*, 175, 179, 180, 181, 189, *192*, 201, 242, *248*
Steinvoll, O., 253, *290*
Stern, H., 306, *343*
Stevenson, R. W. H., 45, *48*, 269, 270, 273, 275, 288, *290*
Stewart, A. T., *96*, 98, 120, 122, *138*, 201, 203, 208, 209, 210, 211, 215, *244, 248*
Stewart, J. W., 312, *345*
Stiller, H., 132, *139*, 362, 377, 378, *410, 411*, 487, *496*
Stone, R. S., 58, *96*
Straub, W. D., 235, *246*
Streetman, G. B., 56, 88, *94*
Stringfellow, M. W., 270, 273, 275, 283, *289*
Strong, K. A., 70, *94*, 213, 214, 215, *247*, 447, *450*, 461, 462, 464, 465, *495, 496*
Stuart, R., 31, 32, *48*
Sturm, W. J., 108, *139*
Sullivan, J. J., 217, *246*
Summerfield, G. C., 299, *345*
Sun, K. H., 179, *192*
Svensson, E. C., 215, *247*
Swenson, C. A., 312, *342*
Syemyenov, V. A., 89, *94*
Szabo, P., 104, *139*

T

Tannenwald, P. E., 274, *290*
Tarina, V., 462, *493*
Taylor, T. I., 456, 460, 473, 481, 482, 486, 487, *495*
Tchernoplekov, N. A., 207, 210, 211, *248*
Tchetserin, A. G., 207, 210, 211, *248*
Teller, E., 228, 232, *246*, 367, 369, *410*, 415, 416, 419, 437, 441, *450, 451*, 454, *495*

Thapar, C. L., 107, 132, *138*
Thomas, G. E., 93, *96*, 185, 186, 189, 190, *191*
Thomson, B. V., 306, *345*
Thorson, I. M., 80, *95, 96*, 237, *246, 343*, 357, 361, *409, 410*, 471, *494*
Todireanu, S., 462, *493*
Tolk, N. H., 70, 72, *96*
Tolpygo, K. B., 217, 221, 226, 228, *245, 247, 248*
Tomacheva, N. S., 185, *192*
Tomita, K., 288, *290*
Torrie, B. H., 270, 273, 275, 283, *289*
Toya, T., 199, 203, 208, *248*
Trammell, G. T., 33, *49*
Trevino, S. F., 489, *494*
Tsitovich, A. P., 57, 62, *95*
Tubbs, N., 456, *496*
Tunkelo, E., *247*, 333, 335, *344*, 353, 356, *410*, 488, *495*
Tunnicliffe, P. R., 112, 113, 116, *138*
Turberfield, K. C., 45, *48*, 69, *96*, 210, 211, *248*, 269, 270, 273, 275, 288, *290*, 387, 391, *411*
Turchin, V. F., 89, *94*, 152, 156, *191*, 293, *345*
Turner, R. E., 303, *344, 345*

U

Uhlenbeck, G. E., 316
Umakantha, N., 65, *96*
Umakantha, R. H., 270, 275, *290*
Usha Deniz, K., 132, 136, *140*, 238, *248*, 260, *289*, 377, *409*, 473, 474, 484, 487, *494, 496*

V

Van Dahl, N., 312, *344*
Van Dingenen, W., 160, 161, 162, 168, *192*
Van Hove, L., 10, 47, *49*, 193, 194, 203, 207, 239, *247, 248*, 259, 278, 279, 280, 287, *290*, 294, 296, 301, 303, 306, *345*, 347, *410*, 447, *451*
Van Itterbeck, A., 312, *344*
Van Leeuwen, J. M. J., 310, *345*
Van Vleck, J. H., 256, 258, 259, *290*

Venkataraman, G., 109, 117, 130, 132, 136, *139*, *140*, 213, 238, *246*, *248*, 260, *289*, 377, *409*, 473, 474, 484, 487, *494*, *496*
Verdan, G., 216, *247*
Vertebnii, V. P., 72, 73, *96*
Vijayaraghavan, P. R., 109, 117, 119, 130, 132, 136, *139*, *140*, 213, 238, *246*, *248*, 484, 487, *496*
Villian, J., 48, *48*, 266, 278, 280, 281, 285, 287, *289*, *290*
Vincent, D. H., 70, *96*
Vineyard, G. H., 13, 21, *49*, 303, 321, 326, 332, *345*
Vinogradov, F., 5, *48*
Visscher, W., 216, *244*
Vladimirskii, V. V., 62, *96*
Voitovetskii, V. K., 185, *192*
Volkin, H. C., 442, *451*, 459, *496*
Von Elbe, G., 170, *192*
Vosko, S. H., 201, *248*

W

Wainwright, T., 318, *345*
Wajima, L. T., 107, 108, 131, *139*, *140*
Wakuta, Y., 488, *495*
Wala, K., 287, *290*
Walker, C. B., 202, 203, *248*
Waller, I., 28, *49*
Wang, M. C., 316
Wanic, A., 269, 274, 287, *290*, 455, 456, 458, 469, 475, *494*, *496*
Ward, D. L., 170, *192*
Warren, J. L., 201, 203, 217, 219, 223, 235, *248*, *249*
Watanabe, H., 267, 268, 273, *289*
Watson, R. E., 34, *48*
Waugh, J. L. T., 217, 218, 221, 229, *245*, *248*
Weak, K. E., 312, *342*
Webb, F. J., 69, *95*, 148, 149, 157, 160, 161, 162, 163, 164, 165, 167, 169, 170, 174, 181, 182, 183, 184, 185, 186, *191*, *192*, 372, *410*, 465, 466, *496*
Weil, L., 167, *192*
Weiner, N., 15, *49*
Weinstock, R., 17, *49*, 393, *411*
Weiss, J. R., 204, *247*
Welton, T. A., 11, *48*, 302, *343*
Wenzel, R. G., 217, 219, 223, 235, *248*, *249*

Westcott, C. H., 91, *96*, 144, *192*
Westphal, W. B., 235, *247*
Wheeler, D. A., 21, *48*
Whitehead, C. D., 113, *138*
Whittemore, W. L., 62, 89, *96*, 153, 154, 155, 156, 157, 160, *192*, 238, *247*, 368, 369, 371, *410*, *411*, 470, 478, 479, 481, *493*, *496*
Wick, G. C., 430, *451*
Wiener, E., 488, *495*
Wigner, E., 196, *244*
Wilkinson, M. K., 280, 282, *290*
Wolfram, T., 215, *248*
Woll, E. J., 204, *248*
Wollan, E. O., 113, *140*, 280, *290*
Wood, R. E., 104, *139*
Woods, A. D. B., 132, *138*, *140*, 200, 203, 204, 205, 206, 208, 209, 211, 217, 225, 226, 227, 228, 232, 238, 239, 242, *244*, *245*, *247*, *248*, 254, *289*, 481, 483, 484, *496*
Wörwag, G., 313, *343*
Wraight, L. A., 174, 179, 180, 181, 182, 183, 184, 185, 186, *192*

Y

Yafet, Y., 38, 40, 44, *48*
Yamada, Y., 256, *290*
Yang, L., 314, *345*
Yarnell, J. L., 117, *140*, 201, 203, 212, 217, 219, 223, 235, *246*, *248*, *249*
Yeater, M. L., 89, *95*, 153, *191*
Yevick, G. J., 310, *344*
Yip, S., 325, *345*
Yoshie, T., 117, *138*
Yoshimori, A., 238, *249*
Young, J. A., 238, *249*

Z

Zemach, A. C., 415, 416, 422, *451*, 455, 462, 463, *496*
Zemlyanov, M. G., 207, 210, 211, *248*, *249*
Zhdanova, N. F., 313, *345*
Zhukovskaya, I., 89, *95*, 152, *191*, 365, *409*
Ziman, J. M., 23, 25, *49*, 195, 201, *249*
Zimmerman, R. L., 144, *192*
Zinn, W. H., 111, 113, *140*
Zweifel, P. F., 72, *96*, 299, 303, *342*, *345*

Subject Index

Numbers in italics are main entries

A

Acoustic attenuation, in classical fluids, *314–315*

Adiabatic approximation, 195, *220*

Alcohols
hindered internal rotations in, 458–459, 471–472
K.N. model for, 458
scattering from, *374–377*, 458, 472

Alloys, cross-section for, *22*

Aluminium
as monochromator, *86–87*, 106, 374
liquid, 388, *396–398*
phonon dispersion relation in, *202–203*

Ammonia
K.N. model for *457*, *465–466*
rotations in, 465, 469
scattering from, *456–457*, *465–466*, 481

Ammonium salts, *481–487*
rotation of NH_4^+ in, 473, *481–487*
torsional vibrations in, *483–487*

Analysers, time-of-flight, 54, 56, *90–92*
use with on-line computers, 92

Andrade formula, *313*

Anharmonicity, in crystals, 26, 124, 125, 225, 231, 235, *239–243*, *306–309*, 327
and shape of neutron groups, *125*
and phonon lifetimes, *239–241*, 306, 308
and phonon frequency shifts, *239–241*
of torsional oscillations, *487*

Antiferromagnets, scattering from, *42–45*, 280, *286–288*

Argon, liquid, 331, *402–407*
phonon dispersion relation in, *405–406*

B

Band theory of alloys, 276

Benzene, scattering from, *470*

BEPO, *145*, 158, 159, 164–165

Beryllium, as moderator, *149*
phonon dispersion relation in, *214*
phonon frequency distribution in, 215

Beryllium detector [filter] method, *132–133*, 362, 374, 483, 486

Born-Mayer [overlap] potential, *200*, 203, 226

Born-von Kármán model, 197, 199–200, *205*, 211, 217, 219, 292, 303, 342

Boron trifluoride counters, 113, 117, 132, 135, *175–178*, 190
discrimination against γ-rays, 175, 190
multidetector arrays of, 178
time uncertainty in, 177

Bragg condition, *19*

Bragg cut-off, *19*, 20, 127

Bragg scattering, *18–21*, 46, *305*, 324
multiple, *21*
+phonon scattering, *205–206*, 213

Braking of relaxation, *281*, 286

Bravais lattice, 26–28, 196, 303

Bromine, liquid, *407–409*

Brookhaven High Flux Beam Reactor, (HFBR), 144

Brownian motion, 309, 316, 338, 386

n-Butane, scattering from, *467*

C

Cauchy relations, 208

Cell model, for liquids, 309, 316, 319, 341

Central-force models, *208*, 226, 309

Choppers
curved-slot, *59–60*, 65
Fermi, 56, *57–59*, 61, 64, 68, 70
materials for, 61, 62, 64, 65
path of neutrons through, *57*, 59
phased, 55, *70–85*, 89
safety of, *93*
transmission of, *57–59*, 60–61

Cluster model, in fluctuation theory, 278

Collective electron theory, 276

Collimators
and intensity of diffraction pattern, *109–111*
design of, *103–104*, *146–148*
effect on neutron beam, *3–4*

Collimators
  for polarized neutrons, 148
  for phonon experiments, 197
  rotating, 76
  totally reflecting, *147–148*
  use in reactors, *146–148*
  use with crystal monochromators, *102*, 105
Collision time, molecular, *429–430*, 433
Compressibility, adiabatic, in classical fluids, 320
Compressibility, isothermal, in classical liquids, *310*, 311, 312
  experimental values of, *312*
Constant-Q method, *123–124*, *224*
Convolution approximation, *321*, 323, 401, 404, 408
Copper
  Born-Mayer potential in, 201
  phonon dispersion relation in, 203
Correlation of position, 9, *10–12*, 320
Correlation, of velocity, *14*, 15, *316*, *318*, 327–328
Correlation function
  density, 296, *319–320*, 324, 325
  distinct [pair], *11*, 321, *389–390*, 424
  force, *316*, *319*
  instantaneous pair, *12*, 22, *295*, 298–300, *309–310*, *320–324*, 326, 389
  magnetic, *45*, 46, *258*, *277–278*, 287
  self, *11*, *295–296*, 303, 321, 324, 326, 332, 364, 424
    in liquid argon, 331
    in liquid lead, 389, *391*
    in liquid sodium, 401
  space-time, *10–12*, *294–298*, 303, 321, 324, *388–391*, 404
    in liquid lead, *388–391*
  velocity, *316*, *318–319*, *327–328*, *338–339*, 357, 365–366
  Vineyard, *13*, *332*
Correlation range
  in liquids, 336, 347
  magnetic, 281, *283*, 284
Correlation times, in liquids, 318, *333–334*, 347, 356, 383–385, 398
  in solids, 9, 17, 347
Coulomb interaction, interionic, 201, *220*
Counters, proportional, 113, 117, 132, 135, *175–178*, 190

shielding for, 113, *173*, 180
  time uncertainty in, *177*, *184*, 187
Critical points, in $z(\nu)$, *203*, 207, 210
Critical scattering, magnetic, *45–48*, 258, *277–288*
  in iron, *282–286*
  in nickel, 282–283
Cross-section
  absorption, 196
  bound atom, *6*
  coherent, *11*, *18*, 19, *27*, *28*, *29*, *35–37*, 194, 210, 298, 319, 321, 448
  differential, *9*, 11, *16–18*, 22, *27–38*, 40, 46, 47, *49–52*, *259*, *278–281*, 393, 414, 423, 428, 448, *460*
  free atom, *7*
  in terms of eigenstates of scatterer, *15–17*, 417, *422–423*
  magnetic, *34–48*, *259*, 277, *278–279*, 281
    antiferromagnetic, 42–45
    for critical processes, *47*, 277, *279*, *281*, 282–283
    for polarized neutrons, 35, *37*
    for unpolarized neutrons, *34–35*, *36*
    diffuse inelastic, *266–267*
    incoherent magnetic, *38*
    magnon, *40*, 271
    paramagnetic, *36*
  molecular scattering, 414, *417–419*, *422–423*, *427–430*, 436, *440–441*, 445
  phonon,
    1-phonon coherent, *28*, *29*, 194, 223, 324, 393
    1-phonon incoherent, *30*, 194, 231, 393, 398
    multiphonon, *31–33*, 194, 309, 324, 398.
  X-ray, 9, *10*
Crystal monochromators
  calculated intensity from, *99–102*
  effects of thickness and mosaic spread, *100–101*, 103
  Fankuchen cut, 87, *106*
  order contamination in, *108–109*
  parasitic reflections in, *106–108*
  rotating, 56, *85–88*
  types of crystal for, *104–106*
Crystal spectrometers, basis of, 111–113
Crystalline electric field, effects of, 36, 253, *254–256*

Curie temperature
    characteristics of, *33*, 45, *257–258, 277*
    in Mn_2O_3, 259
        $MnSO_4$, 260
        rare earth oxides, 256
        spin wave behaviour near, *272–276*

D

Debye approximation, 17, 31, 304, 323, 329, 339, 341–342
Debye temperature, *17–18*, 209, 228–229, *323*, 470
    calculation from phonon $z(f)$, 209, 228
    in argon, 403, 405
    in lead, 388, 390
    in sodium, 209
    in sodium iodide, *228–229*
    in water, 334, 355, 357
Debye-Waller factor, 17, 27, 32, 305, 334, 351, 355, 365, 383, 387
    for molecular vibrations, *436*
    in glycerol, 383, 387
    in water, 355, 357, 365
Defects, modes of, *215–216*
    electronic, 231
Density of states, phonon, 15, *30*, 195, 198, 206–207, 209, 210, 215, 228, 237
Detailed balance, 13, 301, 303
Diatomic molecules, scattering from, *437–442, 489–491*
    bromine, 407–409
    hydrogen, 367–373, 437–442
    nitrogen, 489–490
    oxygen, 489–490
DIDO, *145*, 146, 158–160, 165–167, 168 et seq.
Dielectric function, 201
Diffraction method, in inelastic scattering, *264*, 268, 270–271, 274, 275
Diffusion broadening, *332, 334, 351*, 353–354, 362, 375–387, 399, 404
Diffusion equation, 303, 320, 326, *332*
Diffusive motion, 13, 329–330, 332, 348, 351–352, 474
    of spins, *259*, 280–281, 286, 288
        degrees of freedom for, 338–339, 386–387
Dipole approximation, *221*, 227, 229

Dirac vector model, *39*
Discrimination
    of pulse shape, *182–184*
    of pulse height, *186–187*, 190
Disorder, spin and isotope, 11, 18, 21–23
Dispersion relation, phonon
    experimental methods for, 69, 83, *119–124*, 194
    in liquid and solid argon, *405–406*
    symmetry conditions on, in f.c.c. metals, *202*
    in b.c.c. metals, *208*
    in diamond structure, *218*
    in NaCl structure, 225
Dispersion relation, spin wave, 262, 263, *267–271*, 273, 275
    experimental methods for, *267–271*
    in antiferromagnets, *269*, 275
    in ionic ferromagnets, 275
Distribution function, pair, *22, 23*
Domains, magnetic, *257*
Doppler effect, 354, 415, 447, 477–478, 481
Dubna pulsed fast reactor (IBR-1), *151–152*, 155–156
Dynamical matrix, *24, 196*, 218, 220, 240
    "anharmonic", 240

E

E.A. treatment, *see* Zemach-Glauber theory
Effective mass
    for diffusion, *330, 335–336*, 341
    in molecules, 419, *435*, 436, 444, 454, *456*, 467
Efficiency of detectors, 113, *171, 172–174*, 176, *178*, 180, 182, *184*, 190
    optimum, *173–174*
    to γ-rays, 172, 175, *182*, 190
Eigenstates of scatterer, 15–17
Einstein oscillator, as model for metal hydrides, 238, 480–481
Electron linear accelerators (linacs)
    use as neutron sources, 54, 89–90, *152–155*
Electron–magnon interaction, 276
Electron–phonon interaction, *199*, 208
Electron scattering, 297
Energy, total, in classical liquids, *309*
Equivalent electron energy, in glass scintillators, *185–186*

Ethylene, K.N. model for, 456–457
  scattering from, 455, *457*
Ewald construction, *19*
Ewald lattice sum (theta transformation),
  201, 220
Exchange interaction, *39, 256*, 259, 267,
  269–270, 275, 279
Exchange stiffness constant, 273, 274, *276*
Extinction, primary and secondary, *20–
  21, 99*
Eyring's formula, *336*, 383

                          F

Fankuchen cut, 87, *106*
Fermi chopper, 56, *57–59*, 61, 64, 68
  transmission of, *57–59*
Fermi surface, 201, 211, 212
  electron density of states at, 201
  determination of by Kohn effect, 204
Fermi pseudopotential, *6*, 8, *416*, 419, *422*
Ferroelectrics, *233–235*, 243, *487, 488*
Filters, neutron, 20, *127–137*, 348
  characteristics of, *128–129*
  polycrystalline, *127–130*, 132–137
  single crystal, *130–132*
  use in analysers, *132–137*
  use in filter-chopper, 67–69, 127
  use in chopper-time-of-flight method,
    69, 85
  use in rotating-crystal method, 87, 127
  use in spinning-sample method, 89
  use with crystal monochromators, 109
Filter-chopper method, *67–69*, 351, 355
Fluctuation-dissipation theorem, 11, *301–
  303*, 305, 307, 322, 328 332. 339
Fluctuations of density in fluids, 317–318
Fluctuations of magnetization, *39, 258*,
  266–267, *277–281*, 287–288
  range of, *279*, 281, *283*, 284
Flux, scattered, 8
Flux reflector, *144*
Flux spectrum, from reactors, *3*, 108,
  148–150
  from high-temperature moderators,
    149–150
  from cold sources, *162–163, 167–169*,
    292
Flux trap, *144*

Focusing, in spectrometers
  twin-axis, *110–111*
  triple-axis, 124–125
Form factor, magnetic, *34*, 267
  effect of double Bragg reflections in
    determination of, 108
Fourier series analysis, *199, 204–205*, 236
  and relation to interatomic force con-
    stants, 199–200, 204
  in graphite, 236
  in iron, 208
  in lead, 204–205
  in sodium, 208
  in metals of Group V and VI, 211
Frequency distribution function, *15, 30*,
    195, 198, 206–207, 209, 210, 215, 228,
    237, 304, 308, 328–331
  calculation from cross-section for gra-
    phite, *237*
  effect of impurity modes on, 215
  experimental methods for, 207, *210, 215*
  in liquids, *328–331, 340*, 357, 387, 398,
    399
  in molecules, 447, *449*, 454
  sampling method for calculation of
    in nickel, 206
    in sodium, *209*
Frictional force, in liquids, *316*, 329, 330,
    332, 335–341
Friedel oscillations, 201, *205*, 211

                          G

Gaussian approximation, *326–328*, 357,
    401, 408, *448*
Glass detectors, *184–187*
Globule model for liquids, *335–338*, 387
  comparison with experiment, 337
Globular compounds
  quasi-free rotation in, 489
  scattering from, 489
Graphite
  as moderator, 148, 159
  phonon dispersion relation in, *235–238*
Green's functions, in anharmonicity, 239
Griffing model for molecular scattering,
    453, *463–464*, 465, 474, 487
Group theory
  notation of, for crystal symmetry direc-
    tions, 196, 214

H

Half-angling, 110, 116
  devices for, *112–113*
Harmonic approximation, 17, *23*, 24–26,
  195, 225, *239*, 303–306, 320, 326, 394
Harmonic oscillator
  as model for protons in solids, *476–479*
  scattering from, *416–418*, 441, *476–477*
Heavy water
  as moderator, 148, 159–160
  frequency spectrum in, 361
  quasi-elastic scattering from, 352, 355
  rotations in, 470–471
Helical slot velocity selectors, 54, *65–67*
Helium-3
  in proportional counters, *178*, 190
Hindered rotations
  energy barrier for, *473, 481–483*
  in ammonium salts, *481–487*
    bromine, 408
    glycerol, 384, 387
    organic liquids, 473
    water, *351*, 354–355, 357, 361, *468–471*
  internal, in alcohols and thiols, 458–
    459, 471–472
Hydrides, metal, scattering from, *238*,
  476–481
Hydrogen, liquid
  as moderator, 148–149, *160–161, 164–
  171*, 367
  ortho–para transition in, *367–373*
  scattering of neutrons from, 158, *367–
  373*
Hydrogen fluoride, scattering from, *471–
  472*, 487
Hydrogen molecule
  K.N. model for, 459–460
  ortho–para transition in, 367–373, *441–
  442*
  rotation of, 437, 459
  scattering from, *367–373, 437–442, 460*,
    466
  spin correlation effects in, 426, 437
Hydrogen sulphide
  K.N. effective mass in, *456*
  rotations in, 468
  scattering from, 456, *457*, 465
Hydrogenous liquids
  as moderators, *160–161*

neutron scattering
  from alcohols, *374–377*, 458
  n-butane, 467
  glycerol, 374, *378–387*
  methane, 374, *377–378*, 455, *451*,
    468

I

Ice, 352, 358–360, 470
Incoherent approximation, *31*, 392
Inelastic scattering, from crystals, *23–33*
  from ideal crystals, *23–26*
  incoherent, *30*, 194
  one-phonon coherent, *28–30*, 194
  magnetic, *38–45, 251–290*
  multi-phonon, *31–33*, 194
Infra-red absorption, phonon data from,
  217, *223*, 226
Interatomic force constants, 197, 199–200,
  202
  in aluminium, 202
    copper, 203
    iron, 208
    lead, 204–205
    nickel, 206
    sodium, 208
    vanadium, 210
  use to calculate $z(f)$, *202*, 207, *209*
Interference effects, in liquids, *320–326*,
  361
  in polyatomic molecules, *430–431, 436*,
  446, 455, 489
Intermediate scattering function, *13*, 294,
  297, *298–300, 304*, 319–320, 321–323,
  327, 364, *388–390*
  in Gaussian approximation, *327*
  in liquid lead, *389–390*
  for molecular scattering, *450*
  weighted, for molecular scattering, *423–
  424*, 426, 427, 429–431, *432–435, 444*,
  445
Interplanar force constants, *199–200*, 202,
  236
  in aluminium, 202
  in graphite, 236
Iron
  critical scattering in, *281–286*
  phonon dispersion relation in, 208
  spin waves in, 270–271
Isotopic disorder, 11, 18, 21, 22

J

Jacobian, *28*, 29, *40*, 224
Jump-diffusion model for liquids, *333–335*, 351–352, 356, 380

K

Kinematic relaxation, *280–286*
Kneser liquids, 315
Kohn effect, *199, 201, 203–204*
  in lead, 203–204
  in sodium, 209
Krieger-Nelkin [K.N.] model, 354, *432–437*, 443, 447, 453–455, *457*, 465, 473
  for ammonia, 457, 465–466
    alcohols, 458
    ethylene, 457
    hydrogen, 459–460
    light water, 457, 459, 469
    methane, 457, 468, 473–475

L

Langevin equation, 303, *316*, 318, 319, 326, 329, 332, 342
Lead
  Fermi surface of, 204
  liquid, *388–396*
  phonon dispersion relation in, *203–206*
Lifetime, magnon, *272–275*
  phonon, 26, 215, *229–231, 239–243*, 292
Light water
  as moderator, 148, 159–160
  frequency spectrum in, *358–361*
  hindered rotations in, 351, 354–355, 357, 361, 468
  K.N. model for, *457*, 459
  scattering from, 330, *350–367*, 456, *457*, *468–471*
Linear accelerators (linacs)
  use as neutron sources, 54, *89–90, 152–155*
"Liquid crystal", scattering from, *475–476*, 487
Liquid hydrogen moderator, 148–149, *160–161, 164–171*
  effect of added deuterium, *169*
  effect of p-H_2, *168–169*
  in BEPO, 149, 158, *164–165, 167–169*

  in DIDO, 158, *165–167*, 169–171
  safety of, 169–171
"Localized" modes, *215*
Lyddane-Sachs-Teller [LST] relation, *228*, 232, 233
  for CaF_2, 232
    KBr, 229
    NaI, 229
    $SrTiO_3$, 233
    UO_2, 232

M

Magnetovibrational scattering, 35, *45*, *264–266*
Mandel'shtam-Brillouin scattering, 297, 315, 325
Mass point, *418–421*
Mass tensor, *418–421, 433–434*, 435, 436, 455
  reduced, *421*
Matrix elements for scattering, *15–17*, 417, *422–427*, 437, 445
Maxwellian distribution, *3*, 98, *148–150*, 162, 167, 426, 442
Mean energy transfer, as first moment of scattering law, 298, *299*, 402
Methane
  as moderator, *163*
  effective proton mass in, *456, 462*
  K.N. model for, 457, 468, 473–475
  rotations in, 467–468
  scattering from, 374, *377–378*, 455, *457*, *461–465*, 468, *473–475*, 487
  vibrations in, 462, 487
  Zemach-Glauber theory for, 462–464
Methanethiol, hindered internal rotations in, *458*, 471
  scattering from, 471–472
Methanoic acid (formic acid), scattering from, *470*
Methanol
  hindered internal rotations in, 458–459, 471–472
  K.N. model for, 458
  scattering from, *374–377*, 458, 472
Modes, normal, of vibration, *23–26, 196*, 202, 208, 213, 216, 220, 223, 225, 229–231, 238
  acoustic, 25–26, 213, 216
  defect, 215–216

Modes
  optic, 26, 213, 216, 220, 225, *229–231*, 238, 483
Moderators, *148–150*
  cold, 148–149, *158–169*
  graphite, 148, 159
  heavy water, 148, 159–160
  hot, *149–150*
  [liquid] hydrogen, 148–149, *160–161*, *164–171*
  in linac systems, *154*, *155*
  light water, 148, 159–160
  methane, *163*
  organic, *160–161*
  for pulsed sources, *154–157*
  relation of temperature to neutron spectrum, *3*, *148–150*
Molecular field model, in fluctuation theory, *278–280*
Molecular rotations, *432–434*, 454
  cross-section due to, *428–431*, *442–446*
  hindered, 351, 354–355, 357, 361, 384, *468–471*, 473, *481–487*
  in ammonia, 465
    ammonium salts, *481–487*
    bromine, 408
    globular compounds, 489
    glycerol, 384, 387
    hydrogen, 160, 367, 370, 473
    hydrogen sulphide, 468
    methane, 464
    water, 330, 351, 354–355, 357, 361, *468–471*
  information on from *I.R.* data, 415, 469
  internal, in alcohols, 458–459, 471–472
  moderation by, *160*
  separation from vibrations, 427, 433, 473
Molecular vibrations, 366, 377, 408, 432, *434–435*, 436, 446, 454–455, 483, 491
  cross-section due to, *431–432*, *436*, 442
  in hydrogen bonds, *488*
  in methane, 465
  separation from rotations, 427, 433, 473
Molybdenum
  in window filters, *135*
  phonon dispersion relation in, *211–212*
Moment relations, *298–300*, 321–323, 339, 357, 402
  comparison with experiment, *402*

Mosaic spread
  of monochromator, 20, *99–100*, *104–106*, 109
    and effect on diffracted beam intensity, *109–111*
    and effect on monochromatic beam intensity, *99–102*
  of sample, as difficulty in 1-phonon coherent scattering, 195, *205–206*
Mössbauer effect, 297, 306, 308
Multichannel time analysers, 54, 56, *90–92*
  use with on-line computers, 92
Multiphonon effects
  cross-section, *31–33*, 194, 324
  spectrum due to, 241, 309, 392, 396
Multiple scattering, in samples, 357, 378, *395–397*

N

Navier-Stokes equation, 314, 315, 319
Néel temperature, *257*, 265, 287–288
  behaviour of spin waves near, *272–276*
Nelkin model, for water, *470–471*
Neutron, discovery of, 3
Neutrons, general dependence of scattered on properties of scatterer, 1, *4–6*
Neutron, relationship of wavelength to velocity and energy, *2*, 520
Neutron sources, total flux from, *4*, 142, *145*
Neutron, wave equation for, 7, 8, 49
Nickel
  critical scattering in, *282–283*
  phonon dispersion relation in, 206–207
  phonon frequency distribution in, 207
  spin waves in, 270–271, 275
Niobium, phonon dispersion relation in, *211–212*
Normal modes, *23–26*, *196*, 202, 208, 216, 220, 223, 225, 229–231, 238
N.R.U. reactor, *143*, *145*

O

Occupation number, phonon state, *26*, 28
Order
  in *p*-azoxyanisol, 475–476
  long-range, 46, 310
  short-range, *22*, 258, 260, 310

Order contamination, in crystal monochromator systems, 106, *108–109*
removal of, by filters, 109, 130
Order-disorder transition, effect on neutron
groups, *215*

P

Pair-distribution function, *12*, 22, *295*,
298–300, 309–310, 320–324, 326, 389
Paramagnets, scattering from, *35–36*, *253–
261*, 489–490
Particle density
macroscopic, 295, 310, *311*
microscopic, *296*, 301
operators for, 301
Phased chopper velocity selectors, 55, *70–
85*, 89, 378
at Chalk River, *76–80*, 156
Harwell, *76–80*
M.T.R., *80–85*
Saclay, 85
phasing of, 70, 78–79, 82
power supplies for, 76–78, 82
principles of, 70–72
resolution of, 72–76
use with linac, 89, 156
use with pulsed reactor, 156
Phonon dispersion relations, *194*
experimental methods for, 69, 83–84,
119–124, 196–197
in aluminium, *202–203*
beryllium, *214*
CaF_2, *231–232*
germanium, 223
graphite, *235–238*
lead, *203–206*
magnesium, 213–214
molybdenum, *211–212*
nickel, 206–207
niobium, *211–212*
KBr, 226, *227* et seq.
silicon, *221–223*
sodium, *208–210*
NaI, 226–229
zinc, *213–214*
Phonon-phonon interaction, *239*, 306
Phonon widths and lifetimes, 26, 215, *229–
231*, *239–243*, 292, 306, 308
in β-brass, *215*

in alkali halides, 229–231, 242–243
in aluminium, 242
in lead, 242
in strontium titanate, 243
Placzek mass expansion, *31*, *32*
Polarizability, atomic and ionic, *220*, 226,
232
Polarization vector, phonon, *24*, *28*, *194–
197*, 202, 208, 217, 218, *223–225*, 304,
393
determination of, *223–225*
in symmetry directions, 202, 208
Polarized neutrons, *35*, *37*, 108, 148, *253*
collimators for, *148*
Polycrystal
coherent cross-section for, *19–20*
phonon scattering from, 292, 325–326,
392–393
scattered intensity from sample of, *110*
spin-inelastic scattering from, *47*
Potential, scattering, *6*, *8*, *15*
Primitive cell, 199
Pressure, in classical liquids, *309*
Probability density, *10*
Projection operators, *425*
Proportional counters, 113, 172, *175–178*
boron trifluoride, 113, 117, 132, 135,
175–178
helium-3, *178*
Pseudo-phonons, in liquids, *394*, 405, 407
Pseudopotential, Fermi, *6*, 8, *416*, 419, *422*
interionic, 201, 209
Pulse height, from detectors, 182, *186–187*
resolution of, *187*
Pulse shape discrimination, for scintillator
detectors, *182–184*
Pulsed reactors, 54, *90*, *150–152*, 155–156
at Dubna, *151–152*, 155–156

Q

Quasi-elastic peak, 325, 332–333, 334, 336,
340
in alcohols, 374, 376
argon, 403
bromine, 407
glycerol, 379–381
hydrogen, 373
[liquid] lead, 391

Quasi-elastic peak
　in methane, 378, 463–464
　　water, 351 et seqq., 365
　intensity of, 352, 355
　width of, *332*, *334*, *351*, 353–354, *355–356*, 373, 380–381, 403

R

Rahman-Singwi-Sjölander [R.S.S.] model
　for liquids, *338–341*, 365–366, 386–387
Random phase approximation, 276
Reactors, flux spectrum from, *3*, 108
　total flux of, 142, *145*
Reflectivity, of crystal monochromator,
　100, 101, 102, 103, 108
Relaxation time
　in liquids, 315, *318*, 325, 330, *333–334*,
　　347, 356, 383–385, 398, 399
　magnetic, 45, *280–286*, 328
Resolution width, of pulse height from
　detectors, *186–187*
Resonance absorption of γ-rays [Mössbauer
　effect], 297, 306, 308
"Resonance" modes, *215*
Rigid ion model, *226*, *227*, 232
Rotating crystal spectrometer, *56*, *85–88*,
　348, 352, 363, 377, 389, 403
　time focusing in, 87–88
　order contamination in, 87
　at Chalk River, 86, 87, 88
　intensity of beams in, 88

S

Sachs-Teller theory, *418–421*, 433–434,
　435, 436, 454–455, 459
Scalar-Q method, *125–127*
Scattering law, *12*, 13, 14, 79, 80, *297*,
　298–303, 319–320, 324, 332, 333, 336,
　357, 363, 388–389, 400–401, 481
　detailed balance, 13, *301*, 303
　experimental method for, 79–80, 83,
　　298, 363, 400
　for rigid rotator, *444*, *447*
　in globule model for liquids, *336*, 357
　　Griffing model for methane, *464*
　　jump-diffusion model for liquids, *333*
　　Krieger-Nelkin model, *435*
　in Vineyard model for liquids, *332*

sum rule for, 12
　weighted, in Zemach-Glauber theory,
　　423, *432*
Scattering length [amplitude]
　coherent, *425*
　for hydrogen molecule, *441–442*
　incoherent, *425*
　magnetic, *34*, *35*
　nuclear, 6, *7*, 49, 297, 321, 416, *425*, 445
Scattering surfaces, *29–30*, *41–42*, 44, 262–264
　for phonons, *29–30*
　for spin waves, *41–42*, 44, *262–264*, 284
Schofield time substitution, *302*, *322*, 449
Schrödinger equation
　for neutron near single atom, *6*
　for neutron and diatomic molecule, *437–439*
　time-dependent, 49
Scintillation detectors [scintillators], 172,
　178–190
　discrimination against γ-rays, 172, *182–184*
　glass, *184–187*
　multidetector arrays of, 174, *184*
　zinc sulphide, *178–184*
Second moment, normalized coherent, *300*
Self-diffusion coefficient, 13, 303, 314, 316,
　327, *329*, 330, *332*, 334 et seq., 340,
　351, 381–383, 407
　deduced from quasielastic peak data
　　in alcohols, *376*
　　in argon, *404*
　　in methane, *377–378*
　　in sodium, 399
　　in water, 352, 362, 364
　　in classical fluids, *314*
　　in various models, *334*
Shear dispersion, 315
Shell model, 217, *220*, 226–229
　for alkali halides, *226–229*
　semiconductors, *220*
Small angle scattering, magnetic, 267,
　270–271
Sodium
　Born-Mayer potential in, 201
　liquid, 388, *398–402*
　phonon dispersion relation in, *208–210*
　phonon frequency distribution in, *210*,
　　399

Soller slit collimator, *104*, 109, 115, 116
Sound, velocity of, in liquids, *314, 320*, 405
Source block, 144–145
Specific heat
  of fluids, *311–312*
  of solids, 209, 228, 311
Spectral density, *15*
Spectral tensor function, *307–308*
Spectrometers, crystal, *111–119*, 349
  single-axis, 111, 113
  triple axis, 113, 117, 389, 407
    automation for, 118–119
    at Chalk River, *113–117*
    experimental methods for, *119–124*
Spin cant [spin spiral], *37*
Spinning sample method, 56, *88–89*
Spin correlation, in molecular scattering, *426*, 432, 437, 439–442, 489
Spin diffusion, *259*, 280–281, 286, 288
Spin disorder, 11, 18, 21, 22
Spin fluctuations, *39, 258*, 266–267, *277–281*
Spin-orbit coupling, *252, 253*
Spin wave approximation, 35, *38–40*, 262, 272
Spin wave linewidths and lifetimes, *272–275*
Spin wave resonance, 274
Spin wave scattering, *38–45*, 257, 260, *262–277*, 284
  antiferromagnetic, *42–45*, 266
  distinction from phonon scattering, *265–266*, 271
  ferromagnetic, *38–42*
Static approximations, 12, 45, 47, *429*
Stochastic force model for liquids, *316*, 338–341, 365–366, 386–387
Structure factor
  elastic, 18, *19*
  liquid, *393*, 395, 402, 405, 408
  magnetic, *36, 37, 44*
  phonon inelastic, *28*, 98, 195, 217, 226, 227, 393
Susceptibility, 278, 284
  wavelength-dependent, *278–279*

T

Time-of-flight techniques, 54, 56, 67, 69, 90–93, 152, 176–177, 184, 187

for liquids, 353, 356, 371, 372, 374–375, 378–380, 392, 394 et seq.
for molecular scattering, 465–466, 471 et seq.
Tin [white]
  liquid, *394–395*
  phonon dispersion relation in, 215
Torsional molecular oscillations, 468, *471, 483–487*, 488
  of ammonium ion, 483–487
  of hydronium ion, 486
  of water of crystallization, 488
Total internal reflection, of neutrons, *147–148*
Thermal diffusion coefficient, 324
Thermal expansion coefficient, 311
Thermodynamic relaxation, 277, *280–288*
Time uncertainty, in detectors, *177, 184*, 187

V

Vanadium,
  liquid, 349, 398
  phonon frequency distribution in, *210–211*
Velocity frequency function, *328*
Velocity selectors, phased chopper, 55, *70–85*, 89, 378
  at Chalk River, *76–80*, 156
  at Harwell, *76–80*
  at M.T.R., *80–85*
  at Saclay, 85
  phasing of, 70, 78–79, 82
  power supplies for, 76–78, 82
  principles of, 70–72
  resolution of, 72–76
  use with linac, 89, 156
  use with pulsed reactor, 156
Visco-elastic medium, 315
Viscosity
  of classical fluids, *313*, 320, 330
  of helium, 313
  relation to friction coefficient, *356*
  relation to relaxation time, *384–385*

W

Width function, *13*, 14, *303–309*, 326–327, 329, 332, 335, 339, 341, 365–366, 401
  in Gaussian approximation, *326–327*, 401, *448*

Width function
in globule model for liquids, *335*
R.S.S. model for liquids, *339*
in Vineyard model for liquids, *332*
for molecular scattering, *448–450*
for [liquid] sodium, *401*
Window detector [filter] method, *134–136*

X

X-Rays
cross-sections for, 9, *10*, 18

diffraction of, from liquids, *294*, *299*, 310

Z

Zemach-Glauber theory, *422–432*, 433, 434, 437, 442, 445, 447, 455
for methane [E.A. treatment], *462–464*
Zinc, phonon dispersion relation in, *213–214*
Zinc sulphide, as scintillator, *178–184*

Appendix

Conversion Chart 520

Universal Constants 521

General List of Symbols 522

Conversion Chart

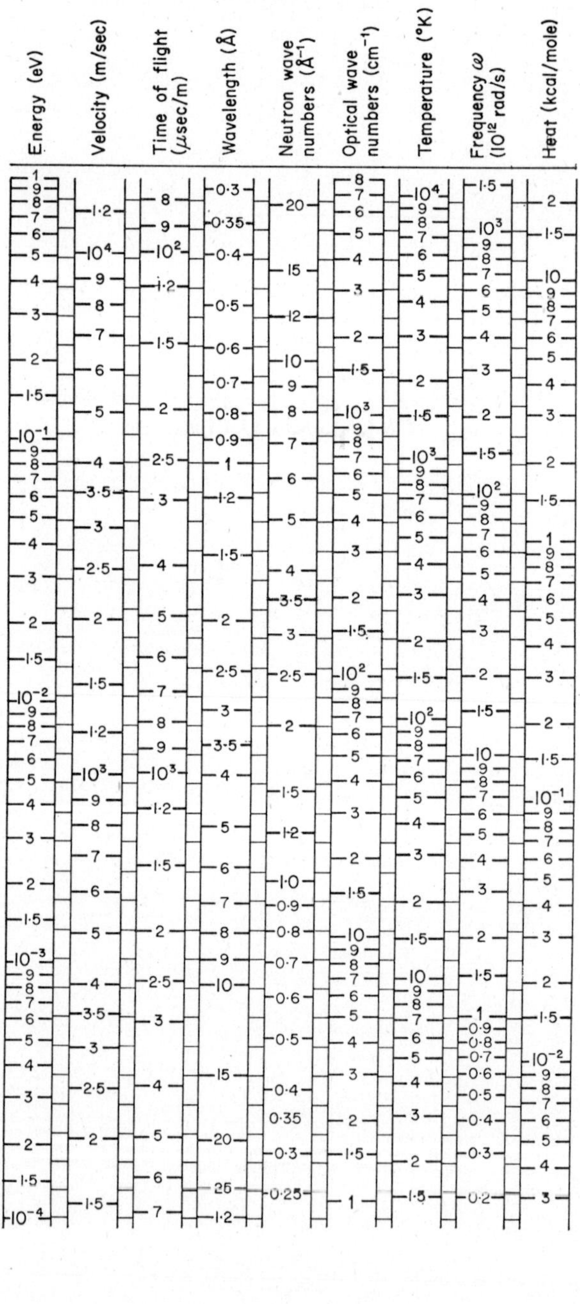

The chart consists of parallel vertical logarithmic scales with the following column headers (left to right):

Energy (eV)	Velocity (m/sec)	Time of flight (μsec/m)	Wavelength (Å)	Neutron wave numbers (Å⁻¹)	Optical wave numbers (cm⁻¹)	Temperature (°K)	Frequency ω (10^{12} rad/s)	Heat (kcal/mole)

Energy (eV): 1, 9, 8, 7, 6, 5, 4, 3, 2, 1·5, 10^{-1}, 9, 8, 7, 6, 5, 4, 3, 2, 1·5, 10^{-2}, 9, 8, 7, 6, 5, 4, 3, 2, 1·5, 10^{-3}, 9, 8, 7, 6, 5, 4, 3, 2, 1·5, 10^{-4}

Velocity (m/sec): 1·2, 10^4, 9, 8, 7, 6, 5, 4, 3·5, 3, 2·5, 2, 1·5, 1·2, 10^3, 9, 8, 7, 6, 5, 4, 3·5, 3, 2·5, 2, 1·5

Time of flight (μsec/m): 8, 9, 10^2, 1·2, 1·5, 2, 2·5, 3, 4, 5, 6, 7, 8, 9, 10^3, 1·2, 1·5, 2, 2·5, 3, 4, 5, 6, 7

Wavelength (Å): 0·3, 0·35, 0·4, 0·5, 0·6, 0·7, 0·8, 0·9, 1, 1·2, 1·5, 2, 2·5, 3, 3·5, 4, 5, 6, 7, 8, 9, 10, 15, 20, 25, 1·2

Neutron wave numbers (Å⁻¹): 20, 15, 12, 10, 9, 8, 7, 6, 5, 4, 3·5, 3, 2·5, 2, 1·5, 1·2, 1·0, 0·9, 0·8, 0·7, 0·6, 0·5, 0·4, 0·35, 0·3, 0·25

Optical wave numbers (cm⁻¹): 8, 7, 6, 5, 4, 3, 2, 1·5, 10^3, 9, 8, 7, 6, 5, 4, 3, 2, 1·5, 10^2, 9, 8, 7, 6, 5, 4, 3, 2, 1·5, 10, 9, 8, 7, 6, 5, 4, 3, 2, 1·5, 1

Temperature (°K): 10^4, 9, 8, 7, 6, 5, 4, 3, 2, 1·5, 10^3, 9, 8, 7, 6, 5, 4, 3, 2, 1·5, 10^2, 9, 8, 7, 6, 5, 4, 3, 2, 1·5, 10, 9, 8, 7, 6, 5, 4, 3, 2, 1·5

Frequency ω (10^{12} rad/s): 1·5, 10^3, 9, 8, 7, 6, 5, 4, 3, 2, 1·5, 10^2, 9, 8, 7, 6, 5, 4, 3, 10, 9, 8, 7, 6, 5, 4, 3, 2, 1, 0·9, 0·8, 0·7, 0·6, 0·5, 0·4, 0·3, 0·2

Heat (kcal/mole): 2, 1·5, 10, 9, 8, 7, 6, 5, 4, 3, 2, 1·5, 1, 9, 8, 7, 6, 5, 4, 3, 2, 1·5, 10^{-1}, 9, 8, 7, 6, 5, 4, 3, 2, 1·5, 10^{-2}, 9, 8, 7, 6, 5, 4, 3

Universal Constants

Velocity of light c	2.9979×10^{10} cm/sec
Electronic charge e	4.803×10^{-10} e.s.u.
Plancks constant h	6.6255×10^{-27} erg sec
Plancks constant $\hbar$	1.054×10^{-27} erg sec
Boltzmanns constant k	1.380×10^{-16} erg/deg
Mass of neutron m	1.00894 A.M.U. (1 A.M.U. $= 1.660 \times 10^{-24}$ g)
Mass of electron m	9.109×10^{-28} g
Magnetic moment of neutron	-1.913 nuclear magneton (1 nuclear magneton $=$ 5.050×10^{-24} erg/gauss)
Avogadro's number	0.6023×10^{24}
1 kilocalorie	4.18×10^{10} ergs
$\hbar/k$	7.64×10^{-12} deg sec
$\hbar/2m$	3.15×10^{-4} cm²/sec
1 electron volt energy	1.602×10^{-12} erg
1 eV is equivalent to	
neutron velocity	1.38×10^{4} m/sec
neutron time-of-flight	72.4 μsec/m
neutron wavelength	0.286Å
neutron wave number	21.95 Å⁻¹
optical wave	
number	8.07×10^{3} cm⁻¹
temperature	1.16×10^{4} °K
frequency	1.52×10^{15} c/s
energy per atom	23.1 kcal/mole

General List of Symbols

b	Bound scattering length
c	Velocity of light
D	Diffusion constant
E	Energy (usually scattered neutron energy)
E_0	Incident neutron energy
$\mathbf{E(q)}$	Dynamical matrix
e	Electronic charge
F_τ	Structure factor
f	Angular frequency of phonons, etc.
$f(\mathbf{Q})$	Form factor
G	[with various subscripts] Force constant
$G(\mathbf{r},\tau)$	Space–time correlation function

$$\widetilde{G}(\mathbf{r},\tau) = G\left(\mathbf{r},\tau + \frac{i\hbar}{2kT}\right)$$

$G_d(\mathbf{r},\tau)$	"Distinct" correlation function for a pair of atoms
$G_s(\mathbf{r},\tau)$	"Self" correlation function
$g(\mathbf{r})$	Pair correlation function
$h, \hbar$	Plancks constant
$I(\mathbf{Q},\tau)$	Intermediate scattering function

$$\widetilde{I}(\mathbf{Q},\tau) = I\left(\mathbf{Q},\tau + \frac{i\hbar}{2kT}\right)$$

J	Exchange integral
$\mathbf{J}$	Total angular momentum $= \mathbf{L}+\mathbf{S}$
J	$/\mathbf{J}/$
$\mathscr{J}$	Jacobian
k	Boltzmanns constant
$\mathbf{k}$	Wave-vector of scattered neutron
$\mathbf{k_0}$	Wave-vector of incident neutron
K_1	Reciprocal of range of spin fluctuations in critical scattering
$\mathbf{L}$	Orbital angular momentum
L	Number of atoms in a unit cell
M	Mass of atom
M^*	Effective mass for diffusion
m	Mass of neutron
$\mathbf{m}$	Mass of electron
n	Number of neutrons, phonons, magnons, etc.
n_D	Total no. of neutrons/unit volume
$n_d(v)$	Total number of neutrons per velocity interval at v, in Maxwell distribution
n_F	Total flux of neutrons in Maxwell distribution

$n_f(\lambda)$	Flux per wavelength interval near λ
$n_f(v)$	Flux per velocity interval near v
$n_f(E)$	Flux per energy interval near E
n_i	Occupation number
N	Number of atoms or unit cells
$\mathbf{P_n}$	Equilibrium position on lattice of atom $\mathbf{n}$
$\mathbf{Q}$	Scattering vector
$\mathbf{q}$	Wave-vector of phonon, magnon, etc.
$\mathbf{R_n}$	Position of atom which has equilibrium position $\mathbf{P_n}$
$\mathbf{S}$	Spin angular momentum
$S(\mathbf{Q},\omega)$	Scattering law

$$\widetilde{S}(\mathbf{Q},\omega) = e^{-\hbar\omega/2kT}S(\mathbf{Q},\omega)$$

$\mathscr{S}$	Incoherent cross-section
s	Branch of phonon spectrum
T	Temperature (sometimes time)
$\mathbf{u_n}(\tau)$	Thermal displacement at time τ of atom which has equilibrium position $\mathbf{P_n}$
$V(\mathbf{q})$	Polarization vector of phonon
$V(\mathbf{r},\tau)$	Potential at time τ at position $\mathbf{r}$
W_n	Debye-Waller factor associated with atom at $\mathbf{P_n}$
$w(\tau)$	Width function
z	Number of nearest neighbours to an atom
$z(f), z(\nu)$	Density of phonon states
$z(\omega)$	Spectral density for motion of single atom
α, β	Sub- or superscripts for Cartesian components of vectors, etc.
γ	Magnetic moment of neutron
$\Delta\tau$	Width of, e.g. τ distribution; taken as full width at half height of distribution
η	Viscosity of liquid
Θ	Debye temperature
θ	Bragg angle or scattering angle
λ	Neutron wavelength
$\boldsymbol{\mu}$	Magnetization direction
ν	Frequency of phonon
$\boldsymbol{\rho_n}$	Equilibrium position in unit cell of atom $\mathbf{n}$
ρ	Density
σ	Cross-section

τ	Elapsed time	χ	Susceptibility
$\boldsymbol{\tau}$	Reciprocal lattice vector (with-out 2π)	Ω	Solid angle
ϕ	Scattering angle	ω	Angular frequency corresponding to $(E_0 - E)/\hbar$

74893

QC   Thermal neutron
721   scattering
.T53
1965